QUANTITATIVE ANALYSIS

FOR BUSINESS DECISION MAKING

Edited by

Gerald I. Harel, Ph.D.

Tej S. Dhakar, Ph.D.

WILEY

CUSTOM SERVICES

BRIEF CONTENTS

CONTENTS

8 Linear and Integer Programming Models 298

9 Applications of Linear and Integer Programming Models 366

CD-ROMS

Applied Management Science

Note: The Contents of this CD-ROM refer to the chapters of Lawrence and Pasternack, *Applied Management Science*, Second Edition, the source of the CD-ROM. The corresponding chapters in the text are as follows:

- Chapter 2 references on the CD-ROM equate to Chapter 8 in the text (i.e., refer to the Chapter 2 Excel files on the CD-ROM to access the Excel files for Chapter 8 in the text).
- Chapter 3 references on the CD-ROM equate to Chapter 9 in the text.
- Chapter 6 references on the CD-ROM equate to Chapter 10 in the text.
- Chapter 10 references on the CD-ROM equate to Chapter 11 in the text; note that Chapter 11 on the CD-ROM and Chapter 11 in the text are not related.

ADDITIONAL CHAPTERS

SUPPLEMENTS

APPENDICES

TEMPLATES

EXCEL SOFTWARE ADD-INS

EXCEL FILES

POWERPOINT SLIDES

PROBLEM MOTIVATIONS

ADDITIONAL PROBLEMS/CASES

SPSS Student Version

WinQSB

PREFACE

The field of statistics and management science has progressed a great deal during the last decade. With the availability of the computer facilities and the infusion of new concepts and new mathematical models, our graduate students have become increasingly sophisticated. Sophistication, in turn, obscures the fundamental difference between theoretical models and applied quantitative approaches towards problem solving.

A good practitioner of the business world is the one whose objective now is to venture into real life and apply the advanced tools to it. A good course in quantitative methods and procedures will give you some real insight into how a business establishment should utilize the tools of "quant" in the process of decision making.

It is not surprising that many business analysts encounter numerous problems often ignored by the profession, since ideal textbook-style examples seldom occur in real life. Thus, this edited book is oriented to the aspects of mathematical and statistical tools to help and solve business problems. The uniqueness of this book is that it enhances Management Science Techniques, Statistical Tools and the World of Computers into one well-integrated whole.

ORGANIZATION OF THE BOOK

This book is organized in three parts.

- The first part is Statistics Review. This part covers the statistical basics that the students are supposed to know from the undergraduate statistics class. These topics have been included in the book in order that you may be able to review these topics and refresh your knowledge.

- The second part of the book is Statistical Applications. This part includes some of the most powerful applications of statistics, i.e., simple and multiple regression and forecasting.

- Part three of the text, Management Science Applications, contains a number of powerful management science techniques, i.e., linear programming, decision analysis, and simulation models. We have selected the applications that we think you will most likely use during your MBA program as well as during your work life.

USE OF COMPUTERS

The text is designed for using computers for almost all quantitative techniques included in the text. Since Excel is the most widely used and accessible quantitative software, most of the examples in the text are based on Excel. With add-ins such as Solver and Data Analysis Tool Pak, Excel can be used for most of the commonly-used and powerful statistical and management science techniques. Many of the major schools have switched to using Excel in teaching quantitative analysis in their MBA programs. Once you are comfortable using

Excel for quantitative analysis, you can go on to learn the use of specialized statistical and management science software such as SAS and LINDO as needed by you.

CD-ROMS

The CD-ROMs that accompany the book contain a wealth of additional and supplementary materials. Use the supplementary materials on the CD-ROMs to gain a better understanding of the topics covered in the classes and use the additional materials on the CD-ROMs to learn new quantitative techniques. Do explore the CD-ROMs, become familiar with their contents and make the best use of what is within your easy reach on the CD-ROMs.

A NOTE TO THE STUDENTS

The intent of this edition is to give the students more than just another textbook. This one is both a good text and an excellent reference book.

Like all rewarding subjects, quantitative methods will not be mastered without effort. A book on "quant" must be worked at. It cannot be read like a novel or poetry. It is a good idea to read any chapter quickly to see the general run of the logical development and solution algorithms, then reread it carefully, making sure that you understand each step of the method or model.

Learning can be best retained through repeated, explicit use of concepts and solving as many problems at the end of each chapter as possible. Therefore, first do things the "old fashioned" way and then use the computer as much as possible.

You should be prepared to spend more time on difficult sections; occasionally you may spend an hour or more on one page or a few pages. Paper, pencil and calculator are indispensable equipment in your reading before approaching the computer.

FINAL NOTE

This is a relatively short book, achieving brevity by omitting much of the purely descriptive material customarily found in "traditional texts." That is, the various topics from several books have been integrated into one edition around the long overdue realism of approaching the process of decision-making from a problem-solving point of view. We hope you will find this text rewarding and stimulating.

Gerald I. Harel, Ph.D.
Tej S. Dhakar, Ph.D.

QUANTITATIVE ANALYSIS

For Business Decision Making

CHAPTER 1

Sampling and Sampling Distributions

LEARNING OBJECTIVES

The two main objectives for Chapter 1 are to give you an appreciation for the proper application of sampling techniques and an understanding of the sampling distributions of two statistics, thereby enabling you to:

1. Determine when to use sampling instead of a census.
2. Distinguish between random and nonrandom sampling.
3. Decide when and how to use various sampling techniques.
4. Be aware of the different types of errors that can occur in a study.
5. Understand the impact of the central limit theorem on statistical analysis.
6. Use the sampling distributions of $\bar{x}$ and $\hat{p}$.

Early in the 1960s, the government of Mexico established the maquiladora program. This program allowed U.S.-owned corporations to build manufacturing facilities inside the Mexican border where they could import supplies and materials from the United States free of duty, to assemble or produce products, and then export the finished items back to the United States. The idea was to entice U.S. firms to build in Mexico because of the cheap labor pool available there, and thus create jobs for Mexicans.

The program has been successful, with more than 3,500 registered companies taking part. By 2000, more than 1.1 million maquiladora workers were employed. An estimated $50 billion (U.S.) was spent by maquiladoras with suppliers in 1999, with maquiladora industry exports at about $65 billion (U.S.). Nearly 85% of maquiladora manufacturing is in Mexico's northern states, those bordering the United States. These firms are concentrated in Ciudad Juarez, Tijuana, Mexicali, Nuevo Laredo, and Matamoras. The maquiladora program now encompasses companies from all over the world including Japan, Korea, China, Canada, and many European countries.

What are the Mexican maquiladora workers like? What are their attitudes toward their jobs and their companies? Are there cultural gaps between company and worker that must be bridged in order to utilize the human resources more effectively? What culture-based attitudes and expectations do the maquiladora laborers bring to the work situation? How does a business researcher go about surveying workers?

Managerial and Statistical Questions

Suppose researchers decide to survey maquiladora workers to ascertain the workers' attitudes toward and expectations of the work environment and the company.

1. Should the researchers take a census of all maquiladora workers or just a sample? What are reasons for each?
2. If a sample is used, what type of sampling technique would gain the most valid information? How can the researchers be certain that the sample of workers is representative of the population?
3. What types of questions should be asked and how should they be stated?
4. Can the questions be analyzed quantitatively? If so, which statistical techniques are most appropriate?
5. In what format can the researchers most effectively convey the results of the study to management?
6. How can management fully utilize the study results to effect a more productive work environment?

Source: Adapted from Cheryl L. Noll, "Mexican Maquiladora Workers: An Attitude Toward Working," *Southwest Journal of Business and Economics*, vol. IX, no. 1 (Spring 1992), pp. 1–8; *Maquila Magazine*, http://www.mexico-maquila.com/mi.htm, accessed 2000; Steven B. Zisser, "Maquiladora 2001 Understanding and Preparing," available at http://www.maqguide.com/zisser1.htm.

This chapter explores the process of sampling and the sampling distributions of some statistics. How do we obtain the data used in statistical analysis? Why do researchers often take a sample rather than conduct a census? What are the differences between random and nonrandom sampling? This chapter addresses these and other questions about sampling.

Also presented are the distributions of two statistics: the sample mean and the sample proportion. It has been determined that statistics such as these are approximately normally distributed under certain conditions. Knowledge of the uses of the sample mean and sample proportion is important in the study of statistics and is basic to much of statistical analysis.

1.1 SAMPLING

Sampling is widely used in business as a means of gathering useful information about a population. Data are gathered from samples and conclusions are drawn about the population as a part of the inferential statistics process. In the Decision Dilemma on maquiladora workers, a random sample of workers could be taken from a wide selection of companies in several industries in many of the key border cities. A carefully constructed questionnaire that is culturally sensitive to Mexicans could be administered to the selected workers to determine work attitudes, expectations, and cultural differences between workers and companies. The researchers could compile and analyze the data gleaned from the responses. Summaries and observations could be made about worker outlook and culture in the maquiladora program. Management and decision makers could then attempt to use the results of the study to improve worker performance and motivation. Often, a sample provides a reasonable means for gathering such useful decision-making information that might be otherwise unattainable and unaffordable.

Reasons for Sampling

Taking a sample instead of conducting a census offers several advantages.

1. The sample can save money.
2. The sample can save time.
3. For given resources, the sample can broaden the scope of the study.
4. Because the research process is sometimes destructive, the sample can save product.
5. If accessing the population is impossible, the sample is the only option.

A sample can be cheaper to obtain than a census for a given magnitude of questions. For example, if an 8-minute telephone interview is being undertaken, conducting the interviews with a sample of 100 customers rather than with a population of 100,000 customers obviously is less expensive. In addition to the cost savings, the significantly smaller number of interviews usually requires less total time. Thus, if obtaining the results is a matter of urgency, sampling can provide them more quickly. With the volatility of some markets and the constant barrage of new competition and new ideas, sampling has a strong advantage over a census in terms of research turnaround time.

If the resources allocated to a research project are fixed, more detailed information can be gathered by taking a sample than by conducting a census. With resources concentrated on fewer individuals or items, the study can be broadened in scope to allow for more specialized questions. One organization budgeted $100,000 for a study and opted to take a census instead of a sample by using a mail survey. The researchers mass-mailed thousands of copies of a computer card that looked like a major league baseball all-star ballot. The card contained 20 questions to which the respondent could answer Yes or No by punching out a perforated hole. The information retrieved amounted to the percentages of respondents who answered Yes and No on the 20 questions. For the same amount of money, the company could have taken a random sample from the population, held interactive one-on-one sessions with highly trained interviewers, and gathered detailed information about the process being studied. By using the money for a sample, the researchers could have spent significantly more time with each respondent and thus increased the potential for gathering useful information.

Some research processes are destructive to the product or item being studied. For example, if light bulbs are being tested to determine how long they burn or if candy bars are being taste tested to determine whether the taste is acceptable, the product is destroyed. If a census were conducted for this type of research, no product would be left to sell. Hence, taking a sample is the only realistic option for testing such products.

Sometimes a population is virtually impossible to access for research. For example, some people refuse to answer sensitive questions, and some telephone numbers are unlisted. Some items of interest (like a 1957 Chevrolet) are so scattered that locating all of them would be extremely difficult. When the population is inaccessible for these or other reasons, sampling is the only option.

Reasons for Taking a Census

Sometimes taking a census makes more sense than using a sample. One reason to take a census is to eliminate the possibility that by chance a randomly selected sample might not be representative of the population. Even when all the proper sampling techniques are implemented, a sample that is nonrepresentative of the population can be selected by chance. For example, if the population of interest is all truck owners in the state of Colorado, a random sample of owners could yield mostly ranchers, when in fact many of the truck owners in Colorado are urban dwellers.

A second reason to take a census is that the client (person authorizing and/or underwriting the study) does not have an appreciation for random sampling and feels more comfortable with conducting a census. Both of these reasons for taking a census are based on the assumption that enough time and money are available to conduct such a census.

Frame

Every research study has a target population that consists of the individuals, institutions, or entities that are the object of investigation. The sample is taken from a population *list, map, directory, or other source used to represent the population.* This list, map, or directory is called the **frame,** which can be school lists, trade association lists, or even lists sold by list brokers. Ideally, a one-to-one correspondence exists between the frame units and the population units. In reality, the frame and the target population are often different. For example, suppose the target population is all families living in Detroit. A feasible frame would be the residential pages of the Detroit telephone books. How would the frame differ from the target population? Some families have no telephone. Other families have unlisted numbers. Still other families might have moved and/or changed numbers since the directory was printed. Some families even have multiple listings under different names.

Frames that have *overregistration* contain all the target population units plus some additional units. Frames that have *underregistration* contain fewer units than does the target population. Sampling is done from the frame, not the target population. In theory, the target population and the frame are the same. In reality, a researcher's goal is to minimize the differences between the frame and the target population.

Random versus Nonrandom Sampling

The two main types of sampling are random and nonrandom. In **random sampling** *every unit of the population has the same probability of being selected into the sample.* Random sampling implies that chance enters into the process of selection. For example, most Americans would like to believe that winners of nationwide magazine sweepstakes are selected by some random draw of numbers. Late in the 1960s when the military draft lottery was being used, most people eligible for the draft trusted that a given birthdate was selected by chance as the first date used to draft people. In both of these situations, members of the population believed that selections were made by chance.

In **nonrandom sampling** *not every unit of the population has the same probability of being selected into the sample.* Members of nonrandom samples are not selected by chance. For example, they might be selected because they are at the right place at the right time or because they know the people conducting the research.

Sometimes random sampling is called *probability sampling* and nonrandom sampling is called *nonprobability sampling.* Because every unit of the population is not equally likely to be selected, assigning a probability of occurrence in nonrandom sampling is impossible. The statistical methods presented and discussed in this text are based on the assumption that the data come from random samples. *Nonrandom sampling methods are not appropriate techniques for gathering data to be analyzed by most of the statistical methods presented in this text.* However, several nonrandom sampling techniques are described in this section, primarily to alert you to their characteristics and limitations.

Random Sampling Techniques

The four basic random sampling techniques are simple random sampling, stratified random sampling, systematic random sampling, and cluster (or area) random sampling. Each technique offers advantages and disadvantages. Some techniques are simpler to use, some are less costly, and others show greater potential for reducing sampling error.

Simple Random Sampling

The most elementary random sampling technique is **simple random sampling.** Simple random sampling can be viewed as the basis for the other random sampling techniques. With simple random sampling, each unit of the frame is numbered from 1 to N (where N is the size of the population). Next, a table of random numbers or a random number generator is used to select n items into the sample. A random number generator is usually a computer program that allows computer-calculated output to yield random numbers. Table 1.1 contains a brief table of random numbers. Table A.1 in Appendix A contains a full table of random numbers. These numbers are random in all directions. The spaces in the table are there only for ease of reading the values. For each number, any of the 10 digits (0–9) is equally likely, so getting the same digit twice or more in a row is possible.

As an example, from the population frame of companies listed in Table 1.2, we will use simple random sampling to select a sample of six companies. First, we number every member of the population. We select as many digits for each unit sampled as there are in the largest number in the population. For example, if a population has 2,000 members, we select four-digit numbers. Because the population in Table 1.2 contains 30 members, only two digits need be selected for each number. The population is numbered from 01 to 30, as shown in Table 1.3.

The object is to sample six companies, so six different two-digit numbers must be selected from the table of random numbers. Because this population contains only 30 companies, all numbers greater than 30 (31–99) must be ignored. If, for example, the number 67 is selected, the process is continued until a value between 1 and 30 is obtained. If the same number occurs more than once, we proceed to another number. For ease of understanding, we start with the first pair of digits in Table 1.1 and proceed across the first row until $n = 6$ different values between 01 and 30 are selected. If additional numbers are needed, we proceed

TABLE 1.1							
A Brief Table of Random Numbers							
91567	42595	27958	30134	04024	86385	29880	99730
46503	18584	18845	49618	02304	51038	20655	58727
34914	63976	88720	82765	34476	17032	87589	40836
57491	16703	23167	49323	45021	33132	12544	41035
30405	83946	23792	14422	15059	45799	22716	19792
09983	74353	68668	30429	70735	25499	16631	35006
85900	07119	97336	71048	08178	77233	13916	47564

TABLE 1.2			
A Population Frame of 30 Companies	Alaska Airlines	DuPont	Lucent
	Alcoa	Exxon Mobil	Mattel
	Ashland	General Dynamics	Mead
	Bank of America	General Electric	Microsoft
	BellSouth	General Mills	Occidental Petroleum
	Chevron	Halliburton	JCPenney
	Citigroup	IBM	Procter & Gamble
	Clorox	Kellogg	Ryder
	Delta Air Lines	Kmart	Sears
	Disney	Lowe's	Time Warner

TABLE 1.3			
Numbered Population of 30 Companies	01 Alaska Airlines	11 DuPont	21 Lucent
	02 Alcoa	12 Exxon Mobil	22 Mattel
	03 Ashland	13 General Dynamics	23 Mead
	04 Bank of America	14 General Electric	24 Microsoft
	05 BellSouth	15 General Mills	25 Occidental Petroleum
	06 Chevron	16 Halliburton	26 JCPenney
	07 Citigroup	17 IBM	27 Procter & Gamble
	08 Clorox	18 Kellogg	28 Ryder
	09 Delta Air Lines	19 Kmart	29 Sears
	10 Disney	20 Lowe's	30 Time Warner

across the second row, and so on. Often a researcher will start at some randomly selected location in the table and proceed in a predetermined direction to select numbers.

In the first row of digits in Table 1.1, the first number is 91. This number is out of range so it is cast out. The next two digits are 56. Next is 74, followed by 25, which is the first usable number. From Table 1.3, we see that 25 is the number associated with Occidental Petroleum, so Occidental Petroleum is the first company selected into the sample. The next number is 95, unusable, followed by 27, which is usable. Twenty-seven is the number for Procter & Gamble, so this company is selected. Continuing the process, we pass over the numbers 95 and 83. The next usable number is 01, which is the value for Alaska Airlines. Thirty-four is next, followed by 04 and 02, both of which are usable. These numbers are associated with Bank of America and Alcoa, respectively. Continuing along the first row, the next usable number is 29, which is associated with Sears. Because this selection is the sixth, the sample is complete. The following companies constitute the final sample.

> Alaska Airlines
> Alcoa
> Bank of America
> Occidental Petroleum
> Procter & Gamble
> Sears

Simple random sampling is easier to perform on small than on large populations. The process of numbering all the members of the population and selecting items is cumbersome for large populations.

Stratified Random Sampling

A second type of random sampling is **stratified random sampling,** in which the population is divided into nonoverlapping subpopulations called strata. The researcher then extracts a simple random sample from each of the subpopulations. The main reason for using stratified random sampling is that it has the potential for reducing sampling error.

Sampling error occurs when, by chance, the sample does not represent the population. With stratified random sampling, the potential to match the sample closely to the population is greater than it is with simple random sampling because portions of the total sample are taken from different population subgroups. However, stratified random sampling is generally more costly than simple random sampling because each unit of the population must be assigned to a stratum before the random selection process begins.

Strata selection is usually based on available information. Such information may have been gleaned from previous censuses or surveys. Stratification benefits increase as the strata differ more. Internally, a stratum should be relatively homogeneous; externally, strata should contrast with each other. Stratification is often done by using demographic variables, such as gender, socioeconomic class, geographic region, religion, and ethnicity. For example, if a U.S. presidential election poll is to be conducted by a market research firm, what important variables should be stratified? The gender of the respondent might make a difference because a gender gap in voter preference has been noted in past elections; that is, men and women tended to vote differently in national elections. Geographic region also provides an important variable in national elections because voters are influenced by local cultural values that differ from region to region. Voters in the South voted almost exclusively for Democrats in the past, but recently they tended to vote for Republican candidates in national elections. Voters in the Rocky Mountain states supported Republican presidential candidates; in the industrial Northeast, voters were more inclined toward Democratic candidates.

In FM radio markets, age of listener is an important determinant of the type of programming used by a station. Figure 1.1 contains a stratification by age with three strata, based on the assumption that age makes a difference in preference of programming. This stratification implies that listeners 20 to 30 years of age tend to prefer the same type of programming, which is different from that preferred by listeners 30 to 40 and 40 to 50 years of age. Within each age subgroup (stratum), *homogeneity* or alikeness is present; between each pair of subgroups a difference, or *heterogeneity,* is present.

Stratified random sampling can be either proportionate or disproportionate. **Proportionate stratified random sampling** occurs *when the percentage of the sample taken from each stratum is proportionate to the percentage that each stratum is within the whole population.* For example, suppose voters are being surveyed in Boston and the sample is being stratified by religion as Catholic, Protestant, Jewish, and others. If Boston's population is 90% Catholic and if a sample of 1,000 voters is taken, the sample would require inclusion of 900 Catholics to achieve proportionate stratification. Any other number of Catholics would be disproportionate stratification. The sample proportion of other religions would also have to follow population percentages. Or consider the city of El Paso, Texas, where the population is approximately 77% Hispanic. If a researcher is conducting a citywide poll in El Paso and if stratification is by ethnicity, a proportionate stratified random sample should contain 77% Hispanics. Hence, an ethnically proportionate stratified

FIGURE 1.1

Stratified Random Sampling of FM Radio Listeners

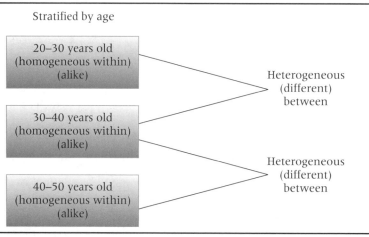

sample of 160 residents from El Paso's 600,000 residents should contain approximately 123 Hispanics. *Whenever the proportions of the strata in the sample are different from the proportions of the strata in the population,* **disproportionate stratified random sampling** occurs.

Systematic Sampling

Systematic sampling is a third random sampling technique. Unlike stratified random sampling, systematic sampling is not done in an attempt to reduce sampling error. Rather, systematic sampling is used because of its convenience and relative ease of administration. With **systematic sampling,** *every k^{th} item is selected to produce a sample of size n from a population of size N.* The value of k, sometimes called the sampling cycle, can be determined by the following formula. If k is not an integer value, the whole-number value should be used.

DETERMINING THE VALUE OF *k*	$$k = \frac{N}{n}$$

where

n = sample size
N = population size
k = size of interval for selection

As an example of systematic sampling, a management information systems researcher wanted to sample the manufacturers in Texas. He had enough financial support to sample 1,000 companies (n). The *Directory of Texas Manufacturers* listed approximately 17,000 total manufacturers in Texas (N) in alphabetical order. The value of k was 17 (17,000/1,000) and the researcher selected every 17th company in the directory for his sample.

Did the researcher begin with the first company listed or the 17th or one somewhere between? In selecting every kth value, a simple random number table should be used to select a value between 1 and k inclusive as a starting point. The second element for the sample is the starting point plus k. In the example, $k = 17$, so the researcher would have gone to a table of random numbers to determine a starting point between 1 and 17. Suppose he selected the number 5. He would have started with the 5th company, then selected the 22nd (5 + 17), and then the 39th, and so on.

Besides convenience, systematic sampling has other advantages. Because systematic sampling is evenly distributed across the frame, a knowledgeable person can easily determine whether a sampling plan has been followed in a study. However, a problem with systematic sampling can occur if the data are subject to any periodicity, and the sampling interval is in syncopation with it. In such a case, the sampling would be nonrandom. For example, if a list of 150 college students is actually a merged list of five classes with 30 students in each class and if each of the lists of the five classes has been ordered with the names of top students first and bottom students last, then systematic sampling of every 30th student could cause selection of all top students, all bottom students, or all mediocre students; that is, the original list is subject to a cyclical or periodic organization. Systematic sampling methodology is based on the assumption that the source of population elements is random.

Cluster (or Area) Sampling

Cluster (or area) sampling is a fourth type of random sampling. **Cluster (or area) sampling** involves dividing the population into nonoverlapping areas or clusters. However, in contrast to stratified random sampling where strata are homogeneous, cluster sampling identifies clusters that tend to be internally heterogeneous. In theory, each cluster contains a wide variety of elements, and the cluster is a miniature, or microcosm, of the population. Examples of clusters are towns, companies, homes, colleges, areas of a city, and geographic regions. Often clusters are naturally occurring groups of the population and are already identified, such as states or Standard Metropolitan Statistical Areas. Although area sampling usually refers to clusters that are areas of the population, such as geographic regions and cities, the terms *cluster sampling* and *area sampling* are used interchangeably in this text.

After choosing the clusters, the researcher randomly selects individual elements into the sample from the clusters. One example of business research that makes use of clustering is test marketing of new products. Often in test marketing, the United States is divided into clusters of test market cities, and individual consumers within the test market cities are surveyed. Figure 1.2 shows some U.S. test market cities that are used as clusters to test products. The Statistics in Business Today feature on test market cities discusses some of the more frequently researched U.S. cities.

Sometimes the clusters are too large, and a second set of clusters is taken from each original cluster. This technique is called **two-stage sampling.** For example, a researcher could divide the United States into clusters of cities. She could then divide the cities into clusters of blocks and randomly select individual houses from the block clusters. The first stage is selecting the test cities and the second stage is selecting the blocks.

Cluster or area sampling offers several advantages. Two of the foremost advantages are convenience and cost. Clusters are usually convenient to obtain, and the cost of sampling from the entire population is reduced because the scope of the study is reduced to the clusters. The cost per element is usually lower in cluster or area sampling than in stratified sampling because of lower element listing or locating costs. The time and cost of contacting elements of the population can be reduced, especially if travel is involved, because clustering reduces the distance to the sampled elements. In addition, administration of the sample survey can be simplified. Sometimes cluster or area sampling is the only feasible approach because the sampling frames of the individual elements of the population are unavailable and therefore other random sampling techniques cannot be used.

Cluster or area sampling also has several disadvantages. If the elements of a cluster are similar, cluster sampling may be statistically less efficient than simple random sampling. In an extreme case—when the elements of a cluster are the same—sampling from the cluster may be no better than sampling a single unit from the cluster. Moreover, the costs and problems of statistical analysis are greater with cluster or area sampling than with simple random sampling.

Nonrandom Sampling

Sampling techniques used to select elements from the population by any mechanism that does not involve a random selection process are called **nonrandom sampling techniques.** Because chance is not used to select items from the samples, these techniques are nonprobability techniques and are not desirable for use in gathering data to be analyzed by the methods of

FIGURE 1.2

Some Test Market Cities

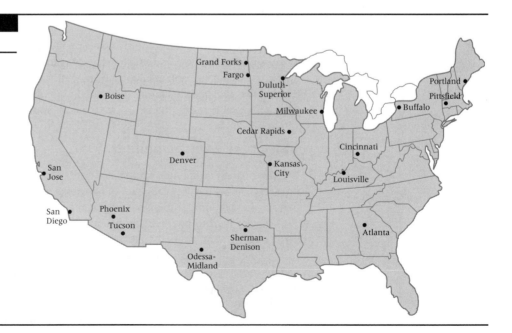

Test Market Cities

Particular cities are chosen as test markets for a variety of reasons, including demographics, psychographics, familiarity, convenience, and others. The most surveyed metropolitan area in the United States is Odessa–Midland, Texas, where residents receive more calls per capita than those in any other area. Odessa–Midland is followed by Portland, Maine, and Boulder–Longmont, Colorado, respectively. The table shows the 10 most surveyed metropolitan areas according to Survey Sampling of Fairfield, Connecticut.

The most surveyed cities are not necessarily the most representative of the United States. Tulsa is not one of the most surveyed cities but is believed to be the city that comes closest to the national demographic profile in terms of population, age, ethnicity, and housing values. The runner-up is Charleston, West Virginia.

Market researchers have different criteria for selecting test market cities. Some of the rationale is proprietary. A test market is sometimes chosen because the company has used that city in a previous test and the product went on to be successful. Other markets are convenient or comfortable to the researcher.

Certain products are targeted toward particular demographic or psychographic segments of the population. The selection of a test market city might be based on which city has the highest number or proportion of people in those targeted segments. Still other factors can enter into the selection of a test market city. Spill-in occurs when two or more markets are so close together that people from other areas come "in" to shop. Spill-over occurs when a test market is influenced by media from other areas. Both are problems that are taken into consideration in selecting a test market city. For example, even though Baltimore is the number one city psychographically, it is affected by spill-in from Washington, D.C., so the Baltimore market is difficult to isolate and study without taking Washington, D.C., into consideration. For this reason and others, *Marketing News* rated Boise, Idaho, as one of the best places to market consumer goods in the United States. It is a microcosm of the nation, yet is an isolated media island that allows for research design control.

MOST SURVEYED METROPOLITAN AREAS

Rank	Metropolitan Area
1	Odessa–Midland, TX
2	Portland, ME
3	Boulder–Longmont, CO
4	Grand Forks, ND–MN
5	Phoenix–Mesa, AZ
6	Denver, CO
7	Fargo–Moorhead, ND–MN
8	Boise, ID
9	Tucson, AZ
10	Pittsfield, MA

inferential statistics presented in this text. Sampling error cannot be determined objectively for these sampling techniques. Four nonrandom sampling techniques are presented here: convenience sampling, judgment sampling, quota sampling, and snowball sampling.

Convenience Sampling

In **convenience sampling,** *elements for the sample are selected for the convenience of the researcher.* The researcher typically chooses elements that are readily available, nearby, or willing to participate. The sample tends to be less variable than the population because in many environments the extreme elements of the population are not readily available. The researcher will select more elements from the middle of the population. For example, a convenience sample of homes for door-to-door interviews might include houses where people are at home, houses with no dogs, houses near the street, first-floor apartments, and houses with friendly people. In contrast, a random sample would require the researcher to gather data only from houses and apartments that have been selected randomly, no matter how inconvenient or unfriendly the location. If a research firm is located in a mall, a convenience sample might be selected by interviewing only shoppers who pass the shop and look friendly.

Judgment Sampling

Judgment sampling occurs when *elements selected for the sample are chosen by the judgment of the researcher.* Researchers often believe they can obtain a representative sample by using sound judgment, which will result in saving time and money. Sometimes ethical, professional researchers might believe they can select a more representative sample than the random process will provide. They might be right! However, some studies show that random sampling methods outperform judgment sampling in estimating the population mean even when the researcher who is administering the judgment sampling is trying to put together a representative sample. When sampling is done by judgment, calculating the probability that an element is going to be selected into the sample is not possible. The sampling error cannot be determined objectively because probabilities are based on *nonrandom* selection.

Other problems are associated with judgment sampling. The researcher tends to make errors of judgment in one direction. These systematic errors lead to what are called *biases*. The researcher also is unlikely to include extreme elements. Judgment sampling provides no objective method for determining whether one person's judgment is better than another's.

Quota Sampling

A third nonrandom sampling technique is **quota sampling,** which appears to be similar to stratified random sampling. Certain population subclasses, such as age group, gender, or geographic region, are used as strata. However, instead of randomly sampling from each stratum, the researcher uses a nonrandom sampling method to gather data from one stratum until the desired quota of samples is filled. Quotas are described by quota controls, which set the sizes of the samples to be obtained from the subgroups. Generally, a quota is based on the proportions of the subclasses in the population. In this case, the quota concept is similar to that of proportional stratified sampling.

Quotas often are filled by using available, recent, or applicable elements. For example, instead of randomly interviewing people to obtain a quota of Italian Americans, the researcher would go to the Italian area of the city and interview there until enough responses are obtained to fill the quota. In quota sampling, an interviewer would begin by asking a few filter questions; if the respondent represents a subclass whose quota has been filled, the interviewer would terminate the interview.

Quota sampling can be useful if no frame is available for the population. For example, suppose a researcher wants to stratify the population into owners of different types of cars but fails to find any lists of Toyota van owners. Through quota sampling, the researcher would proceed by interviewing all car owners and casting out non–Toyota van owners until the quota of Toyota van owners is filled.

Quota sampling is less expensive than most random sampling techniques because it essentially is a technique of convenience. However, cost may not be meaningful because the quality of nonrandom and random sampling techniques cannot be compared. Another advantage of quota sampling is the speed of data gathering. The researcher does not have to call back or send out a second questionnaire if he does not receive a response; he just moves on to the next element. Also, preparatory work for quota sampling is minimal.

The main problem with quota sampling is that, when all is said and done, it still is only a *nonrandom* sampling technique. Some researchers believe that if the quota is filled by *randomly* selecting elements and discarding those not from a stratum, quota sampling is essentially a version of stratified random sampling. However, most quota sampling is carried out by the researcher going where the quota can be filled quickly. The object is to gain the benefits of stratification without the high field costs of stratification. Ultimately, it remains a nonprobability sampling method.

Snowball Sampling

Another nonrandom sampling technique is **snowball sampling,** in which *survey subjects are selected based on referral from other survey respondents.* The researcher identifies a person who fits the profile of subjects wanted for the study. The researcher then asks this person for the names and locations of others who would also fit the profile of subjects wanted for the study. Through these referrals, survey subjects can be identified cheaply and efficiently, which is particularly useful when survey subjects are difficult to locate. It is the main advantage of snowball sampling; its main disadvantage is that it is nonrandom.

Sampling Error

Sampling error occurs *when the sample is not representative of the population.* When random sampling techniques are used to select elements for the sample, sampling error occurs by chance. Many times the statistic computed on the sample is not an accurate estimate of the population parameter because the sample was not representative of the population. This result is caused by sampling error. With random samples, sampling error can be computed and analyzed.

Nonsampling Errors

All errors other than sampling errors are **nonsampling errors.** The many possible nonsampling errors include missing data, recording errors, input processing errors, and analysis errors. Other nonsampling errors result from the measurement instrument, such as errors of unclear definitions, defective questionnaires, and poorly conceived concepts. Improper definition of the frame is a nonsampling error. In many cases, finding a frame that perfectly fits the population is impossible. Insofar as it does not fit, a nonsampling error has been committed.

Response errors are also nonsampling errors. They occur when people do not know, will not say, or overstate. Virtually no statistical method is available to measure or control for nonsampling errors. The statistical techniques presented in this text are based on the assumption that none of these nonsampling errors were committed. The researcher must eliminate these errors through carefully planning and executing the research study.

1.1 PROBLEMS

1.1 Develop a frame for the population of each of the following research projects.
   a. Measuring the job satisfaction of all union employees in a company
   b. Conducting a telephone survey in Utica, New York, to determine the level of interest in opening a new hunting and fishing specialty store in the mall
   c. Interviewing passengers of a major airline about its food service
   d. Studying the quality control programs of boat manufacturers
   e. Attempting to measure the corporate culture of cable television companies

1.2 Make a list of 20 people you know. Include men and women, various ages, various educational levels, and so on. Number the list and then use the random number list in Table 1.1 to select six people randomly from your list. How representative of the population is the sample? Find the proportion of men in your population and in your sample. How do the proportions compare? Find the proportion of 20-year-olds in your sample and the proportion in the population. How do they compare?

1.3 Use the random numbers in Table A.1 of Appendix A to select 10 of the companies from the 30 companies listed in Table 1.2. Compare the types of companies in your sample with the types in the population. How representative of the population is your sample?

1.4 For each of the following research projects, list three variables for stratification of the sample.
   a. A nationwide study of motels and hotels is being conducted. An attempt will be made to determine the extent of the availability of online links for customers. A sample of motels and hotels will be taken.
   b. A consumer panel is to be formed by sampling people in Michigan. Members of the panel will be interviewed periodically in an effort to understand current consumer attitudes and behaviors.
   c. A large soft drink company wants to study the characteristics of the U.S. bottlers of its products, but the company does not want to conduct a census.

    d. The business research bureau of a large university is conducting a project in which the bureau will sample paper-manufacturing companies.

1.5 In each of the following cases, the variable represents one way that a sample can be stratified in a study. For each variable, list some strata into which the variable can be divided.

    a. Age of respondent (person)

    b. Size of company (sales volume)

    c. Size of retail outlet (square feet)

    d. Geographic location

    e. Occupation of respondent (person)

    f. Type of business (company)

1.6 A city's telephone book lists 100,000 people. If the telephone book is the frame for a study, how large would the sample size be if systematic sampling were done on every 200th person?

1.7 If every 11th item is systematically sampled to produce a sample size of 75 items, approximately how large is the population?

1.8 If a company employs 3,500 people and if a random sample of 175 of these employees has been taken by systematic sampling, what is the value of k? The researcher would start the sample selection between what two values? Where could the researcher obtain a frame for this study?

1.9 For each of the following research projects, list at least one area or cluster that could be used in obtaining the sample.

    a. A study of road conditions in the state of Missouri

    b. A study of U.S. offshore oil wells

    c. A study of the environmental effects of petrochemical plants west of the Mississippi River

1.10 Give an example of how judgment sampling could be used in a study to determine how district attorneys feel about attorneys advertising on television.

1.11 Give an example of how convenience sampling could be used in a study of *Fortune* 500 executives to measure corporate attitude toward paternity leave for employees.

1.12 Give an example of how quota sampling could be used to conduct sampling by a company test marketing a new personal computer.

1.2 SAMPLING DISTRIBUTION OF $\bar{x}$

In the inferential statistics process, a researcher selects a random sample from the population, computes a statistic on the sample, and reaches conclusions about the population parameter from the statistic. In attempting to analyze the sample statistic, it is essential to know the distribution of the statistic. So far we studied several distributions, including the binomial distribution, the Poisson distribution, the hypergeometric distribution, the uniform distribution, the normal distribution, and the exponential distribution.

    In this section we explore the sample mean, $\bar{x}$, as the statistic. The sample mean is one of the more common statistics used in the inferential process. To compute and assign the probability of occurrence of a particular value of a sample mean, the researcher must know the distribution of the sample means. One way to examine the distribution possibilities is to take a population with a particular distribution, randomly select samples of a given size, compute the sample means, and attempt to determine how the means are distributed.

    Suppose a small finite population consists of only $N = 8$ numbers:

54   55   59   63   64   68   69   70

Using an Excel-produced histogram, we can see the shape of the distribution of this population of data.

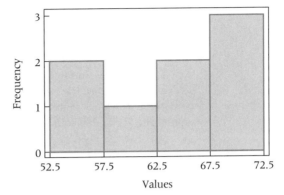

Suppose we take all possible samples of size $n = 2$ from this population with replacement. The result is the following pairs of data.

(54,54)	(55,54)	(59,54)	(63,54)
(54,55)	(55,55)	(59,55)	(63,55)
(54,59)	(55,59)	(59,59)	(63,59)
(54,63)	(55,63)	(59,63)	(63,63)
(54,64)	(55,64)	(59,64)	(63,64)
(54,68)	(55,68)	(59,68)	(63,68)
(54,69)	(55,69)	(59,69)	(63,69)
(54,70)	(55,70)	(59,70)	(63,70)
(64,54)	(68,54)	(69,54)	(70,54)
(64,55)	(68,55)	(69,55)	(70,55)
(64,59)	(68,59)	(69,59)	(70,59)
(64,63)	(68,63)	(69,63)	(70,63)
(64,64)	(68,64)	(69,64)	(70,64)
(64,68)	(68,68)	(69,68)	(70,68)
(64,69)	(68,69)	(69,69)	(70,69)
(64,70)	(68,70)	(69,70)	(70,70)

The means of each of these samples follow.

54	54.5	56.5	58.5	59	61	61.5	62
54.5	55	57	59	59.5	61.5	62	62.5
56.5	57	59	61	61.5	63.5	64	64.5
58.5	59	61	63	63.5	65.5	66	66.5
59	59.5	61.5	63.5	64	66	66.5	67
60	61.5	63.5	65.5	66	68	68.5	69
61.5	62	64	66	66.5	68.5	69	69.5
62	62.5	64.5	66.5	67	69	69.5	70

Again using an Excel-produced histogram, we can see the shape of the distribution of these sample means.

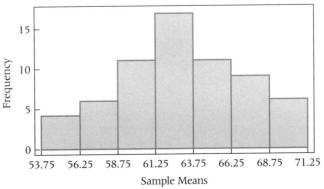

Notice that the shape of the histogram for sample means is quite unlike the shape of the histogram for the population. The sample means appear to "pile up" toward the middle of the distribution and "tail off" toward the extremes.

Figure 1.3 is a MINITAB histogram of the data from a Poisson distribution of values with a population mean of 1.25. Note that the histogram is skewed to the right. Suppose 90 samples of size $n = 30$ are taken randomly from a Poisson distribution with $\lambda = 1.25$ and the means are computed on each sample. The resulting distribution of sample means is displayed in Figure 1.4. Notice that although the samples were drawn from a Poisson distribution, which is skewed to the right, the sample means form a distribution that approaches a symmetrical, nearly normal-curve-type distribution.

Suppose a population is uniformly distributed. If samples are selected randomly from a population with a uniform distribution, how are the sample means distributed? Figure 1.5 displays the MINITAB histogram distributions of sample means from five different sample sizes. Each of these histograms represents the distribution of sample means from 90 samples generated randomly from a uniform distribution in which $a = 10$ and $b = 30$. Observe the shape of the distributions. Notice that even for small sample sizes, the distributions of sample means for samples taken from the uniformly distributed population begin to "pile up" in the middle. As sample sizes become much larger, the sample mean distributions begin to approach a normal distribution and the variation among the means decreases.

So far, we examined three populations with different distributions. However, the sample means for samples taken from these populations appear to be approximately normally distributed, especially as the sample sizes become larger. What would happen to the distribution of sample means if we studied populations with differently shaped distributions? The answer to that question is given in the **central limit theorem**.

FIGURE 1.3

MINITAB Histogram of a
Poisson Distributed Population,
$\lambda = 1.25$

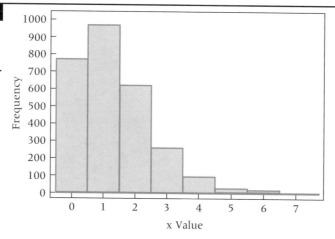

FIGURE 1.4

MINITAB Histogram of
Sample Means

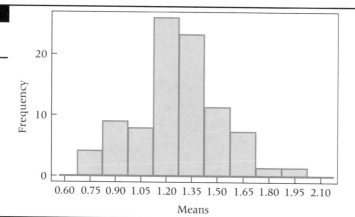

FIGURE I.5

FIGURE I.5   MINITAB Outputs for Sample Means from 90 Samples Ranging in Size from $n = 2$ to $n = 30$ from a Uniformly Distributed Population with $a = 10$ and $b = 30$

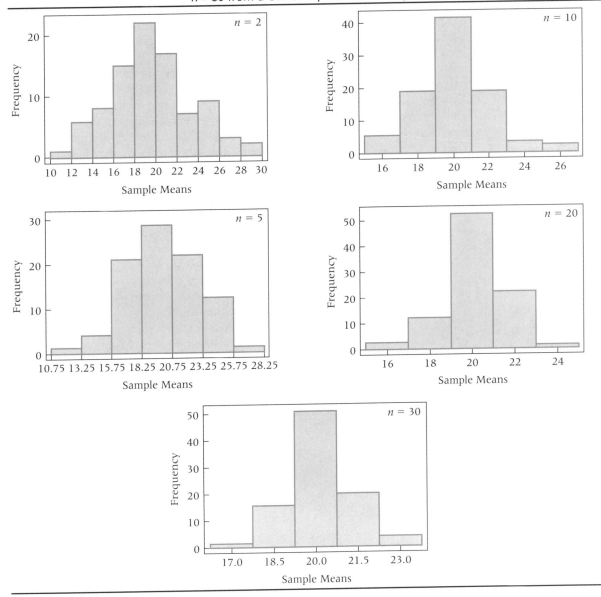

CENTRAL LIMIT THEOREM	If samples of size n are drawn randomly from a population that has a mean of μ and a standard deviation of σ, the sample means, $\bar{x}$, are approximately normally distributed for sufficiently large sample sizes ($n \geq 30$) regardless of the shape of the population distribution. If the population is normally distributed, the sample means are normally distributed for any size sample.

From mathematical expectation,* it can be shown that the mean of the sample means is the population mean.

$$\mu_{\bar{x}} = \mu$$

and the standard deviation of the sample means (called the standard error of the mean) is the standard deviation of the population divided by the square root of the sample size.

$$\sigma_{\bar{x}} = \frac{\sigma}{\sqrt{n}}$$

*The derivations are beyond the scope of this text and are not shown.

The central limit theorem creates the potential for applying the normal distribution to many problems when sample size is sufficiently large. Sample means that have been computed for random samples drawn from normally distributed populations are normally distributed. However, the real advantage of the central limit theorem comes when sample data drawn from populations not normally distributed or from populations of unknown shape also can be analyzed by using the normal distribution because the sample means are normally distributed for sufficiently large sample sizes.* Column 1 of Figure 1.6 shows four different population distributions. Each succeeding column displays the shape of the distribution of the sample means for a particular sample size. Note in the bottom row for the normally distributed population that the sample means are normally distributed even for $n = 2$. Note also that with the other population distributions, the distribution of the sample means begins to approximate the normal curve as n becomes larger. For all four distributions, the distribution of sample means is approximately normal for $n = 30$.

How large must a sample be for the central limit theorem to apply? The sample size necessary varies according to the shape of the population. However, in this text (as in many others), a sample of *size 30 or larger* will suffice. Recall that if the population is normally distributed, the sample means are normally distributed for sample sizes as small as $n = 1$.

The shapes displayed in Figure 1.6 coincide with the results obtained empirically from the random sampling shown in Figures 1.4 and 1.5. As shown in Figure 1.6, and as indicated in Figure 1.5, as sample size increases, the distribution narrows, or becomes more leptokurtic. This trend makes sense because the standard deviation of the mean is $\sigma/\sqrt{n}$. This value will become smaller as the size of n increases.

In Table 1.4, the means and standard deviations of the means are displayed for random samples of various sizes ($n = 2$ through $n = 30$) drawn from the uniform distribution

---

* The actual form of the central limit theorem is a limit function of calculus. As the sample size increases to infinity, the distribution of sample means literally becomes normal in shape.

FIGURE 1.6

Shapes of the Distributions of Sample Means for Three Sample Sizes Drawn from Four Different Population Distributions

| Population distribution | $n = 2$ | $n = 5$ | $n = 30$ |

Exponential

Uniform

U-shaped

Normal

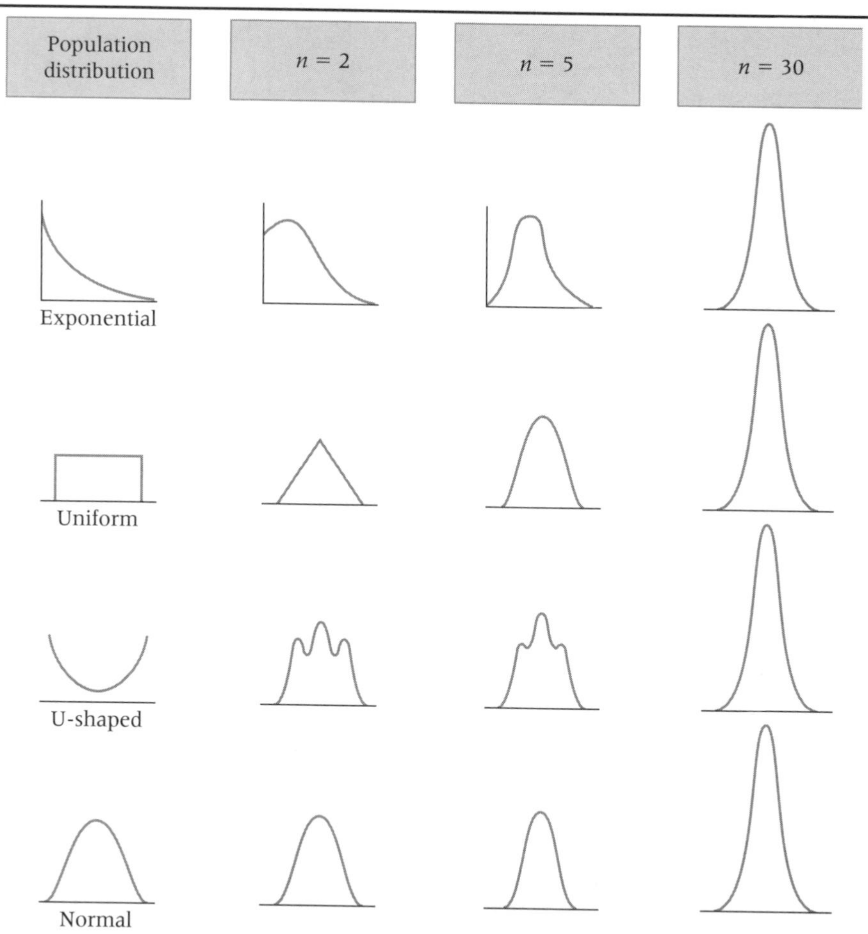

TABLE 1.4

$\mu_{\bar{x}}$ and $\sigma_{\bar{x}}$ of 90 Random Samples for Five Different Sizes*

Sample Size	Mean of Sample Means	Standard Deviation of Sample Means	μ	$\frac{\sigma}{\sqrt{n}}$
$n = 2$	19.92	3.87	20	4.08
$n = 5$	20.17	2.65	20	2.58
$n = 10$	20.04	1.96	20	1.83
$n = 20$	20.20	1.37	20	1.29
$n = 30$	20.25	0.99	20	1.05

*Randomly generated by using MINITAB from a uniform distribution with $a = 10, b = 30$.

of $a = 10$ and $b = 30$ shown in Figure 1.5. The population mean is 20, and the standard deviation of the population is 5.774. Note that the mean of the sample means for each sample size is approximately 20 and that the standard deviation of the sample means for each set of 90 samples is approximately equal to $\sigma/\sqrt{n}$. A small discrepancy occurs between the standard deviation of the sample means and $\sigma/\sqrt{n}$, because not all possible samples of a given size were taken from the population (only 90). In theory, if all possible samples for a given sample size are taken exactly once, the mean of the sample means will equal the population mean and the standard deviation of the sample means will equal the population standard deviation divided by the square root of n.

The central limit theorem states that sample means are normally distributed regardless of the shape of the population for large samples and for any sample size with normally distributed populations. Thus, sample means can be analyzed by using z scores. The formula to determine z scores for individual values from a normal distribution:

$$z = \frac{x - \mu}{\sigma}$$

If sample means are normally distributed, the z score formula applied to sample means would be

$$z = \frac{\bar{x} - \mu_{\bar{x}}}{\sigma_{\bar{x}}}$$

This result follows the general pattern of z scores: the difference between the statistic and its mean divided by the statistic's standard deviation. In this formula, the mean of the statistic of interest is $\mu_{\bar{x}}$, and *the standard deviation of the statistic of interest is* $\sigma_{\bar{x}}$, sometimes referred to as **the standard error of the mean.** To determine $\mu_{\bar{x}}$, the researcher would randomly draw out all possible samples of the given size from the population, compute the sample means, and average them. This task is virtually impossible to accomplish in any realistic period of time. Fortunately, $\mu_{\bar{x}}$ equals the population mean, μ, which is easier to access. Likewise, to determine directly the value of $\sigma_{\bar{x}}$, the researcher would take all possible samples of a given

FIGURE 1.7

Graphical Solution to the Tire Store Example

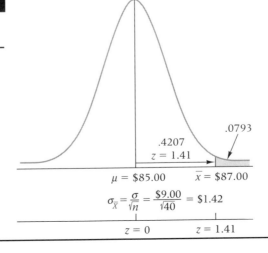

$\mu = \$85.00$ $\bar{x} = \$87.00$

$$\sigma_{\bar{x}} = \frac{\sigma}{\sqrt{n}} = \frac{\$9.00}{\sqrt{40}} = \$1.42$$

$z = 0$ $z = 1.41$

size from a population, compute the sample means, and determine the standard deviation of sample means. This task also is practically impossible. Fortunately, $\sigma_{\bar{x}}$ can be computed by using the population standard deviation divided by the square root of the sample size.

As sample size increases, the standard deviation of the sample means becomes smaller and smaller because the population standard deviation is being divided by larger and larger values of the square root of n. The ultimate benefit of the central limit theorem is a practical, useful version of the z formula for sample means.

z FORMULA FOR SAMPLE MEANS	$$z = \frac{\bar{x} - \mu}{\frac{\sigma}{\sqrt{n}}}$$

When the population is normally distributed and the sample size is 1, this formula for sample means becomes the z formula for individual values. The reason is that the mean of one value is that value, and when $n = 1$ the value of $\sigma/\sqrt{n} = \sigma$.

Suppose, for example, that the mean expenditure per customer at a tire store is $85.00, with a standard deviation of $9.00. If a random sample of 40 customers is taken, what is the probability that the sample average expenditure per customer for this sample will be $87.00 or more? Because the sample size is greater than 30, the central limit theorem can be used, and the sample means are normally distributed. With $\mu = \$85.00$, $\sigma = \$9.00$, and the z formula for sample means, z is computed as

$$z = \frac{\bar{x} - \mu}{\frac{\sigma}{\sqrt{n}}} = \frac{\$87.00 - \$85.00}{\frac{\$9.00}{\sqrt{40}}} = \frac{\$2.00}{\$1.42} = 1.41$$

From the z distribution (Table A.2), $z = 1.41$ produces a probability of .4207. This number is the probability of getting a sample mean between $87.00 and $85.00 (the population mean). Solving for the tail of the distribution yields

$$.5000 - .4207 = .0793$$

which is the probability of $\bar{x} \geq \$87.00$. That is, 7.93% of the time, a random sample of 40 customers from this population will yield a sample mean expenditure of $87.00 or more. Figure 1.7 shows the problem and its solution.

DEMONSTRATION PROBLEM 1.1	Suppose that during any hour in a large department store, the average number of shoppers is 448, with a standard deviation of 21 shoppers. What is the probability that a random sample of 49 different shopping hours will yield a sample mean between 441 and 446 shoppers?

Solution

For this problem, $\mu = 448$, $\sigma = 21$, and $n = 49$. The problem is to determine $P(441 \leq \bar{x} \leq 446)$. The following diagram depicts the problem.

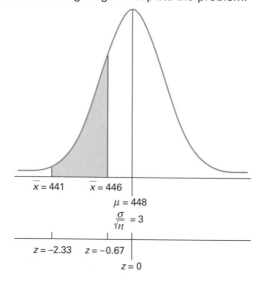

1.14 A population is normally distributed, with a mean of 23.45 and a standard deviation of 3.8. What is the probability of each of the following?

    a. Taking a sample of size 10 and obtaining a sample mean of 22 or more

    b. Taking a sample of size 4 and getting a sample mean of more than 26

1.15 Suppose a random sample of size 36 is drawn from a population with a mean of 278. If 86% of the time the sample mean is less than 280, what is the population standard deviation?

1.16 A random sample of size 81 is drawn from a population with a standard deviation of 12. If only 18% of the time a sample mean greater than 300 is obtained, what is the mean of the population?

1.17 Find the probability in each case.

    a. $N = 1000$, $n = 60$, $\mu = 75$, and $\sigma = 6$; $P(\bar{x} < 76.5) = ?$

    b. $N = 90$, $n = 36$, $\mu = 108$, and $\sigma = 3.46$; $P(107 < \bar{x} < 107.7) = ?$

    c. $N = 250$, $n = 100$, $\mu = 35.6$, and $\sigma = 4.89$; $P(\bar{x} \geq 36) = ?$

    d. $N = 5000$, $n = 60$, $\mu = 125$, and $\sigma = 13.4$; $P(\bar{x} \leq 125) = ?$

1.18 The Statistical Abstract of the United States published by the U.S. Census Bureau reports that the average annual consumption of fresh fruit per person is 99.9 pounds. The standard deviation of fresh fruit consumption is about 30 pounds. Suppose a researcher took a random sample of 38 people and had them keep a record of the fresh fruit they ate for one year.

    a. What is the probability that the sample average would be less than 90 pounds?

    b. What is the probability that the sample average would be between 98 and 105 pounds?

    c. What is the probability that the sample average would be less than 112 pounds?

    d. What is the probability that the sample average would be between 93 and 96 pounds?

1.19 Suppose a subdivision on the southwest side of Denver, Colorado, contains 1,500 houses. The subdivision was built in 1983. A sample of 100 houses is selected randomly and evaluated by an appraiser. If the mean appraised value of a house in this subdivision for all houses is $177,000, with a standard deviation of $8,500, what is the probability that the sample average is greater than $185,000?

1.20 Suppose the average checkout tab at a large supermarket is $65.12, with a standard deviation of $21.45. Twenty-three percent of the time when a random sample of 45 customer tabs is examined, the sample average should exceed what value?

1.21 According to Nielsen Media Research, the average number of hours of TV viewing per household per week in the United States is 50.4 hours. Suppose the standard deviation is 11.8 hours and a random sample of 42 U.S. households is taken.

    a. What is the probability that the sample average is more than 52 hours?

    b. What is the probability that the sample average is less than 47.5 hours?

    c. What is the probability that the sample average is less than 40 hours? If the sample average actually is less than 40 hours, what would it mean in terms of the Nielsen Media Research figures?

    d. Suppose the population standard deviation is unknown. If 71% of all sample means are greater than 49 hours and the population mean is still 50.4 hours, what is the value of the population standard deviation?

1.3 SAMPLING DISTRIBUTION OF $\hat{p}$

Sometimes in analyzing a sample, a researcher will choose to use the sample proportion, denoted $\hat{p}$. If research produces *measurable* data such as weight, distance, time, and income, the sample mean is often the statistic of choice. However, if research results in

FIGURE 1.8

Graphical Solution to the
Electrical Contractor Example

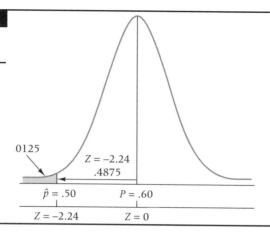

0125

$Z = -2.24$
.4875

$\hat{p} = .50$ $P = .60$

$Z = -2.24$ $Z = 0$

countable items such as how many people in a sample choose Dr. Pepper as their soft drink or how many people in a sample have a flexible work schedule, the sample proportion is often the statistic of choice. Whereas the mean is computed by averaging a set of values, the **sample proportion** is *computed by dividing the frequency with which a given characteristic occurs in a sample by the number of items in the sample.*

SAMPLE PROPORTION	$$\hat{p} = \frac{x}{n}$$

where

x = number of items in a sample that have the characteristic
n = number of items in the sample

For example, in a sample of 100 factory workers, 30 workers might belong to a union. The value of $\hat{p}$ for this characteristic, union membership, is 30/100 = .30. In a sample of 500 businesses in suburban malls, if 10 are shoe stores, then the sample proportion of shoe stores is 10/500 = .02. The sample proportion is a widely used statistic and is usually computed on questions involving Yes or No answers. For example, do you have at least a high school education? Are you predominantly right-handed? Are you female? Do you belong to the student accounting association?

How does a researcher use the sample proportion in analysis? The central limit theorem applies to sample proportions in that the normal distribution approximates the shape of the distribution of sample proportions if $n \cdot p > 5$ and $n \cdot q > 5$ (p is the population proportion and $q = 1 - p$). The mean of sample proportions for all samples of size n randomly drawn from a population is p (the population proportion) and the standard deviation of sample proportions is $\sqrt{(p \cdot q)/n}$, sometimes referred to as the **standard error of the proportion.** Sample proportions also have a z formula.

z FORMULA FOR SAMPLE PROPORTIONS FOR $n \cdot P > 5$ AND $n \cdot Q > 5$	$$z = \frac{\hat{p} - p}{\sqrt{\dfrac{p \cdot q}{n}}}$$

where

$\hat{p}$ = sample proportion
n = sample size
p = population proportion
q = 1 − p

Suppose 60% of the electrical contractors in a region use a particular brand of wire. What is the probability of taking a random sample of size 120 from these electrical contractors and finding that .50 or less use that brand of wire? For this problem,

$$p = .60 \quad \hat{p} = .50 \quad n = 120$$

The z formula yields

$$z = \frac{.50 - .60}{\sqrt{\dfrac{(.60)(.40)}{120}}} = \frac{-.10}{.0447} = -2.24$$

From Table A.2, the probability corresponding to $z = -2.24$ is .4875. For $z < -2.24$ (the tail of the distribution), the answer is $.5000 - .4875 = .0125$. Figure 1.8 shows the problem and solution graphically.

This answer indicates that a researcher would have difficulty (probability of .0125) finding that 50% or less of a sample of 120 contractors use a given brand of wire if indeed the population market share for that wire is .60. If this sample result actually occurs, either it is a rare chance result, the .60 proportion does not hold for this population, or the sampling method may not have been random.

DEMONSTRATION PROBLEM 1.3	If 10% of a population of parts is defective, what is the probability of randomly selecting 80 parts and finding that 12 or more parts are defective?

Solution

Here, $p = .10$, $\hat{p} = 12/80 = .15$, and $n = 80$. Entering these values in the z formula yields

$$z = \frac{.15 - .10}{\sqrt{\dfrac{(.10)(.90)}{80}}} = \frac{.05}{.0335} = 1.49$$

Table A.2 gives a probability of .4319 for a z value of 1.49, which is the area between the sample proportion, .15, and the population proportion, .10. The answer to the question is

$$P(\hat{p} \geq .15) = .5000 - .4319 = .0681.$$

Thus, about 6.81% of the time, 12 or more defective parts would appear in a random sample of 80 parts when the population proportion is .10. If this result actually occurred, the 10% proportion for population defects would be open to question. The diagram shows the problem graphically.

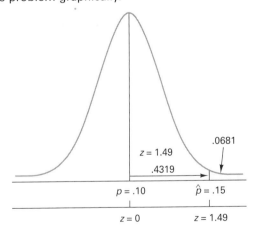

1.3 PROBLEMS

1.22   A given population proportion is .25. For the given value of n, what is the probability of getting each of the following sample proportions?

     a. $n = 110$ and $\hat{p} \leq .21$

     b. $n = 33$ and $\hat{p} > .24$

    c. $\quad n = 59$ and $.24 \leq \hat{p} < .27$

    d. $\quad n = 80$ and $\hat{p} > .30$

    e. $\quad n = 800$ and $\hat{p} > .30$

1.23 A population proportion is .58. Suppose a random sample of 660 items is sampled randomly from this population.

    a. What is the probability that the sample proportion is greater than .60?

    b. What is the probability that the sample proportion is between .55 and .65?

    c. What is the probability that the sample proportion is greater than .57?

    d. What is the probability that the sample proportion is between .53 and .56?

    e. What is the probability that the sample proportion is less than .48?

1.24 Suppose a population proportion is .40, and 80% of the time when you draw a random sample from this population you get a sample proportion of .35 or more. How large a sample were you taking?

1.25 If a population proportion is .28 and if the sample size is 140, 30% of the time the sample proportion will be less than what value if you are taking random samples?

1.26 According to a study by Decision Analyst, 21% of the people who have credit cards are very close to the total limit on the card(s). Suppose a random sample of 600 credit card users is taken. What is the probability that more than 150 credit card users are very close to the total limit on their card(s)?

1.27 According to a survey by Accountemps, 48% of executives believe that employees are most productive on Tuesdays. Suppose 200 executives are randomly surveyed.

    a. What is the probability that fewer than 90 of the executives believe employees are most productive on Tuesdays.

    b. What is the probability that more than 100 of the executives believe employees are most productive on Tuesdays.

    c. What is the probability that more than 80 of the executives believe employees are most productive on Tuesdays

1.28 The Travel Weekly International Air Transport Association survey asked business travelers about the purpose for their most recent business trip. Nineteen percent responded that it was for an internal company visit. Suppose 950 business travelers are randomly selected.

    a. What is the probability that more than 25% of the business travelers say that the reason for their most recent business trip was an internal company visit?

    b. What is the probability that between 15% and 20% of the business travelers say that the reason for their most recent business trip was an internal company visit?

    c. What is the probability that between 133 and 171 of the business travelers say that the reason for their most recent business trip was an internal company visit?

IN RESPONSE

Surveying Maquiladora Workers

Because of limited resources, limited time, and a large population of workers, most work attitude and cultural studies of maquiladora workers probably would be accomplished through the use of random sampling. To ensure the inclusion of certain groups and in an effort to reduce sampling error, a proportionate stratified sampling technique might

1.42 The average cost of a one-bedroom apartment in a town is $550 per month. What is the probability of randomly selecting a sample of 50 one-bedroom apartments in this town and getting a sample mean of less than $530 if the population standard deviation is $100?

1.43 The Aluminum Association reports that the average American uses 56.8 pounds of aluminum in a year. A random sample of 51 households is monitored for one year to determine aluminum usage. If the population standard deviation of annual usage is 12.3 pounds, what is the probability that the sample mean will be each of the following?

  a. More than 60 pounds
  b. More than 58 pounds
  c. Between 56 and 57 pounds
  d. Less than 55 pounds
  e. Less than 50 pounds

1.44 Use Table A.1 to select 20 three-digit random numbers. Did any of the numbers occur more than once? How is it possible for a number to occur more than once? Make a stem and leaf plot of the numbers with the stem being the left digit. Do the numbers seem to be equally distributed, or are they bunched together?

1.45 Direct marketing companies are turning to the Internet for new opportunities. A recent study by Gruppo, Levey, & Co. showed that 73% of all direct marketers conduct transactions on the Internet. Suppose a random sample of 300 direct marketing companies is taken.

  a. What is the probability that between 210 and 234 (inclusive) direct marketing companies are turning to the Internet for new opportunities?

  b. What is the probability that 78% or more of direct marketing companies are turning to the Internet for new opportunities?

  c. Suppose a random sample of 800 direct marketing companies is taken. Now what is the probability that 78% or more are turning to the Internet for new opportunities? How does this answer differ from the answer in part (b)? Why do the answers differ?

1.46 According to the U.S. Bureau of Labor Statistics, 20% of all people 16 years of age or older do volunteer work. Women volunteer slightly more than men, with 22% of women volunteering and 19% of men volunteering. What is the probability of randomly sampling 140 women 16 years of age or older and getting 35 or more who do volunteer work? What is the probability of getting 21 or fewer from this group? Suppose a sample of 300 men and women 16 years of age or older is selected randomly from the U.S. population. What is

the probability that the sample proportion of those who do volunteer work is between 18% and 25%?

1.47 Suppose you work for a large firm that has 20,000 employees. The CEO calls you in and asks you to determine employee attitudes toward the company. She is willing to commit $100,000 to this project. What are the advantages of taking a sample versus conducting a census? What are the trade-offs?

1.48 In a particular area of the Northeast, an estimated 75% of the homes use heating oil as the principal heating fuel during the winter. A random telephone survey of 150 homes is taken in an attempt to determine whether this figure is correct. Suppose 120 of the 150 homes surveyed use heating oil as the principal heating fuel. What is the probability of getting a sample proportion this large or larger if the population estimate is true?

1.49 The U.S. Bureau of Labor Statistics released hourly wage figures for western countries for workers in the manufacturing sector. The hourly wage was $21.24 in Switzerland, $22.00 in Japan, and $19.86 in the United States. Suppose 40 manufacturing workers are selected randomly from across Switzerland and asked what their hourly wage is. What is the probability that the sample average will be between $21 and $22? Suppose 35 manufacturing workers are selected randomly from across Japan. What is the probability that the sample average will exceed $23? Suppose 50 manufacturing workers are selected randomly from across the United States. What is the probability that the sample average will be less than $18.90? Assume that in all three countries, the standard deviation of hourly labor rates is $3.

1.50 Give a variable that could be used to stratify the population for each of the following studies. List at least four subcategories for each variable.

  a. A political party wants to conduct a poll prior to an election for the office of U.S. senator in Minnesota.
  b. A soft drink company wants to take a sample of soft drink purchases in an effort to estimate market share.
  c. A retail outlet wants to interview customers over a one-week period.
  d. An eyeglasses manufacturer and retailer wants to determine the demand for prescription eyeglasses in its marketing region.

1.51 According to Runzheimer International, a typical business traveler spends an average of $281 per day in Chicago. This cost includes hotel, meals, car rental, and incidentals. A survey of 65 randomly selected business travelers who have been to Chicago on business recently is taken. For the population mean of $281 per day, what is the probability of getting a sample average of more than $273 per day if the population standard deviation is $47?

ANALYZING THE DATABASES

see www.wiley.com/college/black

1. Let the manufacturing database be the frame for a population of manufacturers that are to be studied. This database has 140 different SIC Codes. How would you proceed to take a simple random sample of size 6 from these industries? Explain how you would take a systematic sample of size 10 from this frame. Examine the variables in the database. Name two variables that could be used to stratify the population. Explain how these variables could be used in stratification and why they might be important strata.

2. Assume the manufacturing database is the population of interest. Compute the mean and standard deviation for cost of materials on this population. Take a random sample of 32 of the SIC Code categories and compute the sample mean cost of materials on this sample. Using techniques presented in this chapter, determine the probability of getting a mean this large or larger from the population. Note that the population contains only 140 items. Work this problem with and without the finite correction factor. Compare the results and discuss the differences in answers.

3. Use the hospital database to calculate the mean and standard deviation of personnel. Assume that these figures are true for the population of hospitals in the United States. Suppose a random sample of 36 hospitals is taken from hospitals in the United States. What is the probability that the sample mean of personnel is less than 650? What is the probability that the sample mean of personnel is between 700 and 1,100? What is the probability that the sample mean is between 900 and 950?

   Determine the proportion of the hospital database that is under the control of nongovernment not-for-profit organizations (category 2). Assume that this proportion represents the entire population of hospitals. If you randomly selected 500 hospitals from across the United States, what is the probability that 45% or more are under the control of nongovernment not-for-profit organizations? If you randomly selected 100 hospitals, what is the probability that less than 40% are under the control of nongovernment not-for-profit organizations?

CASE: SHELL ATTEMPTS TO RETURN TO PREMIERE STATUS

The Shell Oil Company, which began about 1912, had been for decades a household name as a quality oil company in the United States. However, by the late 1970s much of its prestige as a premiere company had disappeared. How could Shell regain its high status?

In the 1990s, Shell undertook an extensive research effort to find out what it needed to do to improve its image. As a first step, Shell hired Responsive Research and the Opinion Research Corporation to conduct a series of focus groups and personal interviews among various segments of the population. Included in these were youths, minorities, residents in neighborhoods near Shell plants, legislators, academics, and present and past employees of Shell. The researchers learned that people believe that top companies are integral parts of the communities in which the companies are located rather than separate entities. These studies and others led to the development of materials that Shell used to explain their core values to the general public.

Next, PERT Survey Research ran a large quantitative study to determine which values were best received by the target audience. Social issues emerged as the theme with the most support. During the next few months, the advertising agency of Ogilvy & Mather, hired by Shell, developed several campaigns with social themes. Two market research companies were hired to evaluate the receptiveness of the various campaigns. The result was the "Count on Shell" campaign, which featured safety messages with useful information about what to do in various dangerous situations.

A public "Count on Shell" campaign was launched in February 1998 and met with considerable success: the ability to recall Shell advertising jumped from 20% to 32% among opinion influencers; more than 1 million copies of Shell's free safety brochures were distributed; and activity on Shell's Internet "Count on Shell" site remains extremely strong. By promoting itself as a reliable company that cares, Shell seems to be regaining its premiere status.

Today, Shell continues its efforts to be "community friendly." United Way of America announced Shell Oil Company as one of its three Spirit of America Summit Award winners for 2002 and commended the company for its outstanding volunteer and corporate contributions programs. Several Shell employees were recognized by the Houston Minority Business Council for their continued efforts to provide windows of opportunity for minority business owners and strengthen Shell's commitment to supplier diversity. Recently, the Shell Oil Company Foundation donated $120,000 to the National Action Council for Minorities in Engineering in support of the organization's mission to increase the representation of successful African-American, American-Indian and Latino women and men in engineering and technology-, math-, and science-based careers.

Discussion

1. Suppose you were asked to develop a sampling plan to determine what a "premiere company" is to the general public. What sampling plan would you use?

What is the target population? What would you use for a frame? Which of the four types of random sampling discussed in this chapter would you use? Could you use a combination of two or more of the types (two-stage sampling)? If so, how?

2. It appears that at least one of the research companies hired by Shell used some stratification in their sampling. What are some of the variables on which they are stratified? If you were truly interested in ascertaining opinions from a variety of segments of the population with regard to opinions on "premiere" companies or about Shell, what strata might make sense? Name at least five and justify why you would include them.

3. Suppose that in 1979 only 12% of the general adult U.S. public believed that Shell was a "premiere" company. Suppose further that you randomly selected 350 people from the general adult U.S. public this year and 25% said that Shell was a "premiere" company. If only 12% of the general adult U.S. public still believes that Shell is a "premiere" company, how likely is it that the 25% figure is a chance result in sampling 350 people? *Hint:* Use the techniques in this chapter to determine the probability of the 25% figure occurring by chance.

4. PERT Survey Research conducted quantitative surveys in an effort to measure the effectiveness of various campaigns. Suppose they used a 1-to-5 scale where 1 denotes that the campaign is not effective at all, 5 denotes that the campaign is extremely effective, and 2, 3, and 4 fall in between on an interval scale. Suppose also that a particular campaign received an average of 1.8 on the scale with a standard deviation of .7 early in the tests. Later, after the campaign had been critiqued and improved, a survey of 35 people was taken and a sample mean of 2.0 was recorded. What is the probability of this sample mean or greater occurring if the actual population mean is still just 1.8? Based on this probability, do you think that a sample mean of 2.0 is just a chance fluctuation on the 1.8 population mean, or do you think that perhaps it indicates the population mean is now greater than 1.8? Support your conclusion. Suppose a sample mean of 2.5 is attained. What is the likelihood of this result occurring by chance when the population mean is 1.8? Suppose this increase actually happens after the campaign has been improved. What does it mean?

Source: Adapted from "Count on It," *American Demographics*, March 1999, p. 60; "Shell in the U.S.," 2002, available at http://www.shellus.com/.

USING THE COMPUTER

EXCEL

Random numbers can be generated from Excel for several different distributions. The procedure begins with the selection of **Tools** on the menu bar. From the pull-down menu, choose **Data Analysis**. From the menu provided in the **Data Analysis** dialog box, select **Random Number Generation**. In the third line of the Random Number Generation dialog box are the choices of distributions. Select the distribution from which you want to generate random numbers. The options and required responses in the Random Number Generation dialog box will change with the chosen distribution. In each case, the number of variables goes on the first line and the number of random numbers to be generated goes into the second line.

For random number generation from a binomial distribution, place the value of p on the p **Value** = line and n in the **Number of Trials** = line. For random number generation from a normal distribution, place the value of μ on the **Mean** = line and the value of σ on the **Standard Deviation** = line. For random number generation from a Poisson distribution, place the value of λ in the **Lambda** = line. For random number generation from the uniform distribution, place the value of a in the first space after **Between** and the value of b in the second space.

MINITAB

MINITAB Windows has the capability of generating random numbers from many different distributions. We will focus here on the normal distribution, the uniform distribution, the binomial distribution, the Poisson distribution, and the exponential distribution. Begin by selecting **Calc** on the menu bar. On the pull-down menu that appears, select **Random Data**. When the pull-down menu appears, select the distribution from which you want to generate random numbers. A dialog box for the distribution selected will open, which asks you to signify how many rows of data you want to generate. Basically, it wants to know how many random numbers you want to generate for each column. Next, you are asked to signify the columns in which you want the data loaded. For example, if you want to generate 100 random numbers in column 1, you would place 100 (rows of data) on line 1 and C1 on line 2. Each distribution also requires specific parameters. The binomial distribution dialog box asks for **Number of trials:** (place the value of n there) and **Probability of success:** (place the value of p). The exponential distribution dialog box asks for the **Mean:**. Place the value of μ on this line. The normal distribution dialog box asks for the **Mean** (place μ on this line) and the **Standard deviation:** (place σ on this line). The Poisson distribution dialog box asks for the **Mean:**. Place the value of λ on this line. The uniform distribution dialog box asks for the **Lower endpoint:** (place the value of a) and the **Upper endpoint:** (place the value of b).

CHAPTER 2

Statistical Inference: Estimation for Single Populations

LEARNING OBJECTIVES

The overall learning objective of Chapter 2 is to help you understand estimating parameters of single populations, thereby enabling you to:

1. Know the difference between point and interval estimation.
2. Estimate a population mean from a sample mean when σ is known.
3. Estimate a population mean from a sample mean when σ is unknown.
4. Estimate a population proportion from a sample proportion.
5. Estimate the population variance from a sample variance.
6. Estimate the minimum sample size necessary to achieve given statistical goals.

A Report of Surveys on Productivity, Compensation, and Benefits

A number of surveys and studies set out to determine the state of compensation and benefits in the United States. One survey of 1,200 employees found that 25% of U.S. workers believed that they could accomplish at least 50% more on the job each day. Some of the barriers to productivity according to workers and the associated% of the survey respondents who cited them include the following: companies not supervising their work closely enough (37%), companies not involving them enough in decision making (34%), companies not rewarding them for a good job performance (29%), and companies not giving them advancement or promotion opportunities (29%). Twenty-eight% of the workers said that their companies do not train employees to a great extent, and 26% said that companies do not hire the right people.

A survey of 231 human resource specialists conducted by *Compensation & Benefits Review* reported that 12.12% cited managing performance as the dominant issue facing compensation and benefits managers. In addition, 10.39% named team-based pay and 9.96% named competency-based pay as the most pressing issues.

ECS/Watson Wyatt Data Services studied 1,500 companies and found that more than 75% of companies use variable pay for middle managers. The favorite variable pay approach, according to the survey, was annual bonuses. Two-thirds of those companies reporting variable pay plans for middle managers use bonuses. Another survey by Watson Wyatt showed that 26% of supervisors were given cash awards, usually some sort of bonus.

Edward Perlin Associates surveyed sixty-three companies with data-processing professionals to ascertain the prevalence of computer security-related jobs in light of the increase of computer viruses and the compensation for such employees. The average annual compensation including base salary and bonuses for security managers is $79,900. Security heads earn an average total yearly compensation of $94,800. The average figure for security specialists is $42,900.

A survey of 4,800 members of the Institute of Management Accountants showed that the average annual salary in the 30- to 39-year age bracket is $57,937 for certified management accountants compared to $47,332 for uncertified management accountants. In the 19- to 29-year-old age bracket, for certified management accountants the average annual salary is $40,185 and $31,008 for uncertified management accountants.

A survey of 1,935 Internet workers by the Association of Internet Professions revealed that the average annual salary for an online services manager was $59,781, for a software development person was $64,024, and for a media production person was $42,455.

Managerial and Statistical Questions

1. How can the national average salary for computer security positions be estimated using sample data? How much error is involved in such an estimation? How much confidence do we have in this estimation?

2. This Decision Dilemma reports average annual salaries for certified and uncertified management accountants and of Internet workers. However, these figures are based on sample information. How does a business researcher use sample information to estimate population parameters like the mean national average annual salary for accountants? For Internet workers? What is the error in such a process? Are we certain of the results?

3. One survey reported that 37% of the workers felt that companies are not supervising their work enough. This figure came from a survey of 1,200 employees and is only a sample statistic. Can we say from this survey that 37% of all employees in the United States feel this way? Why or why not? Can we use the 37% as an estimate for the population parameter? If we do, how much error is there; and how much confidence do we have in the final results?

4. A survey of 231 human resource specialists found that 12.12% cited that managing performance is the dominant issue facing compensation and benefits managers. Can this figure be used to represent all compensation and benefits managers? If so, how much potential error is there in doing so? Since this sample size is 231 and the sample size for the employee survey on productivity uses a sample size of 1,200, does the accuracy of the results of the two surveys differ? Does the size of the sample enter in to the predictability of a survey's results?

5. Why did these research companies choose to sample 1,200, 231, 1,500, 63, and 4,800 firms or people, respectively? What is the rationale for determining how many to sample other than to sample as few as possible to save time or money? Is a minimum sample size necessary to accomplish estimations?

Source: Adapted from William Lissy and Marlene L. Morgenstern, "Currents in Compensation and Benefits," *Compensation & Benefits Review* (November–December 1995), pp. 15–25; "Compensation by Job Category," *Internet World* (1 February 2000), p. 1.

The central limit theorem presented in Chapter 1 states that certain statistics of interest, such as the sample mean and the sample proportion, are approximately normally distributed for large sample sizes regardless of the shape of the population distribution. The z formulas for each statistic that were developed and discussed can be used in parametric estimation, hypothesis testing, and determination of sample size. This chapter describes how these z formulas can be manipulated algebraically into a format for estimating population parameters and determining the size of samples necessary to conduct research. In addition, mechanisms are introduced for the estimation of population means when the population standard deviation is unknown and for the estimation of population variance.

2.1 ESTIMATING THE POPULATION MEAN USING THE z STATISTIC (σ KNOWN)

On many occasions estimating the population mean is useful in business research. For example, the manager of human resources in a company might want to estimate the average number of days of work an employee misses per year because of illness. If the firm has thousands of employees, direct calculation of a population mean such as this may be practically impossible. Instead, a random sample of employees can be taken, and the sample mean number of sick days can be used to estimate the population mean. Suppose another company developed a new process for prolonging the shelf life of a loaf of bread. The company wants to be able to date each loaf for freshness, but company officials do not know exactly how long the bread will stay fresh. By taking a random sample and determining the sample mean shelf life, they can estimate the average shelf life for the population of bread.

As the cellular telephone industry matures, a cellular telephone company is rethinking its pricing structure. Users appear to be spending more time on the phone and are shopping around for the best deals. To do better planning, the cellular company wants to ascertain the average number of minutes of time used per month by each of its residential users but does not have the resources available to examine all monthly bills and extract the information. The company decides to take a sample of customer bills and estimate the population mean from sample data. A researcher for the company takes a random sample of 85 bills for a recent month and from these bills computes a sample mean of 153 minutes. This sample mean, which is a statistic, is used to estimate the population mean, which is a parameter. If the company uses the sample mean of 153 minutes as an estimate for the population mean, then the sample mean is used as a *point estimate*.

A **point estimate** is *a statistic taken from a sample that is used to estimate a population parameter*. A point estimate is only as good as the representativeness of its sample. If other random samples are taken from the population, the point estimates derived from those samples are likely to vary. Because of variation in sample statistics, estimating a population parameter with an interval estimate is often preferable to using a point estimate. An **interval estimate** (confidence interval) is *a range of values within which the analyst can declare, with some confidence, the population parameter lies.* Confidence intervals can be two-sided or one-sided. This text presents only two-sided confidence intervals. How are confidence intervals constructed?

As a result of the central limit theorem, the following *z* formula for sample means can be used when sample sizes are large, regardless of the shape of the population distribution, or for smaller sizes if the population is normally distributed.

$$z = \frac{\bar{x} - \mu}{\frac{\sigma}{\sqrt{n}}}$$

Rearranging this formula algebraically to solve for μ gives

$$\mu = \bar{x} - z\frac{\sigma}{\sqrt{n}}$$

Because a sample mean can be greater than or less than the population mean, *z* can be positive or negative. Thus the preceding expression takes the following form.

$$\bar{x} \pm z\frac{\sigma}{\sqrt{n}}$$

Rewriting this expression yields the confidence interval formula for estimating μ with large sample sizes.

100(1 – α)% CONFIDENCE INTERVAL TO ESTIMATE μ (2.1)

$$\bar{x} \pm z_{\alpha/2}\frac{\sigma}{\sqrt{n}}$$

or

$$\bar{x} - z_{\alpha/2}\frac{\sigma}{\sqrt{n}} \le \mu \le \bar{x} + z_{\alpha/2}\frac{\sigma}{\sqrt{n}}$$

where

α = the area under the normal curve outside the confidence interval area

$\alpha/2$ = the area in one end (tail) of the distribution outside the confidence interval

---

Alpha (α) is the area under the normal curve in the tails of the distribution outside the area defined by the confidence interval. We will focus more on α in Chapter 3. Here we use α to locate the *z* value in constructing the confidence interval as shown in Figure 2.1. Because the standard normal table is based on areas between a *z* of 0 and $z_{\alpha/2}$, the table *z* value is found by locating the area of .5000 – $\alpha/2$, which is the part of the normal curve between the middle of the curve and one of the tails. Another way to locate this *z* value is to change the confidence level from percentage to proportion, divide it in half, and go to the table with this value. The results are the same.

The confidence interval formula (2.1) yields a range (interval) within which we feel with some confidence the population mean is located. It is not certain that the population mean is in the interval unless we have a 100% confidence interval that is infinitely

---

FIGURE 2.1

z Scores for Confidence Intervals in Relation to α

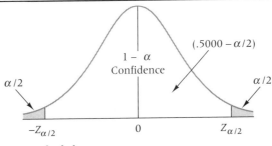

α = shaded area

FIGURE 2.2

Distribution of Sample Means
for 95% Confidence

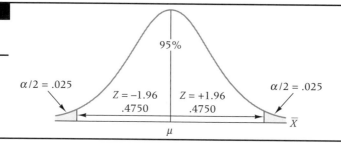

wide. If we want to construct a 95% confidence interval, the level of confidence is 95% or .95. If 100 such intervals are constructed by taking random samples from the population, it is likely that 95 of the intervals would include the population mean and five would not.

As an example, in the cellular telephone company problem of estimating the population mean number of minutes called per residential user per month, from the sample of 85 bills it was determined that the sample mean is 153 minutes. Using this sample mean, a confidence interval can be calculated within which the researcher is relatively confident the actual population mean is located. To make this calculation using formula 2.1, the value of the population standard deviation and the value of z (in addition to the sample mean, 153, and the sample size, 85) must be known. Suppose past history and similar studies indicate that the population standard deviation is 46 minutes.

The value of z is driven by the level of confidence. An interval with 100% confidence is so wide that it is meaningless. Some of the more common levels of confidence used by business researchers are 90%, 95%, 98%, and 99%. Why would a business researcher not just select the highest confidence and always use that level? The reason is that trade-offs between sample size, interval width, and level of confidence must be considered. For example, as the level of confidence is increased, the interval gets wider, provided the sample size and standard deviation remain constant.

FIGURE 2.3

Twenty 95% Confidence
Intervals of μ

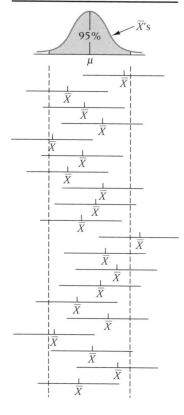

For the cellular telephone problem, suppose the business researcher decided on a 95% confidence interval for the results. Figure 2.2 shows a normal distribution of sample means about the population mean. When using a 95% level of confidence, the researcher selects an interval centered on μ within which 95% of all sample mean values will fall and then uses the width of that interval to create an interval around the *sample mean* within which he has some confidence the population mean will fall.

For 95% confidence, $\alpha = .05$ and $\alpha/2 = .025$. The value of $z_{\alpha/2}$ or $z_{.025}$ is found by looking in the standard normal table under $.5000 - .0250 = .4750$. This area in the table is associated with a z value of 1.96. Another way can be used to locate the table z value. Because the distribution is symmetric and the intervals are equal on each side of the population mean, $\frac{1}{2}(95\%)$, or .4750, of the area is on each side of the mean. Table A.2 yields a z value of 1.96 for this portion of the normal curve. Thus the z value for a 95% confidence interval is always 1.96. In other words, of all the possible $\bar{x}$ values along the horizontal axis of the diagram, 95% of them should be within a z score of 1.96 from the population mean.

The business researcher can now complete the cellular telephone problem. To determine a 95% confidence interval for $\bar{x} = 153$, $\sigma = 46$, $n = 85$, and $z = 1.96$, the researcher estimates the average call length by including the value of z in formula 2.1.

$$153 - 1.96 \frac{46}{\sqrt{85}} \leq \mu \leq 153 + 1.96 \frac{46}{\sqrt{85}}$$

$$153 - 9.78 \leq \mu \leq 153 + 9.78$$

$$143.22 \leq \mu \leq 162.78$$

The confidence interval is constructed from the point estimate, which in this problem is 153 minutes, and the error of this estimate, which is ±9.78 minutes. The resulting confidence interval is $143.22 \leq \mu \leq 162.78$. The cellular telephone company researcher is 95% confident that the average length of a call for the population is between 143.22 and 162.78 minutes.

What does being 95% confident that the population mean is in an interval actually indicate? It indicates that, if the company researcher were to randomly select 100 samples of 85 calls and use the results of each sample to construct a 95% confidence interval, approximately 95 of the 100 intervals would contain the population mean. It also indicates that 5% of the intervals would not contain the population mean. The company researcher is likely to take only a single sample and compute the confidence interval from that sample information. That interval either contains the population mean or it does not. Figure 2.3 depicts the meaning of a 95% confidence interval for the mean. Note that if 20 random samples are taken from the population, 19 of the 20 are likely to contain the population mean if a 95% confidence interval is used ($19/20 = 95\%$). If a 90% confidence interval is constructed, only 18 of the 20 intervals are likely to contain the population mean.

DEMONSTRATION PROBLEM 2.1	A survey was taken of U.S. companies that do business with firms in India. One of the questions on the survey was: Approximately how many years has your company been trading with firms in India? A random sample of 44 responses to this question yielded a mean of 10.455 years. Suppose the population standard deviation for this question is 7.7 years. Using this information, construct a 90% confidence interval for the mean number of years that a company has been trading in India for the population of U.S. companies trading with firms in India.

Solution

Here, $n = 44$, $\bar{x} = 10.455$, and $\sigma = 7.7$. To determine the value of $z_{\alpha/2}$, divide the 90% confidence in half, or take $.5000 - \alpha/2 = .5000 - .0500$. The z distribution of $\bar{x}$ around μ contains .4500 of the area on each side of μ, or $\frac{1}{2}(90\%)$. Table A.2 yields a z value of 1.645 for the area of .4500 (interpolating between .4495 and .4505). The confidence interval is

$$\bar{x} - z\frac{\sigma}{\sqrt{n}} \leq \mu \leq \bar{x} + z\frac{\sigma}{\sqrt{n}}$$

$$10.455 - 1.645\frac{7.7}{\sqrt{44}} \leq \mu \leq 10.455 + 1.645\frac{7.7}{\sqrt{44}}$$

$$10.455 - 1.91 \leq \mu \leq 10.455 + 1.91$$

$$8.545 \leq \mu \leq 12.365$$

TABLE 2.1

Values of z for Common Levels of Confidence

Confidence Level	z Value
90%	1.645
95%	1.96
98%	2.33
99%	2.575

The analyst is 90% confident that if a census of all U.S. companies trading with firms in India were taken at the time of this survey, the actual population mean number of years a company would have been trading with firms in India would be between 8.545 and 12.365. The point estimate is 10.455 years.

For convenience, Table 2.1 contains some of the more common levels of confidence and their associated z values.

Finite Correction Factor

Recall from Chapter 1 that if the sample is taken from a finite population, a finite correction factor may be used to increase the accuracy of the solution. In the case of interval estimation, the finite correction factor is used to reduce the width of the interval. As stated in Chapter 1, if the sample size is less than 5% of the population, the finite correction factor does not significantly alter the solution. If formula 2.1 is modified to include the finite correction factor, the result is formula 2.2.

CONFIDENCE INTERVAL TO ESTIMATE μ USING THE FINITE CORRECTION FACTOR (2.2)	$\bar{x} - z_{\alpha/2}\frac{\sigma}{\sqrt{n}}\sqrt{\frac{N-n}{N-1}} \leq \mu \leq \bar{x} + z_{\alpha/2}\frac{\sigma}{\sqrt{n}}\sqrt{\frac{N-n}{N-1}}$

Demonstration Problem 2.2 shows how the finite correction factor can be used.

DEMONSTRATION PROBLEM 2.2

A study is conducted in a company that employs 800 engineers. A random sample of 50 engineers reveals that the average sample age is 34.3 years. Historically, the population standard deviation of the age of the company's engineers is approximately 8 years. Construct a 98% confidence interval to estimate the average age of all the engineers in this company.

Solution

This problem has a finite population. The sample size, 50, is greater than 5% of the population, so the finite correction factor may be helpful. In this case $N = 800$, $n = 50$, $\bar{x} = 34.3$, and $\sigma = 8$. The z value for a 98% confidence interval is 2.33 (.98 divided into two equal parts yields .4900; the z value is obtained from Table A.2 by using .4900). Substituting into formula 2.2 and solving for the confidence interval gives

$$34.3 - 2.33 \frac{8}{\sqrt{50}} \sqrt{\frac{750}{799}} \leq \mu \leq 34.3 + 2.33 \frac{8}{\sqrt{50}} \sqrt{\frac{750}{799}}$$

$$34.3 - 2.55 \leq \mu \leq 34.3 + 2.55$$

$$31.75 \leq \mu \leq 36.85$$

Without the finite correction factor, the result would have been

$$34.3 - 2.64 \leq \mu \leq 34.3 + 2.64$$

$$31.66 \leq \mu \leq 36.94$$

The finite correction factor takes into account the fact that the population is only 800 instead of being infinitely large. The sample, $n = 50$, is a greater proportion of the 800 than it would be of a larger population, and thus the width of the confidence interval is reduced.

Estimating the Population Mean Using the z Statistic when the Sample Size is Small

In the formulas and problems presented so far in this section, sample size was large ($n \geq 30$). However, quite often in the business world, sample sizes are small. While the Central Limit Theorem applies only when sample size is large, the distribution of sample means is approximately normal even for small sizes **if** the *population* is normally distributed. This is visually displayed in the bottom row of Figure 1.6 in Chapter 1. Thus, if it is known that the population from which the sample is being drawn is normally distributed and if σ is known, the z formulas presented in this section can still be used to estimate a population mean even if the sample size is small ($n < 30$).

As an example, suppose a U.S. car rental firm wants to estimate the average number of miles traveled per day by each of its cars rented in California. A random sample of 20 cars rented in California reveals that the sample mean travel distance per day is 85.5 miles, with a population standard deviation of 19.3 miles. Compute a 99% confidence interval to estimate μ.

Here, $n = 20$, $\bar{x} = 85.5$, and $\sigma = 19.3$. For a 99% level of confidence, a z value of 2.575 is obtained. Assume that number of miles traveled per day is normally distributed in the population. The confidence interval is

$$\bar{x} - z_{\alpha/2} \frac{\sigma}{\sqrt{n}} \leq \mu \leq \bar{x} + z_{\alpha/2} \frac{\sigma}{\sqrt{n}}$$

$$85.5 - 2.575 \frac{19.3}{\sqrt{20}} \leq \mu \leq 85.5 + 2.575 \frac{19.3}{\sqrt{20}}$$

$$85.5 - 11.1 \leq \mu \leq 85.5 + 11.1$$

$$74.4 \leq \mu \leq 96.6$$

FIGURE 2.4
Excel and MINITAB Output for the Cellular Telephone Example

Excel Output

	A	B
1	The sample mean is:	153
2	The error of the interval is:	9.779
3	The confidence interval is:	153 ± 9.779
4	The confidence interval is:	143.221 ≤ Mu ≤.162.779

MINITAB Output

```
        One-Sample z: Minutes

The assumed sigma = 46.0
Variable    n    Mean    StDev      95.0% CI
Minutes    85   153.00     46    (143.22,  162.78)
```

The point estimate indicates that the average number of miles traveled per day by a rental car in California is 85.5. With 99% confidence, we estimate that the population mean is somewhere between 74.4 and 96.6 miles per day.

Using the Computer to Construct *z* Confidence Intervals for the Mean

It is possible to construct a *z* confidence interval for the mean with either Excel or MINITAB. Excel yields the ± error portion of the confidence interval that must be placed with the sample mean to construct the complete confidence interval. MINITAB constructs the complete confidence interval. Figure 2.4 shows both the Excel output and the MINITAB output for the cellular telephone example.

2.1 PROBLEMS

2.1 Use the following information to construct the confidence intervals specified to estimate μ.
   a. 95% confidence for $\bar{x} = 25$, $\sigma = 3.5$, and $n = 60$
   b. 98% confidence for $\bar{x} = 119.6$, $\sigma = 23.89$, and $n = 75$
   c. 90% confidence for $\bar{x} = 3.419$, $\sigma = 0.974$, and $n = 32$
   d. 80% confidence for $\bar{x} = 56.7$, $\sigma = 12.1$, $N = 500$, and $n = 47$

2.2 For a random sample of 36 items and a sample mean of 211, compute a 95% confidence interval for μ if the population standard deviation is 23.

2.3 A random sample of 81 items is taken, producing a sample mean of 47. The population standard deviation is 5.89. Construct a 90% confidence interval to estimate the population mean.

2.4 A random sample of size 70 is taken from a population that has a variance of 49. The sample mean is 90.4 What is the point estimate of μ? Construct a 94% confidence interval for μ.

2.5 A random sample of size 39 is taken from a population of 200 members. The sample mean is 66 and the population standard deviation is 11. Construct a 96% confidence interval to estimate the population mean. What is the point estimate of the population mean?

2.6 A candy company fills a 20-ounce package of Halloween candy with individually wrapped pieces of candy. The number of pieces of candy per package varies because the package is sold by weight. The company wants to estimate the number of pieces per package. Inspectors randomly sample 120 packages of this candy and count the number of pieces in each package. They find that the sample mean number of pieces is 18.72. Assuming a population standard deviation of .8735, what is the point estimate of the number of pieces per package? Construct a 99% confidence interval to estimate the mean number of pieces per package for the population.

2.7 A small lawnmower company produced 1,500 lawnmowers in 1995. In an effort to determine how maintenance-free these units were, the company decided to conduct a multiyear study of the 1995 lawnmowers. A sample of 200 owners of these lawnmowers was drawn randomly from company records and contacted. The owners were given an 800 number and asked to call the company when the first major repair was required for the lawnmowers. Owners who no longer used the lawnmower to cut their grass were disqualified. After many years, 187 of the owners had reported. The other 13 disqualified themselves. The average number of years until the first major repair was 5.3 for the 187 owners reporting. It is believed that the population standard deviation was 1.28 years. If the company wants to advertise an average number of years of repair-free lawn mowing for this lawnmower, what is the point estimate? Construct a 95% confidence interval for the average number of years until the first major repair.

2.8 The average total dollar purchase at a convenience store is less than that at a supermarket. Despite smaller-ticket purchases, convenience stores can still be profitable because of the size of operation, volume of business, and the markup. A researcher is interested in estimating the average purchase amount for convenience stores in suburban Long Island. To do so, she randomly sampled 24 purchases from several convenience stores in suburban Long Island and tabulated the amounts to the nearest dollar. Use the following data to construct a 90% confidence interval for the population average amount of purchases. Assume that the population standard deviation is 3.23 and the population is normally distributed.

$2	$11	$8	$7	$9	$3
5	4	2	1	10	8
14	7	6	3	7	2
4	1	3	6	8	4

2.9 A community health association is interested in estimating the average number of maternity days women stay in the local hospital. A random sample is taken of 36 women who had babies in the hospital during the past year. The following numbers of maternity days each woman was in the hospital are rounded to the nearest day.

3	3	4	3	2	5	3	1	4	3
4	2	3	5	3	2	4	3	2	4
1	6	3	4	3	3	5	2	3	2
3	5	4	3	5	4				

Use these data and a population standard deviation of 1.17 to construct a 98% confidence interval to estimate the average maternity stay in the hospital for all women who have babies in this hospital.

2.10 A meat-processing company in the Midwest produces and markets a package of eight small sausage sandwiches. The product is nationally distributed, and the company is interested in knowing the average retail price charged for this item in stores across the country. The company cannot justify a national census to generate this information. Based on the company information system's list of all retailers who carry the product, a researcher for the company contacts 36 of these retailers and ascertains the selling prices for the product. Use the following price data and a population standard deviation of 0.113 to determine a point estimate for the national retail price of the product. Construct a 90% confidence interval to estimate this price.

$2.23	$2.11	$2.12	$2.20	$2.17	$2.10
2.16	2.31	1.98	2.17	2.14	1.82
2.12	2.07	2.17	2.30	2.29	2.19
2.01	2.24	2.18	2.18	2.32	2.02
1.99	1.87	2.09	2.22	2.15	2.19
2.23	2.10	2.08	2.05	2.16	2.26

2.11 According to the U.S. Census Bureau, the average travel time to work in Philadelphia is 27.4 minutes. Suppose a business researcher wants to estimate the average travel time to work in Cleveland using a 95% level of confidence. A random sample of 45 Cleveland commuters is taken and the travel time to work is obtained from each. The data follow. Assuming a population standard deviation of 5.124, compute a 95% confidence interval on the data. What is the point estimate and what is the error of the interval? Explain what these results means in terms of Philadelphia commuters.

27	25	19	21	24	27	29	34	18	29	16	28
20	32	27	28	22	20	14	15	29	28	29	33
16	29	28	28	27	23	27	20	27	25	21	18
26	14	23	27	27	21	25	28	30			

2.12 In a recent year, turkey prices increased because of a high rate of turkey deaths caused by a heat wave and a fatal illness that spread across North Carolina, the top turkey-producing state. Suppose a random sample of turkey prices is taken from across the nation in an effort to estimate the average turkey price per pound in the United States. Shown here is the MINITAB output for such a sample. Examine the output. What is the point estimate? What is the value of the assumed population standard deviation? How large is the sample? What level of confidence is being used? What table value is associated with this level of confidence? What is the confidence interval? Often the portion of the confidence interval that is added and subtracted from the mean is referred to as the error of the estimate. How much is the error of the estimate in this problem?

```
                    Z CONFIDENCE INTERVALS

The assumed sigma = 0.140
Variable    n    Mean    StDev    SE Mean      95.0 % CI
Price per   41   0.5765  0.1394   0.0219    (0.5336, 0.6193)
```

2.2 ESTIMATING THE POPULATION MEAN USING THE t STATISTIC (σ UNKNOWN)

In Section 2.1, we learned how to estimate a population mean by using the sample mean when the population standard deviation is known. In most instances, if a business researcher desires to estimate a population mean, the population standard deviation will be unknown and thus, techniques presented in Section 2.1 will not be applicable. When the population standard deviation is unknown, the sample standard deviation must be used in the estimation process. In this section, a statistical technique is presented to estimate a population mean using the sample mean when the population standard deviation is unknown.

Suppose a business researcher is interested in estimating the average flying time of a DC-10 jet from New York to Los Angeles. Since the business researcher does not know the population mean or average time, it is likely that she also does not know the population standard deviation. By taking a random sample of flights, the researcher can compute a sample mean and a sample standard deviation from which the estimate can be constructed. Another business researcher is studying the impact of movie video advertisements on consumers using a random sample of people. The researcher wants to estimate the mean response for the population, but has no idea what is the population standard deviation. He will have the sample mean and sample standard deviation available to perform this analysis.

The z formulas presented in Section 2.1 are inappropriate for use when the population standard deviation is unknown (and is replaced by the sample standard deviation). Instead, another mechanism to handle such cases was developed by a British statistician, William S. Gosset.

Gosset was born in 1876 in Canterbury, England. He studied chemistry and mathematics, and in 1899 went to work for the Guinness Brewery in Dublin, Ireland. Gosset was involved in quality control at the brewery, studying variables such as raw materials and temperature. Because of the circumstances of his experiments, Gosset conducted many studies where the population standard deviation was unavailable. He discovered that using the standard z test with a sample standard deviation produced inexact and incorrect distributions. This finding led to his development of the distribution of the sample standard deviation and the t test.

Gosset was a student and close personal friend of Karl Pearson. When Gosset's first work on the t test was published, he used the pen name "Student." As a result, the t test is sometimes referred to as the Student's t test. Gosset's contribution was significant because it led to more exact statistical tests, which some scholars say marked the beginning of the modern era in mathematical statistics.*

The *t* Distribution

Gosset developed the **t distribution,** which is used instead of the z distribution for doing inferential statistics on the population mean when the population standard deviation is unknown and the population is normally distributed. The formula for the **t value** is

$$t = \frac{\bar{x} - \mu}{\frac{s}{\sqrt{n}}}$$

This formula is essentially the same as the z formula, but the distribution table values are different. The t distribution values are contained in Table A.3 and, for convenience, inside the back cover of the text.

The t distribution actually is a series of distributions because every sample size has a different distribution, thereby creating the potential for many t tables. To make these t values more manageable, only select key values are presented; each line in the table contains values from a different t distribution. An assumption underlying the use of the t statistic is that the population is normally distributed. If the population distribution is not normal or is unknown, nonparametric techniques should be used.

Robustness

Most statistical techniques have one or more underlying assumptions. If a statistical technique is relatively insensitive to minor violations in one or more of its underlying assumptions, the technique is said to be **robust** to that assumption. The t statistic for estimating a population mean is relatively robust to the assumption that the population is normally distributed.

Some statistical techniques are not robust, and a statistician should exercise extreme caution to be certain that the assumptions underlying a technique are being met before using

---

*Adapted from Arthur L. Dudycha and Linda W. Dudycha, "Behavioral Statistics: An Historical Perspective," in *Statistical Issues: A Reader for the Behavioral Sciences,* Roger Kirk, ed. (Monterey, CA: Brooks/Cole, 1972).

it or interpreting statistical output resulting from its use. A business analyst should always beware of statistical assumptions and the robustness of techniques being used in an analysis.

Characteristics of the *t* Distribution

Figure 2.5 displays two *t* distributions superimposed on the standard normal distribution. Like the standard normal curve, *t* distributions are symmetric, unimodal, and a family of curves. The *t* distributions are flatter in the middle and have more area in their tails than the standard normal distribution.

An examination of *t* distribution values reveals that the *t* distribution approaches the standard normal curve as *n* becomes large. The *t* distribution is the appropriate distribution to use any time the population variance or standard deviation is unknown, regardless of sample size.

Reading the *t* Distribution Table

To find a value in the *t* distribution table requires knowing the degrees of freedom; each different value of degrees of freedom is associated with a different *t* distribution. The *t* distribution table used here is a compilation of many *t* distributions, with each line of the table having different degrees of freedom and containing *t* values for different *t* distributions. The **degrees of freedom** for the *t* statistic presented in this section are computed by $n - 1$. The term **degrees of freedom** refers to *the number of independent observations for a source of variation minus the number of independent parameters estimated in computing the variation.*[*] In this case, one independent parameter, the population mean, μ, is being estimated by $\bar{x}$ in computing *s*. Thus, the degrees of freedom formula is *n* independent observations minus one independent parameter being estimated $(n - 1)$.

Because the degrees of freedom are computed differently for various *t* formulas, a degrees of freedom formula is given along with each *t* formula in the text.

In Table A.3, the degrees of freedom are located in the left column. The *t* distribution table in this text does not use the area between the statistic and the mean as does the *z* distribution (standard normal distribution). Instead, the *t* table uses the area in the tail of the distribution. The emphasis in the *t* table is on α, and each tail of the distribution contains $\alpha/2$ of the area under the curve when confidence intervals are constructed. For confidence intervals, the table *t* value is found in the column under the value of $\alpha/2$ and in the row of the degrees of freedom (df) value.

For example, if a 90% confidence interval is being computed, the total area in the two tails is 10%. Thus, α is .10 and $\alpha/2$ is .05, as indicated in Figure 2.6. The *t* distribution table shown in Table 2.2 contains only six values of $\alpha/2$ (.10, .05, .025, .01, .005, .001). The *t* value is located at the intersection of the df value and the selected $\alpha/2$ value. So if the degrees of freedom for a given *t* statistic are 24 and the desired $\alpha/2$ value is .05, the *t* value is 1.711.

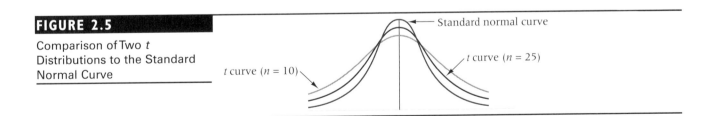

FIGURE 2.5

Comparison of Two *t* Distributions to the Standard Normal Curve

* Roger E. Kirk. *Experimental Design: Procedures for the Behavioral Sciences.* Belmont, California: Brooks/Cole Publishing Company, 1968.

FIGURE 2.6

Distribution with Alpha for 90% Confidence

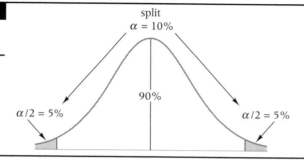

split
$\alpha = 10\%$

90%

$\alpha/2 = 5\%$ $\alpha/2 = 5\%$

TABLE 2.2

t Distribution

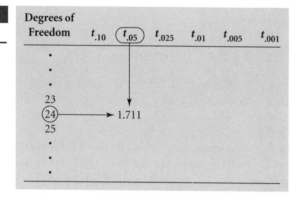

Degrees of Freedom	$t_{.10}$	$t_{.05}$	$t_{.025}$	$t_{.01}$	$t_{.005}$	$t_{.001}$
•						
•						
•						
23						
24	→	1.711				
25						
•						
•						
•						

Confidence Intervals to Estimate the Population Mean Using the *t* Statistic

The *t* formula

$$t = \frac{\bar{x} - \mu}{\frac{s}{\sqrt{n}}}$$

can be manipulated algebraically to produce a formula for estimating the population mean when σ is unknown and the population is normally distributed. The results are the formulas given next.

CONFIDENCE INTERVAL TO ESTIMATE μ: POPULATION STANDARD DEVIATION UNKNOWN AND THE POPULATION NORMALLY DISTRIBUTED (2.3)	$\bar{x} \pm t_{\alpha/2, n-1} \dfrac{s}{\sqrt{n}}$ $\bar{x} - t_{\alpha/2, n-1} \dfrac{s}{\sqrt{n}} \leq \mu \leq \bar{x} + t_{\alpha/2, n-1} \dfrac{s}{\sqrt{n}}$ $\mathrm{df} = n - 1$

Formula 2.3 can be used in a manner similar to methods presented in Section 2.1 for constructing a confidence interval to estimate μ. For example, in the aerospace industry some companies allow their employees to accumulate extra working hours beyond their 40-hour week. These extra hours sometimes are referred to as *green* time, or *comp* time. Many managers work longer than the 8-hour workday preparing proposals, overseeing crucial tasks, and taking care of paperwork. Recognition of such overtime is important. Most managers are usually not paid extra for this work, but a record is kept of this time and occasionally the manager is allowed to use some of this comp time as extra leave or vacation time. Suppose a researcher wants to estimate the average amount of comp time accumulated per week for managers in the aerospace industry. He randomly samples 18 managers and measures the amount of extra time they work during a specific week and obtains the results shown (in hours).

6	21	17	20	7	0	8	16	29
3	8	12	11	9	21	25	15	16

He constructs a 90% confidence interval to estimate the average amount of extra time per week worked by a manager in the aerospace industry. He assumes that comp time is normally distributed in the population. The sample size is 18, so df = 17. A 90% level of confidence results in $\alpha/2 = .05$ area in each tail. The table t value is

$$t_{.05,17} = 1.740$$

The subscripts in the t value denote to other researchers the area in the right tail of the t distribution (for confidence intervals $\alpha/2$) and the number of degrees of freedom. The sample mean is 13.56 hours, and the sample standard deviation is 7.8 hours. The confidence interval is computed from this information as

$$\bar{x} \pm t_{\alpha/2,n-1}\frac{s}{\sqrt{n}}$$

$$13.56 \pm 1.740\frac{7.8}{\sqrt{18}} = 13.56 \pm 3.20$$

$$10.36 \leq \mu \leq 16.76$$

The point estimate for this problem is 13.56 hours, with an error of ±3.20 hours. The researcher is 90% confident that the average amount of comp time accumulated by a manager per week in this industry is between 10.36 and 16.76 hours.

From these figures, aerospace managers could attempt to build a reward system for such extra work or evaluate the regular 40-hour week to determine how to use the normal work hours more effectively and thus reduce comp time.

DEMONSTRATION PROBLEM 2.3	The owner of a large equipment rental company wants to make a rather quick estimate of the average number of days a piece of ditchdigging equipment is rented out per person per time. The company has records of all rentals, but the amount of time required to conduct an audit of *all* accounts would be prohibitive. The owner decides to take a random sample of rental invoices. Fourteen different rentals of ditchdiggers are selected randomly from the files, yielding the following data. She uses these data to construct a 99% confidence interval to estimate the average number of days that a ditchdigger is rented and assumes that the number of days per rental is normally distributed in the population.

$$3 \quad 1 \quad 3 \quad 2 \quad 5 \quad 1 \quad 2 \quad 1 \quad 4 \quad 2 \quad 1 \quad 3 \quad 1 \quad 1$$

Solution

As $n = 14$, the df = 13. The 99% level of confidence results in $\alpha/2 = .005$ area in each tail of the distribution. The table t value is

$$t_{.005,13} = 3.012$$

The sample mean is 2.14 and the sample standard deviation is 1.29. The confidence interval is

$$\bar{x} \pm t\frac{s}{\sqrt{n}}$$

$$2.14 \pm 3.012\frac{1.29}{\sqrt{14}} = 2.14 \pm 1.04$$

$$1.10 \leq \mu \leq 3.18$$

The point estimate of the average length of time per rental is 2.14 days, with an error of ±1.04. With a 99% level of confidence, the company's owner can estimate that the average length of time per rental is between 1.10 and 3.18 days. Combining this figure with variables such as frequency of rentals per year can help the owner estimate potential profit or loss per year for such a piece of equipment.

FIGURE 2.7
Excel and MINITAB Output for the Comp Time Example

Excel Output

	A	B
1	Comp Time	
2	Mean	13.56
3	Standard Error	1.8386
4	Standard Deviation	7.8006
5	Confidence Level (90.0%)	3.20

MINITAB Output

```
One-Sample T: Comp Time

Variable     n    Mean   StDev   SE Mean      90.0% CI
Comp Time   18   13.56   7.80      1.84    (10.36, 16.75)
```

Using the Computer to Construct t Confidence Intervals for the Mean

Both Excel and MINITAB can be used to construct confidence intervals for μ using the t distribution. Figure 2.7 displays Excel output and MINITAB output for the aerospace comp time problem. The Excel output includes the mean, the standard error, the sample standard deviation, and the error of the confidence interval, referred to by Excel as the "confidence level." The standard error of the mean is computed by dividing the standard deviation (7.8006) by square root of n (4.243). When using the Excel output, the confidence interval must be computed from the sample mean and the confidence level (error of the interval).

The MINITAB output yields the confidence interval endpoints (10.36, 16.75). The "SE Mean" is the standard error of the mean. The error of the confidence interval is computed by multiplying the standard error of the mean by the table value of t. Adding and subtracting this error from the mean yields the confidence interval endpoints produced by MINITAB.

2.2 PROBLEMS

2.13 Suppose the following data are selected randomly from a population of normally distributed values.

40   51   43   48   44   57   54

39   42   48   45   39   43

Construct a 95% confidence interval to estimate the population mean.

2.14 Assuming x is normally distributed, use the following information to compute a 90% confidence interval to estimate μ.

313   320   319   340   325   310

321   329   317   311   307   318

2.15 If a random sample of 41 items produces $\bar{x} = 128.4$ and $s = 20.6$, what is the 98% confidence interval for μ? Assume x is normally distributed for the population. What is the point estimate?

2.16 A random sample of 15 items is taken, producing a sample mean of 2.364 with a sample variance of .81. Assume x is normally distributed and construct a 90% confidence interval for the population mean.

2.17 Use the following data to construct a 99% confidence interval for μ.

16.4	17.1	17.0	15.6	16.2
14.8	16.0	15.6	17.3	17.4
15.6	15.7	17.2	16.6	16.0
15.3	15.4	16.0	15.8	17.2
14.6	15.5	14.9	16.7	16.3

Assume x is normally distributed. What is the point estimate for μ?

2.18 According to Runzheimer International, the average cost of a domestic trip for business travelers in the financial industry is $1,250. Suppose another travel industry research company takes a random sample of 22 business travelers in the financial industry and determines that the sample average cost of a domestic trip is $1,192, with a sample standard deviation of $279. Construct a 98% confidence interval for the population mean from these sample data. Assume that the data are normally distributed in the population. Now go back and examine the $1,250 figure published by Runzheimer International. Does it fall into the confidence interval computed from the sample data? What does it tell you?

2.19 A valve manufacturer produces a butterfly valve composed of two semicircular plates on a common spindle that is used to permit flow in one direction only. The semicircular plates are supplied by a vendor with specifications that the plates be 2.37 millimeters thick and have a tensile strength of 5 pounds per millimeter. A random sample of 20 such plates is taken. Electronic calipers are used to measure the thickness of each plate; the measurements are given here. Assuming that the thicknesses of such plates are normally distributed, use the data to construct a 95% level of confidence for the population mean thickness of these plates. What is the point estimate? How much is the error of the interval?

2.4066	2.4579	2.6724	2.1228	2.3238
2.1328	2.0665	2.2738	2.2055	2.5267
2.5937	2.1994	2.5392	2.4359	2.2146
2.1933	2.4575	2.7956	2.3353	2.2699

2.20 Some fast-food chains offer a lower-priced combination meal in an effort to attract budget-conscious customers. One chain test-marketed a burger, fries, and a drink combination for $1.71. The weekly sales volume for these meals was impressive. Suppose the chain wants to estimate the average amount its customers spent on a meal at their restaurant while this combination offer was in effect. An analyst gathers data from 28 randomly selected customers. The following data represent the sample meal totals.

$3.21	5.40	3.50	4.39	5.60	8.65	5.02	4.20	1.25	7.64
3.28	5.57	3.26	3.80	5.46	9.87	4.67	5.86	3.73	4.08
5.47	4.49	5.19	5.82	7.62	4.83	8.42	9.10		

Use these data to construct a 90% confidence interval to estimate the population mean value. Assume the amounts spent are normally distributed.

2.21 The marketing director of a large department store wants to estimate the average number of customers who enter the store every 5 minutes. She randomly selects 5-minute intervals and counts the number of arrivals at the store. She obtains the figures 58, 32, 41, 47, 56, 80, 45, 29, 32, and 78. The analyst assumes the number of arrivals is normally distributed. Using these data, the analyst computes a 95% confidence interval to estimate the mean value for all 5-minute intervals. What interval values does she get?

2.22 Runzheimer International publishes results of studies on overseas business travel costs. Suppose as a part of one of these studies the following per diem travel accounts (in dollars) are obtained for 14 business travelers staying in Johannesburg, South Africa. Use these data to construct a 98% confidence interval to estimate the average per diem expense for businesspeople traveling to

Johannesburg. What is the point estimate? Assume per diem rates for any locale are approximately normally distributed.

| 142.59 | 148.48 | 159.63 | 171.93 | 146.90 | 168.87 | 141.94 |
| 159.09 | 156.32 | 142.49 | 129.28 | 151.56 | 132.87 | 178.34 |

2.3 ESTIMATING THE POPULATION PROPORTION

Business decision makers and researchers often need to be able to estimate a population proportion. For most businesses, estimating market share (their proportion of the market) is important because many company decisions evolve from market share information. Companies spend thousands of dollars estimating the proportion of produced goods that are defective. Market segmentation opportunities come from a knowledge of the proportion of various demographic characteristics among potential customers or clients.

Methods similar to those in Section 2.1 can be used to estimate the population proportion. The central limit theorem for sample proportions led to the following formula in Chapter 1.

$$z = \frac{\hat{p} - p}{\sqrt{\dfrac{p \cdot q}{n}}}$$

where $q = 1 - p$. Recall that this formula can be applied only when $n \cdot p$ and $n \cdot q$ are greater than 5.

Algebraically manipulating this formula to estimate p involves solving for p. However, p is in both the numerator and the denominator, which complicates the resulting formula. For this reason—for confidence interval purposes only and for large sample sizes— $\hat{p}$ is substituted for p in the denominator, yielding

$$z = \frac{\hat{p} - p}{\sqrt{\dfrac{\hat{p} \cdot \hat{q}}{n}}}$$

where $\hat{q} = 1 - \hat{p}$. Solving for p results in the confidence interval in formula (2.4).*

CONFIDENCE INTERVAL TO ESTIMATE p (2.4)

$$\hat{p} - z_{\alpha/2}\sqrt{\frac{\hat{p} \cdot \hat{q}}{n}} \leq p \leq \hat{p} + z_{\alpha/2}\sqrt{\frac{\hat{p} \cdot \hat{q}}{n}}$$

where
$\hat{p}$ = sample proportion
$\hat{q} = 1 - \hat{p}$
p = population proportion
n = sample size

In this formula, $\hat{p}$ is the point estimate and $\pm z_{\alpha/2}\sqrt{\dfrac{\hat{p} \cdot \hat{q}}{n}}$ is the error of the estimation.

---

*Because we are not using the true standard deviation of $\hat{p}$, the correct divisor of the standard error of $\hat{p}$ is $n - 1$. However, for large sample sizes, the effect is negligible. Although technically the minimal sample size for the techniques presented in this section is $n \cdot p$ and $n \cdot q$ greater than 5, in actual practice sample sizes of several hundred are more commonly used. As an example, for $\hat{p}$ and $\hat{q}$ of .50 and $n = 300$, the standard error of $\hat{p}$ is .02887 using n and .02892 using $n - 1$, a difference of only .00005.

Coffee Consumption in the United States

In 1969, more people drank coffee than soft drinks in the United States. In fact, according to Jack Maxwell of *Beverage Digest*, U.S. consumption of coffee in 1969 was close to 40 gallons per capita compared to about 20 gallons of soft drinks. However, by 1998, coffee consumption was down to about 20 gallons per capita annually compared to more than 50 gallons for soft drink consumption. Although coffee lost out to soft drinks as a beverage leader in the past three decades, it made a comeback recently with the increase in the popularity of coffee shops in the United States.

What is the state of coffee consumption in the United States now? A survey conducted by the National Coffee Association revealed that 80 percent of Americans now drink coffee at least occasionally. Out-of-home consumption has grown to 39%. Daily consumption among 18- to 24-year-olds rose to 25% compared to 74% of the over-60-year-olds. The average consumption per drinker rose to 3.3 cups per day. However, the 18- to 24-year-olds who drink coffee average 4.6 cups per day, whereas the over-60-year-olds average only 2.8 cups. Coffee consumption also varies by geographic region. Fifty-three percent of Northeasterners surveyed had drunk coffee the previous day compared to 47% of Westerners. Only 16% of Northeasterners drink their coffee black compared to 33% of Westerners and 42% of people in the North Central region.

How does U.S. consumption of coffee compare to other countries? The U.S. per capita consumption of coffee is 4 kilograms, compared to 5.56 kilograms in Europe in general and 11 kilograms in Finland.

Because much of the information presented here was gleaned from some survey, virtually all of the percentages and means are sample statistics and not population parameters. Thus, what are presented as coffee population statistics are actually point estimates. Using the sample size (3,300) and a level of confidence, confidence intervals can be constructed for the proportions. Confidence intervals for means can be constructed from these point estimates if the value of the standard deviation can be determined.

Source: Adapted from Nikhil Deogun, "Joe Wakes Up, Smells the Soda," *The Wall Street Journal* (8 June 1999), p. B1; "Better Latte than Never," *Prepared Foods* (March 2001), p. 1; "Coffee Consumption on the Rise," *Nation's Restaurant News* (2 July 2001), p. 1. Other sources include the National Coffee Association, Jack Maxwell, the International Coffee Organization, and Datamonitor.

As an example, a study of 87 randomly selected companies with a telemarketing operation revealed that 39% of the sampled companies used telemarketing to assist them in order processing. Using this information, how could a researcher estimate the *population* proportion of telemarketing companies that use their telemarketing operation to assist them in order processing?

The sample proportion, $\hat{p} = .39$, is the *point estimate* of the population proportion, p. For $n = 87$ and $\hat{p} = .39$, a 95% confidence interval can be computed to determine the interval estimation of p. The z value for 95% confidence is 1.96. The value of $\hat{q} = 1 - \hat{p} = 1 - .39 = .61$. The confidence interval estimate is

$$.39 - 1.96\sqrt{\frac{(.39)(.61)}{87}} \leq p \leq .39 + 1.96\sqrt{\frac{(.39)(.61)}{87}}$$

$$.39 - .10 \leq p \leq .39 + .10$$

$$.29 \leq p \leq .49$$

This interval suggests that the population proportion of telemarketing firms that use their operation to assist order processing is somewhere between .29 and .49, based on the point estimate of .39 with an error of ±.10. This result has a 95% level of confidence.

DEMONSTRATION PROBLEM 2.4	Coopers & Lybrand surveyed 210 chief executives of fast-growing small companies. Only 51% of these executives had a management succession plan in place. A spokesperson for Cooper & Lybrand said that many companies do not worry about management succession unless it is an immediate problem. However, the unexpected exit of a corporate leader can disrupt and unfocus a company for long enough to cause it to lose its momentum.

Use the data given to compute a 92% confidence interval to estimate the proportion of *all* fast-growing small companies that have a management succession plan.

Solution

The point estimate is the sample proportion given to be .51. It is estimated that .51, or 51% of all fast-growing small companies have a management succession plan. Realizing that the point estimate might change with another sample selection, we calculate a confidence interval.

The value of n is 210; $\hat{p}$ is .51, and $\hat{q} = 1 - \hat{p} = .49$. Because the level of confidence is 92%, the value of $z_{.04} = 1.75$. The confidence interval is computed as

$$.51 - 1.75\sqrt{\frac{(.51)(.49)}{210}} \leq p \leq .51 + 1.75\sqrt{\frac{(.51)(.49)}{210}}$$

$$.51 - .06 \leq p \leq .51 + .06$$

$$.45 \leq p \leq .57$$

It is estimated with 92% confidence that the proportion of the population of fast-growing small companies that have a management succession plan is between .45 and .57.

DEMONSTRATION PROBLEM 2.5

A clothing company produces men's jeans. The jeans are made and sold with either a regular cut or a boot cut. In an effort to estimate the proportion of their men's jeans market in Oklahoma City that prefers boot-cut jeans, the analyst takes a random sample of 212 jeans sales from the company's two Oklahoma City retail outlets. Only 34 of the sales were for boot-cut jeans. Construct a 90% confidence interval to estimate the proportion of the population in Oklahoma City who prefer boot-cut jeans.

Solution

The sample size is 212, and the number preferring boot-cut jeans is 34. The sample proportion is $\hat{p} = 34/212 = .16$. A point estimate for boot-cut jeans in the population is .16, or 16%. The z value for a 90% level of confidence is 1.645, and the value of $\hat{q} = 1 - \hat{p} = 1 - .16 = .84$. The confidence interval estimate is

$$.16 - 1.645\sqrt{\frac{(.16)(.84)}{212}} \leq p \leq .16 + 1.645\sqrt{\frac{(.16)(.84)}{212}}$$

$$.16 - .04 \leq p \leq .16 + .04$$

$$.12 \leq p \leq .20$$

The analyst estimates that the population proportion of boot-cut jeans purchases is between .12 and .20. The level of confidence in this result is 90%.

Using the Computer to Construct Confidence Intervals of the Population Proportion

MINITAB has the capability of producing confidence intervals for proportions. Figure 2.8 contains MINITAB output for Demonstration Problem 2.5. The output contains the sample size (labeled as N), the number in the sample containing the characteristic of interest (X), the sample proportion, the level of confidence, and the endpoints of the confidence interval. Note that the endpoints of the confidence interval are essentially the same as those computed in Demonstration Problem 2.5.

FIGURE 2.8

MINITAB Output for Demonstration Problem 2.5

```
         TEST AND CI FOR ONE PROPORTION

Test of p = 0.5 vs p not = 0.5

Sample   X    N    Sample p        90.0% CI          P-Value
1       34   212  0.160377  (0.120328, 0.207718)    0.000
```

2.3 PROBLEMS

2.23 Use the information about each of the following samples to compute the confidence interval to estimate p.

    a. $n = 44$ and $\hat{p} = .51$; compute a 99% confidence interval.

    b. $n = 300$ and $\hat{p} = .82$; compute a 95% confidence interval.

    c. $n = 1,150$ and $\hat{p} = .48$; compute a 90% confidence interval.

    d. $n = 95$ and $\hat{p} = .32$; compute an 88% confidence interval.

2.24 Use the following sample information to calculate the confidence interval to estimate the population proportion. Let x be the number of items in the sample having the characteristic of interest.

    a. $n = 116$ and $x = 57$, with 99% confidence

    b. $n = 800$ and $x = 479$, with 97% confidence

    c. $n = 240$ and $x = 106$, with 85% confidence

    d. $n = 60$ and $x = 21$, with 90% confidence

2.25 Suppose a random sample of 85 items has been taken from a population and 40 of the items contain the characteristic of interest. Use this information to calculate a 90% confidence interval to estimate the proportion of the population that has the characteristic of interest. Calculate a 95% confidence interval. Calculate a 99% confidence interval. As the level of confidence changes and the other sample information stays constant, what happens to the confidence interval?

2.26 A study released by Scoop Marketing showed that Universal/PolyGram held a 24.5% share of the music CD market. Suppose this figure is actually a point estimate obtained by interviewing 1,003 people who purchased a music CD. Use this information to compute a 99% confidence interval for the proportion of the market that is held by Universal/PolyGram. Suppose the figure was obtained from a survey of 10,000 people. Recompute the confidence interval and compare your results with the first confidence interval. How did they differ? What might you conclude about sample size and confidence intervals?

2.27 According to the Stern Marketing Group, 9 out of 10 professional women say that financial planning is more important today than it was five years ago. Where do these women go for help in financial planning? Forty-seven percent use a financial advisor (broker, tax consultant, financial planner). Twenty-eight percent use written sources such as magazines, books, and newspapers. Suppose these figures were obtained by taking a sample of 560 professional women who said that financial planning is more important today than it was five years ago. Construct a 95% confidence interval for the proportion of professional women who use a financial advisor. Use the percentage given in this problem as the point estimate. Construct a 90% confidence interval for the proportion of professional women who use written sources. Use the percentage given in this problem as the point estimate.

2.28 What proportion of pizza restaurants that are primarily for walk-in business have a salad bar? Suppose that, in an effort to determine this figure, a random sample of 1,250 of these restaurants across the United States based on the *Yellow Pages* is called. If 997 of the restaurants sampled have a salad bar, what is the 98% confidence interval for the population proportion?

2.29 The highway department wants to estimate the proportion of vehicles on Interstate 25 between the hours of midnight and 5:00 A.M. that are 18-wheel tractor trailers. The estimate will be used to determine highway repair and construction considerations and in highway patrol planning. Suppose researchers for the highway department counted vehicles at different locations on the interstate for several nights during this time period. Of the 3,481 vehicles counted, 927 were 18-wheelers.

    a. Determine the point estimate for the proportion of vehicles traveling Interstate 25 during this time period that are 18-wheelers.

    b. Construct a 99% confidence interval for the proportion of vehicles on Interstate 25 during this time period that are 18-wheelers.

2.30 What proportion of commercial airline pilots are more than 40 years of age? Suppose a researcher has access to a list of all pilots who are members of the Commercial Airline Pilots Association. If this list is used as a frame for the study, she can randomly select a sample of pilots, contact them, and ascertain their ages. From 89 of these pilots so selected, she learns that 48 are more than 40 years of age. Construct an 85% confidence interval to estimate the population proportion of commercial airline pilots who are more than 40 years of age.

2.31 According to Runzheimer International, in a survey of relocation administrators 63% of all workers who rejected relocation offers did so for family considerations. Suppose this figure was obtained by using a random sample of the files of 672 workers who had rejected relocation offers. Use this information to construct a 95% confidence interval to estimate the population proportion of workers who reject relocation offers for family considerations.

2.4 ESTIMATING THE POPULATION VARIANCE

At times in statistical analysis, the researcher is more interested in the population variance than in the population mean or population proportion. For example, in the total quality movement, suppliers who want to earn world-class supplier status or even those who want to maintain customer contracts are often asked to show continual reduction of variation on supplied parts. Tests are conducted with samples in efforts to determine lot variation and to determine whether variability goals are being met.

Estimating the variance is important in many other instances in business. For example, variations between airplane altimeter readings need to be minimal. It is not enough just to know that, on the average, a particular brand of altimeter produces the correct altitude. It is also important that the variation between instruments be small. Thus measuring the variation of altimeters is critical. Parts being used in engines must fit tightly on a consistent basis. A wide variability among parts can result in a part that is too large to fit into its slots or so small that it results in too much tolerance, which causes vibrations. How can variance be estimated?

Sample variance is computed by using the formula

$$s^2 = \frac{\sum (x - \overline{x})^2}{n - 1}$$

Because sample variances are typically used as estimators or estimations of the population variance, as they are here, a mathematical adjustment is made in the denominator by using $n - 1$ to make the sample variance an unbiased estimator of the population variance.

Suppose a researcher wants to estimate the population variance from the sample variance in a manner that is similar to the estimation of the population mean from a sample mean. The relationship of the sample variance to the population variance is captured by the **chi-square distribution** (x^2). The ratio of the sample variance (s^2) multiplied by $n - 1$ to the population variance (σ^2) is approximately chi-square distributed, as shown in formula 2.5, if the population from which the values are drawn is normally distributed.

Caution: *Use of the chi-square statistic to estimate the population variance is extremely sensitive to violations of the assumption that the population is normally distributed. For that reason, some researchers do not include this technique among their statistical repertoire. Although the technique is still rather widely presented as a mechanism for constructing confidence intervals to estimate a population variance, you should proceed with extreme caution and apply the technique only in cases where the population is known to be normally distributed. We can say that this technique lacks robustness.*

Like the *t* distribution, the chi-square distribution varies by sample size and contains a degrees-of-freedom value. The number of degrees of freedom for the chi-square formula (2.5) is $n - 1$.

The business council can estimate with 95% confidence that the population variance of the hourly wages of production workers in manufacturing in Greece is between 0.7648 and 2.4277.

2.4 PROBLEMS

2.32 For each of the following sample results, construct the requested confidence interval. Assume the data come from normally distributed populations.

    a. $n = 12$, $\bar{x} = 28.4$, $s^2 = 44.9$; 99% confidence for σ^2

    b. $n = 7$, $\bar{x} = 4.37$, $s = 1.24$; 95% confidence for σ^2

    c. $n = 20$, $\bar{x} = 105$, $s = 32$; 90% confidence for σ^2

    d. $n = 17$, $s^2 = 18.56$; 80% confidence for σ^2

2.33 Use the following sample data to estimate the population variance. Produce a point estimate and a 98% confidence interval. Assume the data come from a normally distributed population.

27	40	32	41	45	29	33	39
30	28	36	32	42	40	38	46

2.34 The Interstate Conference of Employment Security Agencies says the average workweek in the United States is down to only 35 hours, largely because of a rise in part-time workers. Suppose this figure was obtained from a random sample of 20 workers and that the standard deviation of the sample was 4.3 hours. Assume hours worked per week are normally distributed in the population. Use this sample information to develop a 98% confidence interval for the population variance of the number of hours worked per week for a worker. What is the point estimate?

2.35 A manufacturing plant produces steel rods. During one production run of 20,000 such rods, the specifications called for rods that were 46 centimeters in length and 3.8 centimeters in width. Fifteen of these rods comprising a random sample were measured for length; the resulting measurements are shown here. Use these data to estimate the population variance of length for the rods. Assume rod length is normally distributed in the population. Construct a 99% confidence interval. Discuss the ramifications of the results.

44 cm	47 cm	43 cm	46 cm	46 cm
45 cm	43 cm	44 cm	47 cm	46 cm
48 cm	48 cm	43 cm	44 cm	45 cm

2.36 Suppose a random sample of 14 people 30–39 years of age produced the household incomes shown here. Use these data to determine a point estimate for the population variance of household incomes for people 30–39 years of age and construct a 95% confidence interval. Assume household income is normally distributed.

$37,500	44,800
33,500	36,900
42,300	32,400
28,000	41,200
46,600	38,500
40,200	32,000
35,500	36,800

2.5 ESTIMATING SAMPLE SIZE

In most business research that uses sample statistics to infer about the population, being able to *estimate the size of sample necessary to accomplish the purposes of the study* is important. The need for this **sample-size estimation** is the same for the large corporation investing tens of thousands of dollars in a massive study of consumer preference and for students undertaking a small case study and wanting to send questionnaires to local businesspeople. In either case, such things as level of confidence, sampling error, and width of estimation interval are closely tied to sample size. If the large corporation is undertaking a market study, should it sample 40 people or 4,000 people? The question is an important one. In most cases, because of cost considerations, business researchers do not want to sample any more units or individuals than necessary.

Sample Size When Estimating μ

In research studies when μ is being estimated, the size of sample can be determined by using the z formula for sample means to solve for n. Consider,

$$z = \frac{\bar{x} - \mu}{\frac{\sigma}{\sqrt{n}}}$$

The difference between $\bar{x}$ and μ is the **error of estimation** resulting from the sampling process. Let $E = (\bar{x} - \mu)$ = the error of estimation. Substituting E into the preceding formula yields

$$z = \frac{E}{\frac{\sigma}{\sqrt{n}}}$$

Solving for n yields a formula that can be used to determine sample size.

SAMPLE SIZE WHEN ESTIMATING μ (2.7)	$n = \dfrac{z_{\alpha/2}^2 \sigma^2}{E^2} = \left(\dfrac{z_{\alpha/2} \sigma}{E}\right)^2$

Sometimes in estimating sample size the population variance is known or can be determined from past studies. Other times, the population variance is unknown and must be estimated to determine the sample size. In such cases, it is acceptable to use the following estimate to represent σ.

$$\sigma \approx \frac{1}{4}(range)$$

Using formula (2.7), the business researcher can estimate the sample size needed to achieve the goals of the study before gathering data. For example, suppose a researcher wants to estimate the average monthly expenditure on bread by a family in Chicago. She wants to be 90% confident of her results. How much error is she willing to tolerate in the results? Suppose she wants the estimate to be within $1.00 of the actual figure and the standard deviation of average monthly bread purchases is $4.00. What is the sample size estimation for this problem? The value of z for a 90% level of confidence is 1.645. Using formula (2.7) with $E = \$1.00$, $\sigma = \$4.00$, and $z = 1.645$ gives

$$n = \frac{z_{\alpha/2}^2 \sigma^2}{E^2} = \frac{(1.645)^2 (4)^2}{1^2} = 43.30$$

That is, at least $n = 43.3$ must be sampled randomly to attain a 90% level of confidence and produce an error within $1.00 for a standard deviation of $4.00. Sampling 43.3 units is impossible, so this result should be rounded up to $n = 44$ units.

2.57 According to a survey by Topaz Enterprises, a travel auditing company, the average error by travel agents is $128. Suppose this figure was obtained from a random sample of 41 travel agents and the sample standard deviation is $21. What is the point estimate of the national average error for all travel agents? Compute a 98% confidence interval for the national average error based on these sample results. Assume the travel agent errors are normally distributed in the population. How wide is the interval? Interpret the interval.

2.58 A national survey on telemarketing was undertaken. One of the questions asked was: How long has your organization had a telemarketing operation? Suppose the following data represent some of the answers received to this question. Suppose further that only 300 telemarketing firms comprised the population when this survey was taken. Use the following data to compute a 98% confidence interval to estimate the average number of years a telemarketing organization has had a telemarketing operation. The population standard deviation is 3.06.

5	5	6	3	6	7	5
5	6	8	4	9	6	4
10	5	10	11	5	14	7
5	9	6	7	3	4	3
7	5	9	3	6	8	16
12	11	5	4	3	6	5
8	3	5	9	7	13	4
6	5	8	3	5	8	7
11	5	14	4			

2.59 An entrepreneur wants to open an appliance service repair shop. She would like to know about what the average home repair bill is, including the charge for the service call for appliance repair in the area. She wants the estimate to be within $20 of the actual figure. She believes the range of such bills is between $30 and $600. How large a sample should the entrepreneur take if she wants to be 95% confident of the results?

2.60 A national survey of insurance offices was taken, resulting in a random sample of 245 companies. Of these 245 companies, 189 responded that they were going to purchase new software for their offices in the next year. Construct a 90% confidence interval to estimate the population proportion of insurance offices that intend to purchase new software during the next year.

2.61 A national survey of companies included a question that asked whether the company had at least one bilingual telephone operator. The sample results of 90 companies follow (Y denotes that the company does have at least one bilingual operator; N denotes that it does not).

N	N	N	N	Y	N	Y	N	N
Y	N	N	N	Y	Y	Y	N	N
N	N	Y	N	Y	N	Y	N	Y
Y	Y	N	Y	N	N	N	Y	N
N	Y	N	N	N	N	N	N	N
Y	N	Y	Y	N	N	Y	N	Y
N	N	Y	Y	N	N	N	N	N
Y	N	N	N	N	Y	N	N	N
Y	Y	Y	N	N	Y	N	N	N
N	N	N	Y	Y	N	N	Y	N

Use this information to estimate with 95% confidence the proportion of the population that does have at least one bilingual operator.

2.62 A movie theater has had a poor accounting system. The manager has no idea how many large containers of popcorn are sold per movie showing. She knows that the amounts vary by day of the week and hour of the day. However, she wants to estimate the overall average per movie showing. To do so, she randomly selects 12 movie performances and counts the number of large containers of popcorn sold between 30 minutes before the movie showing and 15 minutes after the movie showing. The sample average was 43.7 containers, with a variance of 228. Construct a 95% confidence interval to estimate the mean number of large containers of popcorn sold during a movie showing. Assume the number of large containers of popcorn sold per movie is normally distributed in the population. Use this information to construct a 98% confidence interval to estimate the population variance.

2.63 According to a survey by Runzheimer International, the average cost of a fast-food meal (quarter-pound cheeseburger, large fries, medium soft drink, excluding taxes) in Seattle is $4.82. Suppose this figure was based on a sample of 27 different establishments and the standard deviation was $0.37. Construct a 95% confidence interval for the population mean cost for all fast-food meals in Seattle. Assume the costs of a fast-food meal in Seattle are normally distributed. Using the interval as a guide, is it likely that the population mean is really $4.50? Why or why not?

2.64 A survey of 77 commercial airline flights of under 2 hours resulted in a sample average late time for a flight of 2.48 minutes. The population standard deviation was 12 minutes. Construct a 95% confidence interval for the average time that a commercial flight of under 2 hours is late. What is the point estimate? What does the interval tell about whether the average flight is late?

2.65 A regional survey of 560 companies asked the vice president of operations how satisfied he or she was with the software support received from the computer staff of the company. Suppose 33% of the 560 vice presidents said they were satisfied. Construct a 99% confidence interval for the proportion of the population of vice presidents who would have said they were satisfied with the software support if a census had been taken.

2.66 A research firm has been asked to determine the proportion of all restaurants in the state of Ohio that serve alcoholic beverages. The firm wants to be 98%

confident of its results but has no idea of what the actual proportion is. The firm would like to report an error of no more than .05. How large a sample should it take?

2.67 A national magazine marketing firm attempts to win subscribers with a mail campaign that involves a contest using magazine stickers. Often when people subscribe to magazines in this manner they sign up for multiple magazine subscriptions. Suppose the marketing firm wants to estimate the average number of subscriptions per customer of those who purchase at least one subscription. To do so, the marketing firm's researcher randomly selects 65 returned contest entries. Twenty-seven contain subscription requests. Of the 27, the average number of subscriptions is 2.10, with a standard deviation of .86. The researcher uses this information to compute a 98% confidence interval to estimate μ and assumes that x is normally distributed. What does the researcher find?

2.68 A national survey showed that Hillshire Farm Deli Select cold cuts were priced, on the average, at $5.20 per pound. Suppose a national survey of 23 retail outlets was taken and the price per pound of Hillshire Farm Deli Select cold cuts was ascertained. If the following data represent these prices, what is a 90% confidence interval for the population variance of these prices? Assume prices are normally distributed in the population.

5.18	5.22	5.25	5.19	5.30
5.17	5.15	5.28	5.20	5.14
5.05	5.19	5.26	5.23	5.19
5.22	5.08	5.21	5.24	5.33
5.22	5.19	5.19		

2.69 The price of a head of iceberg lettuce varies greatly with the season and the geographic location of a store. During February a researcher contacts a random sample of 39 grocery stores across the United States and asks the produce manager of each to state the current price charged for a head of iceberg lettuce. Using the researcher's results that follow, construct a 99% confidence interval to estimate the mean price of a head of iceberg lettuce in February in the United States. Assume that σ is 0.205.

1.59	1.25	1.65	1.40	0.89
1.19	1.50	1.49	1.30	1.39
1.29	1.60	0.99	1.29	1.19
1.20	1.50	1.49	1.29	1.35
1.10	0.89	1.10	1.39	1.39
1.50	1.50	1.55	1.20	1.15
0.99	1.00	1.30	1.25	1.10
1.00	1.55	1.29	1.39	

INTERPRETING THE OUTPUT

2.70 A soft drink company produces a cola in a 12-ounce can. Even though their machines are set to fill the cans with 12 ounces, variation due to calibration, operator error, and other things sometimes precludes the cans having the correct fill. To monitor the can fills, a quality team randomly selects some filled 12-ounce cola cans and measures their fills in the lab. A confidence interval for the population mean is constructed from the data. Shown here is the MINITAB output from this effort. Discuss the output.

```
              One-Sample Z: Can Fills

The assumed sigma = 0.0536

Variable    N    Mean    StDev   SE Mean      99.0% CI
Can Fills   58  11.9788  0.0556   0.0070  (11.9607, 11.9970)
```

2.71 A company has developed a new light bulb that seems to burn longer than most residential bulbs. To determine how long these bulbs burn, the company randomly selects a sample of these bulbs and burns them in the laboratory. The Excel output shown here is a portion of the analysis from this effort. Discuss the output.

	A	B
1	Bulb Burn	
2	Mean	2198.217
3	Standard Deviation	152.9907
4	Count	84
5	Confidence Level (90.0%)	27.76691

2.72 Suppose a researcher wants to estimate the average age of a person who is a first-time home buyer. A random sample of first-time home buyers is taken and their ages are ascertained. The MINITAB output shown here is an analysis of that data. Study the output and explain its implication.

```
              One-Sample T: Ages

Variable    N    Mean   StDev   SE Mean      98.0% CI
Ages       21   27.63   6.54     1.43     (24.02, 31.24)
```

2.73 What proportion of all American workers drive their cars to work? Suppose a poll of American workers is taken in an effort to answer that question, and the MINITAB output shown here is an analysis of the data from the poll. Explain the meaning of the output in light of the question.

```
            Test and CI for One Proportion

Test of p = 0.5 vs p not = 0.5

Sample   X    N   Sample p       95.0% CI          P-Value
1       506  781  0.647887  (0.613240, 0.681413)    0.000
```

CHAPTER **3**

Statistical Inference: Hypothesis Testing for Single Populations

LEARNING OBJECTIVES

The main objective of Chapter 3 is to help you to learn how to test hypotheses on single populations, thereby enabling you to:

1. Understand the logic of hypothesis testing and know how to establish null and alternative hypotheses.
2. Understand Type I and Type II errors and know how to solve for Type II errors.
3. Know how to implement the HTAB system to test hypotheses.
4. Test hypotheses about a single population mean when σ is known.
5. Test hypotheses about a single population mean when σ is unknown.
6. Test hypotheses about a single population proportion.
7. Test hypotheses about a single population variance.

Type I and Type II Errors

Because the hypothesis testing process uses sample statistics calculated from random data to reach conclusions about population parameters, it is possible to make an incorrect decision about the null hypothesis. In particular, two types of errors can be made in testing hypotheses: Type I error and Type II error.

A **Type I error** is committed by *rejecting a true null hypothesis*. With a Type I error, the null hypothesis is true, but the business researcher decides that it is not. As an example, suppose the flour-packaging process actually is "in control" and is averaging 40 ounces of flour per package. Suppose also that a business researcher randomly selects 100 packages, weighs the contents of each, and computes a sample mean. It is possible, by chance, to randomly select 100 of the more extreme packages (mostly heavy weighted or mostly light weighted) resulting in a mean that falls in the rejection region. The decision is to reject the null hypothesis even though the population mean is actually 40 ounces. In this case, the business researcher has committed a Type I error.

The notion of a Type I error can be used outside the realm of statistical hypothesis testing in the business world. For example, if a manager fires an employee because some evidence indicates that she is stealing from the company and if she really is not stealing from the company, then the manager has committed a Type I error. As another example, suppose a worker on the assembly line of a large manufacturer hears an unusual sound and decides to shut the line down (reject the null hypothesis). If the sound turns out not to be related to the assembly line and no problems are occurring with the assembly line, then the worker has committed a Type I error. In U.S. industries in the 1950s, 1960s, and 1970s when U.S. products were in great demand, workers were strongly discouraged from making such Type I errors because the production downtime was so expensive. An analogous courtroom example of a Type I error is when an innocent person is sent to jail.

In Figure 3.3, the rejection regions represent the possibility of committing a Type I error. Means that fall beyond the critical values will be considered so extreme that the business researcher chooses to reject the null hypothesis. However, if the null hypothesis is true, any mean that falls in a rejection region will result in a decision that produces a Type I error. The *probability of committing a Type I error* is called **alpha (α)** or **level of significance.** Alpha equals the area under the curve that is in the rejection region beyond the critical value(s). The value of alpha is always set before the experiment or study is undertaken. As mentioned previously, common values of alpha are .05, .01, .10, and .001.

A **Type II error** is committed when a business researcher *fails to reject a false null hypothesis.* In this case, the null hypothesis is false, but a decision is made to not reject it. Suppose in the case of the flour problem that the packaging process is actually producing a population mean of 41 ounces even though the null hypothesis is 40 ounces. A sample of 100 packages yields a sample mean of 40.2 ounces, which falls in the nonrejection region. The business decision maker decides not to reject the null hypothesis. A Type II error has been committed. The packaging procedure is out-of-control and the hypothesis testing process does not identify it.

Suppose in the business world an employee is stealing from the company. A manager sees some evidence that the stealing is occurring but lacks enough evidence to conclude that the employee is stealing from the company. The manager decides not to fire the employee based on theft. The manager has committed a Type II error. Consider the manufacturing line with the noise. Suppose the worker decides not enough noise is heard to shut the line down, but in actuality, one of the cords on the line is unraveling, creating a dangerous situation. The worker is committing a Type II error. Beginning in the 1980s, U.S. manufacturers started protecting more against Type II errors. They found that in many cases, it was more costly to produce bad product (e.g., scrap/rework costs and loss of market share due to poor quality) than it was to make it right the first time. They encouraged workers to "shut down" the line if the quality of work was seemingly not what it should be (risking a Type I error) rather than allowing poor quality product to be shipped. In a court-of-law, a Type II error is committed when a guilty person is declared innocent.

The probability of committing a Type II error is **beta** (β). Unlike alpha, beta is not usually stated at the beginning of the hypothesis testing procedure. Actually, because beta occurs only when the null hypothesis is not true, the computation of beta varies with the many possible alternative parameters that might occur. For example, in the flour-packaging problem, if the population mean is not 40 ounces, then what is it? It could be 41, 38, or 42 ounces. A value of beta is associated with each of these alternative means.

How are alpha and beta related? First of all, because alpha can only be committed when the null hypothesis is rejected and beta can only be committed when the null hypothesis is not rejected, a business researcher cannot commit both a Type I error and a Type II error at the same time on the same hypothesis test. Generally, alpha and beta are inversely related. If alpha is reduced, then beta is increased, and vice versa. If the rejection regions displayed in Figure 3.3 are reduced, making it harder to reject the 40-ounce weight, it will be easier to not discern when the packaging process is out-of-control. In terms of the manufacturing assembly line, if management makes it harder for workers to shut down the assembly line (reduce Type I error), then there is a greater chance that bad product will be made or that a serious problem with the line will arise (increase Type II error). Legally, if the courts make it harder to send innocent people to jail, then they have made it easier let guilty people go free. One way to reduce both errors is to increase the sample size. If a larger sample is taken, it is more likely that the sample is representative of the population; which translates into a better chance that a business researcher will make the correct choice. Figure 3.4 shows the relationship between the two types of error. The "state of nature" is how things actually are and the "action" is the decision that the business researcher actually makes. Note that each action alternative contains only one of the errors along with the possibility that a correct decision has been made. **Power,** which is equal to $1 - \beta$, is *the probability of a test rejecting the null hypothesis when the null hypothesis is false.* Figure 3.4 shows the relationship between α, β, and power.

3.2 TESTING HYPOTHESES ABOUT A POPULATION MEAN USING THE z STATISTIC (σ KNOWN)

One of the most basic hypothesis tests is a test about a population mean. A business researcher might be interested in testing to determine whether an established or accepted mean value for an industry is still true or in testing a hypothesized mean value for a new theory or product. As an example, a computer products company sets up a telephone service to assist customers by providing technical support. The average wait time during weekday hours is 37 minutes. However, a recent hiring effort added technical consultants to the system, and management believes that the average wait time decreased, and they want to prove it. Other business scenarios resulting in hypothesis tests of a single mean might include the following:

- A financial investment firm wants to test to determine whether the average hourly change in the Dow Jones Average over a 10-year period is +0.25.

- A manufacturing company wants to test to determine whether the average thickness of a plastic bottle is 2.4 millimeters.

FIGURE 3.4
Alpha, Beta, and Power

		State of nature	
		Null true	Null false
Action	Fail to reject null	Correct decision	Type II error (β)
	Reject null	Type I error (α)	Correct decision (power)

- A retail store wants to test to determine whether the average age of its customers is less than 40 years.

Formula (3.1) can be used to test hypotheses about a single population mean if the sample size is large ($n \geq 30$) for any population and for small samples ($n < 30$) if x is known to be normally distributed.

z TEST FOR A SINGLE MEAN (3.1)	$$z = \frac{\bar{x} - \mu}{\frac{\sigma}{\sqrt{n}}}$$

A survey of CPAs across the United States found that the average net income for sole proprietor CPAs is \$74,914.* Because this survey is now more than ten years old, an accounting researcher wants to test this figure by taking a random sample of 112 sole proprietor accountants in the United States to determine whether the net income figure changed. The researcher could use the eight steps of hypothesis testing to do so. Assume the population standard deviation of net incomes for sole proprietor CPAs is \$14,530.

HYPOTHESIZE:

At step 1, the hypotheses must be established. Because the researcher is testing to determine whether the figure has changed, the alternative hypothesis is that the mean net income is not \$74,914. The null hypothesis is that the mean still equals \$74,914. These hypotheses follow.

$$H_0: \mu = \$74,914$$
$$H_a: \mu \neq \$74,914$$

TEST:

Step 2 is to determine the appropriate statistical test and sampling distribution. Because sample size is large ($n = 112$) and the researcher is using the sample mean as the statistic, the z test in formula (3.1) is the appropriate test statistic.

$$z = \frac{\bar{x} - \mu}{\frac{\sigma}{\sqrt{n}}}$$

Step 3 is to specify the Type I error rate, or alpha, which is .05 in this problem. Step 4 is to state the decision rule. Because the test is two-tailed and alpha is .05, there is $\alpha/2$ or .025 area in each of the tails of the distribution. Thus, the rejection region is in the two ends of the distribution with 2.5% of the area in each. There is a .4750 area between the mean and each of the critical values that separate the tails of the distribution (the rejection region) from the nonrejection region. By using this .4750 area and Table A.2, the critical z value can be obtained.

$$z_{\alpha/2} = \pm 1.96$$

Figure 3.5 displays the problem with the rejection regions and the critical values of z. The decision rule is that if the data gathered produce a z value greater than 1.96 or less than -1.96, the test statistic is in one of the rejection regions and the decision is to reject the null hypothesis. If the z value calculated from the data is between -1.96 and $+1.96$, the decision is to not reject the null hypothesis because the calculated z value is in the nonrejection region.

Step 5 is to gather the data. Suppose the 112 CPAs who respond produce a sample mean of \$78,695. At step 6, the value of the test statistic is calculated by using $\bar{x} = \$78,695$, $n = 112$, $\sigma = \$14,530$, and a hypothesized $\mu = \$74,914$:

$$z = \frac{78,695 - 74,914}{\frac{14,530}{\sqrt{112}}} = 2.75$$

---

*Adapted from Daniel J. Flaherty, Raymond A. Zimmerman, and Mary Ann Murray, "Benchmarking Against the Best," *Journal of Accountancy* (July 1995), pp. 85–88.

FIGURE 3.5

CPA Net Income Example

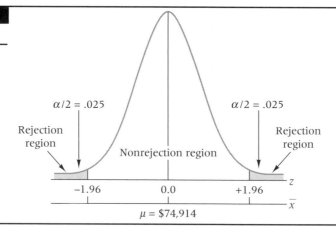

ACTION:

Because this test statistic, $z = 2.75$, is greater than the critical value of z in the upper tail of the distribution, $z = +1.96$, the statistical conclusion reached at step 7 of the hypothesis-testing process is to reject the null hypothesis. *The calculated test statistic* is often referred to as the **observed value.** Thus, the observed value of z for this problem is 2.75 and the critical value of z for this problem is 1.96.

BUSINESS IMPLICATION:

Step 8 is to make a managerial decision. What does this result mean? Statistically, the researcher has enough evidence to reject the figure of $74,914 as the true national average net income for sole proprietor CPAs. Although the researcher conducted a two-tailed test, the evidence gathered indicates that the national average may have increased. The sample mean of $78,695 is $3,781 higher than the national mean being tested. The researcher can conclude that the national average is more than before, but because the $78,695 is only a sample mean, it offers no guarantee that the national average for all sole proprietor CPAs is $3,781 more. If a confidence interval were constructed with the sample data, $78,695 would be the point estimate. Other samples might produce different sample means. Managerially, this statistical finding may mean that CPAs will be more expensive to hire either as full-time employees or as consultants. It may mean that consulting services have gone up in price. For new accountants, it may mean the potential for greater earning power. If the sample mean of $78,695 is the actual new population average for the year 2005, it would represent an increase of $3,781 over a ten-year period. This increase may or may not be substantive depending on one's point of view.

Testing the Mean with a Finite Population

If the hypothesis test for the population mean is being conducted with a known finite population, the population information can be incorporated into the hypothesis-testing formula. Doing so can increase the potential for rejecting the null hypothesis. However, remember from Chapter 1 that if the sample size is less than 5% of the population, the finite correction factor does not significantly alter the solution. Formula (3.1) can be amended to include the population information.

FORMULA TO TEST HYPOTHESES ABOUT μ WITH A FINITE POPULATION (3.2)	$$z = \dfrac{\bar{x} - \mu}{\dfrac{\sigma}{\sqrt{n}} \sqrt{\dfrac{N-n}{N-1}}}$$

In the CPA net income example, suppose only 600 sole proprietor CPAs practice in the United States. A sample of 112 CPAs taken from a population of only 600 CPAs is

18.67% of the population and therefore is much more likely to be representative of the population than a sample of 112 CPAs taken from a population of 20,000 CPAs (.56% of the population). The finite correction factor takes this difference into consideration and allows for an increase in the observed value of z. The observed z value would change to

$$z = \frac{\overline{x} - \mu}{\frac{\sigma}{\sqrt{n}}\sqrt{\frac{N-n}{N-1}}} = \frac{78,695 - 74,914}{\frac{14,530}{\sqrt{112}}\sqrt{\frac{600-112}{600-1}}} = \frac{3,781}{1,239.2} = 3.05$$

Use of the finite correction factor increased the observed z value from 2.75 to 3.05. The decision to reject the null hypothesis does not change with this new information. However, on occasion, the finite correction factor can make the difference between rejecting and failing to reject the null hypothesis.

Using the *p*-Value to Test Hypotheses

Another way to reach a statistical conclusion in hypothesis testing problems is by using the **p-value,** sometimes referred to as **observed significance level.** The p-value is growing in importance with the increasing use of statistical computer packages to test hypotheses. No preset value of α is given in the p-value method. Instead, the probability of getting a test statistic at least as extreme as the observed test statistic (computed from the data) is computed under the assumption that the null hypothesis is true. Virtually every statistical computer program yields this probability (p-value). The p-value defines the smallest value of alpha for which the null hypothesis can be rejected. For example, if the p-value of a test is .038, the null hypothesis cannot be rejected at $\alpha = .01$ because .038 is the smallest value of alpha for which the null hypothesis can be rejected. However, the null hypothesis can be rejected for $\alpha = .05$.

Suppose a researcher is conducting a one-tailed test with a rejection region in the upper tail and obtains an observed test statistic of $z = 2.04$ from the sample data. Using the standard normal table, Table A.2, we find that the probability of randomly obtaining a z value this great or greater by chance is $.5000 - .4793 = .0207$. The p value is .0207. Using this information, the researcher would reject the null hypothesis for $\alpha = .05$ or .10 or any value more than .0207. The researcher would not reject the null hypothesis for any alpha value less than or equal to .0207 (in particular, $\alpha = .01, .001$, etc.).

For a two-tailed test, recall that we split alpha to determine the critical value of the test statistic. With the p-value, the probability of getting a test statistic at least as extreme as the observed value is computed. This p-value is then compared to $\alpha/2$ for two-tailed tests to determine statistical significance. The business researcher should be cautioned that some statistical computer packages are programmed to double the observed probability and report that value as the p-value when the user signifies that a two-tailed test is being requested. The researcher then compares this p-value to alpha values to decide whether to reject the null hypothesis. In other words, rather than the researcher splitting alpha, the probability of the observed test statistic is doubled. The researcher must be sure she understands what the computer software package does to the p-value for a two-tailed test before she reaches a statistical conclusion.

As an example of using p-values with a two-tailed test, consider the CPA net income problem. The observed test statistic for this problem is $z = 2.75$. Using Table A.2, we know that the probability of obtaining a test statistic at least this extreme if the null hypothesis is true is $.5000 - .4970 = .0030$. Observe that in the MINITAB output in Figure 3.6 the p-value is .0060. MINITAB doubles the p-value on a two-tailed test so that the researcher can compare the p-value to α to reach a statistical conclusion. On the other hand, when Excel yields a p-value in its output, it always gives the one-tailed value, which in this case is .003 (see output in Figure 3.6). To reach a statistical conclusion from an Excel produced p-value when doing a two-tailed test, the researcher must either compare the p-value to $\alpha/2$ or double it and compare it to α.

FIGURE 3.6	**MINITAB Output**

FIGURE 3.6

MINITAB and Excel Output
with *p* Values

MINITAB Output

```
                        Z-TEST

Test of mu=74914 vs mu not=74914
The assumed sigma=14530

Variable    N    Mean    StDev   SE Mean    Z      p
Net Income  112  78695   14543    1373    2.75   0.0060
```

Excel Output

	A	B
1	Sample Mean	78695
2	Standard Error	1374
3	Standard Deviation	14543
4	Count (n)	112
5	Hypothesized Value of Mu	74914
6	P-value	0.003

Using the Critical Value Method to Test Hypotheses

Another method of testing hypotheses is the critical value method. In the CPA income example, the null hypothesis was rejected because the computed value of *z* was in the rejection zone. What mean income would it take to cause the observed *z* value to be in the rejection zone? The **critical value method** *determines the critical mean value required for z to be in the rejection region and uses it to test the hypotheses.*

This method also uses formula (3.1). However, instead of an observed *z*, a critical $\bar{x}$ value, $\bar{x}_C$, is determined. The critical table value of z_c is inserted into the formula, along with μ and σ. Thus,

$$z_c = \frac{\bar{x}_c - \mu}{\frac{\sigma}{\sqrt{n}}}$$

Substituting values from the CPA income example gives

$$\pm 1.96 = \frac{\bar{x}_c - 74{,}914}{\frac{14{,}530}{\sqrt{112}}}$$

or

$$\bar{x}_c = 74{,}914 \pm 1.96 \frac{14{,}530}{\sqrt{112}} = 74{,}914 \pm 2{,}691$$

$$\text{lower } \bar{x}_c = 72{,}223 \text{ and upper } \bar{x}_c = 77{,}605.$$

Figure 3.7 depicts graphically the rejection and nonrejection regions in terms of means instead of *z* scores.

With the critical value method, most of the computational work is done ahead of time. In this problem, before the sample means are computed, the analyst knows that a sample mean value of greater than $77,605 or less than $72,223 must be attained to reject the hypothesized population mean. Because the sample mean for this problem was $78,695, which is greater than $77,605, the analyst rejects the null hypothesis. This method is particularly attractive in industrial settings where standards can be set ahead of time and then quality control technicians can gather data and compare actual measurements of products to specifications.

FIGURE 3.7

Rejection and Nonrejection
Regions for Critical
Value Method

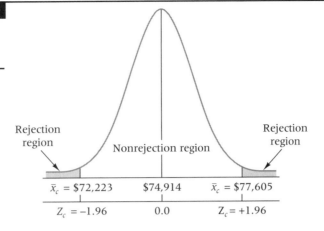

Rejection region   Nonrejection region   Rejection region

$\bar{x}_c = \$72,223$ $\$74,914$ $\bar{x}_c = \$77,605$

$Z_c = -1.96$ 0.0 $Z_c = +1.96$

DEMONSTRATION PROBLEM 3.1

In an attempt to determine why customer service is important to managers in the United Kingdom, researchers surveyed managing directors of manufacturing plants in Scotland.* One of the reasons proposed was that customer service is a means of retaining customers. On a scale from 1 to 5, with 1 being low and 5 being high, the survey respondents rated this reason more highly than any of the others, with a mean response of 4.30. Suppose U.S. researchers believe American manufacturing managers would not rate this reason as highly and conduct a hypothesis test to prove their theory. Alpha is set at .05. Data are gathered and the following results are obtained. Use these data and the eight steps of hypothesis testing to determine whether U.S. managers rate this reason significantly lower than the 4.30 mean ascertained in the United Kingdom. Assume from previous studies that the population standard deviation is 0.574.

```
3  4  5  5  4  5  5  4  4  4  4
4  4  4  4  5  4  4  4  3  4  4
4  3  5  4  4  5  4  4  4  5
```

Solution

HYPOTHESIZE:

STEP 1. Establish hypotheses. Because the U.S. researchers are interested only in "proving" that the mean figure is lower in the United States, the test is one-tailed. The alternative hypothesis is that the population mean is lower than 4.30. The null hypothesis states the equality case.

$$H_0: \mu = 4.30$$
$$H_a: \mu < 4.30$$

TEST:

STEP 2. Determine the appropriate statistical test. The test statistic is

$$z = \frac{\bar{x} - \mu}{\dfrac{\sigma}{\sqrt{n}}}$$

STEP 3. Specify the Type I error rate.

$$\alpha = .05$$

* William G. Donaldson, "Manufacturers Need to Show Greater Commitment to Customer Service," *Industrial Marketing Management*, vol. 24 (October 1995), pp. 421–430. The 1-to-5 scale has been reversed here for clarity of presentation.

STEP 4. State the decision rule. Because this test is a one-tailed test, the critical z value is found by looking up .5000 − .0500 = .4500 as the area in Table A.2. The critical value of the test statistic is $z_{.05} = -1.645$. An observed test statistic must be less than −1.645 to reject the null hypothesis. The rejection region and critical value can be depicted as in the following diagram.

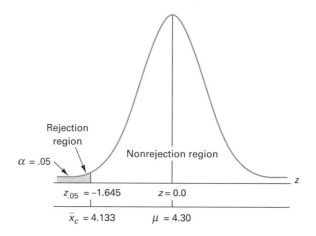

STEP 5. Gather the sample data. The data are shown.
STEP 6. Calculate the value of the test statistic.

$$\bar{x} = 4.156 \qquad \sigma = .574$$

$$z = \frac{4.156 - 4.30}{\frac{.574}{\sqrt{32}}} = -1.42$$

ACTION:

STEP 7. State the statistical conclusion. Because the observed test statistic is not less than the critical value and is not in the rejection region, the statistical conclusion is that the null hypothesis cannot be rejected.

BUSINESS IMPLICATION:

STEP 8. Make a managerial decision. The test does not result in enough evidence to conclude that U.S. managers think it is less important to use customer service as a means of retaining customers than do U.K. managers. Customer service is an important tool for retaining customers in both countries according to managers.

Using the p-value: The observed test statistic is $z = -1.42$. From Table A.2, the probability of getting a z value at least this extreme when the null hypothesis is true is .5000 − .4222 = .0778. Hence, the null hypothesis cannot be rejected at $\alpha = .05$ because the smallest value of alpha for which the null hypothesis can be rejected is .0778.

Using the critical value method: For what sample mean (or more extreme) value would the null hypothesis be rejected? This critical sample mean can be determined by using the critical z value associated with alpha, $z_{.05} = -1.645$.

$$z_c = \frac{\bar{x}_c - \mu}{\frac{\sigma}{\sqrt{n}}}$$

$$-1.645 = \frac{\bar{x}_c - 4.30}{\frac{.574}{\sqrt{32}}}$$

$$\bar{x}_c = 4.133$$

The decision rule is that a sample mean less than 4.133 would be necessary to reject the null hypothesis. Because the mean obtained from the sample data is 4.156, the researchers fail to reject the null hypothesis. The preceding diagram includes a scale with the critical sample mean and the rejection region for the critical value method.

FIGURE 3.8

MINITAB and Excel Output for
Demonstration Problem 3.1

MINITAB Output

```
One-Sample Z: Ratings

Test of mu = 4.3 vs mu < 4.3
The assumed sigma = 0.574

Variable   N   Mean   StDev   SE Mean
Ratings    32  4.156  0.574   0.101

Variable   95.0% Upper Bound    Z      P
Ratings          4.323        -1.42  0.078
```

Excel Output

	A
1	
2	The p-value for the ratings problem is **0.078339**
3	

Using the Computer to Test Hypotheses About a Population Mean Using the *z* Statistic

Both MINITAB and Excel can be used to test hypotheses about a single population mean using the *z* statistic. Figure 3.8 contains output from both MINITAB and Excel for Demonstration Problem 3.1. For *z* tests, MINITAB requires knowledge of the population standard deviation. Note that the standard MINITAB output includes a statement of the one-tailed hypothesis, the observed *z* value, and the *p*-value. Because this test is a one-tailed test, the *p*-value was not doubled. The Excel output contains only the right-tailed *p*-value of the *z* statistic. With a negative observed *z* for Demonstration Problem 3.1, the *p*-value was calculated by taking 1 – (Excel's answer).

3.2 PROBLEMS

3.1 **a.** Use the data given to test the following hypotheses.

$$H_0: \mu = 25 \qquad H_a: \mu \neq 25$$

$$\bar{x} = 28.1, n = 57, \sigma = 8.46, \alpha = .01$$

  b. Use the *p*-value to reach a statistical conclusion

  c. Using the critical value method, what are the critical sample mean values?

3.2 Use the data given to test the following hypotheses. Assume the data are normally distributed in the population.

$$H_0: \mu = 7.48 \qquad H_a: \mu < 7.48$$

$$\bar{x} = 6.91, n = 24, \sigma = 1.21, \alpha = .01$$

3.3 **a.** Use the data given to test the following hypotheses.

$$H_0: \mu = 1200 \qquad H_a: \mu > 1200$$

$$\bar{x} = 1215, n = 113, \sigma = 100, \alpha = .10$$

  b. Use the *p*-value to obtain the results.

  c. Solve for the critical value required to reject the mean.

3.4 The Environmental Protection Agency releases figures on urban air soot in selected cities in the United States. For the city of St. Louis, the EPA claims that the average number of micrograms of suspended particles per cubic meter of air is 82. Suppose St. Louis officials have been working with businesses, commuters, and industries to reduce this figure. These city officials hire an environmental company to take random measures of air soot over a period of several weeks. The resulting data follow. Assume that the population standard deviation is 9.184. Use these data to determine whether the urban air soot in St. Louis is significantly lower than it was when the EPA conducted its measurements. Let $\alpha = .01$. If the null hypothesis is rejected, discuss the substantive hypothesis.

81.6	66.6	70.9	82.5	58.3	71.6	72.4
96.6	78.6	76.1	80.0	73.2	85.5	73.2
68.6	74.0	68.7	83.0	86.9	94.9	75.6
77.3	86.6	71.7	88.5	87.0	72.5	83.0
85.8	74.9	61.7	92.2			

3.5 According to the U.S. Bureau of Labor Statistics, the average weekly earnings of a production worker in 1997 were $424.20. Suppose a labor researcher wants to test to determine whether this figure is still accurate today. The researcher randomly selects 54 production workers from across the United States and obtains a representative earnings statement for one week from each. The resulting sample average is $432.69. Assuming a population standard deviation of $33.90, and a 5% level of significance, determine whether the mean weekly earnings of a production worker have changed.

3.6 According to a study several years ago by the Personal Communications Industry Association, the average wireless phone user earns $62,600 per year. Suppose a researcher believes that the average annual earnings of a wireless phone user are lower now, and he sets up a study in an attempt to prove his theory. He randomly samples 18 wireless phone users and finds out that the average annual salary for this sample is $58,974, with a population standard deviation of $7,810. Use $\alpha = .01$ to test the researcher's theory. Assume wages in this industry are normally distributed.

3.7 A manufacturing company produces valves in various sizes and shapes. One particular valve plate is supposed to have a tensile strength of 5 pounds per millimeter (lbs/mm). The company tests a random sample of 42 such valve plates from a lot of 650 valve plates. The sample mean is a tensile strength of 5.0611 lbs/mm, and the population standard deviation is .2803 lbs/mm. Use $\alpha = .10$ and test to determine whether the lot of valve plates has an average tensile strength of 5 lbs/mm.

3.8 A manufacturing firm has been averaging 18.2 orders per week for several years. However, during a recession, orders appeared to slow. Suppose the firm's production manager randomly samples 32 weeks and finds a sample mean of 15.6 orders. The population standard deviation is 2.3 orders. Test to determine whether the average number of orders is down by using $\alpha = .10$.

3.9 A study conducted by Runzheimer International showed that Paris is the most expensive place to live of the 12 European Union cities. Paris ranks second in housing expense, with a rental unit of six to nine rooms costing an average of $4,292 a month. Suppose a company's CEO believes this figure is too high and decides to conduct her own survey. Her assistant contacts the owners of 55 randomly selected rental units of six to nine rooms and finds that the sample average cost is $4,008. Assume that the population standard deviation is $386. Using the sample results and $\alpha = .01$, test to determine whether the figure published by Runzheimer International is too high. If the null hypothesis is rejected, discuss whether the results are substantive.

3.10 The American Water Works Association estimates that the average person in the United States uses 123 gallons of water per day. Suppose some researchers believe that more water is being used now and want to test to determine whether it is so. They randomly select a sample of Americans and carefully keep track of the water used by each sample member for a day, then analyze the results by using a statistical computer software package. The output is given here. Assume $\alpha = .05$.

How many people were sampled? What was the sample mean? Was this a one- or two-tailed test? What was the result of the study? What decision could be stated about the null hypothesis from these results?

```
             One-Sample Z: Wateruse
_____
Test of mu = 123 vs mu > 123
The assumed sigma = 27.68

Variable   N    Mean    StDev  SE Mean
Wateruse   40  132.36   27.68    4.38

Variable   95.0% Lower Bound    Z      P
Wateruse          125.16       2.14  0.016
```

3.3 TESTING HYPOTHESES ABOUT A POPULATION MEAN USING THE *t* STATISTIC (σ UNKNOWN)

Very often when a business researcher is gathering data to test hypotheses about a single population mean, the value of the population standard deviation is unknown and the researcher must use the sample standard deviation as an estimate of it. In such cases, the *z* test cannot be used.

Chapter 2 presented the *t* distribution, which can be used to analyze hypotheses about a single population mean when σ is unknown if the population is normally distributed for the measurement being studied. In this section, we will examine the *t* test for a single population mean. In general, this *t* test is applicable whenever the researcher is drawing a single random sample to test the value of a population mean (μ), the population standard deviation is unknown, and the population is normally distributed for the measurement of interest. Recall from Chapter 2 that the assumption that the data be normally distributed in the population is rather robust.

The formula for testing such hypotheses follows.

t TEST FOR μ (3.3)	$$t = \frac{\bar{x} - \mu}{\frac{s}{\sqrt{n}}}$$ $$df = n - 1$$

The U.S. Farmers' Production Company builds large harvesters. For a harvester to be properly balanced when operating, a 25-pound plate is installed on its side. The machine that produces these plates is set to yield plates that average 25 pounds. The distribution of plates produced from the machine is normal. However, the shop supervisor is worried that the machine is out of adjustment and is producing plates that do not average 25 pounds. To test this concern, he randomly selects 20 of the plates produced the day before and weighs them. Table 3.1 shows the weights obtained, along with the computed sample mean and sample standard deviation.

The test is to determine whether the machine is out of control, and the shop supervisor has not specified whether he believes the machine is producing plates that are too heavy or too light. Thus a two-tailed test is appropriate. The following hypotheses are tested.

$$H_0: \mu = 25 \text{ pounds}$$
$$H_a: \mu \neq 25 \text{ pounds}$$

An α of .05 is used. Figure 3.9 shows the rejection regions.

Because $n = 20$, the degrees of freedom for this test are 19 $(20 - 1)$. The *t* distribution table is a one-tailed table but the test for this problem is two-tailed, so alpha must be split, which yields $\alpha/2 = .025$, the value in each tail. (To obtain the table *t* value when conducting

TABLE 3.1

Weights in Pounds of a Sample of 20 Plates

22.6	22.2	23.2	27.4	24.5
27.0	26.6	28.1	26.9	24.9
26.2	25.3	23.1	24.2	26.1
25.8	30.4	28.6	23.5	23.6

$\bar{x} = 25.51, s = 2.1933, n = 20$

FIGURE 3.9

Rejection Regions for the
Machine Plate Example

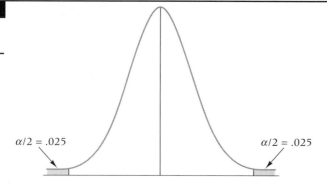

$\alpha/2 = .025$ $\alpha/2 = .025$

FIGURE 3.10

Graph of Observed and Critical
t Values for the Machine Plate
Example

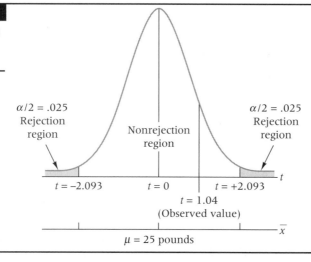

$\alpha/2 = .025$
Rejection
region

Nonrejection
region

$\alpha/2 = .025$
Rejection
region

$t = -2.093$ $t = 0$ $t = +2.093$

$t = 1.04$
(Observed value)

$\mu = 25$ pounds

FIGURE 3.11

MINITAB and Excel Output for
the Machine Plate Example

MINITAB Output

```
One-Sample T: Weight

Test of mu = 25 vs mu not = 25

Variable   N    Mean    StDev   SE Mean
Weight     20   25.510  2.193   0.490

Variable      95.0% CI          T      P
Weight   ( 24.484,  26.536)   1.04   0.311
```

Excel Output

	A	B
1	Mean	25.51
2	Variance	4.810
3	df	19
4	t Stat	1.04
5	P (T<=t) one-tail	0.1557
6	t Critical one-tail	1.73
7	P (T<=t) two-tail	0.3114
8	t Critical two-tail	2.09

a two-tailed test, always split alpha and use $\alpha/2$.) The table *t* value for this example is 2.093. Table values such as this one are often written in the following form:

$$t_{.025,19} = 2.093$$

Figure 3.10 depicts the *t* distribution for this example, along with the critical values, the observed *t* value, and the rejection regions. In this case, the decision rule is to reject the null hypothesis if the observed value of t is less than –2.093 or greater than +2.093 (in the tails of the distribution). Computation of the test statistic yields

$$t = \frac{\bar{x} - \mu}{\frac{s}{\sqrt{n}}} = \frac{25.51 - 25.00}{\frac{2.1933}{\sqrt{20}}} = 1.04 \text{ (observed } t \text{ value)}$$

Because the observed t value is +1.04, the null hypothesis is not rejected. Not enough evidence is found in this sample to reject the hypothesis that the population mean is 25 pounds.

Figure 3.11 shows MINITAB and Excel output for this example. Note that the MINITAB output includes the observed t value (1.04) and the p-value (.311). Since this test is a two-tailed test, MINITAB has doubled the one-tailed p-value for $t = 1.04$. Thus the p-value of .311 can be compared directly to $\alpha = .05$ to reach the conclusion to fail to reject the null hypothesis.

The Excel output contains the observed t value (1.04) plus the p-value and the critical table t value for both a one-tailed and a two-tailed test. Since this test is a two-tailed test, the p-value of .3114 is used to compare to $\alpha = .05$. Excel also gives the table value of $t = 2.09$ for a two-tailed test, which allows one to verify that the statistical conclusion is to fail to reject the null hypothesis because the observed t value is only 1.04, which is less than 2.09.

DEMONSTRATION PROBLEM 3.2

Figures released by the U.S. Department of Agriculture show that the average size of farms has increased since 1940. In 1940, the mean size of a farm was 174 acres; by 1997, the average size was 471 acres. Between those years, the number of farms decreased but the amount of tillable land remained relatively constant, so now farms are bigger. This trend might be explained, in part, by the inability of small farms to compete with the prices and costs of large-scale operations and to produce a level of income necessary to support the farmers' desired standard of living. Suppose an agribusiness researcher believes the average size of farms increased from the 1997 mean figure of 471 acres. To test this notion, she randomly sampled 23 farms across the United States and ascertained the size of each farm from county records. The data she gathered follow. Use a 5% level of significance to test her hypothesis.

445	489	474	505	553	477	454	463	466
557	502	449	438	500	466	477	557	433
545	511	590	561	560				

Solution

HYPOTHESIZE:

STEP 1. The researcher's hypothesis is that the average size of a U.S. farm is more than 471 acres. Because this theory is unproven, it is the alternate hypothesis. The null hypothesis is that the mean is still 471 acres.

$$H_0: \mu = 471$$
$$H_a: \mu > 471$$

TEST:

STEP 2. The statistical test to be used is

$$t = \frac{\bar{x} - \mu}{\frac{s}{\sqrt{n}}}$$

STEP 3. The value of alpha is .05.

STEP 4. With 23 data points, df $= n - 1 = 23 - 1 = 22$. This test is one-tailed, and the critical table t value is

$$t_{.05,22} = 1.717$$

The decision rule is to reject the null hypothesis if the observed test statistic is greater than 1.717.

STEP 5. The gathered data are shown.

STEP 6. The sample mean is 498.78 and the sample standard deviation is 46.94. The observed t value is

$$t = \frac{\bar{x} - \mu}{\frac{s}{\sqrt{n}}} = \frac{498.78 - 471}{\frac{46.94}{\sqrt{23}}} = 2.84$$

ACTION:

STEP 7. The observed t value of 2.84 is greater than the table t value of 1.717, so the business researcher rejects the null hypothesis. She accepts the alternative hypothesis and concludes that the average size of a U.S. farm is now more than 471 acres. The following graph represents this analysis pictorially.

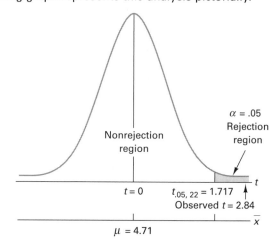

BUSINESS IMPLICATIONS:

STEP 8. Agribusiness researchers can speculate about what it means to have larger farms. If the average size of a farm has increased from 471 acres to almost 500 acres, it may represent a substantive increase.

It could mean that small farms are not financially viable. It might mean that corporations are buying out small farms and that large company farms are on the increase. Such a trend might spark legislative movements to protect the small farm. Larger farm sizes might also affect commodity trading.

FIGURE 3.12
MINITAB and Excel Output for Demonstration Problem 3.2

MINITAB Output

```
One-Sample T: Acres

Test of mu = 471 vs mu > 471

Variable    N     Mean    StDev   SE Mean
Acres       23   498.78   46.94    9.79

Variable   95.0% Lower Bound     T       P
Acres              481.97       2.84   0.005
```

Excel Output

	A	B
1	Mean	498.78
2	Variance	2203.63
3	Observations	23
4	df	22
5	t Stat	2.84
6	P (T<=t) one-tail	0.0048
7	t Critical one-tail	1.72
8	P (T<=t) two-tail	0.0096
9	t Critical two-tail	2.07

Using the Computer to Test Hypotheses About a Population Mean Using the *t* Test

MINITAB has the capability of computing a one-sample *t* test for means. Figure 3.12 contains MINITAB output for Demonstration Problem 3.2. The output contains the hypotheses being tested, the sample statistics, the observed *t* value (2.84), and the *p*-value (.005). Because the *p*-value is less than $\alpha = .05$, the decision is to reject the null hypothesis.

Excel does not have a one-sample *t* test function. However, by using the two-sample *t* test for means with unequal variances, the results for a one-sample test can be obtained. This is accomplished by inputting the sample data for the first sample and the value of the parameter being tested (in this case, $\mu = 471$) for the second sample. The output includes the observed *t* value (2.84) and both the table *t* values and *p*-values for one- and two-tailed tests. Because Demonstration Problem 3.2 was a one-tailed test, the *p*-value of .0048, which is the same value obtained using MINITAB, is used.

3.3 PROBLEMS

3.11 A random sample of size 20 is taken, resulting in a sample mean of 16.45 and a sample standard deviation of 3.59. Assume *x* is normally distributed and use this information and $\alpha = .05$ to test the following hypotheses.

$$H_0: \mu = 16 \qquad H_a: \mu \neq 16$$

3.12 A random sample of 51 items is taken, with $\bar{x} = 58.42$ and $s^2 = 25.68$. Use these data to test the following hypotheses, assuming you want to take only a 1% risk of committing a Type I error and that *x* is normally distributed.

$$H_0: \mu = 60 \qquad H_a: \mu < 60$$

3.13 The following data were gathered from a random sample of 11 items.

1200	1175	1080	1275	1201	1387
1090	1280	1400	1287	1225	

Use these data and a 5% level of significance to test the following hypotheses, assuming that the data come from a normally distributed population.

$$H_0: \mu = 1160 \qquad H_a: \mu > 1160$$

3.14 The following data (in pounds), which were selected randomly from a normally distributed population of values, represent measurements of a machine part that is supposed to weigh, on average, 8.3 pounds.

8.1	8.4	8.3	8.2	8.5	8.6	8.4	8.3	8.4	8.2
8.8	8.2	8.2	8.3	8.1	8.3	8.4	8.5	8.5	8.7

Use these data and $\alpha = .01$ to test the hypothesis that the parts average 8.3 pounds.

3.15 A hole-punch machine is set to punch a hole 1.84 centimeters in diameter in a strip of sheet metal in a manufacturing process. The strip of metal is then creased and sent on to the next phase of production, where a metal rod is slipped through the hole. It is important that the hole be punched to the specified diameter of 1.84 cm. To test punching accuracy, technicians have randomly sampled 12 punched holes and measured the diameters. The data (in centimeters) follow. Use an alpha of .10 to determine whether the holes are being punched an average of 1.84 centimeters. Assume the punched holes are normally distributed in the population.

1.81	1.89	1.86	1.83
1.85	1.82	1.87	1.85
1.84	1.86	1.88	1.85

3.16 Suppose a study reports that the average price for a gallon of self-serve regular unleaded gasoline is $1.16. You believe that the figure is higher in your area of the country. You decide to test this claim for your part of the United States by randomly calling gasoline stations. Your random survey of 25 stations produces the following prices.

$1.27	$1.29	$1.16	$1.20	$1.37
1.20	1.23	1.19	1.20	1.24
1.16	1.07	1.27	1.09	1.35
1.15	1.23	1.14	1.05	1.35
1.21	1.14	1.14	1.07	1.10

Assume gasoline prices for a region are normally distributed. Do the data you obtained provide enough evidence to reject the claim? Use a 1% level of significance.

3.17 Suppose that in past years the average price per square foot for warehouses in the United States has been $32.28. A national real estate investor wants to determine whether that figure has changed now. The investor hires a researcher who randomly samples 19 warehouses that are for sale across the United States and finds that the mean price per square foot is $31.67, with a standard deviation of $1.29. If the researcher uses a 5% level of significance, what statistical conclusion can be reached? What are the hypotheses?

3.18 According to a National Public Transportation survey, the average commuting time for people who commute to a city with a population of 1 to 3 million is 19.0 minutes. Suppose a researcher lives in a city with a population of 2.4 million and wants to test this claim in her city. She takes a random sample of commuters and gathers data. The data are analyzed using both MINITAB and Excel, and the output is shown here. What are the results of the study? What are the hypotheses?

MINITAB Output:

```
One-Sample T: Commute Time

Test of mu = 19 vs mu not = 19

Variable       N    Mean   StDev  SE Mean
Commute Time  26  19.534   4.100    0.804

Variable         95.0% CI          T     P
Commute Time  (17.878, 21.190)  0.66  0.513
```

Excel Output:

	A	B
1	Mean	19.534
2	Variance	16.813
3	Observations	26
4	df	25
5	t Stat	0.66
6	P (T<=t) one-tail	0.256
7	t Critical one-tail	1.71
8	P (T<=t) two-tail	0.513
9	t Critical two-tail	2.06

3.4 TESTING HYPOTHESES ABOUT A PROPORTION

Data analysis used in business decision making often contains proportions to describe such aspects as market share, consumer makeup, quality defects, on-time deliver rate, profitable stocks, and others. Business surveys often produce information expressed in proportion form such as .45 of all businesses offer flexible hours to employees or .88 of all businesses have Web sites. Business researchers conduct hypothesis tests about such proportions to determine whether they have changed in some way. As an example, suppose a company held a 26% or .26 share of the market for several years. Due to a massive marketing effort and improved product quality, company officials believe that the market share increased; and they want to prove it. Other examples of hypothesis testing about a single population proportion might include:

- A market researcher wants to test to determine whether the proportion of new car purchasers who are female has increased.
- A financial researcher wants to test to determine whether the proportion of companies that were profitable last year in the average investment officer's portfolio is .60.
- A quality manager for a large manufacturing firm wants to test to determine whether the proportion of defective items in a batch is less than .04.

Formula (3.4) for inferential analysis of a proportion was introduced in section 1.3 of Chapter 1. Based on the central limit theorem, this formula makes possible the testing of hypotheses about the population proportion in a manner similar to that of the formula used to test sample means. Recall that $\hat{p}$ denotes a sample proportion and p denotes the population proportion. To validly use this test, the sample size must be large enough such that $n \cdot p \geq 5$ and $n \cdot q \geq 5$.

***z* TEST OF A POPULATION PROPORTION (3.4)**	$$z = \frac{\hat{p} - p}{\sqrt{\dfrac{p \cdot q}{n}}}$$

where

$\hat{p}$ = sample proportion
p = population proportion
$q = 1 - p$

A manufacturer believes exactly 8% of its products contain at least one minor flaw. Suppose a company researcher wants to test this belief. The null and alternative hypotheses are

$$H_0: p = .08$$
$$H_a: p \neq .08$$

This test is two-tailed because the hypothesis being tested is whether the proportion of products with at least one minor flaw is .08. Alpha is selected to be .10. Figure 3.13 shows the distribution, with the rejection regions and $z_{.05}$. Because α is divided for a two-tailed test, the table value for an area of $(1/2)(.10) = .05$ is $z_{.05} = \pm 1.645$.

FIGURE 3.13

Distribution with Rejection Regions for Flawed-Product Example

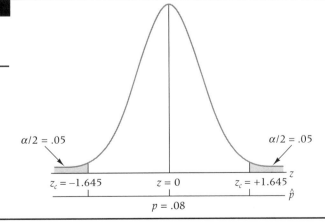

For the business researcher to reject the null hypothesis, the observed z value must be greater than 1.645 or less than -1.645. The business researcher randomly selects a sample of 200 products, inspects each item for flaws, and determines that 33 items have at least one minor flaw. Calculating the sample proportion gives

$$\hat{p} = \frac{33}{200} = .165$$

The observed z value is calculated as:

$$z = \frac{\hat{p} - p}{\sqrt{\dfrac{p \cdot q}{n}}} = \frac{.165 - .080}{\sqrt{\dfrac{(.08)(.92)}{200}}} = \frac{.085}{.019} = 4.43$$

Note that the denominator of the z formula contains the population proportion. Although the business researcher does not actually know the population proportion, he is testing a population proportion value. Hence he uses the hypothesized population value in the denominator of the formula as well as in the numerator. This method contrasts with the confidence interval formula, where the sample proportion is used in the denominator.

The observed value of z is in the rejection region (observed $z = 4.43 >$ table $z_{.05} = +1.645$), so the business researcher rejects the null hypothesis. He concludes that the proportion of items with at least one minor flaw in the population from which the sample of 200 was drawn is not .08. With $\alpha = .10$, the risk of committing a Type I error in this example is .10.

The observed value of $z = 4.43$ is outside the range of most values in virtually all z tables. Thus if the researcher were using the p-value to arrive at a decision about the null hypothesis, the probability would be .0000, and he would reject the null hypothesis.

The MINITAB output shown in Figure 3.14 displays a p-value of .000 for this problem, underscoring the decision to reject the null hypothesis.

Suppose the researcher wanted to use the critical value method. He would enter the table value of $z_{.05} = 1.645$ in the Z formula for single sample proportions, along with the hypothesized population proportion and n, and solve for the critical value of denoted as $\hat{p}_C$. The result is

$$z_{\alpha/2} = \frac{\hat{p}_c - p}{\sqrt{\dfrac{p \cdot q}{n}}}$$

$$\pm 1.645 = \frac{\hat{p}_c - .08}{\sqrt{\dfrac{(.08)(.92)}{200}}}$$

$$\hat{p}_c = .08 \pm 1.645 \sqrt{\frac{(.08)(.92)}{200}} = .08 \pm .032$$

$$= .048 \text{ and } .112$$

Examination of the sample proportion, $\hat{p} = .165$, and Figure 3.15 clearly show that the sample proportion is in the rejection region. The statistical conclusion is to reject the null hypothesis. The proportion of products with at least one flaw is not .08.

FIGURE 3.14	TEST AND CI FOR ONE PROPORTION
MINITAB Output for the Flawed-Product Example	Test of p = 0.08 vs p not = 0.08

```
TEST AND CI FOR ONE PROPORTION

Test of p = 0.08 vs p not = 0.08
Sample   X    N    Sample p        90.0% CI           P-Value
1        33  200   0.165000   (0.123279, 0.214351)    0.000
```

STATISTICS IN BUSINESS TODAY

Testing Hypotheses about Commuting

How do Americans commute to work? A National Public Transportation survey taken a few years ago indicated that almost 80% of U.S. commuters drive alone to work, more than 11% carpool, and approximately 5% use public transportation. Using hypothesis testing methodology presented in this chapter, researchers can test whether these proportions still hold true today as well as how these figures vary by region. For example, in New York City it is almost certain that the proportion of commuters using public transportation is much higher than 5%. In rural parts of the country where public transportation is unavailable, the proportion of commuters using public transportation would be zero.

What is the average travel time of a commute to work in the United States? According to the National Public Transportation Survey, travel time varies according to the type of transportation used. For example, the average travel time of a commute using a private vehicle is 20 minutes as compared to 42 minutes using public transportation. In part, this difference can be accounted for by the travel speed in miles per hour: private vehicles average 35 miles per hour over a commute compared to 19 miles per hour averaged by public transportation vehicles. It is possible to test any of these means using hypothesis testing techniques presented in this chapter to either validate the figures or to determine whether the figures are no longer true.

FIGURE 3.15

Distribution Using Critical Value Method for the Flawed-Product Example

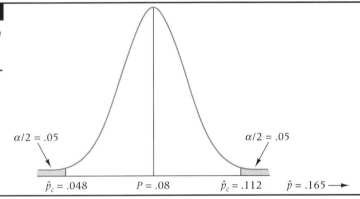

DEMONSTRATION PROBLEM 3.3

A survey of the morning beverage market shows that the primary breakfast beverage for 17% of Americans is milk. A milk producer in Wisconsin, where milk is plentiful, believes the figure is higher for Wisconsin. To test this idea, she contacts a random sample of 550 Wisconsin residents and asks which primary beverage they consumed for breakfast that day. Suppose 115 replied that milk was the primary beverage. Using a level of significance of .05, test the idea that the milk figure is higher for Wisconsin.

Solution

HYPOTHESIZE:

STEP 1. The milk producer's theory is that the proportion of Wisconsin residents who drink milk for breakfast is higher than the national proportion, which is the alternative hypothesis. The null hypothesis is that the proportion in Wisconsin does not differ from the national average. The hypotheses for this problem are

$$H_0: p = .17$$
$$H_a: p > .17$$

TEST:

STEP 2. The test statistic is

$$z = \frac{\hat{p} - p}{\sqrt{\dfrac{p \cdot q}{n}}}$$

STEP 3. The Type I error rate is .05.

STEP 4. This test is a one-tailed test, and the table value is $z_{.05} = +1.645$. The sample results must yield an observed z value greater than 1.645 for the milk producer to reject the null hypothesis. The following diagram shows $z_{.05}$ and the rejection region for this problem.

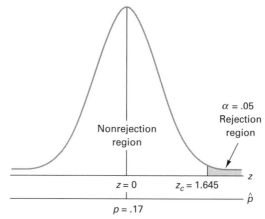

STEP 5. $n = 550$ and $x = 115$

$$\hat{p} = \frac{115}{550} = .209$$

STEP 6. $z = \dfrac{\hat{p} - p}{\sqrt{\dfrac{p \cdot q}{n}}} = \dfrac{.209 - .17}{\sqrt{\dfrac{(.17)(.83)}{550}}} = \dfrac{.039}{.016} = 2.44$

ACTION:

STEP 7. Because $z = 2.44$ is beyond $z_{.05} = 1.645$ in the rejection region, the milk producer rejects the null hypothesis. On the basis of the random sample, the producer is ready to conclude that the proportion of Wisconsin residents who drink milk as the primary beverage for breakfast is higher than the national proportion.

BUSINESS IMPLICATIONS:

STEP 8. If the proportion of residents who drink milk for breakfast is higher in Wisconsin than in other parts of the United States, milk producers might have a market opportunity in Wisconsin that is not available in other parts of the country. Perhaps Wisconsin residents are being loyal to home-state products, in which case marketers of other Wisconsin products might be successful in appealing to residents to support their products. The fact that more milk is sold in Wisconsin might mean that if Wisconsin milk producers appealed to markets outside Wisconsin in the same way they do inside the state, they might increase their market share of the breakfast beverage market in other states. Is a proportion of almost .21 really a substantive increase over .17? Certainly in a market of any size at all, an increase of almost 4% of the market share could be worth millions of dollars and in such a case, would be substantive.

The probability of obtaining a $z \geq 2.44$ by chance is .0073. Because this probability is less than $\alpha = .05$, the null hypothesis is also rejected with the p-value.

A critical proportion can be solved for by

$$z_{.05} = \frac{\hat{p}_c - p}{\sqrt{\dfrac{p \cdot q}{n}}}$$

$$1.645 = \frac{\hat{p}_c - .17}{\sqrt{\dfrac{(.17)(.83)}{550}}}$$

$$\hat{p}_c = .17 + 1.645\sqrt{\frac{(.17)(.83)}{550}} = .17 + .026 = .196$$

With the critical value method, a sample proportion greater than .196 must be obtained to reject the null hypothesis. The sample proportion for this problem is .209, so the null hypothesis is also rejected with the critical value method.

FIGURE 3.16	Test and CI for One Proportion

MINITAB Output for
Demonstration Problem 3.3

```
Test of p = 0.17 vs p > 0.17

                                    Exact
Sample X    N    Sample p    90.0% Lower Bound    P-Value
1     115   550   0.209091    0.186770      0.010
```

Using the Computer to Test Hypotheses About a Population Proportion

MINITAB has the capability of testing hypotheses about a population proportion. Figure 3.16 shows the MINITAB output for Demonstration Problem 3.3. Notice that the output includes a restatement of the hypotheses, the sample proportion, and the *p*-value. From this information, a decision regarding the null hypothesis can be made by comparing the *p*-value (.010) to α (.050). Because the *p*-value is less than α, the decision is to reject the null hypothesis.

3.4 PROBLEMS

3.19 Suppose you are testing H_0: $p = .45$ versus H_a: $p > .45$. A random sample of 310 people produces a value of $\hat{p} = .465$. Use $\alpha = .05$ to test this hypothesis.

3.20 Suppose you are testing H_0: $p = .63$ versus H_a: $p < .63$. For a random sample of 100 people, $x = 55$, where x denotes the number in the sample that have the characteristic of interest. Use a .01 level of significance to test this hypothesis.

3.21 Suppose you are testing H_0: $p = .29$ versus H_a: $p \neq .29$. A random sample of 740 items shows that 207 have this characteristic. With a .05 probability of committing a Type I error, test the hypothesis. For the *p*-value method, what is the probability of the calculated *z* value for this problem? If you had used the critical value method, what would the two critical values be? How do the sample results compare with the critical values?

3.22 The Independent Insurance Agents of America conducted a survey of insurance consumers and discovered that 48% of them always reread their insurance policies, 29% sometimes do, 16% rarely do, and 7% never do. Suppose a large insurance company invests considerable time and money in rewriting policies so that they will be more attractive and easy to read and understand. After using the new policies for a year, company managers want to determine whether rewriting the policies significantly changed the proportion of policyholders who always reread their insurance policy. They contact 380 of the company's insurance consumers who purchased a policy in the past year and ask them whether they always reread their insurance policies. One hundred and sixty-four respond that they do. Use a 1% level of significance to test the hypothesis.

3.23 A study by Hewitt Associates showed that 79% of companies offer employees flexible scheduling. Suppose a researcher believes that in accounting firms this figure is lower. The researcher randomly selects 415 accounting firms and through interviews determines that 303 of these firms have flexible scheduling. With a 1% level of significance, does the test show enough evidence to conclude that a significantly lower proportion of accounting firms offer employees flexible scheduling?

3.24 A survey was undertaken by Bruskin/Goldring Research for Quicken to determine how people plan to meet their financial goals in the next year. Respondents were allowed to select more than one way to meet their goals. Thirty-one percent said that they were using a financial planner to help them meet their goals. Twenty-four percent were using family/friends to help them meet their financial goals followed by broker/accountant (19%), computer software (17%), and books (14%). Suppose another researcher takes a similar survey of 600 people to test these results. If 200 people respond that they are going to use a financial planner to help them meet their goals, is this proportion enough evidence to reject the 31% figure generated in the Bruskin/Goldring survey using $\alpha = .10$? If 130 respond that they are going to use family/friends to help them meet their financial goals, is this result enough evidence to declare that the proportion is significantly lower than Bruskin/Goldring's figure of .24 if $\alpha = .05$?

3.25 Eighteen percent of U.S.-based multinational companies provide an allowance for personal long-distance calls for executives living overseas, according to the Institute for International Human Resources and the National Foreign Trade Council. Suppose a researcher thinks that U.S.-based multinational companies are having a more difficult time recruiting executives to live overseas and that an increasing number of these companies are providing an allowance for personal long-distance calls to these executives to ease the burden of living away from home. To test this hypothesis, a new study is conducted by contacting 376 multinational companies. Twenty-two percent of these surveyed companies are providing an allowance for personal long-distance calls to executives living overseas. Does the test show enough evidence to declare that a significantly higher proportion of multinational companies provide a long-distance call allowance? Let $\alpha = .01$.

3.26 A large manufacturing company investigated the service it received from suppliers and discovered that, in the past, 32% of all materials shipments were received late. However, the company recently installed a just-in-time system in which suppliers are linked more closely to the manufacturing process. A random sample of 118 deliveries since the just-in-time system was installed reveals that 22 deliveries were late. Use this sample information to test whether the proportion of late deliveries was reduced significantly. Let $\alpha = .05$.

3.27 Where do CFOs get their money news? According to Robert Half International, 47% get their money news from newspapers, 15% get it from communication/colleagues, 12% get it from television, 11% from the Internet, 9% from magazines, 5% from radio, and 1% don't know. Suppose a researcher wants to test these results. She randomly samples 67 CFOs and finds that 40 of them get their money news from newspapers. Does the test show enough evidence to reject the findings of Robert Half International? Use $\alpha = .05$.

3.5 TESTING HYPOTHESES ABOUT A VARIANCE

At times a researcher needs to test hypotheses about a population variance. For example, in the area of statistical quality control, manufacturers try to produce equipment and parts that are consistent in measurement. Suppose a company produces industrial wire that is specified to be a particular thickness. Because of the production process, the thickness of the wire will vary slightly from one end to the other and from lot to lot and batch to batch. Even if the average thickness of the wire as measured from lot to lot is on specification, the variance of the measurements might be too great to be acceptable. In other words, on the average the wire is the correct thickness, but some portions of the wire might be too thin and others unacceptably thick. By conducting hypothesis tests for the variance of the thickness measurements, the quality control people can monitor for variations in the process that are too great.

The procedure for testing hypotheses about a population variance is similar to the techniques presented in Chapter 2 for estimating a population variance from the sample variance. Formula (3.5) used to conduct these tests assumes a normally distributed population.

FORMULA FOR TESTING HYPOTHESES ABOUT A POPULATION VARIANCE (3.5)	$\chi^2 = \dfrac{(n-1)s^2}{\sigma^2}$ $$\text{df} = n - 1$$

Note: *As was mentioned in Chapter 2, the chi-square test of a population variance is extremely sensitive to violations of the assumption that the population is normally distributed.*

As an example, a manufacturing firm has been working diligently to implement a just-in-time inventory system for its production line. The final product requires the installation of a pneumatic tube at a particular station on the assembly line. With the just-in-time inventory system, the company's goal is to minimize the number of pneumatic tubes that are piled up at the station waiting to be installed. Ideally, the tubes would arrive just as the operator needs them. However, because of the supplier and the variables involved in getting the tubes to the line, most of the time there will be some buildup of tube inventory. The company expects that, on the average, about 20 pneumatic tubes will be at the station. However, the production superintendent does not want the variance of this inventory to be greater than 4. On a given day, the number of pneumatic tubes piled up at the workstation is determined eight different times and the following numbers of tubes are recorded.

23   17   20   29   21   14   19   24

Using these sample data, we can test to determine whether the variance is greater than 4. The hypothesis test is one-tailed. Assume the number of tubes is normally distributed. The null hypothesis is that the variance is acceptable with no problems—the variance is equal to 4. The alternative hypothesis is that the variance is greater than 4.

$$H_0: \sigma^2 = 4$$

$$H_a: \sigma^2 > 4$$

Suppose alpha is .05. Because the sample size is eight, the degrees of freedom for the critical table chi-square value are $8 - 1 = 7$. Using Table A.5, we find the critical chi-square value.

$$\chi^2_{.05, 7} = 14.0671$$

Because the alternative hypothesis is greater than 4, the rejection region is in the upper tail of the chi-square distribution. The sample variance is calculated from the sample data to be

$$s^2 = 20.9821$$

The observed chi-square value is calculated as

$$\chi^2 = \frac{(8-1)(20.9821)}{4} = 36.72$$

Because this observed chi-square value, $\chi^2 = 36.72$, is greater than the critical chi-square table value, $\chi^2_{.05, 7} = 14.0671$, the decision is to reject the null hypothesis. On the basis of this sample of eight data measurements, the population variance of inventory at this workstation is greater than 4. Company production personnel and managers might want to investigate further to determine whether they can find a cause for this unacceptable variance. Figure 3.17 shows a chi-square distribution with the critical value, the rejection region, the nonrejection region, the value of α, and the observed chi-square value.

Using Excel, the *p*-value of the observed chi-square, 36.72, is determined to be .0000053. Because this value is less than $\alpha = .05$, the conclusion is to reject the null hypothesis using the *p*-value. In fact, using this *p*-value, the null hypothesis could be rejected for

$$\alpha = .00001$$

FIGURE 3.17

Hypothesis Test Distribution for Pneumatic Tube Example

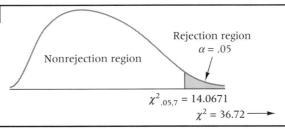

This null hypothesis can also be tested by the critical value method. Instead of solving for an observed value of chi-square, the critical chi-square value for alpha is inserted into formula (3.5) along with the hypothesized value of σ^2 and the degrees of freedom $(n-1)$. Solving for s^2 yields a critical sample variance value, s_c^2.

$$\chi_c^2 = \frac{(n-1)s_c^2}{\sigma^2}$$

$$s_c^2 = \frac{\chi_c^2 \cdot \sigma^2}{(n-1)} = \frac{(14.0671)(4)}{7} = 8.038$$

The critical value of the sample variance is $s_C^2 = 8.038$. Because the observed sample variance actually was 20.9821, which is larger than the critical variance, the null hypothesis is rejected.

DEMONSTRATION PROBLEM 3.4

A small business has 37 employees. Because of the uncertain demand for its product, the company usually pays overtime on any given week. The company assumed that about 50 total hours of overtime per week is required and that the variance on this figure is about 25. Company officials want to know whether the variance of overtime hours has changed. Given here is a sample of 16 weeks of overtime data (in hours per week). Assume hours of overtime are normally distributed. Use these data to test the null hypothesis that the variance of overtime data is 25. Let $\alpha = .10$.

57	56	52	44
46	53	44	44
48	51	55	48
63	53	51	50

Solution

HYPOTHESIZE:

STEP 1. This test is a two-tailed test. The null and alternative hypotheses are

$$H_0: \sigma^2 = 25$$
$$H_a: \sigma^2 \neq 25$$

TEST:

STEP 2. The test statistic is

$$\chi^2 = \frac{(n-1)s^2}{\sigma^2}$$

STEP 3. Because this test is two-tailed, $\alpha = .10$ must be split: $\alpha/2 = .05$.
STEP 4. The degrees of freedom are $16 - 1 = 15$. The two critical chi-square values are

$$\chi^2_{(1-.05),15} = \chi^2_{.95,15} = 7.26094$$
$$\chi^2_{.05,15} = 24.9958$$

The decision rule is to reject the null hypothesis if the observed value of the test statistic is less than 7.26094 or greater than 24.9958.
STEP 5. The data are as listed previously.
STEP 6. The sample variance is

$$s^2 = 28.1$$

The observed chi-square value is calculated as

$$\chi^2 = \frac{(n-1)s^2}{\sigma^2} = \frac{(15)(28.1)}{25} = 16.86$$

ACTION:

STEP 7. This observed chi-square value is in the nonrejection region because $\chi^2_{.95,15} = 7.26094 < \chi^2_{observed} = 16.86 < \chi^2_{.05,15} = 24.9958$. The company fails to reject the null hypothesis. The population variance of overtime hours per week is 25.

BUSINESS IMPLICATIONS:

STEP 8. This result indicates to the company managers that the variance of weekly overtime hours is about what they expected.

3.5 PROBLEMS

3.28   Test each of the following hypotheses by using the given information. Assume the populations are normally distributed.

    a. $H_0: \sigma^2 = 20$
        $H_a: \sigma^2 > 20$
        $\alpha = .05, n = 15, s^2 = 32$

    b. $H_0: \sigma^2 = 8.5$
        $H_a: \sigma^2 \neq 8.5$
        $\alpha = .10, n = 22, s^2 = 17$

    c. $H_0: \sigma^2 = 45$
        $H_a: \sigma^2 < 45$
        $\alpha = .01, n = 8, s = 4.12$

    d. $H_0: \sigma^2 = 5$
        $H_a: \sigma^2 \neq 5$
        $\alpha = .05, n = 11, s^2 = 1.2$

3.29   Previous experience shows the variance of a given process to be 14. Researchers are testing to determine whether this value has changed. They gather the following dozen measurements of the process. Use these data and $\alpha = .05$ to test the null hypothesis about the variance. Assume the measurements are normally distributed.

52	44	51	58	48	49
38	49	50	42	55	51

3.30   A manufacturing company produces bearings. One line of bearings is specified to be 1.64 centimeters (cm) in diameter. A major customer requires that the variance of the bearings be no more than .001 cm². The producer is required to test the bearings before they are shipped, and so the diameters of 16 bearings are measured with a precise instrument, resulting in the following values. Assume bearing diameters are normally distributed. Use the data and $\alpha = .01$ to test the data to determine whether the population of these bearings is to be rejected because of too high a variance.

1.69	1.62	1.63	1.70
1.66	1.63	1.65	1.71
1.64	1.69	1.57	1.64
1.59	1.66	1.63	1.65

3.31   A savings and loan averages about $100,000 in deposits per week. However, because of the way pay periods fall, seasonality, and erratic fluctuations in the local economy, deposits are subject to a wide variability. In the past, the variance for weekly deposits has been about $199,996,164. In terms that make more sense to managers, the standard deviation of weekly deposits has been $14,142. Shown here are data from a random sample of 13 weekly deposits for a recent period. Assume weekly deposits are normally distributed. Use these data and $\alpha = .10$ to test to determine whether the variance for weekly deposits has changed.

$93,000	$135,000	$112,000
68,000	46,000	104,000
128,000	143,000	131,000
104,000	96,000	71,000
87,000		

3.32   A company produces industrial wiring. One batch of wiring is specified to be 2.16 centimeters (cm) thick. A company inspects the wiring in seven locations and determines that, on the average, the wiring is about 2.16 cm thick. However, the measurements vary. It is unacceptable for the variance of the wiring to be more than .04 cm^2. The standard deviation of the seven measurements on this batch of wiring is .34 cm. Use $\alpha = .01$ to determine whether the variance on the sample wiring is too great to meet specifications. Assume wiring thickness is normally distributed.

3.6 SOLVING FOR TYPE II ERRORS

If a researcher reaches the statistical conclusion not to reject the null hypothesis, he makes either a correct decision or a Type II error. If the null hypothesis is true, the researcher makes a correct decision. If the null hypothesis is false, a Type II error results.

In business, failure to reject the null hypothesis may mean staying with the status quo, not implementing a new process, or not making adjustments. If a new process, product, theory, or adjustment is not significantly better than what is currently accepted practice, the decision maker makes a correct decision. However, if the new process, product, theory, or adjustment would significantly improve sales, the business climate, costs, or morale, the decision maker makes an error in judgment (Type II). In business, Type II errors can translate to lost opportunities, poor product quality (as a result of failure to discern a problem in the process), or failure to react to the marketplace. Sometimes the ability to react to changes, new developments, or new opportunities is what keeps a business moving and growing. The Type II error plays an important role in business statistical decision making.

Determining the probability of committing a Type II error is more complex than finding the probability of committing a Type I error. The probability of committing a Type I error either is given in a problem or is stated by the researcher before proceeding with the study. A Type II error, β, varies with possible values of the alternative parameter. For example, suppose a researcher is conducting a statistical test on the following hypotheses.

$$H_0: \mu = 12 \text{ ounces}$$

$$H_a: \mu < 12 \text{ ounces}$$

A Type II error can be committed only when the researcher fails to reject the null hypothesis and the null hypothesis is false. In these hypotheses, if the null hypothesis, $\mu = 12$ ounces, is false, what is the true value for the population mean? Is the mean really 11.99 or 11.90 or 11.5 or 10 ounces? For each of these possible values of the population mean, the researcher can compute the probability of committing a Type II error. Often, when the null hypothesis is false, the value of the alternative mean is unknown, so the researcher will compute the probability of committing Type II errors for several possible values. How can the probability of committing a Type II error be computed for a specific alternative value of the mean?

Suppose that, in testing the preceding hypotheses, a sample of 60 cans of beverage yields a sample mean of 11.985 ounces. Assume that the population standard deviation is 0.10 ounces. From $\alpha = .05$ and a one-tailed test, the table $z_{.05}$ value is −1.645. The observed z value from sample data is

$$z = \frac{11.985 - 12.00}{\frac{.10}{\sqrt{60}}} = -1.16$$

From this observed value of z, the researcher determines not to reject the null hypothesis. By not rejecting the null hypothesis, the researcher either makes a correct decision or commits a Type II error. What is the probability of committing a Type II error in this problem if the population mean actually is 11.99?

The first step in determining the probability of a Type II error is to calculate a critical value for the sample mean, $\bar{x}_c$. In testing the null hypothesis by the critical value method, this value is used as the cutoff for the nonrejection region. For any sample mean obtained that is less than $\bar{x}_c$ (or greater for an upper-tail rejection region), the null hypothesis is rejected. Any sample mean greater than $\bar{x}_c$ (or less for an upper-tail rejection region) causes the researcher to fail to reject the null hypothesis. Solving for the critical value of the mean gives

$$z_C = \frac{\bar{x}_C - \mu}{\frac{\sigma}{\sqrt{n}}}$$

$$-1.645 = \frac{\bar{x}_C - 12}{\frac{.10}{\sqrt{60}}}$$

$$\bar{x}_C = 11.979$$

Figure 3.18(a) shows the distribution of values when the null hypothesis is true. It contains a critical value of the mean, $\bar{x}_c = 11.979$ ounces, below which the null hypothesis will be rejected. Figure 3.18(b) shows the distribution when the alternative mean, $\mu_1 = 11.99$ ounces, is true. How often will the business researcher fail to reject the top distribution as true when, in reality, the bottom distribution is true? If the null hypothesis is false, the researcher will fail to reject the null hypotheses whenever $\bar{x}$ is in the nonrejection region, $\bar{x}_c \geq 11.979$ ounces. If μ actually equals 11.99 ounces, what is the probability of failing to reject $\mu = 12$ ounces when 11.979 ounces is the critical value? The business researcher calculates this probability by extending the critical value ($\bar{x}_c = 11.979$ ounces) from distribution (a) to distribution (b) and solving for the area to the right of $\bar{x}_c = 11.979$.

$$z_1 = \frac{\bar{x}_C - \mu_1}{\frac{\sigma}{\sqrt{n}}} = \frac{11.979 - 11.99}{\frac{.10}{\sqrt{60}}} = -0.85$$

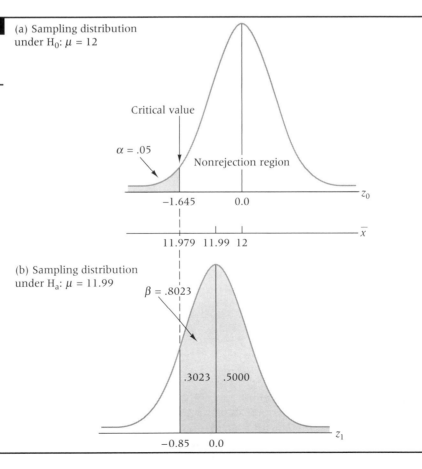

FIGURE 3.18

Type II Error for Soft Drink Example with Alternative Mean = 11.99 Ounces

(a) Sampling distribution under H_0: $\mu = 12$

Critical value

$\alpha = .05$

Nonrejection region

-1.645 0.0 z_0

11.979   11.99   12 $\bar{x}$

(b) Sampling distribution under H_a: $\mu = 11.99$

$\beta = .8023$

.3023   .5000

-0.85 0.0 z_1

This value of z yields an area of .3023. The probability of committing a Type II error is all the area to the right of $\bar{x}_c = 11.979$ in distribution (b), or $.3023 + .5000 = .8023$. Hence there is an 80.23% chance of committing a Type II error if the alternative mean is 11.99 ounces.

DEMONSTRATION PROBLEM 3.5

Recompute the probability of committing a Type II error for the soft drink example if the alternative mean is 11.96 ounces.

Solution

Everything in distribution (a) of Figure 3.18 stays the same. The null hypothesized mean is still 12 ounces, the critical value is still 11.979 ounces, and $n = 60$. However, distribution (b) of Figure 3.18 changes with $\mu_1 = 11.96$ ounces, as the following diagram shows.

The z formula used to solve for the area of distribution (b), $\mu_1 = 11.96$, to the right of 11.979 is

$$z_1 = \frac{\bar{x}_c - \mu_1}{\dfrac{\sigma}{\sqrt{n}}} = \frac{11.979 - 11.96}{\dfrac{.10}{\sqrt{60}}} = 1.47$$

From Table A.2, only .0708 of the area is to the right of the critical value. Thus the probability of committing a Type II error is only .0708, as illustrated in the following diagram.

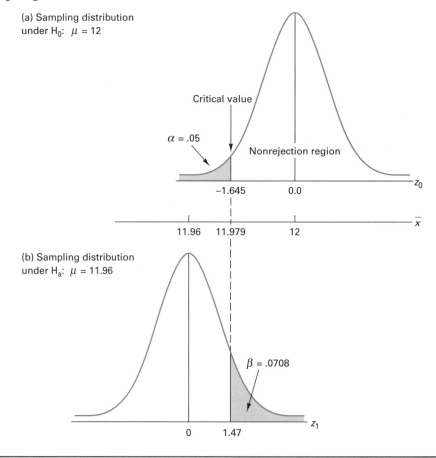

(a) Sampling distribution under H_0: $\mu = 12$

(b) Sampling distribution under H_a: $\mu = 11.96$

DEMONSTRATION PROBLEM 3.6

Suppose you are conducting a two-tailed hypothesis test of proportions. The null hypothesis is that the population proportion is .40. The alternative hypothesis is that the population proportion is not .40. A random sample of 250 produces a sample proportion of .44. With alpha of .05, the table z value for $\alpha/2$ is 1.96. The observed z from the sample information is

$$z = \frac{\hat{p} - p}{\sqrt{\dfrac{p \cdot q}{n}}} = \frac{.44 - .40}{.031} = 1.29$$

Thus the null hypothesis is not rejected. Either a correct decision is made or a Type II error is committed. Suppose the alternative population proportion really is .36. What is the probability of committing a Type II error?

Solution

Solve for the critical value of the proportion.

$$z_c = \frac{\hat{p}_c - p}{\sqrt{\dfrac{p \cdot q}{n}}}$$

$$\pm 1.96 = \frac{\hat{p}_c - .40}{\sqrt{\dfrac{(.40)(.60)}{250}}}$$

$$\hat{p}_c = .40 \pm .06$$

The critical values are .34 on the lower end and .46 on the upper end. The alternative population proportion is .36. The following diagram illustrates these results and the remainder of the solution to this problem.

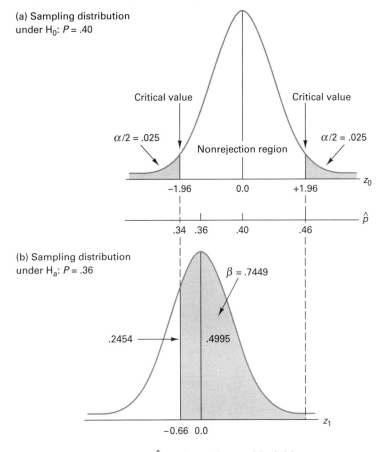

(a) Sampling distribution under H_0: $P = .40$

(b) Sampling distribution under H_a: $P = .36$

Solving for the area between $\hat{p}_c = .34$ and $p_1 = .36$ yields

$$z_1 = \frac{.34 - .36}{\sqrt{\dfrac{(.36)(.64)}{250}}} = -0.66$$

The area associated with $z_1 = -0.66$ is .2454.

The area between .36 and .46 of the sampling distribution under H_a: $p = .36$ (graph (b)) can be solved for by using the following z value.

$$z = \frac{.46 - .36}{\sqrt{\dfrac{(.36)(.64)}{250}}} = 3.29$$

The area from Table A.2 associated with $z = 3.29$ is .4995. Combining this value with the .2454 obtained from the left side of the distribution in graph (b) yields the total probability of committing a Type II error:

$$.2454 + .4995 = .7449$$

With two-tailed tests, both tails of the distribution contain rejection regions. The area between the two tails is the nonrejection region and the region where Type II errors can occur. If the alternative hypothesis is true, the area of the sampling distribution under H_a between the locations where the critical values from H_0 are located is β. In theory, both tails of the sampling distribution under H_a would be non-β area. However, in this problem, the right critical value is so far away from the alternative proportion ($p_1 = .36$) that the area between the right critical value and the alternative proportion is near .5000 (.4995) and virtually no area falls in the upper right tail of the distribution (.0005).

Some Observations About Type II Errors

Type II errors are committed only when the researcher fails to reject the null hypothesis but the alternative hypothesis is true. If the alternative mean or proportion is close to the hypothesized value, the probability of committing a Type II error is high. If the alternative value is relatively far away from the hypothesized value, as in the problem with $\mu = 12$ ounces and $\mu_a = 11.96$ ounces, the probability of committing a Type II error is small. The implication is that when a value is being tested as a null hypothesis against a true alternative value that is relatively far away, the sample statistic obtained is likely to show clearly which hypothesis is true. For example, suppose a researcher is testing to determine whether a company really is filling 2-liter bottles of cola with an average of 2 liters. If the company decides to underfill the bottles by filling them with only 1 liter, a sample of 50 bottles is likely to average a quantity near the 1-liter fill rather than near the 2-liter fill. Committing a Type II error is highly unlikely. Even a customer probably could see by looking at the bottles on the shelf that they are underfilled. However, if the company fills 2-liter bottles with 1.99 liters, the bottles are close in fill volume to those filled with 2.00 liters. In this case, the probability of committing a Type II error is much greater. A customer probably could not catch the underfill just by looking.

In general, if the alternative value is relatively far from the hypothesized value, the probability of committing a Type II error is smaller than it is when the alternative value is close to the hypothesized value. The probability of committing a Type II error decreases as alternative values of the hypothesized parameter move farther away from the hypothesized value. This situation is shown graphically in operating characteristic curves and power curves.

Operating Characteristic and Power Curves

Because the probability of committing a Type II error changes for each different value of the alternative parameter, it is best in managerial decision making to examine a series of possible alternative values. For example, Table 3.2 shows the probabilities of committing a Type II error (β) for several different possible alternative means for the soft drink example discussed in Demonstration Problem 3.5, in which the null hypothesis was H_0: $\mu = 12$ ounces and $\alpha = .05$.

As previously mentioned, power is the probability of rejecting the null hypothesis when it is false and represents the correct decision of selecting the alternative hypothesis when it is true. Power is equal to $1 - \beta$. Note that Table 3.2 also contains the power values for the alternative means and that the β and power probabilities sum to 1 in each case.

These values can be displayed graphically as shown in Figures 3.19 and 3.20. Figure 3.19 is a MINITAB-generated **operating characteristic (OC) curve** *constructed by plotting the β values against the various values of the alternative hypothesis.* Notice that when the alternative means are near the value of the null hypothesis, $\mu = 12$, the probability of committing a Type II error is high because it is difficult to discriminate between a distribution with a mean of 12 and a distribution with a mean of 11.999. However, as the values of the alternative means move away from the hypothesized value, $\mu = 12$, the values of β drop. This visual representation underscores the notion that it is easier to discriminate between a distribution with $\mu = 12$ and a distribution with $\mu = 11.95$ than between distributions with $\mu = 12$ and $\mu = 11.999$.

Figure 3.20 is an Excel **power curve** constructed by *plotting the power values $(1 - \beta)$ against the various values of the alternative hypotheses.* Note that the power increases as the alternative mean moves away from the value of μ in the null hypotheses. This relationship makes sense. As the alternative mean moves farther and farther away from the null hypothesized mean, a correct decision to reject the null hypothesis becomes more likely.

TABLE 3.2

β Values and Power Values for the Soft Drink Example

Alternative Mean	Probability of Committing A Type II Error, β	Power
$\mu_a = 11.999$	.94	.06
$\mu_a = 11.995$	.89	.11
$\mu_a = 11.99$	.80	.20
$\mu_a = 11.98$	.53	.47
$\mu_a = 11.97$	.24	.76
$\mu_a = 11.96$	.07	.93
$\mu_a = 11.95$	.01	.99

FIGURE 3.19

MINITAB Operating-Characteristic Curve for the Soft Drink Example

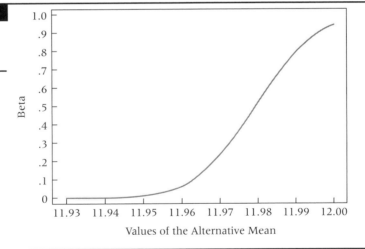

FIGURE 3.20

Excel Power Curve for the Soft Drink Example

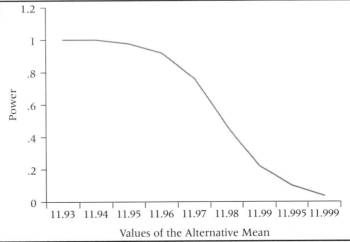

Effect of Increasing Sample Size on the Rejection Limits

The size of the sample affects the location of the rejection limits. Consider the soft drink example in which we were testing the following hypotheses.

$$H_0: \mu = 12.00 \text{ ounces}$$
$$H_a: \mu < 12.00 \text{ ounces}$$

Sample size was 60 ($n = 60$) and the standard deviation was .10 ($\sigma = .10$). With $\alpha = .05$, the critical value of the test statistic was $z_{.05} = -1.645$. From this information, a critical raw score value was computed:

$$z_C = \frac{\bar{x}_C - \mu}{\dfrac{\sigma}{\sqrt{n}}}$$

$$-1.645 = \frac{\bar{x}_C - 12}{\dfrac{.10}{\sqrt{60}}}$$

$$\bar{x}_C = 11.979$$

Any sample mean obtained in the hypothesis-testing process that is less than 11.979 will result in a decision to reject the null hypothesis.

Suppose the sample size is increased to 100. The critical raw score value is

$$-1.645 = \frac{\bar{x}_C - 12}{\dfrac{.10}{\sqrt{100}}}$$

$$\bar{x}_C = 11.984$$

FIGURE 3.21

Type II Error for Soft Drink Example with *n* Increased to 100

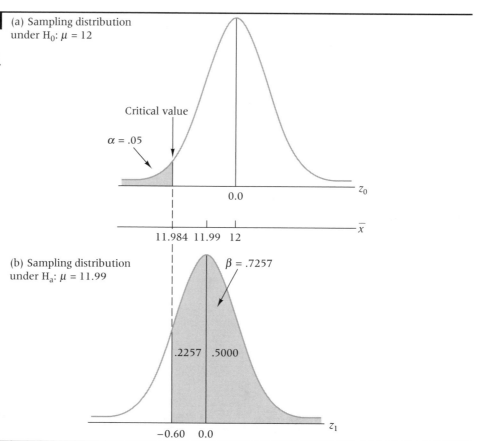

(a) Sampling distribution under H_0: $\mu = 12$

Critical value

$\alpha = .05$

0.0 z_0

11.984   11.99   12 $\bar{x}$

(b) Sampling distribution under H_a: $\mu = 11.99$

$\beta = .7257$

.2257   .5000

−0.60   0.0 z_1

Notice that the critical raw score value is nearer to the hypothesized value ($\mu = 12$) for the larger sample size than it was for a sample size of 60. Because n is in the denominator of the standard error of the mean ($\sigma/\sqrt{n}$), an increase in n results in a decrease in the standard error of the mean, which when multiplied by the critical value of the test statistic ($z_{\alpha/2}$) results in a critical raw score that is closer to the hypothesized value. For $n = 500$, the critical raw score value for this problem is 11.993.

Increased sample size not only affects the distance of the critical raw score value from the hypothesized value of the distribution, but also can result in reducing β for a given value of α. Examine Figure 3.18. Note that the critical raw score value is 11.979 with alpha equal to .05 for $n = 60$. The value of β for an alternative mean of 11.99 is .8023. Suppose the sample size is 100. The critical raw score value (already solved) is 11.984. The value of β is now .7257. The computation is

$$z = \frac{11.984 - 11.99}{\dfrac{.10}{\sqrt{100}}} = -0.60$$

The area under the standard normal curve for $z = -0.60$ is .2257. Adding $.2257 + .5000$ (from the right half of the H_a sampling distribution) results in a β of .7257. Figure 3.21 shows the sampling distributions with α and β for this problem. In addition, by increasing sample size a business researcher could reduce alpha without necessarily increasing beta. It is possible to reduce the probabilities of committing Type I and Type II errors simultaneously by increasing sample size.

3.6 PROBLEMS

3.33 Suppose a null hypothesis is that the population mean is greater than or equal to 100. Suppose further that a random sample of 48 items is taken and the population standard deviation is 14. For each of the following α values, compute the probability of committing a Type II error if the population mean actually is 99.

  a. $\alpha = .10$

  b. $\alpha = .05$

  c. $\alpha = .01$

  d. Based on the answers to parts (a), (b), and (c), what happens to the value of β as α gets smaller?

3.34 For Problem 3.33, use $\alpha = .05$ and solve for the probability of committing a Type II error for the following possible true alternative means.

  a. $\mu_a = 98.5$

  b. $\mu_a = 98$

  c. $\mu_a = 97$

  d. $\mu_a = 96$

  e. What happens to the probability of committing a Type II error as the alternative value of the mean gets farther from the null hypothesized value of 100?

3.35 Suppose a hypothesis states that the mean is exactly 50. If a random sample of 35 items is taken to test this hypothesis, what is the value of β if the population standard deviation is 7 and the alternative mean is 53? Use $\alpha = .01$.

3.36 An alternative hypothesis is that $p < .65$. To test this hypothesis, a random sample of size 360 is taken. What is the probability of committing a Type II error if $\alpha = .05$ and the alternative proportion is as follows?

  a. $p_a = .60$

  b. $p_a = .55$

  c. $p_a = .50$

3.37 The New York Stock Exchange recently reported that the average age of a female shareholder is 44 years. A broker in Chicago wants to know whether this figure is accurate for the female shareholders in Chicago. The broker secures a master list of shareholders in Chicago and takes a random sample of 58 women. Suppose the average age for shareholders in the sample is 45.1 years, with a population standard deviation of 8.7 years. Test to determine whether the broker's sample data differ significantly enough from the 44-years figure released by the New York Stock Exchange to declare that Chicago female shareholders are different in age from female shareholders in general. Use $\alpha = .05$. If no significant difference is noted, what is the broker's probability of committing a Type II error if the average age of a female Chicago shareholder is actually 45 years? 46 years? 47 years? 48 years? Construct an OC curve for these data. Construct a power curve for these data.

3.38 A Harris poll was taken to determine which of 13 major industries are doing a good job of serving their customers. Among the industries rated most highly by Americans for serving their customers were computer hardware and software companies, car manufacturers, and airlines. The industries rated lowest on serving their customers were tobacco companies, managed care providers, and health insurance companies. Seventy-one percent of those polled responded that airlines are doing a good job serving their customers. Suppose due to rising ticket prices, a researcher feels that this figure is now too high. He takes a poll of 463 Americans, and 324 say that the airlines are doing a good job of serving their customers. Does the survey show enough evidence to declare that the proportion of Americans saying that the airlines are doing a good job of serving their customers is significantly lower than stated in the Harris poll? Let alpha equal 10. If the researcher fails to reject the null hypothesis and if the figure is actually 69% now, what is the probability of committing a Type II error? What is the probability of committing a Type II error if the figure is really 66%? 60%?

Business Referrals

In the Decision Dilemma, many data facts are reported from numerous surveys about consumers seeking advice from others before purchasing items or services. Most of the statistics are stated as though they are facts about the population. For example, one study reports that 46% of all consumers seek advice when selecting a physician. Suppose a business researcher believes that this figure is not true, has changed over time, is not true for a particular region of the country, or is different for a particular type of medicine. Using hypothesis techniques presented in Section 3.4 of this chapter, this figure (46%) can be tested as a population proportion. Because the figures presented in the Decision Dilemma have been published and widely disseminated, the researcher who wants to test them would likely place these figures in the null hypothesis (e.g., H_0: $p = .46$), gather a random sample from whichever population is to be studied, and conduct a hypothesis test.

It was reported by Roper Starch Worldwide that influentials make recommendations about office equipment an average of 5.8 times per year. These and any of the other means reported in this study could be tested. The researcher would need to scientifically identify influentials in the population and randomly select a sample. A research mechanism could be set up whereby the number of referrals by each influential could be recorded for a year and averaged thereby producing a sample mean and a sample standard deviation. Using a selected value of alpha, the sample mean could be statistically tested against the population mean (in this case, $H_0: \mu = 5.8$). The probability of falsely rejecting a true null would be alpha. If the null was actually false ($\mu \neq 5.8$), the probability (β) of failing to reject the false null hypothesis would depend upon what the true number of mean referrals per year was for influentials on office equipment.

If a researcher has theories on influentials and these research theories can be stated as statistical hypotheses, the theory should be formulated as an alternate hypothesis; and the null hypothesis should be that the theory is not true. Samples are randomly selected. If the statistic of choice is a mean, then a *z* test or *t* test for a population mean should be used in the analysis dependent on whether or not the population standard deviation is known or unknown. In many studies, the sample standard deviation is used in the analysis instead of the unknown population standard deviation. In these cases, a *t* test should be used when the assumption that the population data are normally distributed can be made. If the statistic is a proportion, then the *z* test for a population proportion is appropriate. Techniques presented in Chapter 2, Section 2.5, can be used to assist the researcher in determining how large a sample to take. Using alpha, a critical table *z* value can be determined and inserted into the sample size determination formulas to determine sample size.

ETHICAL CONSIDERATIONS

The process of hypothesis testing encompasses several areas that could potentially lead to unethical activity, beginning with the null and alternative hypotheses. In the hypothesis-testing approach, the preliminary assumption is that the null hypothesis is true. If a researcher has a new theory or idea that he or she is attempting to prove, it is somewhat unethical to express that theory or idea as the null hypothesis. In doing so, the researcher is assuming that what he or she is trying to prove is true and the burden of proof is on the data to reject this idea or theory. Statistical hypothesis testing is set up so that the new idea or theory is not assumed to be true; the burden of proof is on the researcher to demonstrate through the data and the rejection of the null hypothesis that the new idea or theory is true. The researcher must take great care not to assume that what he or she is attempting to prove is true.

The value of alpha should be established before the experiment is undertaken. Too many researchers "data snoop"—that is, they look at the data and the results of the data analysis and then decide what alpha could be used in order to reject the null hypothesis.

Hypothesis testing through random sampling opens up many possible unethical situations that can occur in sampling, such as identifying a frame that is favorable to the outcome the researcher is seeking or using nonrandom sampling techniques to test hypotheses. In addition, the researcher should be careful to use the proper test statistic for tests of a population mean, particularly when σ is unknown. If *t* tests are used, or in testing a population variance, the researcher should be careful to apply the techniques only when it can be shown with some confidence that the population is normally distributed. The chi-square test of a population variance has been shown to be extremely sensitive to the assumption that the population is normally distributed. Unethical usage of this technique occurs when the statistician does not carefully check the population distribution shape for compliance with this assumption. Failure to do so can easily result in the reporting of spurious conclusions.

It can be unethical from a business decision-making point of view to knowingly use the notion of statistical significance to claim business significance when the results are not substantive. Therefore, it is unethical to intentionally attempt to mislead the business user by inappropriately using the word *significance*.

SUMMARY

Three types of hypotheses were presented in this chapter: research hypotheses, statistical hypotheses, and substantive hypotheses. Research hypotheses are statements of what the researcher believes will be the outcome of an experiment or study. In order to test hypotheses, business researchers formulate their research hypotheses into statistical hypotheses. All statistical hypotheses consist of two parts, a null hypothesis and an alternative hypothesis. The null and alternative hypotheses are structured so that either one or the other is true but not both. In testing hypotheses, the researcher assumes that the null hypothesis is true. By examining the sampled data, the researcher either rejects or does not reject the null hypothesis. If the sample data are significantly in opposition to the null hypothesis, the researcher rejects the null hypothesis and accepts the alternative hypothesis by default.

Hypothesis tests can be one-tailed or two-tailed. Two-tailed tests always utilize = and $\neq$ in the null and alternative hypotheses. These tests are nondirectional in that significant deviations from the hypothesized value that are either greater than or less than the value are in rejection regions. The one-tailed test is directional, and the alternative hypothesis contains < or > signs. In these tests, only one end or tail of the distribution contains a rejection region. In a one-tailed test, the researcher is interested only in deviations from the hypothesized value that are either greater than or less than the value but not both.

Not all statistically significant outcomes of studies are important business outcomes. A substantive result is when the outcome of a statistical study produces results that are important to the decision maker.

When a business researcher reaches a decision about the null hypothesis, the researcher either makes a correct decision or an error. If the null hypothesis is true, the researcher can make a Type I error by rejecting the null hypothesis. The probability of making a Type I error is alpha (α). Alpha is usually set by the researcher when establishing the hypotheses. Another expression sometimes used for the value of α is level of significance.

If the null hypothesis is false and the researcher fails to reject it, a Type II error is committed. Beta (β) is the probability of committing a Type II error. Type II errors must be computed from the hypothesized value of the parameter, α, and a specific alternative value of the parameter being examined. As many possible Type II errors in a problem exist as there are possible alternative statistical values.

If a null hypothesis is true and the researcher fails to reject it, no error is committed, and the researcher makes a correct decision. Similarly, if a null hypothesis is false and it is rejected, no error is committed. Power ($1 - \beta$) is the probability of a statistical test rejecting the null hypothesis when the null hypothesis is false.

An operating characteristic (OC) curve is a graphical depiction of values of β that can occur as various values of the alternative hypothesis are explored. This graph can be studied to determine what happens to β as one moves away from the value of the null hypothesis. A power curve is used in conjunction with an operating characteristic curve. The power curve is a graphical depiction of the values of power as various values of the alternative hypothesis are examined. The researcher can view the increase in power as values of the alternative hypothesis diverge from the value of the null hypothesis.

Included in this chapter were hypothesis tests for a single mean when σ is known and when σ is unknown, a test of a single population proportion, and a test for a population variance. Three different analytic approaches were presented: (1) standard method, (2) p-value, and (3) critical value method.

KEY TERMS

alpha (α)	level of significance	operating characteristic	statistical hypothesis
alternative hypothesis	nonrejection region	(OC) curve	substantive result
beta (β)	null hypothesis	p-value	two-tailed test
critical value	observed significance level	power	Type I error
critical value method	observed value	power curve	Type II error
hypothesis	one-tailed test	rejection region	
hypothesis testing		research hypothesis	

FORMULAS

z test for a single mean (3.1)

$$z = \frac{\bar{x} - \mu}{\frac{\sigma}{\sqrt{n}}}$$

Formula to test hypotheses about μ with a finite population (3.2)

$$z = \frac{\bar{x} - \mu}{\frac{\sigma}{\sqrt{n}} \sqrt{\frac{N-n}{N-1}}}$$

t test for a single mean (3.3)

$$t = \frac{\bar{x} - \mu}{\frac{s}{\sqrt{n}}}$$

$$df = n - 1$$

z test of a population proportion (3.4)

$$z = \frac{\hat{p} - p}{\sqrt{\frac{p \cdot q}{n}}}$$

Formula for testing hypotheses about a population variance (3.5)

$$\chi^2 = \frac{(n-1)s^2}{\sigma^2}$$

$$df = n - 1$$

SUPPLEMENTARY PROBLEMS

CALCULATING THE STATISTICS

3.39 Use the information given and the HTAB system to test the hypotheses. Let $\alpha = .01$.

H_0: $\mu = 36$ H_a: $\mu \neq 36$ $n = 63$ $\bar{x} = 38.4$ $\sigma = 5.93$

3.40 Use the information given and the HTAB system to test the hypotheses. Let $\alpha = .05$. Assume the population is normally distributed.

H_0: $\mu = 7.82$ H_a: $\mu < 7.82$ $n = 17$ $\bar{x} = 17.1$ $s = 1.69$

3.41 For each of the following problems, test the hypotheses. Incorporate the HTAB system with its eight-step process.

    a. H_0: $p = .28$ H_a: $p > .28$ $n = 783$ $x = 230$ $\alpha = .10$
    b. H_0: $p = .61$ H_a: $p \neq .61$ $n = 401$ $\hat{p} = .56$ $\alpha = .05$

3.42 Test the following hypotheses by using the information given and the HTAB system. Let alpha be .01. Assume the population is normally distributed.

H_0: $\sigma^2 = 15.4$ H_a: $\sigma^2 > 15.4$ $n = 18$ $s^2 = 29.6$

3.43 Solve for the value of beta in each of the following problems.

    a. H_0: $\mu = 130$ H_a: $\mu > 130$ $n = 75$ $\sigma = 12$ $\alpha = .01$.
    The alternative mean is actually 135.
    b. H_0: $p = .44$ H_a: $p < .44$ $n = 1095$ $\alpha = .05$.
    The alternative proportion is actually .42.

TESTING YOUR UNDERSTANDING

3.44 According to a survey by ICR for Vienna Systems, a majority of American households have tried to cut long-distance phone bills. Of those who have tried to cut the bills, 32% have done so by switching long-distance companies. Suppose business researchers believe that this figure may be higher today. To test this theory, a researcher conducts another survey by randomly contacting 80 American households who have tried to cut long-distance phone bills. If 39% of the contacted households say they have tried to cut their long-distance phone bills by switching long-distance companies, is this result enough evidence to state that a significantly higher proportion of American households are trying to cut long-distance phone bills by switching companies? Let $\alpha = .01$.

3.45 According to Zero Population Growth, the average urban U.S. resident consumes 3.3 pounds of food per day. Is this figure accurate for rural U.S. residents? Suppose 64 rural U.S. residents are identified by a random procedure and their average consumption per day is 3.45 pounds of food. Assume a population variance of 1.31 pounds of food per day. Use a 5% level of significance to determine whether the Zero Population Growth figure for urban U.S. residents also is true for rural U.S. residents on the basis of the sample data.

3.46 Brokers generally agree that bonds are a better investment during times of low interest rates than during times of high interest rates. A survey of executives during a time of low interest rates showed that 57% of them had some retirement funds invested in bonds. Assume this percentage is constant for bond market investment by executives with retirement funds. Suppose interest rates have risen lately and the proportion of executives with retirement investment money in the bond market may have dropped. To test this idea, a researcher randomly samples 210 executives who have retirement funds. Of these, 93 now have retirement funds invested in bonds. For $\alpha = .10$, does the test show enough evidence to declare that the proportion of executives with retirement fund investments in the bond market is significantly lower than .57?

3.47 Highway engineers in Ohio are painting white stripes on a highway. The stripes are supposed to be approximately 10 feet long. However, because of the machine, the operator, and the motion of the vehicle carrying the equipment, considerable variation occurs among the stripe lengths. Engineers claim that the variance of stripes is not more than 16 inches. Use the sample lengths given here from 12 measured stripes to test the variance claim. Assume stripe length is normally distributed. Let $\alpha = .05$.

Stripe Lengths in Feet

10.3	9.4	9.8	10.1
9.2	10.4	10.7	9.9
9.3	9.8	10.5	10.4

3.48 A computer manufacturer estimates that its line of minicomputers has, on average, 8.4 days of downtime per year. To test this claim, a researcher contacts seven companies that own one of these computers and is allowed to access company computer records. It is determined that, for the sample, the average number of downtime days is 5.6, with a sample standard deviation of 1.3 days. Assuming that number of downtime days is normally distributed, test to determine whether these minicomputers actually average 8.4 days of downtime in the entire population. Let $\alpha = .01$.

3.49 A life insurance salesperson claims the average worker in the city of Cincinnati has no more than $25,000 of personal life insurance. To test this claim, you randomly sample 100 workers in Cincinnati. You find that this sample of workers averages $26,650 of personal life insurance. The population standard deviation is $12,000.

a. Determine whether the test shows enough evidence to reject the null hypothesis posed by the salesperson. Assume the probability of committing a Type I error is .05.

b. If the actual average for this population is $30,000, what is the probability of committing a Type II error?

3.50 A financial analyst has been watching a particular stock for several months. The price of this stock remained fairly stable during this time. In fact, the financial analyst claims that the variance of the price of this stock did not exceed $4 for the entire period. Recently, the market heated up, and the price of this stock appears more volatile. To determine whether it is more volatile, a sample of closing prices of this stock for 8 days is taken randomly. The sample mean price is $36.25, with a sample standard deviation of $7.80. Using a level of significance

of .10, test to determine whether the financial analyst's previous variance figure is now too low. Assume stock prices are normally distributed.

3.51 A study of MBA graduates by Universum for The American Graduate Survey 1999 revealed that MBA graduates have several expectations of prospective employers beyond their base pay. In particular, according to the study 46% expect a performance-related bonus, 46% expect stock options, 42% expect a signing bonus, 28% expect profit sharing, 27% expect extra vacation/personal days, 25% expect tuition reimbursement, 24% expect health benefits, and 19% expect guaranteed annual bonuses. Suppose a study is conducted in an ensuing year to see whether these expectations have changed. If 125 MBA graduates are randomly selected and if 66 expect stock options, does this result provide enough evidence to declare that a significantly higher proportion of MBAs expect stock options? Let $\alpha = .05$. If the proportion really is .50, what is the probability of committing a Type II error?

3.52 Suppose the number of beds filled per day in a medium-sized hospital is normally distributed. A hospital administrator tells the board of directors that, on the average, at least 185 beds are filled on any given day. One of the board members believes this figure is inflated, and she manages to secure a random sample of figures for 16 days. The data are shown here. Use $\alpha = .05$ and the sample data to test whether the hospital administrator's statement is false. Assume the number of filled beds per day is normally distributed in the population.

Number of Beds Occupied per Day

173	149	166	180
189	170	152	194
177	169	188	160
199	175	172	187

3.53 According to the International Data Corporation, Compaq Computers holds a 16% share of the personal computer market in the United States and a 12.7% share of the worldwide market. Suppose a market researcher believes that Compaq holds a higher share of the market in the southwestern region of the United States. To verify this theory, he randomly selects 428 people who purchased a personal computer in the last month in the southwestern region of the United States. Eighty-four of these purchases were Compaq Computers. Using a 1% level of significance, test the market researcher's theory. What is the probability of making a Type I error? If the market share is really .21 in the southwestern region of the United States, what is the probability of making a Type II error?

3.54 A national publication reported that a college student living away from home spends, on average, no more than $15 per month on laundry. You believe this figure is too low and want to disprove this claim. To conduct the test, you randomly select 35 college students and ask them to keep track of the amount of money they spend during a given month for laundry. The sample produces an average expenditure on laundry of $19.34, with a population standard deviation of $4.52. Use these sample data to conduct the hypothesis test. Assume you are willing to take a 10% risk of making a Type I error.

3.55 A local company installs natural-gas grills. As part of the installation, a ditch is dug to lay a small natural-gas line from the grill to the main line. On the average, the depth of these lines seems to run about 1 foot. The company claims that the depth does not vary by more than 16 inches (the variance). To test this claim, a researcher randomly took 22 depth measurements at different locations. The sample average depth was 13.4 inches with a standard deviation of 6 inches. Is this enough evidence to reject the company's claim about the variance? Assume line depths are normally distributed. Let $\alpha = .05$.

3.56 A study of pollutants showed that certain industrial emissions should not exceed 2.5 parts per million. You believe a particular company may be exceeding this average. To test this supposition, you randomly take a sample of nine air tests. The sample average is 3.4 parts per million, with a sample standard deviation of .6. Does this result provide enough evidence for you to conclude that the company is exceeding the safe limit? Use $\alpha = .01$. Assume emissions are normally distributed.

3.57 The average cost per square foot for office rental space in the central business district of Philadelphia is $23.58, according to Cushman & Wakefield. A large real estate company wants to confirm this figure. The firm conducts a telephone survey of 95 offices in the central business district of Philadelphia and asks the office managers how much they pay in rent per square foot. Suppose the sample average is $22.83 per square foot. The population standard deviation is $5.11.

  a. Conduct a hypothesis test using $\alpha = .05$ to determine whether the cost per square foot reported by Cushman & Wakefield should be rejected.

  b. If the decision in part (a) is to fail to reject and if the actual average cost per square foot is $22.30, what is the probability of committing a Type II error?

3.58 The American Water Works Association reports that, on average, men use between 10 and 15 gallons of water daily to shave when they leave the water running. Suppose the following data are the numbers of gallons of water used in a day to shave by 12 randomly selected men and the data come from a normal distribution of data. Use these data and a 5% level of significance to test to determine whether the population variance for such water usage is 2.5 gallons.

10	8	13	17	13	15
12	13	15	16	9	7

INTERPRETING THE OUTPUT

3.59 According to the U.S. Census Bureau, the average American generates 4.4 pounds of garbage per day. Suppose we believe that because of recycling and a greater emphasis on the environment, the figure is now lower. To test this notion, we take a random sample of Americans and have them keep a log of their garbage for a day. We record and analyze the results by using a statistical computer package. The output follows. Describe the sample. What statistical decisions can be made on the basis of this analysis? Let alpha be .05. Discuss any substantive results.

```
One-Sample T: Garbage

Test of mu = 4.4 vs mu < 4.4

Variable    N    Mean    StDev    SE Mean
Garbage    22   3.969   0.866    0.185

Variable    95.0% Upper Bound     T       P
Garbage          4.286          -2.34   0.015
```

3.60 One survey conducted by RHI Management Resources determined that the Lexus is the favorite luxury car for 25% of CFOs. Suppose a financial management association conducts its own survey of CFOs in an effort to determine whether this figure is correct. They use an alpha of .05. Following is the MINITAB output with the results of the survey. Discuss the findings, including the hypotheses, one- or two-tailed tests, sample statistics, and the conclusion. Explain from the data why you reached the conclusion you did. Are these results substantive?

```
Test and CI for One Proportion

Test of p = 0.25 vs p not = 0.25

Sample   X    N    Sample p       95.0% CI          P-Value
1       79   384   0.205729   (0.166399, 0.249663)   0.045
```

3.61 In a recent year, published statistics by the National Cattlemen's Beef Association claimed that the average retail beef price for USDA All Fresh beef was $2.51. Suppose a survey of retailers is conducted this year to determine whether the price of USDA All Fresh beef has increased. The Excel output of the results of the survey are shown here. Analyze the output and explain what it means in this study. An alpha of .05 was used in this analysis. Comment on any substantive results.

	A	B
1	Mean	2.55
2	Variance	0.0218
3	Observations	26
4	df	26
5	t Stat	1.51
6	P (T<=t) one-tail	0.072
7	t Critical one-tail	1.71
8	P (T<=t) two-tail	0.144
9	t Critical two-tail	2.06

3.62 The American Express Retail Index states that the average U.S. household will spend $2,747 on home improvement projects this year. Suppose a large national home improvement company wants to test that figure in the West, theorizing that the average might be lower in the West. The research firm hired to conduct the study arrives at the results shown here. Analyze the data and explain the results. Comment on any substantive findings.

```
One-Sample Z: Home Improv

Test of mu = 2747 vs mu < 2747
The assumed sigma = 1557

  Variable     N   Mean   StDev   SE Mean
Home Improv    67   2349   1818     190

  Variable    95.0%  Upper Bound    Z      P
Home Improv           2662        2.09   0.018
```

ANALYZING THE DATABASES

see www.wiley.com/college/black

1. Suppose the average number of employees per industry group in the manufacturing database is believed to be less than 150 (1,000s). Test this belief as the alternative hypothesis by using the 140 SIC Code industries given in the database as the sample. Let $\alpha = .01$. Assume that the number of employees per industry group are normally distributed in the population. What did you decide and why?

2. Examine the hospital database. Suppose you want to "prove" that the average hospital in the United States averages more than 700 births per year. Use the hospital database as your sample and test this hypothesis. Let alpha be .01. On average, do hospitals in the United States employ fewer than 900 personnel? Use the hospital database as your sample and an alpha of .10 to test this figure as the alternative hypothesis. Assume that the number of births and number of employees in hospitals are normally distributed in the population.

3. Consider the financial database. Are the average earnings per share for companies in the stock market less than $2.50? Use the sample of companies represented by this database to test that hypothesis. Let $\alpha = .05$. Test to determine whether the average return on equity for all companies is equal to 21. Use this database as the sample and $\alpha = .10$. Assume that the earnings per share and return on equity are normally distributed in the population.

4. Fifteen years ago, the average production in the United States for green beans was 166,770 pounds per month. Use the 12 months in 1997 (the last 12 months in the database) in the agriculture database as a sample to test to determine whether the mean monthly production figure for green beans in the United States is now different from the old figure. Let $\alpha = .01$. Assume that the monthly production of beans is normally distributed in the population.

CASE: FRITO-LAY TARGETS THE HISPANIC MARKET

Frito Company was founded in 1932 in San Antonio, Texas, by Elmer Doolin. H. W. Lay & Company was founded in Atlanta, Georgia, by Herman W. Lay in 1938. In 1961, the two companies merged to form Frito-Lay, Inc., with headquarters in Texas. Frito-Lay produced, distributed, and marketed snack foods with particular emphasis on various types of chips. In 1965, the company merged with Pepsi-Cola to form PepsiCo, Inc. Three decades later, Pepsi-Cola combined its domestic and international snack food operations into one business unit called Frito-Lay Company. According to data released by Information Resources, Frito-Lay brands account for more than 60% of the share of the snack chip market.

Despite its overall popularity, Frito-Lay faces a general lack of appeal in the Hispanic market, which is a growing segment of the U.S. population. In an effort to better penetrate that market, Frito-Lay hired various market researchers to determine why Hispanics do not purchase their products as often as company officials had hoped and what could be done about the problem. Driving giant RVs through Hispanic neighborhoods and targeting Hispanic women (who tend to buy most of the groceries for their families), the researchers tested various brands and discovered several things. Hispanics thought Frito-Lay products were too bland, not spicy enough. Hispanics also were relatively unaware of Frito-Lay advertising. In addition, they tended to purchase snacks in small bags rather than in large family-style bags and at small local grocery stores rather than at large supermarkets.

After the "road test," focus groups composed of male teens and male young adults—a group that tends to consume a lot of chips—were formed. The researchers determined that even though many of the teens spoke English at school, they spoke Spanish at home with their family. From this discovery, it was concluded that Spanish advertisements would be needed to reach Hispanics. In addition, the use of Spanish rock music, a growing movement in the Hispanic youth culture, could be effective in some ads.

Researchers also found that using a "Happy Face" logo, which is an icon of Frito-Lay's sister company in Mexico, was effective. Because it reminded the 63% of all Hispanics in the

United States who are Mexican-American of snack foods from home, the logo increased product familiarity.

As a result of this research, Frito-Lay launched its first Hispanic products in San Antonio in 1997. Since that time, sales of the Doritos brand improved 32% in Hispanic areas and Doritos Salsa Verde sales have grown to represent 15% of all sales. Frito-Lay later expanded its line of products into other areas of the United States with large Hispanic populations.

Discussion

In the research process for Frito-Lay Company, many different numerical questions were raised regarding Frito-Lay products, advertising techniques, and purchase patterns among Hispanics. In each of these areas, statistics—in particular, hypothesis testing—plays a central role. Using the case information and the concepts of statistical hypothesis testing, discuss the following:

1. Many proportions were generated in the focus groups and market research that were conducted for this project, including the proportion of the market that is Hispanic, the proportion of Hispanic grocery shoppers that are women, the proportion of chip purchasers that are teens, and so on. Use techniques presented in this chapter to analyze each of the following and discuss how the results might affect marketing decision makers regarding the Hispanic market.

    a. The case information stated that 63% of all U.S. Hispanics are Mexican-American. How might we test that figure? Suppose 850 U.S. Hispanics are randomly selected using U.S. Census Bureau information. Suppose 575 state that they are Mexican-Americans. Test the 63% percentage using an alpha of .05.

    b. Suppose that in the past 94% of all Hispanic grocery shoppers were women. Perhaps due to changing cultural values, we believe that more Hispanic men are now grocery shopping. We randomly sample 689 Hispanic grocery shoppers from around the United States and 606 are women. Does this result provide enough evidence to conclude that a lower proportion of Hispanic grocery shoppers now are women?

    c. What proportion of Hispanics listen primarily to advertisements in Spanish? Suppose one source says that in the past the proportion has been about .83. We want to test to determine whether this figure is true. A random sample of 438 Hispanics is selected, and the MINITAB results of testing this hypothesis are shown here. Discuss and explain this output and the implications of this study using $\alpha = .05$.

```
Test and CI for One Proportion

Test of p = 0.83 vs p not = 0.83
Sample   X    N    Sample p        95.0% CI          P-Value
1        347  438  0.792237  (0.751184, 0.829290)    0.042
```

2. The statistical mean can be used to measure various aspects of the Hispanic culture and the Hispanic market, including size of purchase, frequency of purchase, age of consumer, size of store, and so on. Use techniques presented in this chapter to analyze each of the following and discuss how the results might affect marketing decisions.

    a. What is the average age of a purchaser of Doritos Salsa Verde? Suppose initial tests indicate that the mean age is 31. Is this figure really correct? To test whether it is, a researcher randomly contacts 24 purchasers of Doritos Salsa Verde with results shown in the following Excel output. Discuss the output in terms of a hypothesis test to determine whether the mean age is actually 31. Let α be .01.

	A	B
1	Mean	28.81
2	Variance	50.2651
3	Observations	24
4	df	23
5	t Stat	−1.52
6	P (T<=t) one-tail	0.0716
7	t Critical one-tail	1.71
8	P (T<=t) two-tail	0.1431
9	t Critical two-tail	2.07

    b. What is the average expenditure of a Hispanic customer on chips per year? Suppose it is hypothesized that the figure is $45 per year. A researcher who knows the Hispanic market believes that this figure is too high and wants to prove her case. She randomly selects 18 Hispanics, has them keep a log of grocery purchases for one year, and obtains the following figures. Analyze the data using techniques from this chapter and an alpha of .05. Assume that expenditures per customer are normally distributed in the population.

$55	37	59	57	27	28
16	46	34	62	9	34
4	25	38	58	3	50

Source: Adapted from "From Bland to Brand," *American Demographics* (March 1999), p. 57; Frito-Lay, available at http://www.fritolay.com; and Ronald J. Alsop, ed., *The Wall Street Journal Almanac 1999* (New York: Ballantine Books, 1998), p. 202.

USING THE COMPUTER

EXCEL

Excel has somewhat limited capability for doing hypothesis testing with single samples. It can compute z tests for single population means by using the Paste Function. Begin by clicking on the Paste Function f_x on the standard tool bar. The Paste Function dialog box will appear. From the **Function category** on the left, select **Statistical**. A menu of statistical techniques will appear on the right. Select **ZTEST** from this list. A dialog box will appear. This box requires the location of the data array in the first space beside **Array**. Place the hypothesized value of the mean in the second space beside **X**. Record the population standard deviation in the third line beside **Sigma**. The output is the right-tailed p-value for the test statistic. If the z value is negative, subtract $1 - $ (Excel output) to obtain the p-value for the left tail.

A single-sample t test can be computed in Excel by "fooling" the Excel dialog box for **t-Test: Two-Sample Assuming Unequal Variances**. First load the single-sample data in a column. Next, place the value of the hypothesized mean in another column in as many cells as there are data in the single-sample data column. Next, select **Tools** from the menu bar. Select **Data Analysis** from the pull-down menu. From the Data Analysis dialog box, select **t-Test: Two-Sample Assuming Unequal Variances**. In the dialog box that appears, place the location of the cells containing the single-sample data in **Variable 1 Range**. Place the location of the cells containing the repeated value of the hypothesized mean in **Variable 2 Range**. Place 0 in **Hypothesized Mean Difference**. Finally, fill in the labels and alpha information. The result will be the output for a single-sample t test.

MINITAB

MINITAB Windows conducts hypothesis tests by using the same commands, pull-down menus, and dialog boxes as those used to construct confidence intervals (discussed in Chapter 2). Begin by selecting **Stat** from the menu bar. From the pull-down menu that appears, select **Basic Statistics**. A second pull-down menu will appear. To conduct hypothesis tests in which the population standard deviation is known, select **1–sample Z**. To conduct hypothesis tests in which the population standard deviation is unknown, select **1–sample t**.

In the dialog boxes of each, enter the column location of the data being tested in the first space, **Variables**. (If a z test is being conducted, enter the value of the known population standard deviation in the space labeled **Sigma**.) In the **Test Mean** space enter the hypothesized value of μ. Select **Options**. From the Options dialog box enter the level of confidence if different from 95% and select whether the alternative hypothesis is **less than**, **greater than**, or **not equal**. The output includes a statement of the hypotheses, the sample size, the sample mean and standard deviation, the standard error of the mean, the t statistics, and the p-value of the statistic.

MINITAB is able to test hypotheses about single proportions using the same process presented in Chapter 2. Begin the process by selecting **Stat** from the menu bar. From the pull-down menu, select **Basic Statistics**. From that pull-down menu, select **1 Proportion**. In the dialog box that appears, select either **Samples in columns** or **Summarized data**. If the data are in columns and if only one of two possible values is in each cell, then select **Samples in columns**. If you want to enter the summary data, select **Summarized data**. Using this option, place the size of the sample in the **Number of trials** space, and the number of items containing characteristic of interest, x, in the **Number of successes** space. To test a hypothesis, select **Options**. This command allows you to place the hypothesized proportion in **Test proportion**. Beside **Alternative** select the appropriate alternative hypothesis being tested. The resulting output includes a sample proportion, a confidence interval, and a p-value.

Simple Regression Analysis

LEARNING OBJECTIVES

The overall objective of this chapter is to give you an understanding of bivariate linear regression analysis, thereby enabling you to:

1. Compute the equation of a simple regression line from a sample of data and interpret the slope and intercept of the equation.
2. Understand the usefulness of residual analysis in testing the assumptions underlying regression analysis and in examining the fit of the regression line to the data.
3. Compute a standard error of the estimate and interpret its meaning.
4. Compute a coefficient of determination and interpret it.
5. Test hypotheses about the slope of the regression model and interpret the results.
6. Estimate values of y by using the regression model.

Predicting the Annual Sales Volume of Real Estate Brokerage Firms by the Average Price of the Sale

What are some of the factors that determine the total annual sales volume of a real estate brokerage firm? Certainly, number of units sold would be a factor. Selling more houses/properties would result in higher total sales revenue for a real estate firm. Other factors might also play a role, such as size of houses/properties, location of houses/properties, number of realtors, amount spent on advertising, number of real estate offices, number of cities with real estate offices, and so on. Still another possibility is the average price of a unit sold by a company. It seems feasible that if the average price per sale at a firm is higher, then the total sales volume would be higher.

The following total sales volumes for the top 25 real estate brokerage firms in the United States are given here for a recent year along with the average price of a sale for that same year for each company. Sales volume is given in millions of dollars and the sales prices are given in thousands of dollars.

Company	Sales Volume	Average Price
NRT	50,031	244
Weichert, Realtors	13,000	205
Long & Foster Real Estate	7,791	175
Burnet Financial Group	6,603	176
Prudential Florida Realty	4,927	170
Fred Sands Realtors	4,410	367
Edina Realty	4,055	137
John L. Scott Real Estate	3,721	189
Coldwell Banker Hunneman & Co.	3,700	273
DeWolfe New England	3,593	209
Prudential California Realty	3,439	311
Realty Executives	3,355	138
Fox & Roach Realtors	3,194	179
Realty One	2,712	135
O'Conor, Piper & Flynn	2,711	127
Baird & Warner	2,400	200
Gundaker Realtors/Better Homes and Gardens	2,210	121
Ebby Halliday, Realtors	2,164	166
Prudential Connecticut Realty	2,140	221
Coldwell Banker Premier Van Schaack	2,024	156
Crye-Leike	1,969	126
Henry S. Miller Co., Realtors	1,918	157
Smythe, Cramer	1,912	156
RE/MAX North Atlanta	1,845	174
Pacific Union Residential Brokerage	1,829	439

Managerial and Statistical Questions

1. What variables among the several mentioned are related to the total sales volume for a brokerage firm in any given year? How strongly related to total sales volume are they? What are some other variables besides those mentioned that might be related to total sales volume? How do we determine how strongly one variable is related to another variable?

2. Data are given for the top 25 real estate brokerage firms in the United States for a recent year. In particular, the dollar figures are shown for the two variables, sales volume and average price. Are these two variables related; and if so, how strongly are they related? Just because a firm sells more expensive properties/houses does that mean the firm has higher total revenues? Why or why not?

3. Is there a way to predict a firm's total sales volume for the year by using the average price of a sale? If it were possible to predict a firm's total sales volume by the average price of a sale, how good would the prediction be?

Source: Adapted from data appearing in "REAL Trends, Dallas, Texas," *The Wall Street Journal Almanac 1999.* Ronald J. Alsop, ed. (New York: Ballantine Books), 1999, p. 336.

———

In many business research situations, the key to decision making lies in understanding the relationships between two or more variables. For example, in an effort to predict the value of airline stock from day to day, an analyst might find it helpful to determine whether the price of an airline stock is related to the price of West Texas intermediate (WTI) crude oil. In studying the behavior of the bond market, a broker might find it useful to know whether the interest rate of bonds is related to the prime interest rate. In studying the effect of advertising on sales, an account executive might find it useful to know how strong the relationship is between advertising dollars and sales dollars for a company. What variables are related to unemployment rates? Are minimum hourly wage rates, the inflation rate, or the wholesale price index usable for predicting an unemployment rate?

This chapter presents regression analysis in which mathematical models are developed to predict one variable from another. Using regression analysis, business researchers attempt to determine the functional relationship between the variables. Also, included in this chapter are statistical tools for testing the strength and predictability of the regression model.

4.1 INTRODUCTION TO SIMPLE REGRESSION ANALYSIS

Regression analysis is the process of constructing a mathematical model or function that can be used to predict or determine one variable by another variable. The most elementary regression model is called **simple regression**, which is *bivariate linear regression,* which means that it involves only two variables. One variable is predicted by another variable. *The variable to be predicted* is called the **dependent variable** and is designated as *y. The predictor* is called the **independent variable,** or *explanatory variable,* and is designated as *x.* In simple regression analysis, only a straight-line relationship between two variables is examined. Nonlinear relationships and regression models with more than one independent variable can be explored by using multiple regression models, which are presented in Chapters 5 and 6.

Can the cost of flying a commercial airliner be predicted using regression analysis? If so, what variables are related to such cost? A few of the many variables that can potentially contribute are type of plane, distance, number of passengers, amount of luggage/freight, weather conditions, direction of destination, and perhaps even pilot skill. Suppose a study is conducted using only Boeing 737s traveling 500 miles on comparable routes during the same season of the year in an effort to reduce the number of possible predictor variables. Can the number of passengers predict the cost of flying such routes? It seems logical that more passengers result in more weight and more baggage, which could, in turn, result in increased fuel consumption and other costs. Suppose the data displayed in Table 4.1 are the costs and associated number of passengers for twelve 500-mile commercial airline flights using Boeing 737s during the same season of the year. We will use these data to develop a regression model to predict cost by number of passengers.

Usually, the first step in simple regression analysis is to construct a **scatter plot** (or scatter diagram). Graphing the data in this way yields preliminary information about the shape and spread of the data. Figure 4.1 is an Excel scatter plot of the data in Table 4.1. Figure 4.2 is a close-up view of the scatter plot produced by MINITAB. Try to imagine a line passing through the points. Is a linear fit possible? Would a curve fit the data better? The scatter plot gives some idea of how well a regression line fits the data. Later in the chapter, we present statistical techniques that can be used to determine more precisely how well a regression line fits the data.

4.2 DETERMINING THE EQUATION OF THE REGRESSION LINE

The first step in determining the equation of the regression line that passes through the sample data is to establish the equation's form. Several different types of equations of lines are discussed in algebra, finite math, or analytic geometry courses. Recall that among these equations of a line are the two-point form, the point-slope form, and the slope-intercept form. In regression analysis, researchers use the slope-intercept equation of a line. In math courses, the slope-intercept form of the equation of a line often takes the form

$$y = mx + b$$

where

$m =$ slope of the line
$b = y$ intercept of the line

In statistics, the slope-intercept form of the equation of the regression line through the population points is

$$\hat{y} = \beta_0 + \beta_1 x$$

where

$\hat{y} = $ the predicted value of y
$\beta_0 = $ the population y intercept
$\beta_1 = $ the population slope

For any specific dependent variable value, y_i,

$$y_i = \beta_0 + \beta_1 x_i + \epsilon_i$$

where

$x_i = $ the value of the independent variable for the ith value

TABLE 4.1

Airline Cost Data

Number of Passengers	Cost ($1,000)
61	4.280
63	4.080
67	4.420
69	4.170
70	4.480
74	4.300
76	4.820
81	4.700
86	5.110
91	5.130
95	5.640
97	5.560

FIGURE 4.1

Excel Scatter Plot of Airline Cost Data

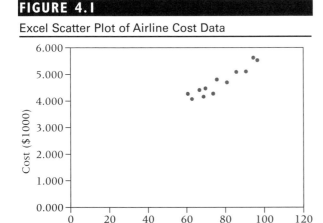

FIGURE 4.2

Close-Up MINITAB Scatter Plot of Airline Cost Data

y_i = the value of the dependent variable for the ith value
β_0 = the population y intercept
β_1 = the population slope
$\in_i$ = the error of prediction for the ith value

Unless the points being fitted by the regression equation are in perfect alignment, the regression line will miss at least some of the points. In the preceding equation, $\in_i$ represents the error of the regression line in fitting these points. If a point is on the regression line, $\in_i = 0$.

These mathematical models can be either deterministic models or probabilistic models. **Deterministic models** are *mathematical models that produce an "exact" output for a given input.* For example, suppose the equation of a regression line is

$$y = 1.68 + 2.40x$$

For a value of $x = 5$, the exact predicted value of y is

$$y = 1.68 + 2.40(5) = 13.68$$

We recognize, however, that most of the time the values of y will not equal exactly the values yielded by the equation. Random error will occur in the prediction of the y values for values of x because it is likely that the variable x does not explain all the variability of the variable y. For example, suppose we are trying to predict the volume of sales (y) for a company through regression analysis by using the annual dollar amount of advertising (x) as the predictor. Although sales are often related to advertising, other factors related to sales are not accounted for by amount of advertising. Hence, a regression model to predict sales volume by amount of advertising probably involves some error. For this reason, in regression, we present the general model as a probabilistic model. A **probabilistic model** is *one that includes an error term that allows for the y values to vary for any given value of x.*

A deterministic regression model is

$$y = \beta_0 + \beta_1 x$$

The probabilistic regression model is

$$y = \beta_0 + \beta_1 x + \in$$

$\beta_0 + \beta_1 x$ is the deterministic portion of the probabilistic model, $\beta_0 + \beta_1 x + \in$. In a deterministic model, all points are assumed to be on the line and in all cases $\in$ is zero.

Virtually all regression analyses of business data involve sample data, not population data. As a result, β_0 and β_1 are unattainable and must be estimated by using the sample statistics, b_0 and b_1. Hence the equation of the regression line contains the sample y intercept, b_0, and the sample slope, b_1.

EQUATION OF THE SIMPLE REGRESSION LINE

$$\hat{y} = b_0 + b_1 x$$

where

b_0 = the sample intercept
b_1 = the sample slope

To determine the equation of the regression line for a sample of data, the researcher must determine the values for b_0 and b_1. This process is sometimes referred to as least squares analysis. **Least squares analysis** is *a process whereby a regression model is developed by producing the minimum sum of the squared error values.* On the basis of this premise and calculus, a particular set of equations has been developed to produce components of the regression model.*

Examine the regression line fit through the points in Figure 4.3. Observe that the line does not actually pass through any of the points. The vertical distance from each point to the line is the error of the prediction. In theory, an infinite number of lines could be constructed to pass through these points in some manner. The least squares regression line is the regression line that results in the smallest sum of errors squared.

---

*Derivation of these formulas is beyond the scope of information being discussed here, but is presented on the eGrade Plus Web site..

Formula (4.1) is an equation for computing the value of the sample slope. Several versions of the equation are given to afford latitude in doing the computations.

SLOPE OF THE REGRESSION LINE (4.1)	$b_1 = \dfrac{\Sigma(x-\bar{x})(y-\bar{y})}{\Sigma(x-\bar{x})^2} = \dfrac{\Sigma xy - n\bar{x}\bar{y}}{\Sigma x^2 - n\bar{x}^2} = \dfrac{\Sigma xy - \dfrac{(\Sigma x)(\Sigma x)}{n}}{\Sigma x^2 - \dfrac{(\Sigma x)^2}{n}}$

The expression in the numerator of the slope formula (4.1) appears frequently in this chapter and is denoted as SS_{xy}.

$$SS_{xy} = \Sigma(x-\bar{x})(y-\bar{y}) = \Sigma xy - \frac{(\Sigma x)(\Sigma y)}{n}$$

The expression in the denominator of the slope formula (4.1) also appears frequently in this chapter and is denoted as SS_{xx}.

$$SS_{xx} = \Sigma(x-\bar{x})^2 = \Sigma x^2 - \frac{(\Sigma x)^2}{n}$$

With these abbreviations, the equation for the slope can be expressed as in Formula (4.2).

ALTERNATIVE FORMULA FOR SLOPE (4.2)	$b_1 = \dfrac{SS_{xy}}{SS_{xx}}$

Formula (4.3) is used to compute the sample y intercept. The slope must be computed before the y intercept.

y INTERCEPT OF THE REGRESSION LINE (4.3)	$b_0 = \bar{y} - b_1\bar{x} = \dfrac{\Sigma y}{n} - b_1\dfrac{(\Sigma x)}{n}$

Formulas 4.1, 4.2, and 4.3 show that the following data are needed from sample information to compute the slope and intercept: Σx, Σy, Σx^2, and Σxy, unless sample means are used. Table 4.2 contains the results of solving for the slope and intercept and determining the equation of the regression line for the data in Table 4.1.

The least squares equation of the regression line for this problem is

$$\hat{y} = 1.57 + .0407x$$

The slope of this regression line is .0407. Because the x values were recoded for the ease of computation and are actually in $1,000 denominations, the slope is actually $40.70. One interpretation of the slope in this problem is that for every unit increase in x (every person added to the flight of the airplane), there is a $40.70 increase in the cost of the flight. The y intercept is the point where the line crosses the y axis (where x is zero). Sometimes in regression analysis, the y intercept is meaningless in terms of the variables studied. However, in this problem, one interpretation of the y intercept, which is 1.570 or $1,570, is that even if there were no passengers on the commercial flight, it would still cost $1,570. In other words, costs are associated with a flight that carries no passengers.

FIGURE 4.3

MINITAB Plot of a
Regression Line

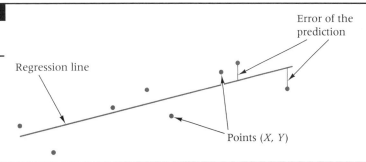

TABLE 4.2

Solving for the Slope and the y Intercept of the Regression Line for the Airline Cost Example

Number of Passengers	Cost ($1,000)		
x	y	x^2	xy
61	4.280	3,721	261.080
63	4.080	3,969	257.040
67	4.420	4,489	296.140
69	4.170	4,761	287.730
70	4.480	4,900	313.600
74	4.300	5,476	318.200
76	4.820	5,776	366.320
81	4.700	6,561	380.700
86	5.110	7,396	439.460
91	5.130	8,281	466.830
95	5.640	9,025	535.800
97	5.560	9,409	539.320

$\Sigma x = 930 \quad \Sigma y = 56.690 \quad \Sigma x^2 = 73,764 \quad \Sigma xy = 4462.220$

$$SS_{xy} = \Sigma xy - \frac{(\Sigma x)(\Sigma x)}{n} = 4462.22 - \frac{(930)(56.69)}{12} = 68.745$$

$$SS_{xx} = \Sigma x^2 - \frac{(\Sigma x)^2}{n} = 73,764 - \frac{(930)^2}{12} = 1689$$

$$b_1 = \frac{SS_{xy}}{SS_{xx}} = \frac{68.745}{1689} = .0407$$

$$b_0 = \frac{\Sigma y}{n} - b_1 \frac{\Sigma x}{n} = \frac{56.69}{12} - (.0407)\frac{930}{12} = 1.57$$

$$\hat{y} = 1.57 + .0407x$$

FIGURE 4.4

Excel Graph of Regression Line for the Airline Cost Example

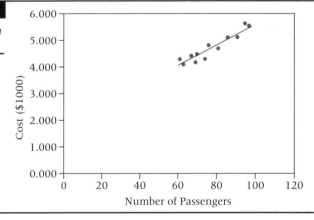

Superimposing the line representing the least squares equation for this problem on the scatter plot indicates how well the regression line fits the data points, as shown in the Excel graph in Figure 4.4. The next several sections explore mathematical ways of testing how well the regression line fits the points.

DEMONSTRATION PROBLEM 4.1

A specialist in hospital administration stated that the number of FTEs (full-time employees) in a hospital can be estimated by counting the number of beds in the hospital (a common measure of hospital size). A healthcare business researcher decided to develop a regression model in an attempt to predict the number of FTEs of a hospital by the number of beds. She surveyed 12 hospitals and obtained the following data. The data are presented in sequence, according to the number of beds.

Number of Beds	FTEs	Number of Beds	FTEs
23	69	50	138
29	95	54	178
29	102	64	156
35	118	66	184
42	126	76	176
46	125	78	225

Solution

The following MINITAB graph is a scatter plot of these data. Note the linear appearance of the data.

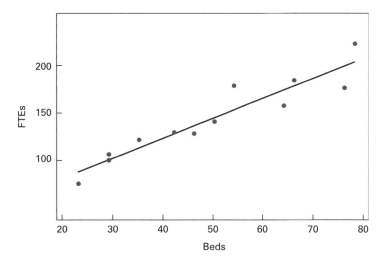

Next, the researcher determined the values of Σx, Σy, Σx^2, and Σxy.

Hospital	Number of Beds x	FTEs y	x^2	xy
1	23	69	529	1,587
2	29	95	841	2,755
3	29	102	841	2,958
4	35	118	1,225	4,130
5	42	126	1,764	5,292
6	46	125	2,116	5,750
7	50	138	2,500	6,900
8	54	178	2,916	9,612
9	64	156	4,096	9,984
10	66	184	4,356	12,144
11	76	176	5,776	13,376
12	78	225	6,084	17,550
	$\Sigma x = 592$	$\Sigma y = 1,692$	$\Sigma x^2 = 33,044$	$\Sigma xy = 92,038$

Using these values, the researcher solved for the sample slope (b_1) and the sample y intercept (b_0).

$$SS_{xy} = \Sigma xy - \frac{(\Sigma x)(\Sigma y)}{n} = 92,038 - \frac{(592)(1692)}{12} = 8566$$

$$SS_{xx} = \Sigma x^2 - \frac{(\Sigma x)^2}{n} = 33,044 - \frac{(592)^2}{12} = 3838.667$$

$$b_1 = \frac{SS_{xy}}{SS_{xx}} = \frac{8566}{3838.667} = 2.232$$

$$b_0 = \frac{\Sigma y}{n} - b_1\frac{\Sigma x}{n} = \frac{1692}{12} - (2.232)\frac{592}{12} = 30.888$$

The least squares equation of the regression line is

$$\hat{y} = 30.888 + 2.232x$$

The slope of the line, $b_1 = 2.232$, means that for every unit increase of x (every bed), y (number of FTEs) is predicted to increase by 2.232. Even though the y intercept helps the researcher sketch the graph of the line by being one of the points on the line (0, 30.888), it has limited usefulness in terms of this solution because $x = 0$ denotes a hospital with no beds. On the other hand, it could be interpreted that a hospital has to have at least 31 FTEs to open its doors even with no patients—a sort of "fixed cost" of personnel.

4.2 PROBLEMS

4.1 Sketch a scatter plot from the following data, and determine the equation of the regression line.

x	12	21	28	8	20
y	17	15	22	19	24

4.2 Sketch a scatter plot from the following data, and determine the equation of the regression line.

x	140	119	103	91	65	29	24
y	25	29	46	70	88	112	128

4.3 A corporation owns several companies. The strategic planner for the corporation believes dollars spent on advertising can to some extent be a predictor of total sales dollars. As an aid in long-term planning, she gathers the following sales and advertising information from several of the companies for 2002 ($ millions).

Advertising	Sales
12.5	148
3.7	55
21.6	338
60.0	994
37.6	541
6.1	89
16.8	126
41.2	379

Develop the equation of the simple regression line to predict sales from advertising expenditures using these data.

4.4 Investment analysts generally believe the interest rate on bonds is inversely related to the prime interest rate for loans; that is, bonds perform well when lending rates are down and perform poorly when interest rates are up. Can the bond rate be predicted by the prime interest rate? Use the following data to construct a least squares regression line to predict bond rates by the prime interest rate.

Bond Rate	Prime Interest Rate
5%	16%
12	6
9	8
15	4
7	7

4.5 Is it possible to predict the annual number of business failures in the United States by the number of business starts the previous year? It might seem that the more business starts there are in a given year, the more potential there is for business failure the next year. The following data from Dun & Bradstreet show the number of business failures from 1989 to 1999 and the number of business starts for each of the previous years. Use these data to develop the equation of a regression line to predict the number of business failures from the number of business starts the previous year. Discuss the slope and y intercept of the model.

Number of Business Starts for the Previous Year	Number of Business Failures
233,710	57,097
199,091	50,361
181,645	60,747
158,930	88,140
155,672	97,069
164,086	86,133
166,154	71,558
188,387	71,128
168,158	71,931
170,475	83,384
166,740	71,857

4.6   It appears that over the past 35 years, the number of farms in the United States declined while the average size of farms increased. The following data provided by the U.S. Department of Agriculture show five-year interval data for U.S. farms. Use these data to develop the equation of a regression line to predict the average size of a farm by the number of farms. Discuss the slope and y intercept of the model.

Year	Number of Farms (millions)	Average Size (acres)
1950	5.65	213
1955	4.65	258
1960	3.96	297
1965	3.36	340
1970	2.95	374
1975	2.52	420
1980	2.44	426
1985	2.29	441
1990	2.15	460
1995	2.07	469
2000	2.17	434

4.7   Can the annual new orders for manufacturing in the United States be predicted by the raw steel production in the United States? Shown here are the annual new orders for 10 years according to the U.S. Census Bureau and the raw steel production for the same 10 years as published by the American Iron & Steel Institute. Use these data to develop a regression model to predict annual new orders by raw steel production. Construct a scatter plot and draw the regression line through the points.

Raw Steel Production (100,000s of net tons)	New Orders ($ trillions)
99.9	2.74
97.9	2.87
98.9	2.93
87.9	2.87
92.9	2.98
97.9	3.09
100.6	3.36
104.9	3.61
105.3	3.75
108.6	3.95

4.3 RESIDUAL ANALYSIS

How does a researcher test a regression line to determine mathematically whether the line is a good fit of the data? One type of information available is the *historical data* used to construct the equation of the line. In other words, actual y values correspond to the x values used in constructing the regression line. Why not insert the historical x values into the equation of the sample regression line and get predicted y values (denoted $\hat{y}$) and then compare these predicted values to the actual y values to determine how much error the equation of the regression line produced? *Each difference between the actual y values and the predicted y values is the error of the regression line at a given point, $y - \hat{y}$, and is referred* to as the **residual.** It is the sum of squares of these residuals that is minimized to find the least squares line.

Table 4.3 shows $\hat{y}$ values and the residuals for each pair of data for the airline cost regression model developed in Section 4.2. The predicted values are calculated by inserting an x value into the equation of the regression line and solving for $\hat{y}$. For example, when $x = 61$, $\hat{y} = 1.57 + .0407(61) = 4.053$, as displayed in column 3 of the table. Each of these predicted y values is subtracted from the actual y value to determine the error, or residual. For example, the first y value listed in the table is 4.280 and the first predicted value is 4.053, resulting in a residual of $4.280 - 4.053 = .227$. The residuals for this problem are given in column 4 of the table.

Note that the sum of the residuals is approximately zero. Except for rounding error, the sum of the residuals is *always zero*. The reason is that a residual is geometrically the vertical distance from the regression line to a data point. The equations used to solve for the slope and intercept place the line geometrically in the middle of all points. Therefore, vertical distances from the line to the points will cancel each other and sum to zero. Figure 4.5 is a MINITAB-produced scatter plot of the data and the residuals for the airline cost example.

An examination of the residuals may give the researcher an idea of how well the regression line fits the historical data points. The largest residual for the airline cost example is –.282, and the smallest is .040. Because the objective of the regression analysis was to predict the cost of flight in $1,000s, the regression line produces an error of $282 when there are 74 passengers and an error of only $40 when there are 86 passengers. This result presents the *best* and *worst* cases for the residuals. The researcher must examine other residuals to determine how well the regression model fits other data points.

Sometimes residuals are used to locate outliers. **Outliers** are *data points that lie apart from the rest of the points.* Outliers can produce residuals with large magnitudes and are usually easy to identify on scatter plots. Outliers can be the result of misrecorded or miscoded data, or they may simply be data points that do not conform to the general trend.

TABLE 4.3			
Predicted Values and Residuals for the Airline Cost Example			
Number of Passengers x	**Cost ($1,000)** y	**Predicted Value** $\hat{y}$	**Residual** $y - \hat{y}$
61	4.280	4.053	.227
63	4.080	4.134	–.054
67	4.420	4.297	.123
69	4.170	4.378	–.208
70	4.480	4.419	.061
74	4.300	4.582	–.282
76	4.820	4.663	.157
81	4.700	4.867	–.167
86	5.110	5.070	.040
91	5.130	5.274	–.144
95	5.640	5.436	.204
97	5.560	5.518	.042

$$\Sigma(y - \hat{y}) = -.001$$

FIGURE 4.5

Close-up MINITAB Scatter Plot with Residuals for the Airline Cost Example

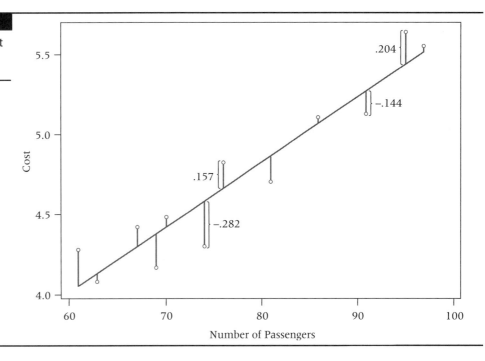

The equation of the regression line is influenced by every data point used in its calculation in a manner similar to the arithmetic mean. Therefore, outliers sometimes can unduly influence the regression line by "pulling" the line toward the outliers. The origin of outliers must be investigated to determine whether they should be retained or whether the regression equation should be recomputed without them.

Residuals are usually plotted against the x axis, which reveals a view of the residuals as x increases. Figure 4.6 shows the residuals plotted by Excel against the x axis for the airline cost example.

Using Residuals to Test the Assumptions of the Regression Model

One of the major uses of residual analysis is to test some of the assumptions underlying regression. The following are the assumptions of simple regression analysis.

1. The model is linear.
2. The error terms have constant variances.
3. The error terms are independent.
4. The error terms are normally distributed.

A particular method for studying the behavior of residuals is the residual plot. The **residual plot** is *a type of graph in which the residuals for a particular regression model are plotted along with their associated value of x as an ordered pair (x, y − ŷ).* Information about how well the regression assumptions are met by the particular regression model can be gleaned by examining the plots. Residual plots are more meaningful with larger sample sizes. For small sample sizes, residual plot analyses can be problematic and subject to over-interpretation. Hence, because the airline cost example is constructed from only 12 pairs of data, one should be cautious in reaching conclusions from Figure 4.6. The residual plots in Figures 4.7, 4.8, and 4.9, however, represent large numbers of data points and therefore are more likely to depict overall trends accurately.

If a residual plot such as the one in Figure 4.7 appears, the assumption that the model is linear does not hold. Note that the residuals are negative for low and high values of x and are positive for middle values of x. The graph of these residuals is parabolic, not linear. The residual plot does not have to be shaped in this manner for a nonlinear relationship to exist. Any significant deviation from an approximately linear residual plot may mean that a nonlinear relationship exists between the two variables.

Excel Graph of Residuals for
the Airline Cost Example

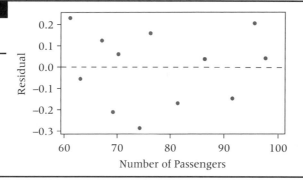

The assumption of *constant error variance* sometimes is called **homoscedasticity.** If *the error variances are not constant* (called **heteroscedasticity**), the residual plots might look like one of the two plots in Figure 4.8. Note in Figure 4.8(a) that the error variance is greater for small values of *x* and smaller for large values of *x*. The situation is reversed in Figure 4.8(b).

If the error terms are not independent, the residual plots could look like one of the graphs in Figure 4.9. According to these graphs, instead of each error term being independent of the one next to it, the value of the residual is a function of the residual value next to it. For example, a large positive residual is next to a large positive residual and a small negative residual is next to a small negative residual.

The graph of the residuals from a regression analysis that meets the assumptions—a *healthy residual graph*—might look like the graph in Figure 4.10. The plot is relatively linear; the variances of the errors are about equal for each value of *x*, and the error terms do not appear to be related to adjacent terms.

Using the Computer for Residual Analysis

Some computer programs contain mechanisms for analyzing residuals for violations of the regression assumptions. MINITAB has the capability of providing graphical analysis of residuals. Figure 4.11 displays MINITAB's residual graphic analyses for a regression model developed to predict the production of carrots in the United States per month by the total production of sweet corn. The data were gathered over a time period of 168 consecutive months (see the CD-ROM for the agricultural database).

These MINITAB residual model diagnostics consist of four different plots. The graph on the lower right is a plot of the residuals versus the fits. Note that this residual plot "flares out" as *x* gets larger. This pattern is an indication of heteroscedasticity, which is a violation of the assumption of constant variance for error terms. The graph in the upper left is a normal probability plot of the residuals. A straight line indicates that the residuals are normally distributed. Observe that this normal plot is relatively close to being a straight line, indicating that the residuals are nearly normal in shape. This normal distribution is confirmed by the graph on the lower left, which is a histogram of the residuals. The histogram groups residuals in classes so the researcher can observe where groups of the residuals lie without having to rely on the residual plot and to validate the notion that the residuals are approximately normally distributed. In this

Nonlinear Residual Plot

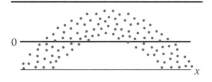

Nonconstant Error Variance

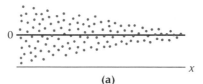

(a)

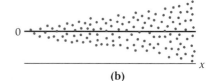

(b)

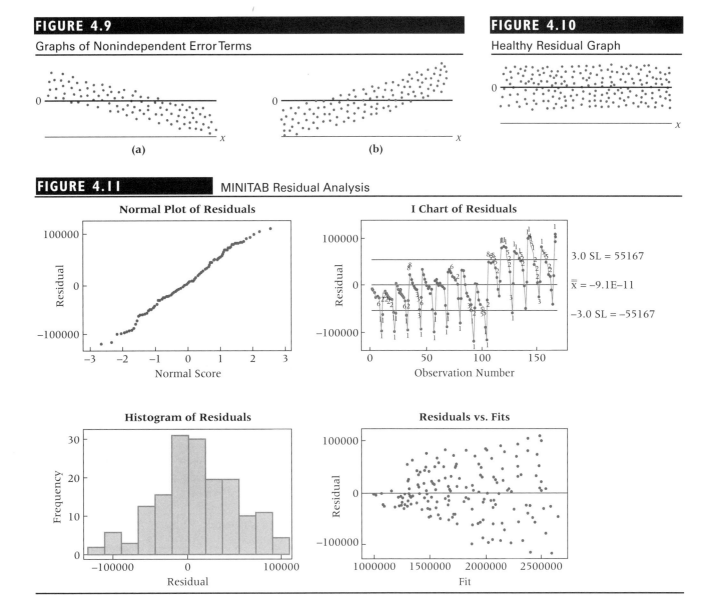

FIGURE 4.9
Graphs of Nonindependent Error Terms

(a)

(b)

FIGURE 4.10
Healthy Residual Graph

FIGURE 4.11 MINITAB Residual Analysis

Normal Plot of Residuals

I Chart of Residuals

3.0 SL = 55167

$\bar{\bar{x}}$ = −9.1E−11

−3.0 SL = −55167

Histogram of Residuals

Residuals vs. Fits

problem, the pattern is indicative of at least a mound-shaped distribution of residuals. The I Chart of Residuals on the upper right is a presentation of the residuals in a control chart form. UCL is the upper control limit and is generally located three standard deviations above the centerline, which here is 0.000. The LCL is the lower control limit and is generally located three standard deviations below the centerline. In control chart analysis, observations outside UCL or LCL are an indication of an out-of-control system. In addition, a relatively random pattern of residuals should occur above and below the centerline. In this chart, a few residuals fall outside the UCL and LCL. In addition, it appears that the residuals are not independent as evidenced by the apparent patterns in the I Chart. The data used to produce this regression model are time-series data, which are discussed in further detail in Chapter 7. However, the seasonal effect in these agricultural data is likely to account for the lack of independence of error terms.

DEMONSTRATION PROBLEM 4.2

Compute the residuals for Demonstration Problem 4.1 in which a regression model was developed to predict the number of full-time equivalent workers (FTEs) by the number of beds in a hospital. Analyze the residuals by using MINITAB graphic diagnostics.

Solution

The data and computed residuals are shown in the following table.

Hospital	Number of Beds x	FTES y	Predicted Value $\hat{y}$	Residuals $y - \hat{y}$
1	23	69	82.22	−13.22
2	29	95	95.62	−.62
3	29	102	95.62	6.38
4	35	118	109.01	8.99
5	42	126	124.63	1.37
6	46	125	133.56	−8.56
7	50	138	142.49	−4.49
8	54	178	151.42	26.58
9	64	156	173.74	−17.74
10	66	184	178.20	5.80
11	76	176	200.52	−24.52
12	78	225	204.98	20.02

$$\Sigma(y - \hat{y}) = -.01$$

Note that the regression model fits these particular data well for hospitals 2 and 5, as indicated by residuals of −.62 and 1.37 FTEs, respectively. For hospitals 1, 8, 9, 11, and 12, the residuals are relatively large, indicating that the regression model does not fit the data for these hospitals well. The Residuals vs. Fits graph indicates that the residuals seem to increase as x increases, indicating a potential problem with heteroscedasticity. This is confirmed by examining the I Chart, which shows that while the residuals appear to be "under control," the variance of them is increasing. The normal plot of residuals indicates that the residuals are nearly normally distributed. The histogram of residuals shows that the residuals pile up in the middle, but are somewhat skewed toward the larger positive values.

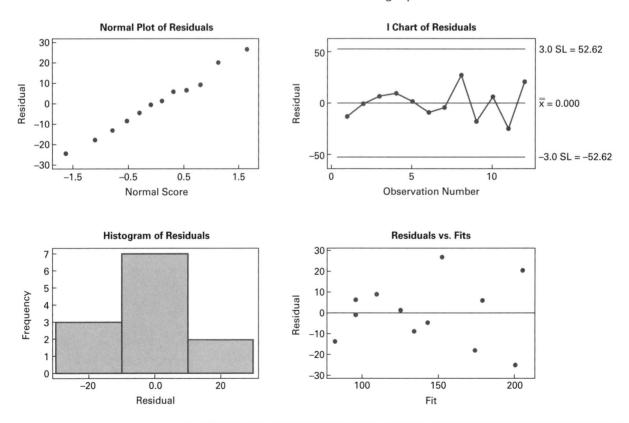

4.3 PROBLEMS

4.8 Determine the equation of the regression line for the following data, and compute the residuals.

x	15	8	19	12	5
y	47	36	56	44	21

4.9 Solve for the predicted values of y and the residuals for the data in Problem 4.1. The data are provided here again:

x	12	21	28	8	20
y	17	15	22	19	24

4.10 Solve for the predicted values of y and the residuals for the data in Problem 4.2. The data are provided here again:

x	140	119	103	91	65	29	24
y	25	29	46	70	88	112	128

4.11 Solve for the predicted values of y and the residuals for the data in Problem 4.3. The data are provided here again:

Advertising	12.5	3.7	21.6	60.0	37.6	6.1	16.8	41.2
Sales	148	55	338	994	541	89	126	379

4.12 Solve for the predicted values of y and the residuals for the data in Problem 4.4. The data are provided here again:

Bond Rate	5%	12%	9%	15%	7%
Prime Interest Rate	16%	6%	8%	4%	7%

4.13 The equation of a regression line is

$$\hat{y} = 50.506 - 1.646x$$

and the data are as follows.

x	5	7	11	12	19	25
y	47	38	32	24	22	10

Solve for the residuals and graph a residual plot. Do these data seem to violate any of the assumptions of regression?

4.14 Wisconsin is an important milk-producing state. Some people might argue that because of transportation costs, the cost of milk increases with the distance of markets from Wisconsin. Suppose the milk prices in eight cities are as follows.

Cost of Milk (per gallon)	Distance from Madison (miles)
$2.64	1,245
2.31	425
2.45	1,346
2.52	973
2.19	255
2.55	865
2.40	1,080
2.37	296

Use the prices along with the distance of each city from Madison, Wisconsin, to develop a regression line to predict the price of a gallon of milk by the number of miles the city is from Madison. Use the data and the regression equation to compute residuals for this model. Sketch a graph of the residuals in the order of the x values. Comment on the shape of the residual graph.

4.15   Graph the following residuals, and indicate which of the assumptions underlying regression appear to be in jeopardy on the basis of the graph.

x	$y - \hat{y}$
213	−11
216	−5
227	−2
229	−1
237	+6
247	+10
263	+12

4.16   Graph the following residuals, and indicate which of the assumptions underlying regression appear to be in jeopardy on the basis of the graph.

x	$y - \hat{y}$	x	$y - \hat{y}$
5	−21	13	−7
6	+16	14	+5
8	+14	17	−2
9	−11	18	+1
12	−8		

4.17   Graph the following residuals, and indicate which of the assumptions underlying regression appear to be in jeopardy on the basis of the graph.

x	$y - \hat{y}$	x	$y - \hat{y}$
10	+6	14	−3
11	+3	15	+2
12	−1	16	+5
13	−11	17	+8

4.18   Study the following MINITAB Residuals vs. Fits graphic for a simple regression analysis. Comment on the residual evidence of lack of compliance with the regression assumptions.

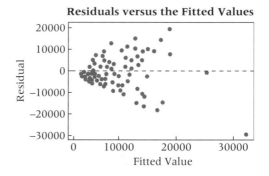

4.4 STANDARD ERROR OF THE ESTIMATE

Residuals represent errors of estimation for individual points. With large samples of data, residual computations become laborious. Even with computers, a researcher sometimes has difficulty working through pages of residuals in an effort to understand the error of the regression model. An alternative way of examining the error of the model is the standard error of the estimate, which provides a single measurement of the regression error.

Because the sum of the residuals is zero, attempting to determine the total amount of error by summing the residuals is fruitless. This zero-sum characteristic of residuals can be avoided by squaring the residuals and then summing them.

Table 4.4 contains the airline cost data from Table 4.1, along with the residuals and the residuals squared. The *total of the residuals squared* column is called the **sum of squares of error (SSE).**

SUM OF SQUARES OF ERROR	$$\text{SSE} = \Sigma(y - \hat{y})^2$$

In theory, infinitely many lines can be fit to a sample of points. However, formulas (4.1) and (4.3) produce a line of best fit for which the SSE is the smallest for any line that can be fit to the sample data. This result is guaranteed, because formulas (4.1) and (4.3) are derived from calculus to minimize SSE. For this reason, the regression process used in this chapter is called *least squares* regression.

A computational version of the equation for computing SSE is less meaningful in terms of interpretation than $\Sigma(y - \hat{y})^2$ but it is usually easier to compute. The computational formula for SSE follows.

COMPUTATIONAL FORMULA FOR SSE	$$\text{SSE} = \Sigma y^2 - b_0 \Sigma y - b_1 \Sigma xy$$

For the airline cost example,

$$\Sigma y^2 = \Sigma\,[(4.280)^2 + (4.080)^2 + (4.420)^2 + (4.170)^2 + (4.480)^2 + (4.300)^2 + (4.820)^2 +$$
$$(4.700)^2 + (5.110)^2 + (5.130)^2 + (5.640)^2 + (5.560)^2] = 270.9251$$

$$b_0 \ = 1.5697928$$
$$b_1 \ = .0407016^*$$
$$\Sigma y \ = 56.69$$
$$\Sigma xy \ = 4462.22$$
$$\text{SSE} \ = \Sigma y^2 - b_0 \Sigma y - b_1 \Sigma xy$$
$$= 270.9251 - (1.5697928)(56.69) - (.0407016)(4462.22) = .31405$$

The slight discrepancy between this value and the value computed in Table 4.4 is due to rounding error.

The sum of squares error is in part a function of the number of pairs of data being used to compute the sum, which lessens the value of SSE as a measurement of error. A more useful measurement of error is the standard error of the estimate. The **standard error of the estimate,** denoted s_e, is *a standard deviation of the error of the regression model* and has a more practical use than SSE. The standard error of the estimate follows.

*Note: In previous sections, the values of the slope and intercept were rounded off for ease of computation and interpretation. They are shown here with more precision in an effort to reduce rounding error.

TABLE 4.4

Determining SSE for the Airline Cost Example

Number of Passengers x	Cost ($1,000) y	Residual $y - \hat{y}$	$(y - \hat{y})^2$
61	4.280	.227	.05153
63	4.080	−.054	.00292
67	4.420	.123	.01513
69	4.170	−.208	.04326
70	4.480	.061	.00372
74	4.300	−.282	.07952
76	4.820	.157	.02465
81	4.700	−.167	.02789
86	5.110	.040	.00160
91	5.130	−.144	.02074
95	5.640	.204	.04162
97	5.560	.042	.00176
		$\Sigma(y - \hat{y}) = -.001$	$\Sigma(y - \hat{y})^2 = .31434$

Sum of squares of error = SSE = .31434

STANDARD ERROR OF THE ESTIMATE	$s_e = \sqrt{\dfrac{SSE}{n-2}}$

The standard error of the estimate for the airline cost example is

$$s_e = \sqrt{\frac{SSE}{n-2}} = \sqrt{\frac{.31434}{10}} = .1773$$

How is the standard error of the estimate used? As previously mentioned, the standard error of the estimate is a standard deviation of error. If data are approximately normally distributed, the empirical rule states that about 68% of all values are within $\mu \pm 1\sigma$ and that about 95% of all values are within $\mu \pm 2\sigma$. One of the assumptions for regression states that for a given x the error terms are normally distributed. Because the error terms are normally distributed, s_e is the standard deviation of error, and the average error is zero, approximately 68% of the error values (residuals) should be within $0 \pm 1s_e$ and 95% of the error values (residuals) should be within $0 \pm 2s_e$. By having knowledge of the variables being studied and by examining the value of s_e, the researcher can often make a judgment about the fit of the regression model to the data by using s_e. How can the s_e value for the airline cost example be interpreted?

The regression model in that example is used to predict airline cost by number of passengers. Note that the range of the airline cost data in Table 4.1 is from 4.08 to 5.64 ($4,080 to $5,640). The regression model for the data yields an s_e of .1773. An interpretation of s_e is that the standard deviation of error for the airline cost example is $177.30. If the error terms were normally distributed about the given values of x, approximately 68% of the error terms would be within $\pm$177.30 and 95% would be within $\pm 2(\$177.30) = \pm\$354.60$. Examination of the residuals reveals that 100% of the residuals are within $2s_e$. The standard error of the estimate provides a single measure of error, which, if the researcher has enough background in the area being analyzed, can be used to understand the magnitude of errors in the model. In addition, some researchers use the standard error of the estimate to identify outliers. They do so by looking for data that are outside $\pm 2s_e$ or $\pm 3s_e$.

DEMONSTRATION PROBLEM 4.3

Compute the sum of squares of error and the standard error of the estimate for Demonstration Problem 4.1, in which a regression model was developed to predict the number of FTEs at a hospital by the number of beds.

Solution

Hospital	Number of Beds x	FTES y	Residuals $y - \hat{y}$	$(y - \hat{y})^2$
1	23	69	−13.22	174.77
2	29	95	−.62	−0.38
3	29	102	6.38	40.70
4	35	118	8.99	80.82
5	42	126	1.37	1.88
6	46	125	−8.56	73.27
7	50	138	−4.49	20.16
8	54	178	26.58	706.50
9	64	156	−17.74	314.71
10	66	184	5.80	33.64
11	76	176	−24.52	601.23
12	78	225	20.02	400.80
	$\Sigma x = 592$	$\Sigma y = 1692$	$\Sigma(y - \hat{y}) = -.01$	$\Sigma(y - \hat{y})^2 = 2448.86$

SSE = 2448.86

$$s_e = \sqrt{\frac{SSE}{n-2}} = \sqrt{\frac{2448.86}{10}} = 15.65$$

The standard error of the estimate is 15.65 FTEs. An examination of the residuals for this problem reveals that eight of 12 (67%) are within $\pm 1s_e$ and 100% are within $\pm 2s_e$. Is this size of error acceptable? Hospital administrators probably can best answer that question.

4.4 PROBLEMS

4.19   Determine the sum of squares of error (SSE) and the standard error of the estimate (s_e) for Problem 4.1. Determine how many of the residuals computed in Problem 4.9 (for Problem 4.1) are within one standard error of the estimate. If the error terms are normally distributed, approximately how many of these residuals should be within $\pm 1s_e$?

4.20   Determine the SSE and the s_e for Problem 4.2. Use the residuals computed in Problem 4.10 (for Problem 4.2) and determine how many of them are within $\pm 1s_e$ and $\pm 2s_e$. How do these numbers compare with what the empirical rule says should occur if the error terms are normally distributed?

4.21   Determine the SSE and the s_e for Problem 4.3. Think about the variables being analyzed by regression in this problem and comment on the value of s_e.

4.22   Determine the SSE and s_e for Problem 4.4. Examine the variables being analyzed by regression in this problem and comment on the value of s_e.

4.23   Use the data from Problem 4.13 and determine the s_e.

4.24   Determine the SSE and the s_e for Problem 4.14. Comment on the size of s_e for this regression model, which is used to predict the cost of milk.

4.25   Determine the equation of the regression line to predict annual sales of a company from the yearly stock market volume of shares sold in a recent year. Compute the standard error of the estimate for this model. Does volume of shares sold appear to be a good predictor of a company's sales? Why or why not?

Company	Annual Sales ($ billions)	Annual Volume (millions of shares)
Merck	10.5	728.6
Philip Morris	48.1	497.9
IBM	64.8	439.1
Eastman Kodak	20.1	377.9
Bristol-Myers Squibb	11.4	375.5
General Motors	123.8	363.8
Ford Motors	89.0	276.3

4.5 COEFFICIENT OF DETERMINATION

A widely used measure of fit for regression models is the **coefficient of determination,** or r^2. The coefficient of determination is *the proportion of variability of the dependent variable (y) accounted for or explained by the independent variable (x).*

The coefficient of determination ranges from 0 to 1. An r^2 of zero means that the predictor accounts for none of the variability of the dependent variable and that there is no regression prediction of y by x. An r^2 of 1 means perfect prediction of y by x and that 100% of the variability of y is accounted for by x. Of course, most r^2 values are between the extremes. The researcher must interpret whether a particular r^2 is high or low, depending on the use of the model and the context within which the model was developed.

In exploratory research where the variables are less understood, low values of r^2 are likely to be more acceptable than they are in areas of research where the parameters are more developed and understood. One NASA researcher who uses vehicular weight to predict mission cost searches for the regression models to have an r^2 of .90 or higher. However, a business researcher who is trying to develop a model to predict the motivation level of employees might be pleased to get an r^2 near .50 in the initial research.

The dependent variable, y, being predicted in a regression model has a variation that is measured by the sum of squares of y (SS_{yy}):

$$SS_{yy} = \Sigma(y - \bar{y})^2 = \Sigma y^2 - \frac{(\Sigma y)^2}{n}$$

and is the sum of the squared deviations of the y values from the mean value of y. This variation can be broken into two additive variations: the *explained variation*, measured by the sum of squares of regression (SSR), and the *unexplained variation*, measured by the sum of squares of error (SSE). This relationship can be expressed in equation form as

$$SS_{yy} = SSR + SSE$$

If each term in the equation is divided by SS_{yy}, the resulting equation is

$$1 = \frac{SSR}{SS_{yy}} + \frac{SSE}{SS_{yy}}$$

The term r^2 is the proportion of the y variability that is explained by the regression model and represented here as

$$r^2 = \frac{SSR}{SS_{yy}}$$

Substituting this equation into the preceding relationship gives

$$1 = r^2 + \frac{SSE}{SS_{yy}}$$

Solving for r^2 yields formula (4.4).

COEFFICIENT OF DETERMINATION (4.4)	$$r^2 = 1 - \frac{SSE}{SS_{yy}} = 1 - \frac{SSE}{\Sigma y^2 - \dfrac{(\Sigma y)^2}{n}}$$

Note: $0 \leq r^2 \leq 1$

The value of r^2 for the airline cost example is solved as follows:

$$SSE = .31434$$

$$SS_{yy} = \Sigma y^2 - \frac{(\Sigma y)^2}{n} = 270.9251 - \frac{(56.69)^2}{12} = 3.11209$$

$$r^2 = 1 - \frac{SSE}{SS_{yy}} = 1 - \frac{.31434}{3.11209} = .899$$

That is, 89.9% of the variability of the cost of flying a Boeing 737 airplane on a commercial flight is explained by variations in the number of passengers. This result also means that 11.1% of the variance in airline flight cost, y, is unaccounted for by x or unexplained by the regression model.

The coefficient of determination can be solved for directly by using

$$r^2 = \frac{SSR}{SS_{yy}}$$

It can be shown through algebra that

$$SSR = b_1{}^2 SS_{xx}$$

From this equation, a computational formula for r^2 can be developed.

COMPUTATIONAL FORMULA FOR r^2	$$r^2 = \frac{b_1{}^2 SS_{xx}}{SS_{yy}}$$

For the airline cost example, $b_1 = .0407016$, $SS_{xx} = 1689$, and $SS_{yy} = 3.11209$. Us. computational formula for r^2 yields

$$r^2 = \frac{(.0407016)^2(1689)}{3.11209} = .899$$

DEMONSTRATION PROBLEM 4.4

Compute the coefficient of determination (r^2) for Demonstration Problem 4.1, in which a regression model was developed to predict the number of FTEs of a hospital by the number of beds.

Solution

$$SSE = 2448.6$$

$$SS_{yy} = 260,136 - \frac{(1692)^2}{12} = 21,564$$

$$r^2 = 1 - \frac{SSE}{SS_{yy}} = 1 - \frac{2448.6}{21,564} = .886$$

This regression model accounts for 88.6% of the variance in FTEs, leaving only 11.4% unexplained variance.

Using $SS_{xx} = 3838.667$ and $b_1 = 2.232$ from Demonstration Problem 4.1, we can solve for r^2 with the computational formula:

$$r^2 = \frac{b_1^2 SS_{xx}}{SS_{yy}} = \frac{(2.232)^2(3838.667)}{21,564} = .886$$

Relationship between r and r^2

Is r, the coefficient of correlation, related to r^2, the coefficient of determination in linear regression? The answer is yes: r^2 equals $(r)^2$. The coefficient of determination is the square of the coefficient of correlation. In Demonstration Problem 4.1, a regression model was developed to predict FTEs by number of hospital beds. The r^2 value for the model was .886. Taking the square root of this value yields $r = .941$, which is the correlation between the sample number of beds and FTEs. A word of caution here: Because r^2 is always positive, solving for r by taking $\sqrt{r^2}$ gives the correct magnitude of r but may give the wrong sign. The researcher must examine the sign of the slope of the regression line to determine whether a positive or negative relationship exists between the variables and then assign the appropriate sign to the correlation value.

4.5 PROBLEMS

4.26 Compute r^2 for Problem 4.19 (Problem 4.1). Discuss the value of r^2 obtained.

4.27 Compute r^2 for Problem 4.20 (Problem 4.2). Discuss the value of r^2 obtained.

4.28 Compute r^2 for Problem 4.21 (Problem 4.3). Discuss the value of r^2 obtained.

4.29 Compute r^2 for Problem 4.22 (Problem 4.4). Discuss the value of r^2 obtained.

4.30 Compute r^2 for Problem 4.23 (Problem 4.13). Discuss the value of r^2 obtained.

4.31 The Conference Board produces a Consumer Confidence Index (CCI) that reflects people's feelings about general business conditions, employment opportunities, and their own income prospects. Some researchers may feel that consumer confidence is a function of the median household income. Shown here are the CCIs for 9 years and the median household incomes for the same 9 years published by the U.S. Census Bureau. Determine the equation of the regression line to predict the CCI from the median household income. Compute the standard error of the estimate for this model. Compute the value of r^2. Does median household income appear to be a good predictor of the CCI? Why or why not?

CCI	Median Household Income ($1,000)
116.8	37.415
91.5	36.770
68.5	35.501
61.6	35.047
65.9	34.700
90.6	34.942
100.0	35.887
104.6	36.306
125.4	37.005

4.6 HYPOTHESIS TESTS FOR THE SLOPE OF THE REGRESSION MODEL AND TESTING THE OVERALL MODEL

Testing the Slope

A hypothesis test can be conducted on the sample slope of the regression model to determine whether the population slope is significantly different from zero. This test is another way to determine how well a regression model fits the data. Suppose a researcher decides that it is not worth the effort to develop a linear regression model to predict y from x. An alternative approach might be to average the y values and use $\bar{y}$ as the predictor of y for all values of x. For the airline cost example, instead of using number of passengers as the predictor, the researcher would use the average value of airline cost, $\bar{y}$, as the predictor. In this case the average value of y is

$$\bar{y} = \frac{56.69}{12} = 4.7242, \text{ or } \$4,724.20$$

Using this result as a model to predict y, if the number of passengers is 61, 70, or 95— or any other number—the predicted value of y is still 4.7242. Essentially, this approach fits the line of $\bar{y} = 4.7242$ through the data, which is a horizontal line with a slope of zero. Would a regression analysis offer anything more than the $\bar{y}$ model? Using this nonregression model (the $\bar{y}$ model) as a worst case, the researcher can analyze the regression line to determine whether it adds a more significant amount of predictability of y than does the $\bar{y}$ model. Because the slope of the $\bar{y}$ line is zero, one way to determine whether the regression line adds significant predictability is to test the population slope of the regression line to find out whether the slope is different from zero. As the slope of the regression line diverges from zero, the regression model is adding predictability that the $\bar{y}$ line is not generating. For this reason, testing the slope of the regression line to determine whether the slope is different from zero is important. If the slope is not different from zero, the regression line is doing nothing more than the $\bar{y}$ line in predicting y.

How does the researcher go about testing the slope of the regression line? Why not just examine the observed sample slope? For example, the slope of the regression line for the airline cost data is .0407. This value is obviously not zero. The problem is that this slope is obtained from a sample of 12 data points; and if another sample was taken, it is likely that a different slope would be obtained. For this reason, the population slope is statistically tested using the sample slope. The question is: If all the pairs of data points for the population were available, would the slope of that regression line be different from zero? Here the sample slope, b_1, is used as evidence to test whether the population slope is different from zero. The hypotheses for this test follow.

$$H_0: \beta_1 = 0$$
$$H_a: \beta_1 \neq 0$$

Note that this test is two-tailed. The null hypothesis can be rejected if the slope is either negative or positive. A negative slope indicates an inverse relationship between x and y. That is, larger values of x are related to smaller values of y, and vice versa. Both negative and positive slopes can be different from zero. To determine whether there is a significant positive relationship between two variables, the hypotheses would be one-tailed, or

$$H_0: \beta_1 = 0$$
$$H_a: \beta_1 > 0$$

To test for a significant negative relationship between two variables, the hypotheses also would be one-tailed, or

$$H_0: \beta_1 = 0$$
$$H_a: \beta_1 < 0$$

In each case, testing the null hypothesis involves a t test of the slope.

***t* TEST OF SLOPE**

$$t = \frac{b_1 - \beta_1}{s_b}$$

where

$$s_b = \frac{s_e}{\sqrt{SS_{xx}}}$$

$$s_e = \sqrt{\frac{SSE}{n-2}}$$

$$SS_{xx} = \Sigma x^2 - \frac{(\Sigma x)^2}{n}$$

β_1 = the hypothesized slope
df = $n - 2$

The test of the slope of the regression line for the airline cost regression model for $\alpha = .05$ follows. The regression line derived for the data is

$$\hat{y} = 1.57 + .0407x$$

The sample slope is $.0407 = b_1$. The value of s_e is .1773, $\Sigma x = 930$, $\Sigma x^2 = 73{,}764$, and $n = 12$. The hypotheses are

$$H_0: \beta_1 = 0$$
$$H_a: \beta_1 \neq 0$$

The df = $n - 2 = 12 - 2 = 10$. As this test is two-tailed, $\alpha/2 = .025$. The table t value is $t_{.025,10} = \pm 2.228$. The observed t value for this sample slope is

$$t = \frac{.0407 - 0}{.1773 \Big/ \sqrt{73{,}764 - \frac{(930)^2}{12}}} = 9.43$$

As shown in Figure 4.12, the t value calculated from the sample slope falls in the rejection region. The null hypothesis that the population slope is zero is rejected. This linear regression model is adding significantly more predictive information to the $\bar{y}$ model (no regression).

It is desirable to reject the null hypothesis in testing the slope of the regression model. In rejecting the null hypothesis of a zero population slope, we are stating that the regression model is adding something to the explanation of the variation of the dependent variable that the average value of y model does not. Failure to reject the null hypothesis in this test causes the researcher to conclude that the regression model has no predictability of the dependent variable, and the model, therefore, has little or no use.

FIGURE 4.12

t Test of Slope from
Airline Cost Example

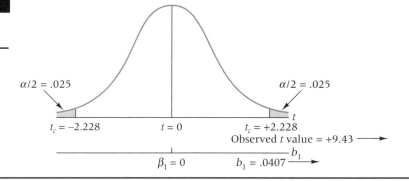

$\alpha/2 = .025$　　　　　　　　　　　　$\alpha/2 = .025$

$t_c = -2.228$　　　　$t = 0$　　　　$t_c = +2.228$　t

Observed *t* value = +9.43 ⟶

$\beta_1 = 0$　　　　$b_1 = .0407$ ⟶ b_1

STATISTICS IN BUSINESS TODAY

Predicting the Price of an SUV

What variables are good predictors of the base price of a new car? In a *Wall Street Journal* article on the 2003 Ford Expedition, data are displayed for five variables on five different makes of large SUVs. The variables are base price, engine horsepower, weight (in pounds), towing capacity (in pounds), and city EPA mileage. The SUV makes are Ford Expedition Eddie Bauer 4×4, Toyota Sequoia Limited, Chevrolet Tahoe LT, Acura MDX, and Dodge Durango R/T. The base prices of these five models ranged from $34,700 to $42,725. Suppose a business researcher wanted to develop a regression model to predict the base price of these cars. What variable would be the strongest predictor and how strong would the prediction be?

Using a correlation matrix constructed from the data for the five variables, it was determined that weight was most correlated with base price and had the greatest potential as a predictor. Towing capacity had the second highest correlation with base price, followed by city EPA mileage, and horsepower. City EPA mileage was negatively related to base price indicating that the more expensive SUVs tended to be "gas guzzlers."

A regression model was developed using weight as a predictor of base price. The MINITAB output from the data follows. Excel output contains similar items.

Regression Analysis: Base Price versus Weight

```
The regression equation is
Base Price = 10140 + 5.77 Weight

Predictor  Coef   SE Coef     T      P
Constant  10140     8473   1.20  0.317
Weight    5.769    1.679   3.44  0.041
S = 1699  R-Sq = 79.7%  R-Sq(adj) = 73.0%
```

Note that the r^2 for this model is almost 80% and that the *t* statistic is significant at $\alpha = .05$. In the regression equation, the slope indicates that for every pound of weight increase there is a $5.77 increase in the price. The *y* intercept indicates that if the SUV weighed nothing at all, it would still cost $10,140! The standard error of the estimate is $1,699.

Regression models were developed for each of the other possible predictor variables. Towing capacity was the next best predictor variable producing an r^2 of 31.4%. City EPA mileage produced an r^2 of 20%, and horsepower produced an r^2 of 6.9%.

Source: Adapted from Jonathan Welsh, "The Biggest Station Wagon of Them All," *The Wall Street Journal*, 7 June 2002, p. W15C.

DEMONSTRATION PROBLEM 4.5

Test the slope of the regression model developed in Demonstration Problem 4.1 to predict the number of FTEs in a hospital from the number of beds to determine whether there is a significant positive slope. Use $\alpha = .01$.

Solution

The hypotheses for this problem are

$$H_0: \beta_1 = 0$$
$$H_a: \beta_1 > 0$$

The level of significance is .01. With 12 pairs of data, df = 10. The critical table *t* value is $t_{.01,10} = 2.764$. The regression line equation for this problem is

$$\hat{y} = 30.888 + 2.232x$$

The sample slope, b_1, is 2.232, and $s_e = 15.65$, $\Sigma x = 592$, $\Sigma x^2 = 33,044$, and $n = 12$. The observed *t* value for the sample slope is

$$t = \frac{2.232 - 0}{15.65 \bigg/ \sqrt{33,044 - \dfrac{(592)^2}{12}}} = 8.84$$

The observed t value (8.84) is in the rejection region because it is greater than the critical table t value of 2.764. The null hypothesis is rejected. The population slope for this regression line is significantly different from zero in the positive direction. This regression model is adding significant predictability over the $\bar{Y}$ model.

Testing the Overall Model

It is common in regression analysis to compute an F test to determine the overall significance of the model. Most computer software packages include the F test and its associated ANOVA table as standard regression output. In multiple regression (Chapters 5 and 6), this test determines whether at least one of the regression coefficients (from multiple predictors) is different from zero. Simple regression provides only one predictor and only one regression coefficient to test. Because the regression coefficient is the slope of the regression line, the F test for overall significance is testing the same thing as the t test in simple regression. The hypotheses being tested in simple regression by the F test for overall significance are

$$H_0: \beta_1 = 0$$
$$H_a: \beta_1 \neq 0$$

In the case of simple regression analysis, $F = t^2$. Thus, for the airline cost example, the F value is

$$F = t^2 = (9.43)^2 = 88.92$$

The F value is computed directly by

$$F = \frac{SS_{reg} \big/ df_{reg}}{SS_{err} \big/ df_{err}} = \frac{MS_{reg}}{MS_{err}}$$

where

$$df_{reg} = k$$
$$df_{err} = n - k - 1$$
$$k = \text{the number of independent variables}$$

The values of the sum of squares (SS), degrees of freedom (df), and mean squares (MS) are obtained from the analysis of variance table, which is produced with other regression statistics as standard output from statistical software packages. Shown here is the analysis of variance table produced by MINITAB for the airline cost example.

```
Analysis of Variance
Source          DF       SS      MS       F       p
Regression       1   2.7980  2.7980   89.09   0.000
Residual Error  10   0.3141  0.0314
Total           11   3.1121
```

The F value for the airline cost example is calculated from the analysis of variance table information as

$$F = \frac{2.7980 \big/ 1}{.3141 \big/ 10} = \frac{2.7980}{.03141} = 89.09$$

The difference between this value (89.09) and the value obtained by squaring the t statistic (88.92) is due to rounding error. The probability of obtaining an F value this large or larger by chance if there is no regression prediction in this model is .000 according to the ANOVA output (the p-value). This output value means it is highly unlikely that the population slope is zero and that there is no prediction due to regression from this model given the sample statistics obtained. Hence, it is highly likely that this regression model adds significant predictability of the dependent variable.

Note from the ANOVA table that the degrees of freedom due to regression are equal to 1. Simple regression models have only one independent variable; therefore, $k = 1$. The degrees of freedom error in simple regression analysis is always $n - k - 1 = n - 1 - 1 = n - 2$. With the degrees of freedom due to regression (1) as the numerator degrees of freedom and the degrees of freedom due to error $(n - 2)$ as the denominator degrees of freedom, Table A.4 can be used to obtain the critical F value $(F_{\alpha,1,n-2})$ to help make the hypothesis-testing decision about the overall regression model if the p-value of F is not given in the computer output. This critical F value is always found in the right tail of the distribution. In simple regression, the relationship between the critical t value to test the slope and the critical F value of overall significance is

$$t^2_{\alpha/2,\, n-2} = F_{\alpha,1,n-2}$$

For the airline cost example with a two-tailed test and $\alpha = .05$, the critical value of $t_{.025,10}$ is ± 2.228 and the critical value of $F_{.05,1,10}$ is 4.96.

$$t^2_{.025,10} = (\pm 2.228)^2 = 4.96 = F_{.05,1,10}$$

4.6 PROBLEMS

4.32   Test the slope of the regression line determined in Problem 4.1. Use $\alpha = .05$.

4.33   Test the slope of the regression line determined in Problem 4.2. Use $\alpha = .01$.

4.34   Test the slope of the regression line determined in Problem 4.3. Use $\alpha = .10$.

4.35   Test the slope of the regression line determined in Problem 4.4. Use a 5% level of significance.

4.36   Shown here is an incomplete analysis of variance table produced by using MINITAB for a simple regression analysis. Compute the value of F and determine whether it is statistically significant by using Table A.4. From this value, compute the value of t. What is the statistical significance of the overall model? Is the slope of the regression line significant? Explain.

```
Analysis of Variance

Source        DF      SS     MS    F
Regression     1    5165
Error          7   18554
Total          8   23718
```

4.37   Study the following analysis of variance table, which was generated from a simple regression analysis. Discuss the F test of the overall model. Determine the value of t and test the slope of the regression line.

```
Analysis of Variance

Source        DF       SS       MS       F      p
Regression     1    116.65   116.65    8.26   0.021
Error          8    112.95    14.12
Total          9    229.60
```

4.7 ESTIMATION

One of the main uses of regression analysis is as a prediction tool. If the regression function is a good model, the researcher can use the regression equation to determine values of the dependent variable from various values of the independent variable. For example, financial brokers would like to have a model with which they could predict the selling price of a particular stock on a certain day by a variable such as unemployment rate or producer price index. Marketing managers would like to have a site location model with which they could predict the sales volume of a new location by variables such as population density or number of competitors. The airline cost example presents a regression model that has the potential to predict the cost of flying an airplane by the number of passengers.

In simple regression analysis, a point estimate prediction of y can be made by substituting the associated value of x into the regression equation and solving for y. From the airline cost example, if the number of passengers is $x = 73$, the predicted cost of the airline flight can be computed by substituting the x value into the regression equation determined in Section 4.2:

$$\hat{y} = 1.57 + .0407x = 1.57 + .0407(73) = 4.5411$$

The point estimate of the predicted cost is 4.5411 or $4,541.10.

Confidence Intervals to Estimate the Conditional Mean of y: $\mu_{y|x}$

Although a point estimate is often of interest to the researcher, the regression line is determined by a sample set of points; and if a different sample is taken, a different line will result, yielding a different point estimate. Hence computing a *confidence interval* for the estimation is often useful. Because for any value of x (independent variable) there can be many values of y (dependent variable), one type of **confidence interval** is *an estimate of the average value of y for a given x*. This average value of y is denoted $E(y_x)$—the expected value of y and can be computed using formula (4.5).

CONFIDENCE INTERVAL TO ESTIMATE $E(y_x)$ FOR A GIVEN VALUE OF x (4.5)	$\hat{y} \pm t_{\alpha/2, n-2} s_e \sqrt{\dfrac{1}{n} + \dfrac{(x_0 - \bar{x})^2}{SS_{xx}}}$ where x_0 = a particular value of x $SS_{xx} = \Sigma x^2 - \dfrac{(\Sigma x)^2}{n}$

The application of this formula can be illustrated with construction of a 95% confidence interval to estimate the average value of y (airline cost) for the airline cost example when x (number of passengers) is 73. For a 95% confidence interval, $\alpha = .05$ and $\alpha/2 = .025$. The df $= n - 2 = 12 - 2 = 10$. The table t value is $t_{.025,10} = 2.228$. Other needed values for this problem, which were solved for previously, are

$$s_e = .1773 \quad \Sigma x = 930 \quad \bar{x} = 77.5 \quad \Sigma x^2 = 73,764$$

For $x_0 = 73$, the value of $\hat{y}$ is 4.5411. The computed confidence interval for the average value of y, $E(y_{73})$, is

$$4.5411 \pm (2.228)(.1773) \sqrt{\dfrac{1}{12} + \dfrac{(73 - 77.5)^2}{73,764 - \dfrac{(930)^2}{12}}} = 4.5411 \pm .1220$$

$$4.4191 \leq E(y_{73}) \leq 4.6631$$

That is, with 95% confidence the average value of y for $x = 73$ is between 4.4191 and 4.6631.

Table 4.5 shows confidence intervals computed for the airline cost example for several values of x to estimate the average value of y. Note that as x values get farther from the mean x value (77.5), the confidence intervals get wider; as the x values get closer to the mean, the confidence intervals narrow. The reason is that the numerator of the second term under the radical sign approaches zero as the value of x nears the mean and increases as x departs from the mean.

Prediction Intervals to Estimate a Single Value of y

A second type of interval in regression estimation is a **prediction interval** to *estimate a single value of y for a given value of x.*

PREDICTION INTERVAL TO ESTIMATE y FOR A GIVEN VALUE OF x (4.6)	$\hat{y} \pm t_{\alpha/2, n-2} s_e \sqrt{1 + \dfrac{1}{n} + \dfrac{(x_0 - \bar{x})^2}{SS_{xx}}}$ where x_0 = a particular value of x $SS_{xx} = \Sigma x^2 - \dfrac{(\Sigma x)^2}{n}$

TABLE 4.5	x	Confidence Interval	
Confidence Intervals to	62	$4.0934 \pm .1876$	3.9058 to 4.2810
Estimate the Average Value of y	68	$4.3376 \pm .1461$	4.1915 to 4.4837
for Some x Values in the Airline	73	$4.5411 \pm .1220$	4.4191 to 4.6631
Cost Example	85	$5.0295 \pm .1349$	4.8946 to 5.1644
	90	$5.2230 \pm .1656$	5.0674 to 5.3986

Formula (4.6) is virtually the same as formula (4.5), except for the additional value of 1 under the radical. This additional value widens the prediction interval to estimate a single value of y from the confidence interval to estimate the average value of y. This result seems logical because the average value of y is toward the middle of a group of y values. Thus the confidence interval to estimate the average need not be as wide as the prediction interval produced by formula (4.6), which takes into account all the y values for a given x.

A 95% prediction interval can be computed to estimate the single value of y for $x = 73$ from the airline cost example by using formula (4.6). The same values used to construct the confidence interval to estimate the average value of y are used here.

$$t_{.025,10} = 2.228, s_e = .1773, \Sigma x = 930, \bar{x} = 77.5, \Sigma x^2 = 73,764$$

For $x_0 = 73$, the value of $\hat{y} = 4.5411$. The computed prediction interval for the single value of y is

$$4.5411 \pm (2.228)(.1773)\sqrt{1 + \frac{1}{12} + \frac{(73 - 77.5)^2}{73,764 - \frac{(930)^2}{12}}} = 4.5411 \pm .4134$$

$$4.1277 \leq y \leq 4.9545$$

Prediction intervals can be obtained by using the computer. Shown in Figure 4.13 is the computer output for the airline cost example. The output displays the predicted value for $x = 73$ ($\hat{y} = 4.5411$), a 95% confidence interval for the average value of y for $x = 73$, and a 95% prediction interval for a single value of y for $x = 73$. Note that the resulting values are virtually the same as those calculated in this section.

Figure 4.14 displays MINITAB confidence intervals for various values of x for the average y value and the prediction intervals for a single y value. Note that the intervals flare out toward the ends, as the values of x depart from the average x value. Note also that the intervals for a single y value are always wider than the intervals for the average y value for any given value of x.

An examination of the prediction interval formula to estimate y for a given value of x explains why the intervals flare out.

$$\hat{y} \pm t_{\alpha/2,n-2} s_e \sqrt{1 + \frac{1}{n} + \frac{(x_0 - \bar{x})^2}{SS_{xx}}}$$

As we enter different values of x_0 from the regression analysis into the equation, the only thing that changes in the equation is $(x_0 - \bar{x})^2$. This expression increases as individual values of x_0 get farther from the mean, resulting in an increase in the width of the interval. The interval is narrower for values of x_0 nearer $\bar{x}$ and wider for values of x_0 farther from $\bar{x}$. A comparison of formulas (4.5) and (4.6) reveals them to be identical except that formula (4.6)—to compute a prediction interval to estimate y for a given value of x—con-

FIGURE 4.13

MINITAB Output for
Prediction Intervals

```
Fit      StDev Fit  95.0% CI          95.0% PI
4.5410   0.0547     (4.4191, 4.6629)  (4.1278, 4.9543)
```

FIGURE 4.14

MINITAB Intervals
for Estimation

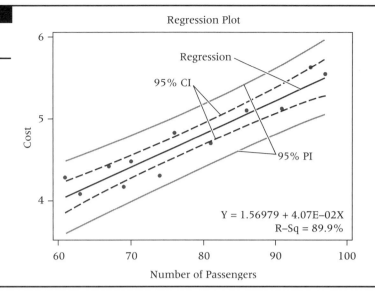

tains a 1 under the radical sign. This distinction ensures that formula (4.6) will yield wider intervals than (4.5) for otherwise identical data.

Caution: *A regression line is determined from a sample of points. The line, the r^2, the s_e, and the confidence intervals change for different sets of sample points. That is, the linear relationship developed for a set of points does not necessarily hold for values of x outside the domain of those used to establish the model. In the airline cost example, the domain of x values (number of passengers) varied from 61 to 97. The regression model developed from these points may not be valid for flights of say 40, 50, or 100 because the regression model was not constructed with x values of those magnitudes. However, decision makers sometimes extrapolate regression results to values of x beyond the domain of those used to develop the formulas (often in time-series sales forecasting). Understanding the limitations of this type of use of regression analysis is essential.*

**DEMONSTRATION
PROBLEM 4.6**

Construct a 95% confidence interval to estimate the average value of y (FTEs) for Demonstration Problem 4.1 when $x = 40$ beds. Then construct a 95% prediction interval to estimate the single value of y for $x = 40$ beds.

Solution

For a 95% confidence interval, $\alpha = .05$, $n = 12$, and df $= 10$. The table t value is $t_{.025,10} = 2.228$; $s_e = 15.65$, $\Sigma x = 592$, $\bar{x} = 49.33$, and $\Sigma x^2 = 33,044$. For $x_0 = 40$, $\hat{y} = 120.17$. The computed confidence interval for the average value of y is

$$120.17 \pm (2.228)(15.65)\sqrt{\frac{1}{12} + \frac{(40 - 49.33)^2}{33,044 - \frac{(592)^2}{12}}} = 120.17 \pm 11.35$$

$$108.82 \leq E(y_{40}) \leq 131.52$$

With 95% confidence, the statement can be made that the average number of FTEs for a hospital with 40 beds is between 108.82 and 131.52.

The computed prediction interval for the single value of y is

$$120.17 \pm (2.228)(15.65)\sqrt{1 + \frac{1}{12} + \frac{(40 - 49.33)^2}{33,044 - \frac{(592)^2}{12}}} = 120.17 \pm 36.67$$

$$83.5 \leq y \leq 156.84$$

With 95% confidence, the statement can be made that a single number of FTEs for a hospital with 40 beds is between 83.5 and 156.84. Obviously this interval is much wider than the 95% confidence interval for the average value of y for $x = 40$.

The following MINITAB graph depicts the 95% interval bands for both the average y value and the single y values for all 12 x values in this problem. Note once again the flaring out of the bands near the extreme values of x.

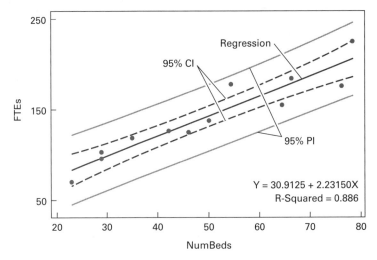

4.7 PROBLEMS

4.38 Construct a 95% confidence interval for the average value of y for Problem 4.1. Use $x = 25$.

4.39 Construct a 90% prediction interval for a single value of y for Problem 4.2; use $x = 100$. Construct a 90% prediction interval for a single value of y for Problem 4.2; use $x = 130$. Compare the results. Which prediction interval is greater? Why?

4.40 Construct a 98% confidence interval for the average value of y for Problem 4.3; use $x = 20$. Construct a 98% prediction interval for a single value of y for Problem 4.3; use $x = 20$. Which is wider? Why?

4.41 Construct a 99% confidence interval for the average bond rate in Problem 4.4 for a prime interest rate of 10%. Discuss the meaning of this confidence interval.

4.8 INTERPRETING THE OUTPUT

Although manual computations can be done, most regression problems are analyzed by using a computer. In this section, computer output from both MINITAB and Excel will be presented and discussed.

At the top of the MINITAB regression output, shown in Figure 4.15, is the regression equation. Next is a table that describes the model in more detail. "Coef" stands for coefficient of the regression terms. The coefficient of "Number of Passengers," the x variable, is 0.040702. This value is equal to the slope of the regression line and is reflected in the regression equation. The coefficient shown next to the constant term (1.5698) is the value of the constant, which is the y intercept and also a part of the regression equation. The "T" values are a t test for the slope and a t test for the intercept or constant. (We generally do not interpret the t test for the constant.) The t value for the slope, $t = 9.44$ with an associated probability of .000, is the same as the value obtained manually in Section 4.6. Because the probability of the t value is given, the p-value method can be used to interpret the t value.

The next row of output is the standard error of the estimate s_e, S = 0.1772; the coefficient of determination, r^2, R-Sq = 89.9%; and the adjusted value of r^2, R-Sq(adj) = 88.9%.

FIGURE 4.15

MINITAB Regression Analysis of the Airline Cost Example

Regression Analysis: Cost versus Passengers

```
The regression equation is
Cost = 1.57 + 0.0407 Passengers

Predictor        Coef    SE Coef     T       P
Constant       1.5698    0.3381    4.64    0.001
Passenge      0.040702  0.004312   9.44    0.000
S = 0.1772   R-Sq = 89.9%   R-Sq(adj) = 88.9%

Analysis of Variance
Source             DF       SS       MS       F        P
Regression          1    2.7980   2.7980   89.09   0.000
Residual Error     10    0.3141   0.0314
Total              11    3.1121

Obs    Passenge   Cost     Fit     SE Fit   Residual   St Resid
 1       61.0    4.2800   4.0526   0.0876    0.2274      1.48
 2       63.0    4.0800   4.1340   0.0808   -0.0540     -0.34
 3       67.0    4.4200   4.2968   0.0683    0.1232      0.75
 4       69.0    4.1700   4.3782   0.0629   -0.2082     -1.26
 5       70.0    4.4800   4.4189   0.0605    0.0611      0.37
 6       74.0    4.3000   4.5817   0.0533   -0.2817     -1.67
 7       76.0    4.8200   4.6631   0.0516    0.1569      0.93
 8       81.0    4.7000   4.8666   0.0533   -0.1666     -0.99
 9       86.0    5.1100   5.0701   0.0629    0.0399      0.24
10       91.0    5.1300   5.2736   0.0775   -0.1436     -0.90
11       95.0    5.6400   5.4364   0.0912    0.2036      1.34
12       97.0    5.5600   5.5178   0.0984    0.0422      0.29
```

(Adjusted r^2 will be discussed in Chapter 5.) Following these items is the analysis of variance table. Note that the value of $F = 89.09$ is used to test the overall model of the regression line. The final item of the output is the predicted value and the corresponding residual for each pair of points.

Although the Excel regression output, shown in Figure 4.16 for Demonstration Problem 4.1, is somewhat different from the MINITAB output, the same essential regression features are present. The regression equation is found under Coefficients at the bottom of ANOVA. The slope or coefficient of x is 2.2315 and the y intercept is 30.9125. The standard error of the estimate for the hospital problem is given as the fourth statistic under Regression Statistics at the top of the output, Standard Error = 15.6491. The r^2 value is given as 0.886 on the second line. The t test for the slope is found under t Stat near the bottom of the ANOVA section on the "Number of beds" (x variable) row, $t = 8.83$. Adjacent to the t Stat is the P-value, which is the probability of the t statistic occurring by chance if the null hypothesis is true. For this slope, the probability shown is 0.000005. The ANOVA table is in the middle of the output with the F value having the same probability as the t statistic, 0.000005, and equaling t^2. The predicted values and the residuals are shown in the Residual Output section.

Predicting the Annual Sales Volume

Chapter 4 contains techniques for bivariate regression. Using these techniques along with the coefficient of correlation, it is possible to measure the strength of the relationship between two variables. The Decision Dilemma posed several possible variables that might

FIGURE 4.16

Excel Regression Output for
Demonstration Problem 4.1

	A	B	C	D	E	F
1	SUMMARY OUTPUT					
2	Regression Statistics					
3	Multiple R	0.942				
4	R Square	0.886				
5	Adjusted R Square	0.875				
6	Standard Error	15.6491				
7	Observations	12				
8						
9	ANOVA					
10		df	SS	MS	F	Significance F
11	Regression	1	19115.0632	19115.0632	78.05	.000005
12	Residual	10	2448.9368	244.8937		
13	Total	11	21564			
14						
15		Coefficients	Standard Error	t Stat	P-value	
16	Intercepts	30.9125	13.2542	2.33	0.041888	
17	Beds	2.2315	0.2526	8.83	0.000005	
18						
19	RESIDUAL OUTPUT					
20	Observation	Predicted FTEs	Residuals			
21	1	82.237	−13.237			
22	2	95.626	−0.626			
23	3	95.626	6.374			
24	4	109.015	8.985			
25	5	124.636	1.364			
26	6	133.562	−8.562			
27	7	142.488	−4.488			
28	8	151.414	26.586			
29	9	173.729	−17.729			
30	10	178.192	5.808			
31	11	200.507	−24.507			
32	12	204.970	20.030			

be related to the total annual sales volume of a real estate brokerage firm. Some of the more promising variables are number of offices, size of sales force, and number of houses/properties sold. In particular, data were given on total annual sales volume and average price of a sale for the top 25 firms in the United States for a recent year. A regression model can be developed in an attempt to predict sales volume (y) by average price (x). What are the results of such an effort? Both the Excel output and MINITAB output for a regression analysis to predict sales volume by average price follow.

Excel Regression Output

	A	B	C	D	E	F
1	SUMMARY OUTPUT					
2	Regression Statistics					
3	Multiple R	0.129				
4	R Square	0.017				
5	Adjusted R Square	−0.026				
6	Standard Error	9719				
7	Observations	25				
8						
9	ANOVA					
10		df	SS	MS	F	Significance F
11	Regression	1	36477544.53	36477544.53	0.39	0.540
12	Residual	23	2172553428	94458844.7		
13	Total	24	2209030973			
14						
15		Coefficients	Standard Error	t Stat	P-value	
16	Intercept	2357.92	5426.17	0.43	0.668	
17	Average Price	15.90	25.58	0.62	0.540	

MINITAB Regression Output:

Regression Analysis: Sales Volume versus Average Price

```
The regression equation is
Sales Volume = 2358 + 15.9 Average Price
Predictor           Coef          SE Coef      T       P
Constant            2358             5426    0.43   0.668
Average            15.90            25.58    0.62   0.540
S = 9719    R-Sq = 1.7%   R-Sq(adj) = 0.0%
Analysis of Variance
Source             DF          SS          MS      F      P
Regression          1    36477545    36477545   0.39   0.540
Residual Error     23  2172553428    94458845
Total              24  2209030973
```

In studying the regression output, we find several indicators that tell us the model is weak. The r^2 value ($.017 = 1.7\%$) is almost zero showing virtually no predictability in the model. In addition, the value of F yields a p-value of .540, indicating no overall significance in the predictability of this model. The standard error of the estimate is more than \$9.7 billion, which is more than all but two of the companies' annual sales volume.

This example shows how a regression model can be made to fit virtually any two variables of data. It becomes imperative that the researcher is able to study the output and determine the strength of the predictability of the model (if any at all). Presenting this regression model as a way to predict the overall sales volume of a real estate firm would be a misuse of statistics. The student is encouraged to find other data that are more useful in establishing relationships between total sales volume in the real estate industry and other variables.

ETHICAL CONSIDERATIONS

Regression analysis offers several opportunities for unethical behavior. Business researchers who knowingly violate the assumptions underlying statistical techniques are acting unethically. Regression analysis requires equal error variance and independence of error terms. Through the use of residual plots and other statistical techniques, a researcher can search to determine whether such assumptions are being met. To present a regression model as fact when the assumptions underlying regression are being grossly violated is unethical behavior.

Another ethical problem that arises in regression analysis is using the regression model to predict values of the independent variable that are outside the domain of values used to develop the model. The airline cost model used in this chapter was built with between 61 and 97 passengers. A linear relationship appeared to be evident between flight costs and number of passengers over this domain. This model is not guaranteed to fit values outside the domain of 61 to 97 passengers, however. In fact, either a nonlinear relationship or no relationship may be present between flight costs and number of passengers if values from outside this domain are included in the model-building process. It is a mistake and probably unethical behavior to make claims for a regression model outside the perview of the domain of values for which the model was developed.

SUMMARY

Regression is a procedure that produces a mathematical model (function) that can be used to predict one variable by other variables. Simple regression is bivariate (two variables) and linear (only a line fit is attempted). Simple regression analysis produces a model that attempts to predict a y variable, referred to as the dependent variable, by an x variable, referred to as the independent variable. The general form of the equation of the simple regression line is the slope-intercept equation of a line. The equation of the simple regression model consists of a slope of the line as a coefficient of x and a y intercept value as a constant.

After the equation of the line has been developed, several statistics are available that can be used to determine how well the line fits the data. Using the historical data values of x, predicted values of y (denoted as $\hat{y}$) can be calculated by inserting values of x into the regression equation. The predicted values can then be compared to the actual values of y to determine how well the regression equation fits the known data. The difference between a specific y value and its associated predicted y value is called the residual or error of prediction. Examination of the residuals can offer insight into the magnitude of the errors produced by a model. In addition, residual analysis can be used to help determine whether the assumptions underlying the regression analysis have been met. Specifically, graphs of the residuals can reveal (1) lack of linearity, (2) lack of homogeneity of error variance, and (3) independence of error terms. Geometrically, the residuals are the vertical distances from the y values to the regression line. Because the equation that yields the regression line is derived in such a way that the line is in the geometric middle of the points, the sum of the residuals is zero.

A single value of error measurement called the standard error of the estimate, s_e, can be computed. The standard error of the estimate is the standard deviation of error of a model. The value of s_e can be used as a single guide to the magnitude of the error produced by the regression model as opposed to examining all the residuals.

Another widely used statistic for testing the strength of a regression model is r^2, or the coefficient of determination. The coefficient of determination is the proportion of total variance of the y variable accounted for or predicted by x. The coefficient of determination ranges from 0 to 1. The higher the r^2 is, the stronger is the predictability of the model.

Testing to determine whether the slope of the regression line is different from zero is another way to judge the fit of the regression model to the data. If the population slope of the regression line is not different from zero, the regression model is not adding significant predictability to the dependent variable. A t statistic is used to test the significance of the slope. The overall significance of the regression model can be tested using an F statistic. In simple regression, because only one predictor is present, this test accomplishes the same thing as the t test of the slope and $F = t^2$.

One of the most prevalent uses of a regression model is to predict the values of y for given values of x. Recognizing that the predicted value is often not the same as the actual value, a confidence interval has been developed to yield a range within which the mean y value for a given x should fall. A prediction interval for a single y value for a given x value also is specified. This second interval is wider because it allows for the wide diversity of individual values, whereas the confidence interval for the mean y value reflects only the range of average y values for a given x.

KEY TERMS

coefficient of determination (r^2)

confidence interval

dependent variable

deterministic model

heteroscedasticity

homoscedasticity

independent variable

least squares analysis

outliers

prediction interval

probabilistic model

regression analysis

residual

residual plot

scatter plot

simple regression

standard error of the estimate (s_e)

sum of squares of error (SSE)

FORMULAS

Equation of the simple regression line

$$\hat{y} = \beta_0 + \beta_1 x$$

Sum of squares

$$SS_{xx} = \Sigma x^2 - \frac{(\Sigma x)^2}{n}$$

$$SS_{yy} = \Sigma y^2 - \frac{(\Sigma y)^2}{n}$$

$$SS_{xy} = \Sigma xy - \frac{\Sigma x \Sigma y}{n}$$

Slope of the regression line

$$b_1 = \frac{\Sigma(x-\bar{x})(y-\bar{y})}{\Sigma(x-\bar{x})^2} = \frac{\Sigma xy - n\bar{x}\bar{y}}{\Sigma x^2 - n\bar{x}^2} = \frac{\Sigma xy - \frac{(\Sigma x)(\Sigma y)}{n}}{\Sigma x^2 - \frac{(\Sigma x)^2}{n}}$$

y intercept of the regression line

$$b_0 = \bar{y} - b_1\bar{x} = \frac{\Sigma y}{n} - b_1\frac{(\Sigma x)}{n}$$

Sum of Squares of Error

$$\text{SSE} = \Sigma(y - \hat{y})^2 = \Sigma y^2 - b_0 \Sigma y - b_1 \Sigma xy$$

Standard error of the estimate

$$s_e = \sqrt{\frac{\text{SSE}}{n-2}}$$

Coefficient of determination

$$r^2 = 1 - \frac{\text{SSE}}{\text{SS}_{yy}} = 1 - \frac{\text{SSE}}{\Sigma y^2 - \frac{(\Sigma y)^2}{n}}$$

Computational formula for r^2

$$r^2 = \frac{b_1{}^2 \text{SS}_{xx}}{\text{SS}_{yy}}$$

t test of slope

$$t = \frac{b_1 - \beta_1}{s_b}$$

$$s_b = \frac{s_e}{\sqrt{\text{SS}_{xx}}}$$

Confidence interval to estimate $E(y_x)$ for a given value of x

$$\hat{y} \pm t_{\alpha/2, n-2} s_e \sqrt{\frac{1}{n} + \frac{(x_0 - \bar{x})^2}{\text{SS}_{xx}}}$$

Prediction interval to estimate y for a given value of x

$$\hat{y} \pm t_{\alpha/2, n-2} s_e \sqrt{1 + \frac{1}{n} + \frac{(x_0 - \bar{x})^2}{\text{SS}_{xx}}}$$

SUPPLEMENTARY PROBLEMS

CALCULATING THE STATISTICS

4.42 Use the following data for parts (a) through (f).

x	5	7	3	16	12	9
y	8	9	11	27	15	13

a. Determine the equation of the least squares regression line to predict y by x.
b. Using the x values, solve for the predicted values of y and the residuals.
c. Solve for s_e.
d. Solve for r^2.
e. Test the slope of the regression line. Use $\alpha = .01$.
f. Comment on the results determined in parts (b) through (e), and make a statement about the fit of the line.

4.43 Use the following data for parts (a) through (g).

x	53	47	41	50	58	62	45	60
y	5	5	7	4	10	12	3	11

a. Determine the equation of the simple regression line to predict y from x.
b. Using the x values, solve for the predicted values of y and the residuals.
c. Solve for SSE.
d. Calculate the standard error of the estimate.
e. Determine the coefficient of determination.
f. Test the slope of the regression line. Assume $\alpha = .05$. What do you conclude about the slope?
g. Comment on parts (d) and (e).

4.44 If you were to develop a regression line to predict y by x, what value would the coefficient of determination have?

x	213	196	184	202	221	247
y	76	65	62	68	71	75

4.45 Determine the equation of the least squares regression line to predict y from the following data.

x	47	94	68	73	80	49	52	61
y	14	40	34	31	36	19	20	21

a. Construct a 95% confidence interval to estimate the mean y value for $x = 60$.
b. Construct a 95% prediction interval to estimate an individual y value for $x = 70$.
c. Interpret the results obtained in parts (a) and (b).

TESTING YOUR UNDERSTANDING

4.46 A manager of a car dealership believes there is a relationship between the number of salespeople on duty and the number of cars sold. Suppose the following sample is used to develop a simple regression model to predict the number of cars sold by the number of salespeople. Solve for r^2 and explain what r^2 means in this problem.

Week	Number of Cars Sold	Number of Salespeople
1	79	6
2	64	6
3	49	4
4	23	2
5	52	3

4.47 Executives of a video rental chain want to predict the success of a potential new store. The company's researcher begins by gathering information on number of rentals and average family income from several of the chain's present outlets.

Rentals	Average Family Income ($1,000)
710	65
529	43
314	29
504	47
619	52
428	50
317	46
205	29
468	31
545	43
607	49
694	64

Develop a regression model to predict the number of rentals per day by the average family income. Comment on the output.

4.48 It seems logical that restaurant chains with more units (restaurants) would have greater sales. This assumption is mitigated, however, by several possibilities: some units may be more profitable than others, some units may be larger, some units may serve more meals, some units may serve more expensive meals, and so on. The data shown here were published by Technomic. Perform a simple regression analysis to predict a restaurant chain's sales by its number of units. How strong is the relationship?

Chain	Sales ($ billions)	Number of Units (1,000)
McDonald's	17.1	12.4
Burger King	7.9	7.5
Taco Bell	4.8	6.8
Pizza Hut	4.7	8.7
Wendy's	4.6	4.6
KFC	4.0	5.1
Subway	2.9	11.2
Dairy Queen	2.7	5.1
Hardee's	2.7	2.9

4.49 According to the National Marine Fisheries Service, the current landings in millions of pounds of fish by U.S. fleets are almost double what they were in the 1970s. In other words, fishing has not faded as an industry. However, the growth of this industry has varied by region as shown in the following data. Some regions have remained relatively constant, the South Atlantic region has dropped in pounds caught, and the Pacific-Alaska region has grown more than threefold.

Fisheries	1977	2000
New England	581	571
Mid-Atlantic	213	220
Chesapeake	668	492
South Atlantic	345	221
Gulf of Mexico	1,476	1,760
Pacific-Alaska	1,776	5,750

Develop a simple regression model to predict the 2000 landings by the 1977 landings. According to the model, if a region had 700 landings in 1977, what would the predicted number be for 2000? Construct a confidence interval for the average y value for the 700 landings. Use the t statistic to test to determine whether the slope is significantly different from zero. Use $\alpha = .05$.

4.50 People in the aerospace industry believe the cost of a space project is a function of the weight of the major object being sent into space. Use the following data to develop a regression model to predict the cost of a space project by the weight of the space object. Determine r^2 and s_e.

Weight (tons)	Cost ($ millions)
1.897	$ 53.6
3.019	184.9
0.453	6.4
0.988	23.5
1.058	33.4
2.100	110.4
2.387	104.6

4.51 The following data represent a breakdown of state banks and all savings organizations in the United States every five years over a 60-year span according to the Federal Reserve System.

Time Period	State Banks	All Savings
1	1,342	2,330
2	1,864	2,667
3	1,912	3,054
4	1,847	3,764
5	1,641	4,423
6	1,405	4,837
7	1,147	4,694
8	1,046	4,407
9	997	4,328
10	1,070	3,626
11	1,009	2,815
12	1,042	2,030
13	992	1,779

Develop a regression model to predict the total number of state banks by the number of all savings organizations. Comment on the strength of the model.

4.52 Is the amount of money spent by companies on advertising a function of the total sales of the company? Shown are sales income and advertising cost data for seven companies, published by *Advertising Age*.

Company	Advertising ($ millions)	Sales ($ billions)
Procter & Gamble	$1,703.1	37.1
Philip Morris	1,319.0	56.1
Ford Motor	973.1	153.6
PepsiCo	797.4	20.9
Time Warner	779.1	13.3
Johnson & Johnson	738.7	22.6
MCI	455.4	19.7

Use the data to develop a regression line to predict the amount of advertising by sales. Compute s_e and r^2. Assuming $\alpha = .05$, test the slope of the regression line. Comment on the strength of the regression model.

4.53 Can the consumption of water in a city be predicted by temperature? The following data represent a sample of a day's water consumption and the high temperature for that day.

Water Use (millions of gallons)	Temperature (degrees Fahrenheit)
219	103°
56	39
107	77
129	78
68	50
184	96
150	90
112	75

Develop a least squares regression line to predict the amount of water used in a day in a city by the high temperature for that day. What would be the predicted water usage for a temperature of 100°? Evaluate the regression model by calculating s_e, by calculating r^2, and by testing the slope. Let $\alpha = .01$.

INTERPRETING THE OUTPUT

4.54 Study the following MINITAB output from a regression analysis to predict y from x.

a. What is the equation of the regression model?

b. What is the meaning of the coefficient of x?

c. What is the result of the test of the slope of the regression model? Let $\alpha = .10$. Why is the t ratio negative?

d. Comment on r^2 and the standard error of the estimate.

e. Comment on the relationship of the F value to the t ratio for x.

f. The correlation coefficient for these two variables is $-.7918$. Is this result surprising to you? Why or why not?

```
Regression Analysis: Y versus X

The regression equation is
Y = 67.2 - 0.0565 X

Predictor   Coef      SE Coef     T        p
Constant    67.231    5.046       13.32    0.000
X           -0.05650  0.01027     -5.50    0.000

S = 10.32   R-Sq = 62.7%   R-Sq(adj) = 60.6%

Analysis of Variance
Source          DF    SS       MS       F       P
Regression      1     3222.9   3222.9   30.25   0.000
Residual Error  18    1918.0   106.6
Total           19    5141.0
```

4.55 Study the following Excel regression output for an analysis attempting to predict the number of union members in the United States by the size of the labor force for selected years over a 30-year period from data published by the U.S. Bureau of Labor Statistics. Analyze the computer output. Discuss the strength of the model in terms of proportion of variation accounted for, slope, and overall predictability. Using the equation of the regression line, attempt to predict the number of union members when the labor force is 100,000. Note that the model was developed with data already recoded in 1,000 units. Use the data in the model as is.

	A	B	C	D	E	F
1	SUMMARY OUTPUT					
2	Regression Statistics					
3	Multiple R	0.610				
4	R Square	0.372				
5	Adjusted R Square	0.320				
6	Standard Error	982.219				
7	Observations	14				
8						
9	ANOVA					
10		df	SS	MS	F	Significance F
11	Regression	1	6868285.79	6868286	7.12	0.0205
12	Residual	12	11577055.64	967455		
13	Total	13	18445341.43			
14						
15		Coefficients	Standard Error	t Stat	P-value	
16	Intercept	22348.97	1846.37	12.10	.000000044	
17	X Variable 1	-0.0524	0.02	-2.67	0.0205	
18						
19	RESIDUAL OUTPUT					
20	Observation	Predicted Y	Residuals			
21	1	19161.39	-1862.39			
22	2	18631.75	749.25			
23	3	18315.95	1295.05			
24	4	17602.12	2240.88			
25	5	17516.68	-176.68			
26	6	17394.71	-398.71			
27	7	17269.86	-294.86			
28	8	17144.07	-231.07			
29	9	17033.79	-31.79			
30	10	16925.13	34.87			
31	11	16902.86	-162.86			
32	12	16961.51	-393.51			
33	13	16914.23	-524.23			
34	14	16841.95	-243.95			

4.56 Study the following MINITAB residual diagnostic graphs. Comment on any possible violations of regression assumptions.

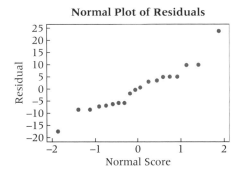

Normal Plot of Residuals

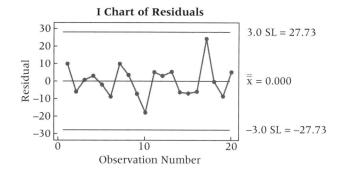

I Chart of Residuals

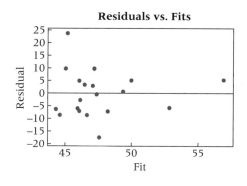

Residuals vs. Fits

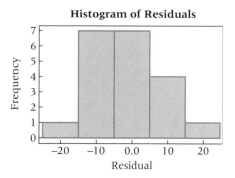

Histogram of Residuals

ANALYZING THE DATABASES

see www.wiley.com/college/black

1. Develop a regression model from the manufacturing database to predict New Capital Expenditures from Value Added by Manufacture. Discuss the model and its strength on the basis of indicators presented in this chapter. Does it seem logical that dollars spent on New Capital Expenditure could be predicted by Value Added by Manufacture?

2. Using the hospital database, develop a regression model to predict the number of Personnel by the number of Births. Now develop a regression model to predict number of Personnel by number of Beds. Examine the regression output. Which model is stronger in predicting number of Personnel? Explain why, using techniques presented in this chapter. Use the second regression model to predict the number of Personnel in a hospital that has 110 beds. Construct a 95%

confidence interval around this prediction for the average value of y.

3. Analyze all the variables except Type in the financial database by using a correlation matrix. The seven variables in this database are capable of producing 21 pairs of correlations. Which are most highly correlated? Select the variable that is most highly correlated with P/E ratio and use it as a predictor to develop a regression model to predict P/E ratio. How did the model do?

4. Use the stock market database to develop a regression model to predict the Utility Index by the Stock Volume. How well did the model perform? Did it perform as you expected? Why or why not? Construct a correlation matrix for the variables of this database (excluding Part of Month) so that you can explore the stock market. Did you discover any apparent relationships between variables?

CASE: DELTA WIRE USES TRAINING AS A WEAPON

The Delta Wire Corporation was founded in 1978 in Clarksdale, Mississippi. The company manufactures high-carbon specialty steel wire for global markets and at present employs about 100 people. For the past few years, sales increased each year.

A few years ago, however, things did not look as bright for Delta Wire because it was caught in a potentially disastrous bind. With the dollar declining in value, foreign competition was becoming a growing threat to Delta's market position. In addition to the growing foreign competition, industry quality requirements were becoming tougher each year.

Delta officials realized that some conditions, such as the value of the dollar, were beyond their control. However, one area that they could improve upon was employee education. The company worked with training programs developed by the state of Mississippi and a local community college to set up its own school. Delta employees were introduced to statistical process control and other quality assurance techniques. Delta reassured its customers that the company was working hard on improving quality and staying competitive. Customers were invited to sit in on the educational sessions. Because of this effort, Delta has been able to weather the storm and continues to sustain a leadership position in the highly competitive steel wire industry.

Delta continued its training and education program. In the 1990s, Delta instituted a basic skills training program that eventually led to a decrease in nonconforming material from 6 percent to 2 percent and a productivity increase from 70,000 to 90,000 pounds per week. In addition, this initiative resulted in a "best in class" award from Goodyear, its largest customer.

Discussion

1. Delta Wire prides itself on its efforts in the area of employee education. Employee education can pay off in many ways. Discuss some of them. One payoff can be the renewed interest and excitement generated toward the job and the company. Some people theorize that because of a more positive outlook and interest in implementing things learned, the more education received by a worker, the less likely he or she is to miss work days. Suppose the following data represent the number of days of sick leave taken by 20 workers last year along with the number of contact hours of employee education/training they each received in the past year. Use the techniques learned in this chapter to analyze the data. Include both regression and correlation techniques. Discuss the strength of the relationship and any models that are developed.

Employee	Hours of Education	Sick Days	Employee	Hours of Education	Sick Days
1	24	5	11	8	8
2	16	4	12	60	1
3	48	0	13	0	9
4	120	1	14	28	3
5	36	5	15	15	8
6	10	7	16	88	2
7	65	0	17	120	1
8	36	3	18	15	8
9	0	12	19	48	0
10	12	8	20	5	10

2. Many companies find that the implementation of total quality management eventually results in improved sales. Companies that fail to adopt quality efforts lose market share in many cases or go out of business. One measure of the effect of a company's quality improvement efforts is customer satisfaction. Suppose Delta Wire hired a research firm to measure customer satisfaction each year. The research firm developed a customer satisfaction scale in which totally satisfied customers can award a score as high as 50 and totally unsatisfied customers can award scores as low as 0. The scores are measured across many different industrial customers and averaged for a yearly mean customer score. Do sales increase with increases in customer satisfaction scores? To study this notion, suppose the average customer satisfaction score each year for Delta Wire is paired with the company's total sales of that year for the last 15 years, and a regression analysis is run on the data. Assume the following MINITAB and Excel outputs are the result. Suppose you were asked by Delta Wire to analyze the data and summarize the results. What would you find?

MINITAB OUTPUT

Regression Analysis: Sales versus Satisfaction

The regression equation is
Sales = 1.73 + 0.162 CustSat

```
Predictor     Coef     StDev       T       p
Constant    1.7332    0.4364    3.97   0.002
CustSat     0.16245   0.01490  10.90   0.000
```

S = 0.4113   R-Sq = 90.1% R-Sq(adj) = 89.4%

Analysis of Variance

```
Source            DF   SS        MS      F        p
Regression         1   20.098   20.098  118.80   0.000
Residual Error    13   2.199    0.169
Total             14   22.297
```

EXCEL OUTPUT

	A	B	C	D	E	F
1	SUMMARY OUTPUT					
2	Regression Statistics					
3	Multiple R	0.949				
4	R Square	0.901				
5	Adjusted R Square	0.894				
6	Standard Error	0.411				
7	Observations	15				
8						
9	ANOVA					
10		df	SS	MS	F	Significance F
11	Regression	1	20.098	20.098	118.80	0.000
12	Residual	13	2.199	0.169		
13	Total	14	22.297			
14						
15		Coefficients	Standard Error	t Stat	P-value	
16	Intercept	1.733	0.436	3.97	0.0016	
17	CustSat	0.162	0.015	10.90	0.0000	

Cumulative Hours of Training	Productivity (in pounds per week)
0	70,000
100	70,350
250	70,500
375	72,600
525	74,000
750	76,500
875	77,000
1,100	77,400
1,300	77,900
1,450	77,200
1,660	78,900
1,900	81,000
2,300	82,500
2,600	84,000
2,850	86,500
3,150	87,000
3,500	88,600
4,000	90,000

Source: Adapted from "Delta Wire Corporation," Strengthening America's Competitiveness: Resource Management Insights for Small Business Success. Published by Warner Books on behalf of Connecticut Mutual Life Insurance Company and the U.S. Chamber of Commerce in association with The Blue Chip Enterprise Initiative, 1991, International Monetary Fund; Terri Bergman, "TRAINING: The Case for Increased Investment," *Employment Relations Today*, Winter 1994–1995, pp. 381–391, available at http://www.ed.psu.edu/nwac/document/train/invest.html.

3. Delta Wire increased productivity from 70,000 to 90,000 pounds per week during a time when it instituted a basic skills training program. Suppose this program was implemented over an 18-month period and that the following data are the number of total cumulative basic skills hours of training and the per week productivity figures taken once a month over this time. Use techniques from this chapter to analyze the data and make a brief report to Delta about the predictability of productivity from cumulative hours of training.

USING THE COMPUTER

EXCEL

Excel has the capability of doing simple regression analysis. For a more inclusive analysis, use the Data Analysis dialog box. Begin the procedure by selecting **Tools** on the menu bar. From the pull-down menu that appears, choose **Data Analysis.** From the **Data Analysis** dialog box select **Regression.** In the **Regression** dialog box, input the location of the y values in **Input Y Range.** Input the location of the x values in **Input X Range.** If you so desire, input **Labels** and the **Confidence Level.** If you want the line to pass through the origin, check the **Constant is Zero** slot. A variety of output features are available by checking the appropriate slot, including a printout of raw residuals (**Residuals**), residuals converted to z scores (**Standardized Residuals**), a plot of the residuals (**Residual Plots**), and a plot of the line through the points (**Line Fit Plots**). The standard output includes such features as r, r^2, s_e, and an ANOVA table with the F test for overall significance, the slope and intercept, t statistic and associated p-value, and any optional requested output such as graphs or residuals.

By using Excel's Paste function, several of the individual measures presented in this chapter can be produced. Begin the process by clicking on the Paste function key, f_x, on the standard toolbar. The Paste function dialog box will appear. Select **Statistical** from the choices on the left side. Several measures of regression can be obtained by selecting the desired measure from the right side of this dialog box. We present four here. Select the desired measure, either **INTERCEPT** (returns the intercept of the linear regression line), **RSQ** (returns the square of the Pearson product-moment correlation coefficient), **SLOPE** (returns the slope of the linear regression line), or **STEYX** (returns the standard error of the predicted y value for each x in the regression). For each of these measures, a dialog box appears. Input the location of the range of data points for each of x and y. The output is the numerical value of the measure.

MINITAB WINDOWS

MINITAB Windows has a relatively thorough capability to perform regression analysis. Begin by selecting **Stat** on the menu bar and producing the **Stat** pull-down menu.

To perform a regression analysis, select **Regression** from the pull-down menu. A second pull-down menu will appear. Select **Regression** from this menu. A regression dialog box will appear. In the **Response** slot, place the location of the y variable. In the **Predictors** slot, place the location of the x variable.

Four buttons in the dialog box can be used to alter output. The **Graphs** button yields a dialog box with several options for residual plots. The **Options** button allows you to select confidence intervals and prediction intervals for particular values of x. The **Results** button allows you to control the regression display, including such things as unusual observations and residuals along with typical regression output. The **Storage** button allows you to store such things as fits and/or residuals for use in other analyses. The standard output for the **Regression** feature includes the regression equation, the t and F statistics and their associated p-values, an ANOVA table, standard error of the estimate, and the coefficient of determination.

The rather extensive residual diagnosis displayed in this chapter can be obtained through MINITAB. Some preliminary setup is necessary. In performing the initial regression analysis, select the **Storage** button in the **Regression** dialog box. In the **Storage** dialog box, check **Fits** and **Residuals** and click OK. When you run the regression analysis, two columns of additional data will be computed and placed into your worksheet: the regression line fits and the residuals. Now, go back to the menu bar and select **Stat**; from the pull-down menu that appears, select **Regression.** From the **Regression** pull-down menu, select **Residual Plots.** In the Residuals slot, place the column location containing the residuals that were just produced (the column with the residuals may be titled RESI1). In the Fits slot, place the column location containing the regression fits that were just produced (the column with the fits may be titled FITS1). Placing a title on the graph is optional. Click OK to get the residual diagnosis output with the four graphs.

To obtain a fitted line plot for the regression analysis, select **Stat** on the menu bar. From the pull-down menu that appears, select **Regression.** From the next pull-down menu that appears, select **Fitted Line Plot.** A dialog box will appear. Place the column location of the y values in the first slot and the location of the x values in the second slot. Select either the **Linear, Quadratic,** or **Cubic** model. (This chapter examined only linear models.) To display confidence bands and/or prediction bands (as discussed in Section 4.7), select **Options.** From the **Options** dialog box, check **Display confidence bands** and/or **Display prediction bands.** MINITAB will default to 95% confidence. For other levels of confidence, place the level desired in the slot labeled **Confidence level.** Placing a title on the graph is optional. The output is a scatter plot of the ordered pairs of points along with a regression line fit through the data. If the confidence bands and/or prediction bands are selected as an option, they will appear in the graph also.

CHAPTER 5

Multiple Regression Analysis

LEARNING OBJECTIVES

This chapter presents the potential of multiple regression analysis as a tool in business decision making and its applications, thereby enabling you to:

1. Develop a multiple regression model.
2. Understand and apply significance tests of the regression model and its coefficients.
3. Compute and interpret residuals, the standard error of the estimate, and the coefficient of multiple determination.
4. Interpret multiple regression computer output.

Are You Going to Hate Your New Job?

Getting a new job can be an exciting and energizing event in your life.

But what if you discover after a short time on the job that you hate your job? Is there any way to determine ahead of time whether you will love or hate your job? Sue Shellenbarger of *The Wall Street Journal* discusses some of the things to look for when interviewing for a position that may provide clues as to whether you will be happy on that job.

Among other things, work cultures vary from hip, freewheeling start-ups to old-school organizational-driven domains. Some organizations place pressure on workers to feel tense and to work long hours while others place more emphasis on creativity and the bottom line. Shellenbarger suggests that job interviewees pay close attention to how they are treated in an interview. Are they just another cog in the wheel or are they valued as an individual? Is a work-life balance apparent within the company? Ask what a typical workday is like at that firm. Inquire about the values that undergird the management by asking questions such as "What is your proudest accomplishment?" Ask about flexible schedules and how job training is managed. For example, does the worker have to go to job training on their own time?

A "Work Trends" survey undertaking by the John J. Heldrich Center for Workforce Development at Rutgers University and the Center for Survey Research and Analysis at the University of Connecticut posed several questions to employees in a survey to ascertain their job satisfaction. Some of the themes included in these questions were relationship with your supervisor, overall quality of the work environment, total hours worked each week, and opportunities for advancement at the job.

Suppose another researcher gathered survey data from 19 employees on these questions and also asked the employees to rate their job satisfaction on a scale from 0 to 100 (with 100 being perfectly satisfied). Suppose the following data represent the results of this survey. Assume that relationship with supervisor is rated on a scale from 1 to 5 (1 represents poor relationship and 5 represents an excellent relationship), overall quality of the work environment is rated on a scale from 0 to 10 (0 represents poor work environment and 10 represents an excellent work environment), and opportunities for advancement is rated on a scale from 1 to 5 (1 represents no opportunities and 5 represents excellent opportunities).

Job Satisfaction	Relationship with Supervisor	Overall Quality of Work Environment	Total Hours Worked per Week	Opportunities for Advancement
55	3	6	55	4
20	1	1	60	3
85	4	8	45	1
65	4	5	65	5
45	3	4	40	3
70	4	6	50	4
35	2	2	75	2
60	4	7	40	3
95	5	8	45	5
65	3	7	60	1
85	3	7	55	3
10	1	1	50	2
75	4	6	45	4
80	4	8	40	5
50	3	5	60	5
90	5	10	55	3
75	3	8	70	4
45	2	4	40	2
65	3	7	55	1

Managerial and Statistical Questions

1. Several variables are presented that may be related to job satisfaction. Which variables are stronger predictors of job satisfaction? Might other variables not mentioned here be related to job satisfaction?

2. Is it possible to develop a mathematical model to predict job satisfaction using the data given? If so, how strong is the model? With four independent variables, will we need to develop four different simple regression models and compare their results?

Source: Adapted from Sue Shellenbarger, "How to Find Out If You're Going to Hate a New Job Before You Agree to Take It," *The Wall Street Journal,* 13 June 2002, p. D1.

Simple regression analysis (discussed in Chapter 4) is bivariate linear regression in which one **dependent variable,** *y,* is predicted by one **independent variable,** *x.* Examples of simple regression applications include models to predict retail sales by population density, Dow Jones averages by prime interest rates, crude oil production by energy consumption, and CEO compensation by quarterly sales. However, in many cases, other independent variables, taken in conjunction with these variables, can make the regression model a better fit in predicting the dependent variable. For example, sales could be predicted by the size of store and number of competitors in addition to population density. A model to predict the Dow Jones average of 30 industrials could include, in addition to the prime interest rate, such predictors as yesterday's volume, the bond interest rate, and the producer price index. A model to predict CEO compensation could be developed by using variables such as company earnings per share, age of CEO, and size of company in addition to quarterly sales. A model could perhaps be developed to predict the cost of outsourcing by such variables as unit price, export taxes, cost of money, damage in transit, and other factors. Each of these examples contains only one dependent variable, *y,* as with simple regression analysis. However, multiple independent variables, *x* (predictors) are involved. *Regression analysis with two or more independent variables or with at least one nonlinear predictor* is called **multiple regression** analysis.

5.1 THE MULTIPLE REGRESSION MODEL

Multiple regression analysis is similar in principle to simple regression analysis. However, it is more complex conceptually and computationally. Recall from Chapter 4 that the equation of the probabilistic simple regression model is

$$y = \beta_0 + \beta_1 x + \epsilon$$

where

y = the value of the dependent variable
β_0 = the population y intercept
β_1 = the population slope
ϵ = the error of prediction

Extending this notion to multiple regression gives the general equation for the probabilistic multiple regression model.

$$y = \beta_0 + \beta_1 x_1 + \beta_2 x_2 + \beta_3 x_3 + \dots + \beta_k x_k + \epsilon$$

where

y = the value of the dependent variable
β_0 = the regression constant
β_1 = the partial regression coefficient for independent variable 1
β_2 = the partial regression coefficient for independent variable 2
β_3 = the partial regression coefficient for independent variable 3
β_k = the partial regression coefficient for independent variable k
k = the number of independent variables

In multiple regression analysis, the dependent variable, y, is sometimes referred to as the **response variable.** The **partial regression coefficient** of an independent variable, β_i, *represents the increase that will occur in the value of y from a 1-unit increase in that independent variable if all other variables are held constant.* The "full" (versus partial) regression coefficient of an independent variable is a coefficient obtained from the bivariate model (simple regression) in which the independent variable is the sole predictor of y. The partial regression coefficients occur because more than one predictor is included in a model. The partial regression coefficients are analogous to β_1, the slope of the simple regression model in Chapter 4.

In actuality, the partial regression coefficients and the regression constant of a multiple regression model are population values and are unknown. In virtually all research, these values are estimated by using sample information. Shown here is the form of the equation for estimating y with sample information.

$$\hat{y} = b_o + b_1 x_1 + b_2 x_2 + b_3 x_3 + \ldots + b_k x_k$$

where

$\hat{y}$ = the predicted value of y
β_0 = the estimate of the regression constant
β_1 = the estimate of regression coefficient 1
β_2 = the estimate of regression coefficient 2
β_3 = the estimate of regression coefficient 3
β_k = the estimate of regression coefficient k
k = the number of independent variables

Multiple Regression Model with Two Independent Variables (First-Order)

The simplest multiple regression model is one constructed with two independent variables, where the highest power of either variable is 1 (first-order regression model). The regression model is

$$y = \beta_0 + \beta_1 x_1 + \beta_2 x_2 + \in$$

The constant and coefficients are estimated from sample information, resulting in the following model.

$$\hat{y} = b_o + b_1 x_1 + b_2 x_2$$

Figure 5.1 is a three-dimensional graph of a series of points (x_1, x_2, y) representing values from three variables used in a multiple regression model to predict the sales price of a house by the number of square feet in the house and the age of the house. Simple regression models yield a line that is fit through data points in the xy plane. In multiple regression analysis, the resulting model produces a **response surface.** In the multiple regression model shown here with two independent first-order variables, the response surface is a **response plane.** The response plane for such a model is fit in a three-dimensional space (x_1, x_2, y).

If such a response plane is fit into the points shown in Figure 5.1, the result is the graph in Figure 5.2. Notice that most of the points are not on the plane. As in simple regression, an error in the fit of the model in multiple regression is usually present. The distances shown in the graph from the points to the response plane are the errors of fit, or residuals $(y - \hat{y})$. Multiple regression models with three or more independent variables involve more than three dimensions and are difficult to depict geometrically.

Observe in Figure 5.2 that the regression model attempts to fit a plane into the three-dimensional plot of points. Notice that the plane intercepts the y axis. Figure 5.2 depicts some values of y for various values of x_1 and x_2. The error of the response plane $(\in)$ in predicting or determining the y values is the distance from the points to the plane.

FIGURE 5.1

Points in a Sample Space

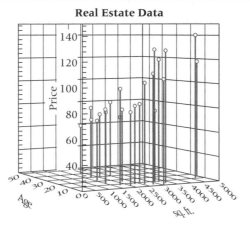

Real Estate Data

FIGURE 5.2

Response Plane for a First-Order Two-Predictor Multiple Regression Model

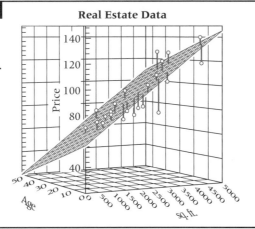

Real Estate Data

Determining the Multiple Regression Equation

The simple regression equations for determining the sample slope and intercept given in Chapter 4 are the result of using methods of calculus to minimize the sum of squares of error for the regression model. The procedure for developing these equations involves solving two simultaneous equations with two unknowns, b_0 and b_1. Finding the sample slope and intercept from these formulas requires the values of Σx, Σy, Σxy, and Σx^2.

The procedure for determining formulas to solve for multiple regression coefficients is similar. The formulas are established to meet an objective of *minimizing the sum of squares of error for the model.* Hence, the regression analysis shown here is referred to as **least squares analysis.** Methods of calculus are applied, resulting in $k + 1$ equations with $k + 1$ unknowns (b_0 and k values of b_i) for multiple regression analyses with k independent variables. Thus, a regression model with six independent variables will generate seven simultaneous equations with seven unknowns (b_0, b_1, b_2, b_3, b_4, b_5, b_6).

For multiple regression models with two independent variables, the result is three simultaneous equations with three unknowns (b_0, b_1, and b_2).

$$b_0 n + b_1 \Sigma x_1 + b_2 \Sigma x_2 = \Sigma y$$
$$b_0 \Sigma x_1 + b_1 \Sigma x_1^2 + b_2 \Sigma x_1 x_2 = \Sigma x_1 y$$
$$b_0 \Sigma x_2 + b_1 \Sigma x_1 x_2 + b_2 \Sigma x_2^2 = \Sigma x_2 y$$

The process of solving these equations by hand is tedious and time-consuming. Solving for the regression coefficients and regression constant in a multiple regression model with two independent variables requires Σx_1, Σx_2, Σy, Σx_1^2, Σx_2^2, $\Sigma x_1 x_2$, $\Sigma x_1 y$, and $\Sigma x_2 y$. In actuality, virtually all business researchers use computer statistical software packages to solve for the regression coefficients, the regression constant, and other pertinent information. In this chapter, we will discuss computer output and assume little or no hand calculation. The emphasis will be on the interpretation of the computer output.

A Multiple Regression Model

A real estate study was conducted in a small Louisiana city to determine what variables, if any, are related to the market price of a home. Several variables were explored, including the number of bedrooms, the number of bathrooms, the age of the house, the number of square feet of living space, the total number of square feet of space, and the number of garages. Suppose the researcher wants to develop a regression model to predict the market price of a home by two variables, "total number of square feet in the house" and "the age of the house." Listed in Table 5.1 are the data for these three variables.

A number of statistical software packages can perform multiple regression analysis, including Excel and MINITAB. The output for the MINITAB multiple regression analysis on the real estate data is given in Figure 5.3. (Excel output is shown in Demonstration Problem 5.1.)

The MINITAB output for regression analysis begins with "The regression equation is." From Figure 5.3, the regression equation for the real estate data in Table 5.1 is

$$\hat{y} = 57.4 + .0177x_1 - .666x_2$$

The regression constant, 57.4, is the y intercept. The y intercept is the value of $\hat{y}$ if both x_1 (number of square feet) and x_2 (age) are zero. In this example, a practical understanding of the y intercept is meaningless. It makes little sense to say that a house containing no square feet ($x_1 = 0$) and no years of age ($x_2 = 0$) would cost $57,400. Note in Figure 5.2 that the response plane crosses the y (price) axis at 57.4.

The coefficient of x_1 (total number of square feet in the house) is .0177, which means that a 1-unit increase in square footage would result in a predicted increase of $.0177 \cdot (\$1,000) = \$17.70$ in the price of the home if age were held constant. All other variables being held constant, the addition of 1 square foot of space in the house results in a predicted increase of $17.70 in the price of the home.

TABLE 5.1	Market Price ($1,000)	Total Number of Square Feet	Age of House (Years)
Real Estate Data	y	x_1	x_2
	63.0	1605	35
	65.1	2489	45
	69.9	1553	20
	76.8	2404	32
	73.9	1884	25
	77.9	1558	14
	74.9	1748	8
	78.0	3105	10
	79.0	1682	28
	83.4	2470	30
	79.5	1820	2
	83.9	2143	6
	79.7	2121	14
	84.5	2485	9
	96.0	2300	19
	109.5	2714	4
	102.5	2463	5
	121.0	3076	7
	104.9	3048	3
	128.0	3267	6
	129.0	3069	10
	117.9	4765	11
	140.0	4540	8

FIGURE 5.3

MINITAB Output of Regression
for the Real Estate Example

```
Regression Analysis: Price versus Square Feet, Age

The regression equation is
Price = 57.4 + 0.0177 Square Feet - 0.666 Age

Predictor           Coef      SE Coef         T        P
Constant           57.35        10.01      5.73    0.000
Square Feet     0.017718     0.003146      5.63    0.000
Age              -0.6663       0.2280     -2.92    0.008

S = 11.96     R-Sq = 74.1%     R-Sq(adj) = 71.5%

Analysis of Variance

Source          DF       SS        MS        F        P
Regression       2   8189.7    4094.9    28.63    0.000
Error           20   2861.0     143.1
Total           22  11050.7
```

The coefficient of x_2 (age) is –.666. The negative sign on the coefficient denotes an inverse relationship between the age of a house and the price of the house: the older the house, the lower the price. In this case, if the total number of square feet in the house is kept constant, a 1-unit increase in the age of the house (1 year) will result in –.666 · ($1000) = –$666, a predicted $666 drop in the price.

In examining the regression coefficients, it is important to remember that the independent variables are often measured in different units. It is usually not wise to compare the regression coefficients of predictors in a multiple regression model and decide that the variable with the largest regression coefficient is the best predictor. In this example, the two variables are in different units, square feet and years. Just because x_2 has the larger coefficient (.666) does not necessarily make x_2 the strongest predictor of y.

Some statistical software packages do not specifically print as output "The regression equation is," but rather produce a table, as shown here.

Predictor	Coef
Constant	57.35
Square Feet	0.017718
Age	–0.6663

The table is also part of MINITAB regression output. In this case, Coef means regression coefficient and the value given beside Constant is the regression constant value. Hence, the regression equation given previously for the data from Table 5.1 can also be gleaned from the output shown here. Note that the columns in MINITAB were named for the variables of interest and that MINITAB prints out values with more precision in the table than in the regression equation model shown previously. The remaining portion of this computer output will be discussed in Section 5.2.

This regression model can be used to predict the price of a house in this small Louisiana city. If the house has 2,500 square feet total and is 12 years old, $x_1 = 2,500$ and $x_2 = 12$. Substituting these values into the regression model yields

$$\hat{y} = 57.4 + .0177x_1 - .666x_2$$
$$= 57.4 + .0177(2,500) - .666(12) = 93.658$$

The predicted price of the house is $93,658. Figure 5.2 is a graph of these data with the response plane and the residual distances.

DEMONSTRATION PROBLEM 5.1*

Much of the freight cargo in the world is transported over roads. The volume of freight cargo shipped over roads varies from country to country depending on the size of the country, the amount of commerce, the wealth of the country, and other

---

* *Source:* World Data; World Road Statistics; George Thomas Kurian, *The Illustrated Book of World Rankings* (Armonk, NY: M.E. Sharpe, Inc., 1997).

factors. Shown here are seven of the top 10 countries in which freight cargo is shipped over roads, along with the number of miles of roads and the number of commercial vehicles (trucks and buses) for each country. Use these data to develop a multiple regression model to predict the volume of freight cargo shipped over roads by the length of roads and the number of commercial vehicles. Determine the predicted volume of freight cargo over roads if the length of roads is 600,000 miles and the number of commercial vehicles is 3 million.

Country	Freight Cargo Shipped by Road (millions of short-ton miles)	Length of Roads (miles)	Number of Commercial Vehicles
China	278,806	673,239	5,010,000
Brazil	178,359	1,031,693	1,371,127
India	144,000	1,342,000	1,980,000
Germany	138,975	395,367	2,923,000
Italy	125,171	188,597	2,745,500
Spain	105,824	206,271	2,859,438
Mexico	96,049	157,036	3,758,034

Solution

The following output shows the results of analyzing the data by using the regression portion of Excel.

	A	B	C	D	E	F
	Summary Output					
	Regression Statistics					
1	Multiple R	0.812				
2	R Square	0.659				
3	Adjusted R Square	0.488				
4	Standard Error	44273.86677				
5	Observations	7				
6						
7	ANOVA					
8		df	SS	MS	F	Significance F
9	Regression	2	15148592381	7574296191	3.86	0.116
10	Residual	4	784070114	1960175278		
11	Total	6	22989293495			
12						
13		Coefficients	Standard Error	t Stat	P-value	
14	Intercept	−26425.45085	67624.938	-0.39	0.716	
15	Length	0.101820862	0.0435	2.34	0.079	
16	Vehicles	0.04094856	0.0171	2.39	0.075	

The regression equation is

$$\hat{y} = -26,425.45 + .1018x_1 + .0410x_2$$

where

$\hat{y}$ = volume of freight cargo shipped
x_1 = length of roads
x_2 = number of commercial vehicles

The model indicates that for every 1-unit (1 mile) increase in length of roads, the predicted volume of freight cargo shipped increases by .1018 million short-ton miles, or 101,800 short-ton miles, if the number of commercial vehicles is held constant. If the number of commercial vehicles is increased by 1 unit, the predicted volume of freight cargo shipped increases by .0410 million short-ton miles, or 41,000 short-ton miles, if the length of roads is held constant.

If x_1 (length of roads) is 600,000 and x_2 (number of commercial vehicles) is 3 million, the model predicts that the volume of freight cargo shipped will be 157,655 million short-ton miles:

$$\hat{y} = 26,425.45 + .1018(600,000) + .0410(3,000,000) = 157,655$$

5.1 PROBLEMS

5.1 Use a computer to develop the equation of the regression model for the following data. Comment on the regression coefficients. Determine the predicted value of y for $x_1 = 200$ and $x_2 = 7$.

y	x_1	x_2
12	174	3
18	281	9
31	189	4
28	202	8
52	149	9
47	188	12
38	215	5
22	150	11
36	167	8
17	135	5

5.2 Use a computer to develop the equation of the regression model for the following data. Comment on the regression coefficients. Determine the predicted value of y for $x_1 = 33$, $x_2 = 29$, and $x_3 = 13$.

y	x_1	x_2	x_3
114	21	6	5
94	43	25	8
87	56	42	25
98	19	27	9
101	29	20	12
85	34	45	21
94	40	33	14
107	32	14	11
119	16	4	7
93	18	31	16
108	27	12	10
117	31	3	8

5.3 Using the following data, determine the equation of the regression model. How many independent variables are there? Comment on the meaning of these regression coefficients.

Predictor	Coefficient
Constant	121.62
x_1	−.174
x_2	6.02
x_3	.00026
x_4	.0041

5.4 Use the following data to determine the equation of the multiple regression model. Comment on the regression coefficients.

Predictor	Coefficient
Constant	31,409.5
x_1	.08425
x_2	289.62
x_3	−.0947

5.5 Is there a particular product that is an indicator of per capita consumption around the world? Shown here are data on per capita consumption, paper consumption, fish consumption, and gasoline consumption for nine countries. Use the data to determine the equation of the multiple regression model to predict per capita consumption by paper consumption, fish consumption, and gasoline consumption. Discuss the impact of increasing paper consumption by 1 unit on the predicted per capita consumption. Discuss the impact of a 1-unit increase in fish consumption on the predicted per capita consumption and the impact of a 1-unit increase in gasoline consumption on the predicted per capita consumption.

Country	Per Capita Consumption	Paper Consumption (kg per 1,000 people)	Fish Consumption (pounds)	Gasoline Consumption (1,000 barrels per day)
Japan	$19,700	76,892	158.7	5,454
Portugal	5,570	24,126	132.7	277
United States	16,500	84,579	47.0	17,033
Venezuela	2,090	6,860	31.1	430
Greece	4,490	15,641	42.1	331
Italy	10,790	43,098	44.3	1,936
Norway	13,400	41,575	90.6	183
United Kingdom	9,040	52,335	43.9	1,803
Philippines	640	940	76.3	235

Sources: World Development Report; Pulp & Paper Industry; Fishery Statistic Yearbook; Energy Statistics Yearbook; George Thomas Kurian, *The Illustrated Book of World Rankings* (Armonk, NY: M. E. Sharpe, Inc., 1997).

5.6 Jensen, Solberg, and Zorn investigated the relationship of insider ownership, debt, and dividend policies in companies. One of their findings was that firms with high insider ownership choose lower levels of both debt and dividends. Shown here is a sample of data of these three variables for 11 different industries. Use the data to develop the equation of the regression model to predict insider ownership by debt ratio and dividend payout. Comment on the regression coefficients.

Industry	Insider Ownership	Debt Ratio	Dividend Payout
Mining	8.2	14.2	10.4
Food and beverage	18.4	20.8	14.3
Furniture	11.8	18.6	12.1
Publishing	28.0	18.5	11.8
Petroleum refining	7.4	28.2	10.6
Glass and cement	15.4	24.7	12.6
Motor vehicle	15.7	15.6	12.6
Department store	18.4	21.7	7.2
Restaurant	13.4	23.0	11.3
Amusement	18.1	46.7	4.1
Hospital	10.0	35.8	9.0

Source: R. Gerald Jensen, Donald P. Solberg, and Thomas S. Zorn, "Simultaneous Determination of Insider Ownership, Debt, and Dividend Policies," *Journal of Financial and Quantitative Analysis*, vol. 27, no. 2 (June 1992).

5.2 SIGNIFICANCE TESTS OF THE REGRESSION MODEL AND ITS COEFFICIENTS

Multiple regression models can be developed to fit almost any data set if the level of measurement is adequate and enough data points are available. Once a model has been constructed, it is important to test the model to determine whether it fits the data well and whether the assumptions underlying regression analysis are met. Assessing the adequacy of the regression model can be done in several ways, including testing the overall significance of the model, studying the significance tests of the regression coefficients, computing the residuals, examining the standard error of the estimate, and observing the coefficient of determination. In this section, we examine significance tests of the regression model and of its coefficients.

Testing the Overall Model

With simple regression, a t test of the slope of the regression line is used to determine whether the population slope of the regression line is different from zero—that is, whether the independent variable contributes significantly in linearly predicting the dependent variable. The hypotheses for this test, presented in Chapter 4, are

$$H_0: \beta_1 = 0$$
$$H_a: \beta_1 \neq 0$$

For multiple regression, an analogous test makes use of the F statistic. The overall significance of the multiple regression model is tested with the following hypotheses.

$$H_0: \beta_1 = \beta_2 = \beta_3 = \ldots = \beta_k = 0$$
$$H_a: \text{At least one of the regression coefficients is} \neq 0.$$

If we fail to reject the null hypothesis, we are stating that the regression model has no significant predictability for the dependent variable. A rejection of the null hypothesis indicates that at least one of the independent variables is adding significant predictability for y.

This F test of overall significance is often printed as a part of the standard multiple regression output from statistical software packages. The output appears as an analysis of variance (ANOVA) table. Shown here is the ANOVA table for the real estate example taken from the MINITAB output in Figure 5.3.

```
Analysis of Variance
```

Source	DF	SS	MS	F	P
Regression	2	8189.7	4094.9	28.63	0.000
Residual Error	20	2861.0	143.1		
Total	22	11050.7			

The F value is 28.63; because $p = .000$, the F value is significant at $\alpha = .001$. The null hypothesis is rejected, and there is at least one significant predictor of house price in this analysis.

The F value is calculated by the following equation.

$$F = \frac{MS_{reg}}{MS_{err}} = \frac{SS_{reg}/df_{reg}}{SS_{err}/df_{err}} = \frac{SSR/k}{SSE/N-k-1}$$

where

$MS=$ mean square
SS = sum of squares
df = degrees of freedom
k = number of independent variables
N = number of observations

Note that in the ANOVA table for the real estate example, $df_{reg} = 2$. The degrees of freedom formula for regression is the number of regression coefficients plus the regression constant minus 1. The net result is the number of regression coefficients, which equals the number of independent variables, k. The real estate example uses two independent variables, so $k = 2$. Degrees of freedom error in multiple regression equals the total number of observations minus the number of regression coefficients minus the regression constant, or $N - k - 1$. For the real estate example, $N = 23$; thus, $df_{err} = 23 - 2 - 1 = 20$.

As you may know, $MS = SS/df$. The F ratio is formed by dividing MS_{reg} by MS_{err}. In using the F distribution table to determine a critical value against which to test the observed F value, the degrees of freedom numerator is df_{reg} and the degrees of freedom denominator is df_{err}. The table F value is obtained in the usual manner. With $\alpha = .01$ for the real estate example, the table value is

$$F_{.01,2,20} = 5.85$$

Comparing the observed F of 28.63 to this table value shows that the decision is to reject the null hypothesis. This same conclusion was reached using the p-value method from the computer output.

If a regression model has only one linear independent variable, it is a simple regression model. In that case, the F test for the overall model is the same as the t test for significance of the population slope. The F value displayed in the regression ANOVA table is related to the t test for the slope in the simple regression case as follows.

$$F = t^2$$

In simple regression, the F value and the t value give redundant information about the overall test of the model.

Most researchers who use multiple regression analysis will observe the value of F and its p-value rather early in the process. If F is not significant, then no population regression coefficient is significantly different from zero, and the regression model has no predictability for the dependent variable.

Significance Tests of the Regression Coefficients

In multiple regression, individual significance tests can be computed for each regression coefficient using a t test. Each of these t tests is analogous to the t test for the slope used in Chapter 4 for simple regression analysis. The hypotheses for testing the regression coefficient of each independent variable take the following form:

$$H_0: \beta_1 = 0$$
$$H_a: \beta_1 \neq 0$$
$$H_0: \beta_2 = 0$$
$$H_a: \beta_2 \neq 0$$
$$\vdots$$
$$H_0: \beta_k = 0$$
$$H_a: \beta_k \neq 0$$

Most multiple regression computer packages yield observed t values to test the individual regression coefficients as standard output. Shown here are the t values and their associated probabilities for the real estate example as displayed with the multiple regression output in Figure 5.3.

Variable	T	p
Square feet	5.63	.000
Age	−2.92	.008

At $\alpha = .05$, the null hypothesis is rejected for both variables because the probabilities (p) associated with their t values are less than .05. If the t ratios for any predictor variables are not significant (fail to reject the null hypothesis), the researcher might decide to drop that variable(s) from the analysis as a nonsignificant predictor(s). Other factors can enter into this decision. In Chapter 6, we will explore techniques for model building in which some variable sorting is required.

The degrees of freedom for each of these individual tests of regression coefficients are $n - k - 1$. In this particular example because there are $k = 2$ predictor variables, the degrees of freedom are $23 - 2 - 1 = 20$. With $\alpha = .05$ and a two-tailed test, the critical table t value is

$$t_{.025,20} = \pm 2.086$$

Notice from the t ratios shown here that if this critical table t value had been used as the hypothesis test criterion instead of the p-value method, the results would have been the same. Testing the regression coefficients not only gives the researcher some insight into the fit of the regression model, but it also helps in the evaluation of how worthwhile individual independent variables are in predicting y.

5.2 PROBLEMS

5.7 Examine the MINITAB output shown here for a multiple regression analysis. How many predictors were there in this model? Comment on the overall significance of the regression model. Discuss the t ratios of the variables and their significance.

```
The regression equation is
```

$$Y = 4.096 - 5.111\ X_1 + 2.662\ X_2 + 1.557\ X_3 + 1.141\ X_4 + 1.650$$
$$X_5 - 1.248\ X_6 + 0.436\ X_7 + 0.962\ X_8 + 1.289\ X_9$$

Predictor	Coef	Stdev	T	p
Constant	4.096	1.2884	3.24	.006
X_1	-5.111	1.8700	2.73	.011
X_2	2.662	2.0796	1.28	.212
X_3	1.557	1.2811	1.22	.235
X_4	1.141	1.4712	0.78	.445
X_5	1.650	1.4994	1.10	.281
X_6	-1.248	1.2735	0.98	.336
X_7	0.436	0.3617	1.21	.239
X_8	0.962	1.1896	0.81	.426
X_9	1.289	1.9182	0.67	.508

```
S = 3.503 R-sq = 40.8%R-sq(adj.) = 20.3%
```

```
Analysis of Variance
```

Source	DF	SS	MS	F	p
Regression	9	219.746	24.416	1.99	.0825
Error	26	319.004	12.269		
Total	35	538.750			

5.8 Displayed here is the MINITAB output for a multiple regression analysis. Study the ANOVA table and the t ratios and use these to discuss the strengths of the regression model and the predictors. Does this model appear to fit the data well? From the information here, what recommendations would you make about the predictor variables in the model?

```
The regression equation is
```

$$Y = 34.7 + 0.0763\ X_1 + 0.00026\ X_2 - 1.12\ X_3$$

Predictor	Coef	Stdev	T	p
Constant	34.672	5.256	6.60	.000
X_1	0.07629	0.02234	3.41	.005
X_2	0.000259	0.001031	0.25	.805
X_3	-1.1212	0.9955	-1.13	.230

```
S = 9.722  R-sq = 51.5%  R-sq(adj) = 40.4%
```

Analysis of Variance

Source	DF	SS	MS	F	p
Regression	3	1306.99	435.66	4.61	.021
Error	13	1228.78	94.52		
Total	16	2535.77			

5.9   Using the data in Problem 5.5, develop a multiple regression model to predict per capita consumption by the consumption of paper, fish, and gasoline. Discuss the output and pay particular attention to the F test and the t tests.

5.10   Using the data from Problem 5.6, develop a multiple regression model to predict insider ownership from debt ratio and dividend payout. Comment on the strength of the model and the predictors by examining the ANOVA table and the t tests.

5.11   Develop a multiple regression model to predict y from x_1, x_2, and x_3 using the following data. Discuss the values of F and t.

y	x_1	x_2	x_3
5.3	44	11	401
3.6	24	40	219
5.1	46	13	394
4.9	38	18	362
7.0	61	3	453
6.4	58	5	468
5.2	47	14	386
4.6	36	24	357
2.9	19	52	206
4.0	31	29	301
3.8	24	37	243
3.8	27	36	228
4.8	36	21	342
5.4	50	11	421
5.8	55	9	445

5.12   Use the following data to develop a regression model to predict y from x_1 and x_2. Comment on the output. Develop a regression model to predict y from x_1 only. Compare the results of this model with those of the model using both predictors. What might you conclude by examining the output from both regression models?

y	x_1	x_2
28	12.6	134
43	11.4	126
45	11.5	143
49	11.1	152
57	10.4	143
68	9.6	147
74	9.8	128
81	8.4	119
82	8.8	130
86	8.9	135
101	8.1	141
112	7.6	123
114	7.8	121
119	7.4	129
124	6.4	135

5.13   Study the following Excel multiple regression output. How many predictors are in this model? How many observations? What is the equation of the regression line? Discuss the strength of the model in terms *F*. Which predictors, if any, are significant? Why or why not? Comment on the overall effectiveness of the model.

	A	B	C	D	E	F
1	Summary Output					
2	Regression Statistics					
3	Multiple R	0.842				
4	R Square	0.710				
5	Adjusted R Square	0.630				
6	Standard Error	109.430				
7	Observations	15				
8						
9	ANOVA					
10		df	SS	MS	F	Significance F
11	Regression	3	321946.82	107315.6	8.96	0.0027
12	Residual	11	131723.20	11974.8		
13	Total	14	453670			
14						
15		Coefficents	Standard Error	t Stat	P-value	
16	Intercept	657.053	167.460	3.92	.0024	
17	X Variable 1	5.7103	1.792	3.19	.0087	
18	X Variable 2	-0.4169	0.322	-1.29	.2222	
19	X Variable 3	-3.4715	1.443	-2.41	.0349	

5.3 RESIDUALS, STANDARD ERROR OF THE ESTIMATE, AND R^2

Three more statistical tools for examining the strength of a regression model are the residuals, the standard error of the estimate, and the coefficient of multiple determination.

Residuals

The **residual,** or error, of the regression model is *the difference between the y value and the predicted value, $\hat{y}$.*

$$\text{Residual} = y - \hat{y}$$

The residuals for a multiple regression model are solved for in the same manner as they are with simple regression. First, a predicted value, $\hat{y}$, is determined by entering the value for each independent variable for a given set of observations into the multiple regression equation and solving for $\hat{y}$. Next, the value of $y - \hat{y}$ is computed for each set of observations. Shown here are the calculations for the residuals of the first set of observations from Table 5.1. The predicted value of y for $x_1 = 1605$ and $x_2 = 35$ is

$$\hat{y} = 57.4 + .0177(1605) - .666(35) = 62.50$$

Actual value of y = 63.0
Residual = $y - \hat{y}$ = 63.0 – 62.50 = 0.50

All residuals for the real estate data and the regression model displayed in Table 5.1 and Figure 5.3 are displayed in Table 5.2.

An examination of the residuals in Table 5.2 can reveal some information about the fit of the real estate regression model. The business researcher can observe the residuals and decide whether the errors are small enough to support the accuracy of the model. The house price figures are in units of $1,000. Two of the 23 residuals are more than 20.00, or more than $20,000 off in their prediction. On the other hand, two residuals are less than 1, or $1,000 off in their prediction.

Residuals are also helpful in locating outliers. **Outliers** are *data points that are apart, or far, from the mainstream of the other data.* They are sometimes data points that were mistakenly recorded or measured. Because every data point influences the regression model,

TABLE 5.2

Residuals for the Real Estate Regression Model

y	$\hat{y}$	$y - \hat{y}$
63.0	62.499	.501
65.1	71.485	−6.385
69.9	71.568	−1.668
76.8	78.639	−1.839
73.9	74.097	−.197
77.9	75.653	2.247
74.9	83.012	−8.112
78.0	105.699	−27.699
79.0	68.523	10.477
83.4	81.139	2.261
79.5	88.282	−8.782
83.9	91.335	−7.435
79.7	85.618	−5.918
84.5	95.391	−10.891
96.0	85.456	10.544
109.5	102.774	6.726
102.5	97.665	4.835
121.0	107.183	13.817
104.9	109.352	−4.452
128.0	111.230	16.770
129.0	105.061	23.939
117.9	134.415	−16.515
140.0	132.430	7.570

outliers can exert an overly important influence on the model based on their distance from other points. In examining the residuals in Table 5.2 for outliers, the eighth residual listed is −27.699. This error indicates that the regression model was not nearly as successful in predicting house price on this particular house as it was with others (an error of more than $27,000). For whatever reason, this data point stands somewhat apart from other data points and may be considered an outlier.

Residuals are also useful in testing the assumptions underlying regression analysis. Figure 5.4 displays MINITAB diagnostic techniques for the real estate example. In the bottom right is a graph of the residuals. Notice that residual variance seems to increase in the right half of the plot, indicating potential heteroscedasticity. As discussed in Chapter 4, one of the assumptions underlying regression analysis is that the error terms have homoscedasticity or homogeneous variance. That assumption might be violated in this example. The normal plot of residuals is nearly a straight line, indicating that the assumption of normally distributed error terms probably has not been violated.

SSE and Standard Error of the Estimate

One of the properties of a regression model is that the residuals sum to zero. As pointed out in Chapter 4, this property precludes the possibility of computing an "average" residual as a single measure of error. In an effort to compute a single statistic that can represent the error in a regression analysis, the zero-sum property can be overcome by *squaring the residuals and then summing the squares.* Such an operation produces the sum of squares of error (SSE).

The formula for computing the sum of squares error (SSE) for multiple regression is the same as it is for simple regression.

$$SSE = \Sigma(y - \hat{y})^2$$

For the real estate example, SSE can be computed by squaring and summing the residuals displayed in Table 5.2.

$$
\begin{aligned}
SSE = \ & [(.501)^2 + (−6.385)^2 + (−1.668)^2 + (−1.839)^2 \\
& + (−.197)^2 + (2.247)^2 + (−8.112)^2 + (−27.699)^2 \\
& + (10.477)^2 + (2.261)^2 + (−8.782)^2 + (−7.435)^2 \\
& + (−5.918)^2 + (−10.891)^2 + (10.544)^2 + (6.726)^2 \\
& + (4.835)^2 + (13.817)^2 + (−4.452)^2 + (16.770)^2 \\
& + (23.939)^2 + (−16.515)^2 + (7.570)^2] \\
= \ & 2861.0
\end{aligned}
$$

FIGURE 5.4

MINITAB Residual Diagnosis for the Real Estate Example

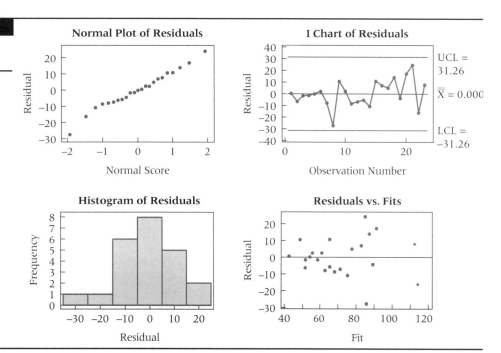

SSE can also be obtained directly from the multiple regression computer output by selecting the value of SS (sum of squares) listed beside error. Shown here is the ANOVA portion of the output displayed in Figure 5.3, which is the result of a multiple regression analysis model developed to predict house prices. Note that the SS for error shown in the ANOVA table equals the value of $\Sigma(y - \hat{y})^2$ just computed (2861.0).

SSE

Analysis of Variance

Source	DF	SS	MS	F	p
Regression	2	8189.7	4094.9	28.63	.000
Error	20	(2861.0)	143.1		
Total	22	11050.7			

SSE has limited usage as a measure of error. However, it is a tool used to solve for other, more useful measures. One of those is the **standard error of the estimate s_e**, which is essentially *the standard deviation of residuals (error) for the regression model.* As explained in Chapter 4, an assumption underlying regression analysis is that the error terms are approximately normally distributed with a mean of zero. With this information and by the empirical rule, approximately 68% of the residuals should be within $\pm 1s_e$ and 95% should be within $\pm 2s_e$. This property makes the standard error of the estimate a useful tool in estimating how accurately a regression model is fitting the data.

The standard error of the estimate is computed by dividing SSE by the degrees of freedom of error for the model and taking the square root.

$$s_e = \sqrt{\frac{SSE}{n - k - 1}}$$

where

n = number of observations
k = number of independent variables

The value of s_e can be computed for the real estate example as follows.

$$s_e = \sqrt{\frac{SSE}{n - k - 1}} = \sqrt{\frac{2861}{23 - 2 - 1}} = 11.96$$

The standard error of the estimate, s_e, is usually given as standard output from regression analysis by computer software packages. The MINITAB output displayed in Figure 5.3 contains the standard error of the estimate for the real estate example.

$$S = 11.96$$

By the empirical rule, approximately 68% of the residuals should be within $\pm 1s_e = \pm 1(11.96) = \pm 11.96$. Because house prices are in units of $1,000, approximately 68% of the predictions are within $\pm 11.96(\$1,000)$, or $\pm\$11,960$. Examining the output displayed in Table 5.2, 18/23, or about 78%, of the residuals are within this span. According to the empirical rule, approximately 95% of the residuals should be within $\pm 2s_e$, or $\pm 2(11.96) = \pm 23.92$. Further examination of the residual values in Table 5.2 shows that 21 of 23, or 91%, fall within this range. The business researcher can study the standard error of the estimate and these empirical rule–related ranges and decide whether the error of the regression model is sufficiently small to justify further use of the model.

Coefficient of Multiple Determination (R^2)

The **coefficient of multiple determination (R^2)** is analogous to the coefficient of determination (r^2) discussed in Chapter 4. R^2 represents *the proportion of variation of the dependent variable, y, accounted for by the independent variables in the regression model.* As with r^2, the range of possible values for R^2 is from 0 to 1. An R^2 of 0 indicates no relationship between the predictor variables in the model and y. An R^2 of 1 indicates that 100% of the variability of y has been accounted for by the predictors. Of course, it is desirable for R^2 to be high, indicating the strong predictability of a regression model. The coefficient of multiple determination can be calculated by the following formula:

$$R^2 = \frac{SSR}{SS_{yy}} = 1 - \frac{SSE}{SS_{yy}}$$

R^2 can be calculated in the real estate example by using the sum of squares regression (SSR), the sum of squares error (SSE), and sum of squares total (SS_{yy}) from the ANOVA portion of Figure 5.3.

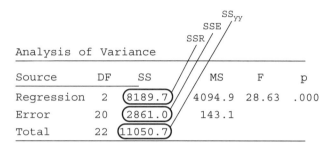

```
                                    SS_yy
                               SSE /
                          SSR //
Analysis of Variance          //
                             // /
Source      DF    SS        / MS     F      p
Regression   2  (8189.7)  / 4094.9  28.63  .000
Error       20  (2861.0)    143.1
Total       22 (11050.7)
```

$$R^2 = \frac{SSR}{SS_{yy}} = \frac{8189.7}{11050.7} = .741$$

or

$$R^2 = 1 - \frac{SSE}{SS_{yy}} = 1 - \frac{2861.0}{11050.7} = .741$$

In addition, virtually all statistical software packages print out R^2 as standard output with multiple regression analysis. A reexamination of Figure 5.3 reveals that R^2 is given as

R-sq = 74.1%

This result indicates that a relatively high proportion of the variation of the dependent variable, house price, is accounted for by the independent variables in this regression model.

Adjusted R^2

As additional independent variables are added to a regression model, the value of R^2 cannot decrease, and in most cases it will increase. In the formulas for determining R^2,

$$R^2 = \frac{SSR}{SS_{yy}} = 1 - \frac{SSE}{SS_{yy}}$$

The value of SS_{yy} for a given set of observations will remain the same as independent variables are added to the regression analysis because SS_{yy} is the sum of squares for the dependent variable. Because additional independent variables are likely to increase SSR at least by some amount, the value of R^2 will probably increase for any additional independent variables.

However, sometimes additional independent variables add no *significant* information to the regression model, yet R^2 increases. R^2 therefore may yield an inflated figure. Statisticians have developed an **adjusted R^2** *to take into consideration both the additional information each new independent variable brings to the regression model and the changed degrees of freedom of regression.* Many standard statistical computer packages now compute and report adjusted R^2 as part of the output. The formula for computing adjusted R^2 is

$$\text{Adjusted } R^2 = 1 - \frac{SSE/_{n-k-1}}{SS_{yy}/_{n-1}}$$

The value of adjusted R^2 for the real estate example can be solved by using information from the ANOVA portion of the computer output in Figure 5.3.

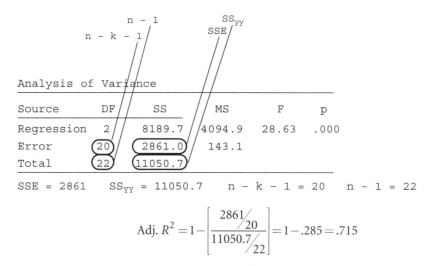

$$\text{Analysis of Variance}$$

Source	DF	SS	MS	F	p
Regression	2	8189.7	4094.9	28.63	.000
Error	20	2861.0	143.1		
Total	22	11050.7			

$$\text{SSE} = 2861 \quad \text{SS}_{YY} = 11050.7 \quad n - k - 1 = 20 \quad n - 1 = 22$$

$$\text{Adj. } R^2 = 1 - \left[\frac{2861/20}{11050.7/22}\right] = 1 - .285 = .715$$

The standard MINITAB regression output in Figure 5.3 contains the value of the adjusted R^2 already computed. For the real estate example, this value is shown as

$$\text{R-sq (adj.)} = 71.5\%$$

A comparison of R^2 (.741) with the adjusted R^2 (.715) for this example shows that the adjusted R^2 reduces the overall proportion of variation of the dependent variable accounted for by the independent variables by a factor of .026, or 2.6%. The gap between the R^2 and adjusted R^2 tends to increase as nonsignificant independent variables are added to the regression model. As n increases, the difference between R^2 and adjusted R^2 becomes less.

5.3 PROBLEMS

5.14 Study the MINITAB output shown in Problem 5.7. Comment on the overall strength of the regression model in light of S, R^2, and adjusted R^2

STATISTICS IN BUSINESS TODAY

Using Regression Analysis to Help Select a Robot

Several factors contribute to the success of a manufacturing firm in the world markets. Some examples are creating more efficient plants, lowering labor costs, increasing the quality of products, improving the standards of supplier materials, and learning more about international markets. Basically, success boils down to producing a better product for less cost.

One way to achieve that goal is to improve the technology of manufacturing facilities. Many companies are now using robots in plants to increase productivity and reduce labor costs. The use of such technology is relatively new. The science of selecting and purchasing robots is imperfect and often involves considerable subjectivity.

Two researchers, Moutaz Khouja and David Booth, devised a way to use multiple regression to assist decision makers in robot selection. After sorting through 20 of the more promising variables, they found that the most important variables related to robot performance are repeatability, accuracy, load capacity, and velocity. Accuracy is measured by the distance between where the

robot goes on a single trial and the center of all points to which it goes on repeated trials. Repeatability is the radius of the circle that just includes all points to which the robot goes on repeated trials. Repeatability is of most concern to decision makers because it is hardest to correct. Accuracy can be viewed as bias and is easier to correct. Load capacity is the maximum weight that the robot can handle, and velocity is the maximum tip velocity of the robot arm.

Khouja and Booth used data gathered from 27 robots and regression analysis to develop a multiple regression model that attempts to predict repeatability of robots (the variable of most concern for decision makers) by the velocity and load capacity of robots. Using the resulting regression model and the residuals of the fit, they developed a ranking system for selecting robots that takes into account repeatability, load capacity, velocity, and cost.

Source: Adapted from Moutaz Khouja and David E. Booth, "A Decision Model for the Robot Selection Problem Using Robust Regression," *Decision Sciences* 22, no. 3 (July/August 1991): 656–62. The *Decision Sciences* journal is published by the Decision Sciences Institute, located at Georgia State University.

5.15 Study the MINITAB output shown in Problem 5.8. Comment on the overall strength of the regression model in light of S, R^2, and adjusted R^2.

5.16 Using the regression output obtained by working Problem 5.5, comment on the overall strength of the regression model using S, R^2, and adjusted R^2.

5.17 Using the regression output obtained by working Problem 5.6, comment on the overall strength of the regression model using S, R^2, and adjusted R^2.

5.18 Using the regression output obtained by working Problem 5.11, comment on the overall strength of the regression model using S, R^2, and adjusted R^2.

5.19 Using the regression output obtained by working Problem 5.12, comment on the overall strength of the regression model using S, R^2, and adjusted R^2.

5.20 Study the Excel output shown in Problem 5.13. Comment on the overall strength of the regression model in light of S, R^2, and adjusted R^2.

5.21 Study the MINITAB residual diagnostic output that follows. Discuss any potential problems with meeting the regression assumptions for this regression analysis based on the residual graphics.

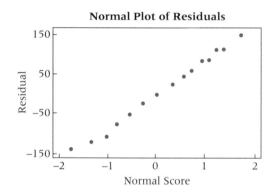

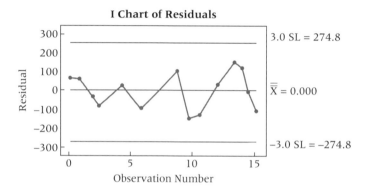

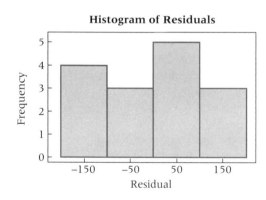

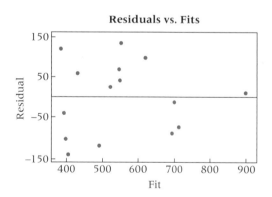

5.4 INTERPRETING MULTIPLE REGRESSION COMPUTER OUTPUT

A Reexamination of the Multiple Regression Output

Figure 5.5 shows again the MINITAB multiple regression output for the real estate example. Many of the concepts discussed thus far in the chapter are highlighted. Note the following items:

1. The equation of the regression model
2. The ANOVA table with the F value for the overall test of the model
3. The t ratios, which test the significance of the regression coefficients
4. The value of SSE
5. The value of s_e
6. The value of R^2
7. The value of adjusted R^2

FIGURE 5.5

Annotated Version of the
MINTAB Output of Regression
for the Real Estate Example

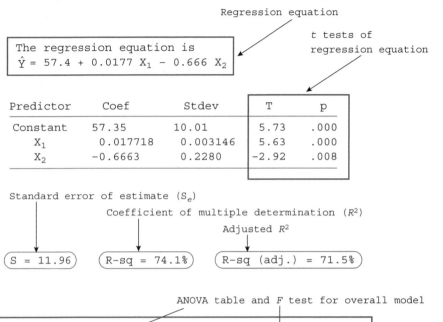

Regression equation

The regression equation is
$\hat{Y} = 57.4 + 0.0177 X_1 - 0.666 X_2$

t tests of
regression equation

Predictor	Coef	Stdev	T	p
Constant	57.35	10.01	5.73	.000
X_1	0.017718	0.003146	5.63	.000
X_2	-0.6663	0.2280	-2.92	.008

Standard error of estimate (S_e)

Coefficient of multiple determination (R^2)

Adjusted R^2

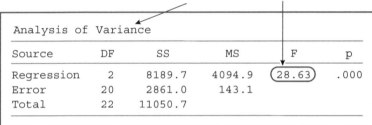

S = 11.96   R-sq = 74.1%   R-sq (adj.) = 71.5%

ANOVA table and F test for overall model

Analysis of Variance

Source	DF	SS	MS	F	p
Regression	2	8189.7	4094.9	28.63	.000
Error	20	2861.0	143.1		
Total	22	11050.7			

**DEMONSTRATION
PROBLEM 5.2**

Discuss the Excel multiple regression output for Demonstration Problem 5.1. Comment on the F test for the overall significance of the model, the t tests of the regression coefficients, and the values of s_e, R^2, and adjusted R^2.

Solution

This regression analysis was done to predict the volume of freight cargo shipped annually in a country by road using the predictors "length of roads" and "number of commercial vehicles." The equation of the regression model was presented in the solution of Demonstration Problem 5.1. Shown here is the complete multiple regression output from the Excel analysis of the data.

The value of F for this problem is 3.86, with a p-value of .1163, which is not significant at $\alpha = .05$. On the basis of this information, the null hypothesis would not be rejected for the overall test of significance. None of the regression coefficients are significantly different from zero, and no significant predictability of the volume of freight cargo shipped by road is given from this regression model.

An examination of the t ratios support this conclusion using an $\alpha = .05$. The t ratio for length of roads is 2.34 with an associated p-value of .0793, and the t ratio for number of commercial vehicles is 2.39 with an associated p-value of .0750. Neither p-value is less than .05.

The standard error of the estimate is $s_e = 44,273.87$, indicating that approximately 68% of the residuals are within $\pm 44,273.87$. An examination of the Excel-produced residuals shows that actually five out of seven, or 71.4%, of the residuals fall in this interval. Approximately 95% of the residuals should be within $\pm 2(44,273.87) = \pm 88,547.74$, and an examination of the Excel-produced residuals shows that seven out of seven, or 100%, of the residuals are within this interval. Shipping industry researchers could examine the value of the standard error of the estimate to determine whether this model produces results with small enough error to suit their needs.

	A	B	C	D	E	F
1	Summary Output					
2	Regression Statistics					
3	Multiple R	0.812				
4	R Square	0.659				
5	Adjusted R Square	0.488				
6	Standard Error	44273.87				
7	Obervations	7				
8						
9	ANOVA					
10		df	SS	MS	F	Significance F
11	Regression	2	15148592381	7574296191	3.86	0.1163
12	Residual	4	7840701114	1960175278		
13	Total	6	22989293495			
14						
15		Coefficients	Standard Error	t Stat	P-value	
16	Intercept	-26425.45	67624.94	-0.39	0.7159	
17	Length	0.10182	0.04350	2.34	0.0793	
18	Vehicles	0.04095	0.01712	2.39	0.0750	
19						
20	Residual Output					
21	Observation	Predicted Miles	Residuals			
22	1	247276.61	31529.39			
23	2	134768.10	43590.90			
24	3	191296.29	-47296.29			
25	4	133523.80	5451.20			
26	5	105201.93	19969.07			
27	6	111667.11	-5843.11			
	7	143450.17	-47401.17			

R^2 for this regression analysis is .659 or 65.9%; that is, 65.9% of the variation in the volume of freight cargo is accounted for by these two independent variables. Conversely, 34.1% of the variation is unaccounted for by this model. The adjusted R^2 is only .488 or 48.8%, indicating that the value of R^2 is considerably inflated. Thus, it could be that the two predictors of the regression model actually account for less than half of the variation of the dependent variable when R^2 is adjusted.

This problem highlights the notion that a regression model can be developed for data and not really fit the data in a significant way. By examining the values of F, t, s_e, R^2, and adjusted R^2, the business researcher can begin to understand whether the regression model is providing any significant predictability for y.

5.4 PROBLEMS

5.22 Study the MINITAB regression output that follows. How many predictors are there? What is the equation of the regression model? Using the key statistics discussed in this chapter, discuss the strength of the model and the predictors.

Regression Analysis: Y versus X1, X2, X3, X4

```
The regression equation is
Y = - 55.9 + 0.0105 X1 - 0.107 X2 + 0.579 X3 - 0.870 X4
Predictor      Coef   SE Coef      T      P
Constant      -55.93    24.22   -2.31  0.025
      X1      0.01049  0.02100   0.50  0.619
      X2     -0.10720  0.03503  -3.06  0.003
      X3      0.57922  0.07633   7.59  0.000
      X4      -0.8695   0.1498  -5.81  0.000
S = 9.025   R-Sq = 80.2%   R-Sq(adj) = 78.7%
```

Analysis of Variance

Source	DF	SS	MS	F	P
Regression	4	18088.5	4522.1	55.52	0.000
Residual Error	55	4479.7	81.4		
Total	59	22568.2			

5.23 Study the Excel regression output that follows. How many predictors are there? What is the equation of the regression model? Using the key statistics discussed in this chapter, discuss the strength of the model and its predictors.

	A	B	C	D	E	F
1	Summary Output					
2	Regression Statistics					
3	Multiple R	0.814				
4	R Square	0.663				
5	Adjusted R Square	0.636				
6	Standard Error	51.761				
7	Obervations	28				
8						
9	ANOVA					
10		df	SS	MS	F	Significance F
11	Regression	2	131567.0243	65783.5121	24.55	0.0000013
12	Residual	25	66979.6543	2679.1862		
13	Total	27	198546.6786			
14						
15		Coefficients	Standard Error	t Stat	P-value	
16	Intercept	203.3937	67.5177	3.01	0.0059	
17	X1	1.1151	0.5278	2.11	0.0448	
18	X2	-2.2115	0.5667	-3.90	0.0006	

IN RESPONSE

Are You Going to Hate Your New Job?

In the Decision Dilemma, several variables are considered in attempting to determine whether a person will like his or her new job. Four predictor (independent) variables are given with the data set: relationship with supervisor, overall quality of work environment, total hours worked per week, and opportunities for advancement. Other possible variables might include openness of work culture, amount of pressure, how the interviewee is treated during the interview, availability of flexible scheduling, size of office, amount of time allotted for lunch, availability of management, interesting work, and many others.

Using the data that are given, a multiple regression model can be developed to predict job satisfaction from the four independent variables. Such an analysis allows the business researcher to study the entire data set in one model rather than constructing four different simple regression models, one for each independent variable. In the multiple regression model, job satisfaction is the dependent variable. There are 19 observations. The Excel regression output for this problem follows.

The test for overall significance of the model produced an F of 33.89 with a p-value of .00000046 (significant at $\alpha = .000001$). The R^2 of .906 and adjusted R^2 of .880 indicate strong predictability in the model. The standard error of the estimate, 8.03, can be viewed in light of the job satisfaction values that ranged from 10 to 95 and the residuals, which are not shown here. Sixteen of the 19 residuals (over 84%) are within the standard error of the estimate. Examining the t statistics and their associated p-values reveals that only one independent variable, "overall quality of work environment" ($t = 3.92$, p-value = .0015), is significant at $\alpha = .01$. Using a more generous α of .10, one could argue that "relationship with supervisor" is also a significant predictor of job satisfaction. Judging by their large p-values, it appears that "total hours worked per week" and "opportunities for advancement" are not good predictors of job satisfaction.

	A	B	C	D	E	F
1	Summary Output					
2	Regression					
3	Multiple R	0.952				
4	R Square	0.906				
5	Adjusted R Square	0.880				
6	Standard Error	8.03				
7	Observations	19				
8						
9	ANOVA					
10		df	SS	MS	F	Significance F
11	Regression	4	8748.967	2187.242	33.89	0.00000046
12	Residual	14	903.664	64.547		
13	Total	18	9652.632			
14						
15		Coefficients	Standard Error	t Stat	P-value	
16	Intercept	-2.6961	13.0047	-0.21	0.8387	
17	Relationship with Supervisior	6.9211	3.7741	1.83	0.0880	
18	Overall Quality of Work Environment	6.0814	1.5499	3.92	0.0015	
19	Total Hours Worked per Week	0.1063	0.1925	0.55	0.5895	
20	Opportunities for Advancement	0.3881	1.6322	0.24	0.8155	

ETHICAL CONSIDERATIONS

Multiple regression analysis can be used either intentionally or unintentionally in questionable or unethical ways. When degrees of freedom are small, an inflated value of R^2 can be obtained, leading to overenthusiastic expectations about the predictability of a regression model. To prevent this type of reliance, a researcher should take into account the nature of the data, the variables, and the value of the adjusted R^2.

Another misleading aspect of multiple regression can be the tendency of researchers to assume cause-and-effect relationships between the dependent variable and predictors. Just because independent variables produce a significant R^2 does not necessarily mean those variables are causing the deviation of the y values. Indeed, some other force not in the model may be driving both the independent variables and the dependent variable over the range of values being studied.

Some people use the estimates of the regression coefficients to compare the worth of the predictor variables; the larger the coefficient, the greater is its worth. At least two problems can be found in this approach. The first is that most variables are measured in different units. Thus, regression coefficient weights are partly a function of the unit of measurement of the variable. Second, if multicollinearity (discussed in Chapter 6) is present, the interpretation of the regression coefficients is questionable. In addition, the presence of multicollinearity raises several issues about the interpretation of other regression output. Researchers who ignore this problem are at risk of presenting spurious results.

Another danger in using regression analysis is in the extrapolation of the model to values beyond the range of values used to derive the model. A regression model that fits data within a given range does not necessarily fit data outside that range. One of the uses of regression analysis is in the area of forecasting. Users need to be aware that what has occurred in the past is not guaranteed to continue to occur in the future. Unscrupulous and sometimes even well-intentioned business decision makers can use regression models to project conclusions about the future that have little or no basis. The receiver of such messages should be cautioned that regression models may lack validity outside the range of values in which the models were developed.

SUMMARY

Multiple regression analysis is a statistical tool in which a mathematical model is developed in an attempt to predict a dependent variable by two or more independent variables or in which at least one predictor is nonlinear. Because doing multiple regression analysis by hand is extremely tedious and time-consuming, it is almost always done on a computer.

The standard output from a multiple regression analysis is similar to that of simple regression analysis. A regression equation is produced with a constant that is analogous to the y intercept in simple regression and with estimates of the regression coefficients that are analogous to the estimate of the slope in simple regression. An F test for the overall model is computed to determine whether at least one of the regression coefficients is significantly different from zero. This F value is usually displayed in an ANOVA table, which is part of the regression output. The ANOVA table also contains the sum of squares of error and sum of squares of regression, which are used to compute other statistics in the model.

Most multiple regression computer output contains t values, which are used to determine the significance of the regression coefficients. Using these t values, statisticians can make decisions about including or excluding variables from the model.

Residuals, standard error of the estimate, and R^2 are also standard computer regression output with multiple regression. The coefficient of determination for simple regression models is denoted r^2, whereas for multiple regression it is R^2. The interpretation of residuals, standard error of the estimate, and R^2 in multiple regression is similar to that in simple regression. Because R^2 can be inflated with nonsignificant variables in the mix, an adjusted R^2 is often computed. Unlike R^2, adjusted R^2 takes into account the degrees of freedom and the number of observations.

KEY TERMS

adjusted R^2

coefficient of multiple determination (R^2)

dependent variable

independent variable

least squares analysis

multiple regression

outliers

partial regression coefficient

residual

response plane

response surface

response variable

standard error of the estimate (s_e)

sum of squares of error (SSE)

FORMULAS

The F value

$$F = \frac{MS_{reg}}{MS_{err}} = \frac{SS_{reg}/df_{reg}}{SS_{err}/df_{err}} = \frac{SSR/k}{SSE/N-k-1}$$

Sum of squares of error

$$SSE = \Sigma(y - \hat{y})^2$$

Standard error of the estimate

$$s_e = \sqrt{\frac{SSE}{n-k-1}}$$

Coefficient of multiple determination

$$R^2 = \frac{SSR}{SS_{yy}} = 1 - \frac{SSE}{SS_{yy}}$$

Adjusted R^2

$$\text{Adjusted } R^2 = 1 - \frac{SSE/n-k-1}{SS_{yy}/n-1}$$

SUPPLEMENTARY PROBLEMS

CALCULATING THE STATISTICS

5.24 Use the following data to develop a multiple regression model to predict y from x_1 and x_2. Discuss the output, including comments about the overall strength of the model, the significance of the regression coefficients, and other indicators of model fit.

y	x_1	x_2
198	29	1.64
214	71	2.81
211	54	2.22
219	73	2.70
184	67	1.57
167	32	1.63
201	47	1.99
204	43	2.14
190	60	2.04
222	32	2.93
197	34	2.15

5.25 Given here are the data for a dependent variable, y, and independent variables. Use these data to develop a regression model to predict y. Discuss the output.

y	x_1	x_2	x_3
14	51	16.4	56
17	48	17.1	64
29	29	18.2	53
32	36	17.9	41
54	40	16.5	60
86	27	17.1	55
117	14	17.8	71
120	17	18.2	48
194	16	16.9	60
203	9	18.0	77
217	14	18.9	90
235	11	18.5	67

TESTING YOUR UNDERSTANDING

5.26 The U.S. Bureau of Mines produces data on the price of minerals. Shown here are the average prices per year for several minerals over a decade. Use these data and multiple regression to produce a model to predict the average price of gold from the other variables. Comment on the results of the process.

Gold ($ per oz.)	Copper (cents per lb.)	Silver ($ per oz.)	Aluminum (cents per lb.)
161.1	64.2	4.4	39.8
308.0	93.3	11.1	61.0
613.0	101.3	20.6	71.6
460.0	84.2	10.5	76.0
376.0	72.8	8.0	76.0
424.0	76.5	11.4	77.8
361.0	66.8	8.1	81.0
318.0	67.0	6.1	81.0
368.0	66.1	5.5	81.0
448.0	82.5	7.0	72.3
438.0	120.5	6.5	110.1
382.6	130.9	5.5	87.8

5.27 The Shipbuilders Council of America in Washington, D.C., publishes data about private shipyards. Among the variables reported by this organization are the employment figures (per 1,000), the number of naval vessels under construction, and the number of repairs or conversions done to commercial ships (in $ millions). Shown here are the data for these three variables over a 7-year period. Use the data to develop a regression model to predict private shipyard employment from number of naval vessels under construction and repairs or conversions of commercial ships. Comment on the regression model and its strengths and its weaknesses.

	Commercial Ship	
Employment	Naval Vessels	Repairs or Conversions
133.4	108	431
177.3	99	1,335
143.0	105	1,419
142.0	111	1,631
130.3	100	852
120.6	85	847
120.4	79	806

5.28 The U.S. Bureau of Labor Statistics produces consumer price indexes for several different categories. Shown here are the percentage changes in consumer price indexes over a period of 20 years for food, shelter, apparel, and fuel oil. Also displayed are the percentage changes in consumer price indexes for all commodities. Use these data and multiple regression to develop a model that attempts to predict all commodities by the other four variables. Comment on the result of this analysis.

All Commodities	Food	Shelter	Apparel	Fuel Oil
.9	1.0	2.0	1.6	3.7
.6	1.3	.8	.9	2.7
.9	.7	1.6	.4	2.6
.9	1.6	1.2	1.3	2.6
1.2	1.3	1.5	.9	2.1
1.1	2.2	1.9	1.1	2.4
2.6	5.0	3.0	2.5	4.4
1.9	.9	3.6	4.1	7.2
3.5	3.5	4.5	5.3	6.0
4.7	5.1	8.3	5.8	6.7
4.5	5.7	8.9	4.2	6.6
3.6	3.1	4.2	3.2	6.2
3.0	4.2	4.6	2.0	3.3
7.4	14.5	4.7	3.7	4.0
11.9	14.3	9.6	7.4	9.3
8.8	8.5	9.9	4.5	12.0
4.3	3.0	5.5	3.7	9.5
5.8	6.3	6.6	4.5	9.6
7.2	9.9	10.2	3.6	8.4
11.3	11.0	13.9	4.3	9.2

5.29 The U.S. Department of Agriculture publishes data annually on various selected farm products. Shown here are the unit production figures (in millions of bushels) for three farm products for 10 years during a 20-year period. Use these data and multiple regression analysis to predict corn production by the production of soybeans and wheat. Comment on the results.

Corn	Soybeans	Wheat
4,152	1,127	1,352
6,639	1,798	2,381
4,175	1,636	2,420
7,672	1,861	2,595
8,876	2,099	2,424
8,226	1,940	2,091
7,131	1,938	2,108
4,929	1,549	1,812
7,525	1,924	2,037
7,933	1,922	2,739

5.30 The American Chamber of Commerce Researchers Association compiles cost-of-living indexes for selected metropolitan areas. Shown here are cost-of-living indexes for 25 different cities on five different items for a recent year. Use the data to develop a regression model to predict the grocery cost-of-living index by the indexes of housing, utilities, transportation, and healthcare. Discuss the results, highlighting both the significant and nonsignificant predictors.

City	Grocery Items	Housing	Utilities	Transportation	Healthcare
Albany	108.3	106.8	127.4	89.1	107.5
Albuquerque	96.3	105.2	98.8	100.9	102.1
Augusta, GA	96.2	88.8	115.6	102.3	94.0
Austin	98.0	83.9	87.7	97.4	94.9
Baltimore	106.0	114.1	108.1	112.8	111.5
Buffalo	103.1	117.3	127.6	107.8	100.8
Colorado Springs	94.5	88.5	74.6	93.3	102.4
Dallas	105.4	98.9	108.9	110.0	106.8
Denver	91.5	108.3	97.2	105.9	114.3
Des Moines	94.3	95.1	111.4	105.7	96.2
El Paso	102.9	94.6	90.9	104.2	91.4
Indianapolis	96.0	99.7	92.1	102.7	97.4
Jacksonville	96.1	90.4	96.0	106.0	96.1
Kansas City	89.8	92.4	96.3	95.6	93.6
Knoxville	93.2	88.0	91.7	91.6	82.3
Los Angeles	103.3	211.3	75.6	102.1	128.5
Louisville	94.6	91.0	79.4	102.4	88.4
Memphis	99.1	86.2	91.1	101.1	85.5
Miami	100.3	123.0	125.6	104.3	137.8
Minneapolis	92.8	112.3	105.2	106.0	107.5
Mobile	99.9	81.1	104.9	102.8	92.2
Nashville	95.8	107.7	91.6	98.1	90.9
New Orleans	104.0	83.4	122.2	98.2	87.0
Oklahoma City	98.2	79.4	103.4	97.3	97.1
Phoenix	95.7	98.7	96.3	104.6	115.2

INTERPRETING THE OUTPUT

5.31 Shown here are the data for y and three predictors, $x_1, x_2,$ and x_3. A multiple regression analysis has been done on these data; the MINITAB results are given. Comment on the outcome of the analysis in light of the data.

y	x_1	x_2	x_3
94	21	1	204
97	25	0	198
93	22	1	184
95	27	0	200
90	29	1	182
91	20	1	159
91	18	1	147
94	25	0	196
98	26	0	228
99	24	0	242
90	28	1	162
92	23	1	180
96	25	0	219

Regression Analysis: Y versus X1, X2, X3

The regression equation is

Y = 87.9 - 0.256 X1 - 2.71 X2 + 0.0706 X3

Predictor	Coef	SE Coef	T	P
Constant	87.890	3.445	25.51	0.000
X1	-0.25612	0.08317	-3.08	0.013
X2	-2.7137	0.7306	-3.71	0.005
X3	0.07061	0.01353	5.22	0.001

S = 0.8503 R-Sq = 94.1% R-Sq(adj) = 92.1%

Analysis of Variance

Source	DF	SS	MS	F	P
Regression	3	103.185	34.395	47.57	0.000
Residual Error	9	6.507	0.723		
Total	12	109.692			

5.32 MINITAB residual diagnostic output from the multiple regression analysis for the data given in Problem 5.30 follows. Discuss any potential problems with meeting the regression assumptions for this regression analysis based on the residual graphics.

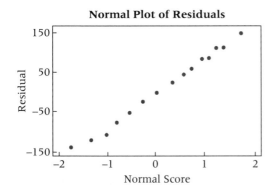

Normal Plot of Residuals

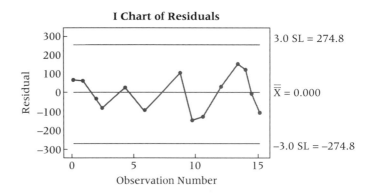

I Chart of Residuals

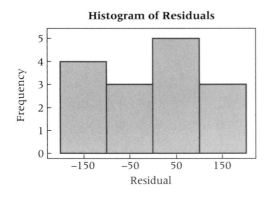

Histogram of Residuals

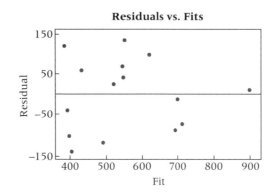

Residuals vs. Fits

ANALYZING THE DATABASES

see **www.wiley.com/college/black**

1. Use the manufacturing database to develop a multiple regression model to predict Cost of Materials by Number of Employees, New Capital Expenditures, Value Added by Manufacture, and End-of-Year Inventories. Discuss the results of the analysis.

2. Develop a regression model using the financial database. Use Total Revenues, Total Assets, Return on Equity, Earnings Per Share, Average Yield, and Dividends Per Share to predict the average P/E ratio for a company. How strong is the model? Which variables seem to be the best predictors?

3. Use the stock market database to develop a regression model to predict the composite index from Stock Volume, Reported Trades, Dollar Value, and Warrants Volume. Discuss the outcome including the model, the strength of the model, and the strength of the predictors.

CASE: STARBUCKS INTRODUCES DEBIT CARD

Starbucks is a resounding restaurant success story. Beginning with its first coffee house in 1971, Starbucks has grown to more than 5,200 locations with projections of reaching 10,000 by the year 2005. Opening up its first international outlet in the mid 1990s, Starbucks now operates in more than 22 countries (900 coffee houses) outside of North America. Besides selling beverages, pastries, confections, and coffee-related accessories and equipment at its retail outlets, Starbucks also purchases and roasts high-quality coffee beans in several locations. The company's objective is to become the most recognized and respected brand in the world. Starbucks maintains a strong environmental orientation and is committed to taking a leadership position environmentally. In addition, the company has won awards for corporate social responsibility through its community building programs, its strong commitment to its origins (coffee producers, family, community), and the Starbucks Foundation, which is dedicated to creating hope, discovery, and opportunity in the communities where Starbucks resides.

In November 2001, Starbucks launched its prepaid (debit) Starbucks Card. The card, which holds between $5 and $500, can be used at virtually any Starbucks location. The card was so popular when it first was released that many stores ran out. By mid-2002, Starbucks had activated more than 5 million of these cards. It is believed that the card accounted for a large portion of the company's 7% same store increase in sales in early 2002 and that it is responsible for attracting many new patrons to the store. As customers "reload" the cards, it appears they are placing more money on them than the initial value of the card.

Discussion

1. Starbucks enjoyed considerable success with its debit cards, which they sell for $5 to $500. Since the card was introduced in November 2001, sales revenues increased. Suppose Starbucks management wants to study the reasons why some people purchase debit cards with higher prepaid amounts than do other people. Suppose a study of 25 randomly selected prepaid card purchasers is taken. Respondents are asked the amount of the prepaid card, the customer's age, the number of days per month the customer makes a purchase at Starbucks, the number of cups of coffee the customer drinks per day, and the customer's income. The data follow. Using these data, develop a multiple regression model to study how well the amount of the prepaid card can be predicted by the other variables and which variables seem to be more promising in doing

the prediction. What sales implications might be evident from this analysis?

Amount of Prepaid Card ($)	Age	Days per Month at Starbucks	Cups of Coffee per Day	Income ($1,000)
5	25	4	1	20
25	30	12	5	35
10	27	10	4	30
5	42	8	5	30
15	29	11	8	25
50	25	12	5	60
10	50	8	3	30
15	45	6	5	35
5	32	16	7	25
5	23	10	1	20
20	40	18	5	40
35	35	12	3	40
40	28	10	3	50
15	33	12	2	30
200	40	15	5	80
15	37	3	1	30
40	51	10	8	35
5	20	8	4	25
30	26	15	5	35
100	38	19	10	45
30	27	12	3	35
25	29	14	6	35
25	34	10	4	45
50	30	6	3	55
15	22	8	5	30

2. Suppose marketing wants to be able to profile frequent visitors to a Starbucks store. Using the same data set already provided, develop a multiple regression model to predict Days per month at Starbucks by Age, Income, and Number of cups of coffee per day. How strong is the model? Which particular independent variables seem to have more promise in predicting how many days per month a customer visits Starbucks? What marketing implications might be evident from this analysis?

3. Over the past decade or so, Starbucks has grown quite rapidly. As they add stores and increase the number of drinks, their sales revenues increase. In reflecting about this growth, think about some other variables that might be related to the increase in Starbucks sales revenues. Some data for the past

seven years on the number of Starbucks stores (worldwide), approximate sales revenue (in $ millions), number of different drinks sold, and average weekly earnings of U.S. production workers are given here. Most figures are approximate. Develop a multiple regression model to predict sales revenue by number of drinks sold, number of stores, and average weekly earnings. How strong is the model? What are the key predictors, if any? How might this analysis help Starbucks management in attempting to determine what drives sales revenues?

Sales Year	Revenue	Number of Stores	Number of Drinks	Average Weekly Earnings
1	400	676	15	386
2	700	1015	15	394
3	1000	1412	18	407
4	1350	1886	22	425
5	1650	2135	27	442
6	2200	3300	27	457
7	2600	4709	30	474

Source: Adapted from Shirley Leung, "Starbucks May Indeed be a Robust Staple," The Wall Street Journal, 26 July 2002, p. B4; Starbucks, available at http://www.starbucks.com/aboutus; James Peters, "Starbucks' Growth Still Hot; Gift Card Jolts Chain's Sales," Nation's Restaurant News, 11 February, 2002, pp. 1–2.

USING THE COMPUTER

EXCEL

The Using the Computer section at the end of Chapter 4 contains directions for doing simple regression analysis by using Excel. Multiple regression analysis can be performed by using the same commands as those used for simple regression and explained in Chapter 4. Select **Tools** on the menu bar. From the pull-down menu that appears choose **Data Analysis.** This selection will produce the **Data Analysis** dialog box. From this, select **Regression.** In the dialog box shown, input the range of the *y* values in the first slot, **Input Y Range.** In the second slot, **Input X Range,** input the range of the *x* values. The *x* value range may include several columns and Excel will determine the number of predictor variables from the number of columns entered in this box. Other options and the standard output features are presented and explained in Chapter 4.

MINITAB WINDOWS

MINITAB Windows has the capability of generating multiple regression models and other regression techniques (explained and presented in Chapter 6). To analyze data with a multiple regression model, follow the procedures outlined in the Using the Computer section at the end of Chapter 4. Select **Stat** on the menu bar, followed by the selection of **Regression** on the pull-down menu and **Regression** again on the next pull-down menu. In the dialog box that appears, enter the column name of the dependent variable in the slot beside **Response** and the column names of the independent variables in the slot beside **Predictors.** The output described in Chapter 4 will result. The graphical residual analysis and other options are explained in Chapter 4.

CHAPTER 6

Building Multiple Regression Models

LEARNING OBJECTIVES

This chapter presents several advanced topics in multiple regression analysis enabling you to:

1. Analyze and interpret nonlinear variables in multiple regression analysis.
2. Understand the role of qualitative variables and how to use them in multiple regression analysis.
3. Learn how to build and evaluate multiple regression models.
4. Detect influential observations in regression analysis.

Determining Compensation for CEOs

Chief executive officers for large companies receive widely varying amounts of compensation for their work. Why is the range so wide? What are some of the variables that seem to contribute to the diversity of CEO compensation packages?

As a starting place, one might examine the role of company size as measured by sales volume, number of employees, number of plants, and so on in driving CEO compensation. It could be argued that CEOs of larger companies carry larger responsibilities and hence should receive higher compensation. Some researchers believe CEO compensation is related to such things as industry performance of the firm, percentage of stock that has outside ownership, and proportion of insiders on the board. At least a significant proportion of CEOs are likely to be compensated according to the performance of their companies during the fiscal period preceding compensation. Company performance can be measured by such variables as earnings per share, percentage change in profit, sales, and profit. In addition, some theorize that companies with outside ownership are more oriented toward declaring dividends to stockholders than toward large CEO compensation packages.

Do CEOs' individual and family characteristics play a role in their compensation? Do such things as CEO age, degrees obtained, marital status, military experience, and number of children matter in compensation? Do type of industry and geographic location of the company matter? What are the significant factors in determining CEO compensation?

What follow are CEO compensation data generated by using management compensation models published by Wyatt Data Services. In the first column on the left are cash compensation figures (in $1,000) for 20 CEOs. Those figures represent salary, bonuses, and any other cash remuneration given to the CEO as part of compensation. The four columns to the right contain data on four variables associated with each CEO's company: sales, number of employees, capital investment, and whether the company is in manufacturing. Sales figures and capital investment figures are given in $ millions.

Cash Compensation	Sales	Number of Employees	Capital Investment	Manufacturing
212	35.0	248.00	10.5	1
226	27.2	156.00	3.8	0
237	49.5	348.00	14.9	1
239	34.0	196.00	5.0	0
242	52.8	371.00	15.9	1
245	37.6	216.00	5.7	0
253	60.7	425.00	18.3	1
262	49.2	285.00	8.0	0
271	75.1	524.00	22.6	1
285	69.0	401.00	12.3	0
329	137.2	947.00	41.4	1
340	140.1	825.00	30.3	0
353	162.9	961.00	36.7	0
384	221.7	1,517.00	67.1	1
405	261.6	1,784.00	79.2	1
411	300.1	1,788.00	79.8	0
456	455.5	2,733.00	135.7	0
478	437.6	2,957.00	132.7	1
525	802.1	4,857.00	278.4	0
564	731.5	4,896.00	222.2	1

Managerial and Statistical Questions

1. Is it possible to sort out variables that appear to be related to CEO compensation and determine which variables are more significant predictors?

2. Can a model be developed to predict CEO compensation?

3. If a model is developed, how can the model be evaluated to determine whether it is valid?

4. Are some of the variables related to CEO compensation but in a nonlinear manner?

5. Are some variables highly interrelated and redundant in their potential for determining CEO compensation?

Sources: Adapted from Jeffrey L. Kerr and Leslie Kren, "Effect of Relative Decision Monitoring on Chief Executive Compensation," *Academy of Management Journal*, vol. 35, no. 2 (June 1992). Used with permission. Robin L. Bartlett, James H. Grant, and Timothy I. Miller, "The Earnings of Top Executives: Compensating Differentials for Risky Business," *Quarterly Reviews of Economics and Finance*, vol. 32, no. 1 (Spring 1992). Used with permission. Database derived using models published in *1993/1994 Top Management Compensation Regression Analysis Report*, 44th ed. (Fort Lee, NJ: Wyatt Data Services/ECS, December 1994).

6.1 NONLINEAR MODELS: MATHEMATICAL TRANSFORMATION

The regression models presented thus far are based on the general linear regression model, which has the form

(6.1)
$$y = \beta_0 + \beta_1 x_1 + \beta_2 x_2 + \ldots + \beta_k x_k + \epsilon,$$

where

β_0 = the regression constant

$\beta_1, \beta_2, \ldots, \beta_k$ are the partial regression coefficients for the k independent variables

$x_1, \ldots, x_k$ are the independent variables

k = the number of independent variables

In this general linear model, the parameters, β_i, are linear. It does not mean, however, that the dependent variable, y, is necessarily linearly related to the predictor variables. Scatter plots sometimes reveal a curvilinear relationship between x and y. Multiple regression response surfaces are not restricted to linear surfaces and may be curvilinear.

To this point, the variables, x_i, have represented different predictors. For example, in the real estate example presented in Chapter 5, the variables, x_1, x_2, represented two predictors: number of square feet in the house and the age of the house, respectively. Certainly, regression models can be developed for more than two predictors. For example, a marketing site location model could be developed in which sales, as the response variable, is predicted by population density, number of competitors, size of the store, and number of salespeople. Such a model could take the form

$$y = \beta_0 + \beta_1 x_1 + \beta_2 x_2 + \beta_3 x_3 + \beta_4 x_4 + \epsilon$$

This regression model has four x_i variables, each of which represents a different predictor.

The general linear model also applies to situations in which some x_i represent recoded data from a predictor variable already represented in the model by another independent variable. In some models, x_i represents variables that have undergone a mathematical transformation to allow the model to follow the form of the general linear model.

In this section of this chapter, we explore some of these other models, including polynomial regression models, regression models with interaction, and models with transformed variables.

Polynomial Regression

Regression models in which the highest power of any predictor variable is 1 and in which there are no interaction terms—cross products $(x_i \cdot x_j)$—are referred to as *first-order models*. Simple regression models like those presented in Chapter 4 are *first-order models with one independent variable*. The general model for simple regression is

$$y = \beta_0 + \beta_1 x_1 + \in$$

If a second independent variable is added, the model is referred to as a first-order model with two independent variables and appears as

$$y = \beta_0 + \beta_1 x_1 + \beta_2 x_2 + \in$$

Polynomial regression models are regression models that are second- or higher-order models. They contain squared, cubed, or higher powers of the predictor variable(s) and contain response surfaces that are curvilinear. Yet, they are still special cases of the general linear model given in formula (6.1).

Consider a regression model with one independent variable where the model includes a second predictor, which is the independent variable squared. Such a model is referred to as a second-order model with one independent variable because the highest power among the predictors is 2, but there is still only one independent variable. This model takes the following form:

$$y = \beta_0 + \beta_1 x_1 + \beta_2 x_1^2 + \in$$

This model can be used to explore the possible fit of a quadratic model in predicting a dependent variable. A **quadratic model** is *a multiple regression model in which the predictors are a variable and the square of the variable*. How can this be a special case of the general linear model? Let x_2 of the general linear model be equal to x_1^2 then $y = \beta_0 + \beta_1 x_1 + \beta_2 x_1^2 + \in$, becomes $y = \beta_0 + \beta_1 x_1 + \beta_2 x_2 + \in$. Through what process does a researcher go to develop the regression constant and coefficients for a curvilinear model such as this one?

Multiple regression analysis assumes a linear fit of the regression coefficients and regression constant, but not necessarily a linear relationship of the independent variable values (x). Hence, a researcher can often accomplish curvilinear regression by recoding the data before the multiple regression analysis is attempted.

As an example, consider the data given in Table 6.1. This table contains sales volumes (in $ millions) for 13 manufacturing companies along with the number of manufacturer's representatives associated with each firm. A simple regression analysis to predict sales by the number of manufacturer's representatives results in the Excel output in Figure 6.1. This

TABLE 6.1 Sales Data for 13 Manufacturing Companies	Manufacturer	Sales ($ millions)	Number of Manufacturing Representatives
	1	2.1	2
	2	3.6	1
	3	6.2	2
	4	10.4	3
	5	22.8	4
	6	35.6	4
	7	57.1	5
	8	83.5	5
	9	109.4	6
	10	128.6	7
	11	196.8	8
	12	280.0	10
	13	462.3	11

FIGURE 6.1

Excel Simple Regression
Output for Manufacturing
Example

	A	B	C	D	E	F
1	SUMMARY OUTPUT					
2	Regression Statistics					
3	Multiple R	0.933				
4	R Square	0.870				
5	Adjusted R Square	0.858				
6	Standard Error	51.098				
7	Observations	13				
8						
9	ANOVA					
10		df	SS	MS	F	Significant F
11	Regression	1	192395.416	192395.416	73.69	0.0000033
12	Residual	11	28721.452	2611.041		
13	Total	12	221116.868			
14						
15		Coefficients	Standard Error	t Stat	P-value	
16	Intercept	-107.029	28.7373	-3.72	0.0033561	
17	Reps	41.026	4.7794	8.58	0.0000033	

regression output shows a regression model with an r^2 of 87.0%, a standard error of the estimate equal to 51.10, a significant overall F test for the model, and a significant t ratio for the predictor number of manufacturer's representatives.

Figure 6.2(a) is a scatter plot for the data in Table 6.1. Notice that the plot of number of representatives and sales is not a straight line and is an indication that the relationship between the two variables may be curvilinear. To explore the possibility that a quadratic relationship may exist between sales and number of representatives, the business researcher creates a second predictor variable, (number of manufacturer's representatives)^2, to use in the regression analysis to predict sales along with number of manufacturer's representatives, as shown in Table 6.2. Thus, a variable can be created to explore second-order parabolic relationships by squaring the data from the independent variable of the linear model and entering it into the analysis. Figure 6.2(b) is a scatter plot of sales with (number of manufacturer's reps)^2. Note that this graph, with the squared term, more closely approaches a straight line than does the graph in Figure 6.2(a). By recoding the predictor variable, the researcher creates a potentially better regression fit.

With these data, a multiple regression model can be developed. Figure 6.3 shows the Excel output for the regression analysis to predict sales by number of manufacturer's representatives and (number of manufacturer's representatives)^2.

Examine the output in Figure 6.3 and compare it with the output in Figure 6.1 for the simple regression model. The R^2 for this model is 97.3%, which is an increase from the r^2 of 87.0% for the single linear predictor model. The standard error of the estimate for this model is 24.59, which is considerably lower than the 51.10 value obtained from the simple

FIGURE 6.2   MINITAB Scatter Plots of Manufacturing Data

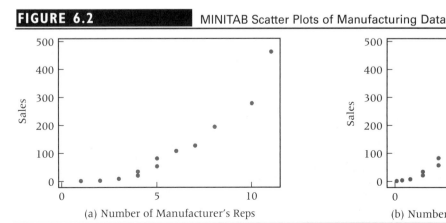

(a) Number of Manufacturer's Reps

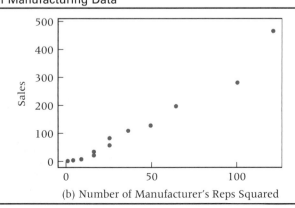

(b) Number of Manufacturer's Reps Squared

TABLE 6.2

Display of Manufacturing Data with Newly Created Variable

Manufacturer	Sales ($ millions) y	Number of Mgfr. Reps x_1	(Mgfr. Reps)^2 $x_2 = (x_1)^2$
1	2.1	2	4
2	3.6	1	1
3	6.2	2	4
4	10.4	3	9
5	22.8	4	16
6	35.6	4	16
7	57.1	5	25
8	83.5	5	25
9	109.4	6	36
10	128.6	7	49
11	196.8	8	64
12	280.0	10	100
13	462.3	11	121

FIGURE 6.3

Excel Output for Quadratic Model of Manufacturing Example

	A	B	C	D	E	F
1	SUMMARY OUTPUT					
2	Regression Statistics					
3	Multiple R	0.986				
4	R Square	0.973				
5	Adjusted R Square	0.967				
6	Standard Error	24.593				
7	Observations	13				
8						
9	ANOVA					
10		df	SS	MS	F	Significant F
11	Regression	2	215068.6001	107534.3	177.79	0.000000015
12	Residual	10	6048.3	604.8		
13	Total	12	221116.8677			
14						
15		Coefficients	Standard Error	t Stat	P-value	
16	Intercept	18.067	24.673	0.73	0.4808	
17	Reps	-15.723	9.550	-1.65	0.1307	
18	RepsSq	4.750	0.776	6.12	0.0001	

regression model. Remember, the sales figures were $ millions. The quadratic model reduced the standard error of the estimate by 26.51($1,000,000), or $26,510,000. It appears that the quadratic model is a better model for predicting sales.

An examination of the t statistic for the squared term and its associated probability in Figure 6.3 shows that it is statistically significant at $\alpha = .001$ ($t = 6.12$ with a probability of .0001). If this t statistic were not significant, the researcher would most likely drop the squared term and revert to the first-order model (simple regression model).

In theory, third- and higher-order models can be explored. Generally, business researchers tend to utilize first- and second-order regression models more than higher-order models. Remember that most regression analysis is used in business to aid decision making. Higher-power models (third, fourth, etc.) become difficult to interpret and difficult to explain to decision makers. In addition, the business researcher is usually looking for trends and general directions. The higher the order in regression modeling, the more the model tends to follow irregular fluctuations rather than meaningful directions.

Tukey's Ladder of Transformations

As just shown with the manufacturing example, recoding data can be a useful tool in improving the regression model fit. Many other ways of recoding data can be explored in this process. John W. Tukey* presents a "ladder of expressions" that can be explored to straighten out a plot of x and y, thereby offering potential improvement in the predictability of the regression model. **Tukey's ladder of transformations** gives the following expressions for both x and y.

Ladder for x
← Up Ladder ↓ Neutral Down Ladder →

$$\ldots, x^4, x^3, x^2, x, \sqrt{x}, x, \log x, \; -\frac{1}{\sqrt{x}}, \; -\frac{1}{x}, \; -\frac{1}{x^2}, \; -\frac{1}{x^3}, \; -\frac{1}{x^4}, \ldots$$

Ladder for y
← Up Ladder ↓ Neutral Down Ladder →

$$\ldots, y^4, y^3, y^2, y, \sqrt{y}, y, \log y, \; -\frac{1}{\sqrt{y}}, \; -\frac{1}{y}, \; -\frac{1}{y^2}, \; -\frac{1}{y^3}, \; -\frac{1}{y^4}, \ldots$$

These ladders suggest to the user potential ways to recode the data. Tukey published a **four-quadrant approach** to determining which expressions on the ladder are more appropriate for a given situation. This approach is based on the shape of the scatter plot of x and y. Figure 6.4 shows the four quadrants and the associated recoding expressions. For example, if the scatter plot of x and y indicates a shape like that shown in the upper left quadrant, recoding should move "down the ladder" for the x variable toward

$$\log x, \; -\frac{1}{\sqrt{x}}, \; -\frac{1}{x}, \; -\frac{1}{x^2}, \; -\frac{1}{x^3}, \; -\frac{1}{x^4}, \ldots$$

or "up the ladder" for the y variable toward

$$y^2, y^3, y^4, \ldots$$

Or, if the scatter plot of x and y indicates a shape like that of the lower right quadrant, the recoding should move "up the ladder" for the x variable toward

$$x^2, x^3, x^4, \ldots$$

or "down the ladder" for the y variable toward

$$\log y, -\frac{1}{\sqrt{y}}, -\frac{1}{y}, -\frac{1}{y^2}, -\frac{1}{y^3} - \frac{1}{y^4}, \ldots$$

In the manufacturing example, the graph in Figure 6.2(a) is shaped like the curve in the lower right quadrant of Tukey's four-quadrant approach. His approach suggests that

---

FIGURE 6.4

Tukey's Four-Quadrant Approach

Move toward $y^2, y^3, \ldots$ or toward $\log x, -1/\sqrt{x}, \ldots$ | Move toward $y^2, y^3, \ldots$ or toward x^2, x^3

Move toward $\log y, -1/\sqrt{y}, \ldots$ or toward $\log x, -1/\sqrt{x}, \ldots$ | Move toward $\log y, -1/\sqrt{y}, \ldots$ or toward $x^2, x^3, \ldots$

** John W. Tukey, *Exploratory Data Analysis*. Reading, MA, Addison-Wesley, 1977.*

the business researcher move "up the ladder" on x as was done by using the squared term. The researcher could have explored other options such as continuing on up the ladder of x or going down the ladder of y. Tukey's ladder is a continuum and leaves open other recoding possibilities between the expressions. For example, between x^2 and x^3 are many possible powers of x that can be explored, such as $x^{2.1}$, $x^{2.5}$, or $x^{2.86}$.

Regression Models with Interaction

Often when two different independent variables are used in a regression analysis, an *interaction* occurs between the two variables. In this interaction, one variable will act differently over a given range of values for the second variable than it does over another range of values for the second variable. For example, in a manufacturing plant, temperature and humidity might interact in such a way as to have an effect on the hardness of the raw material. The air humidity may affect the raw material differently at different temperatures.

In regression analysis, interaction can be examined as a separate independent variable. An interaction predictor variable can be designed by multiplying the data values of one variable by the values of another variable, thereby creating a new variable. A model that includes an interaction variable is

$$y = \beta_0 + \beta_1 x_1 + \beta_2 x_2 + \beta_3 x_1 x_2 + \in$$

The $x_1 x_2$ term is the interaction term. Even though this model has 1 as the highest power of any one variable, it is considered to be a second-order equation because of the $x_1 x_2$ term.

Suppose the data in Table 6.3 represent the closing stock prices for three corporations over a period of 15 months. An investment firm wants to use the prices for stocks 2 and 3 to develop a regression model to predict the price of stock 1. The form of the general linear regression equation for this model is

$$y = \beta_0 + \beta_1 x_1 + \beta_2 x_2 + \in$$

where

y = price of stock 1
x_1 = price of stock 2
x_2 = price of stock 3

Using MINITAB to develop this regression model, the firm's researcher obtains the first output displayed in Figure 6.5. This regression model is a first-order model with two predictors, x_1 and x_2. This model produced a modest R^2 of .472. Both of the t ratios are small and statistically nonsignificant ($t = -.62$ with a p-value of .549 and $t = -.36$ with a p-value of .728). Although the overall model is statistically significant, $F = 5.37$ with probability of .022, neither predictor is significant.

Sometimes the effects of two variables are not additive because of the interacting effects between the two variables. In such a case, the researcher can use multiple regression analysis to explore the interaction effects by including an interaction term in the equation.

$$y = \beta_0 + \beta_1 x_1 + \beta_2 x_2 + \beta_3 x_1 x_2 + \in$$

The equation fits the form of the general linear model

$$y = \beta_0 + \beta_1 x_1 + \beta_2 x_2 + \beta_3 x_3 + \in$$

where $x_3 = x_1 x_2$. Each individual observation of x_3 is obtained through a recoding process by multiplying the associated observations of x_1 and x_2.

Applying this procedure to the stock example, the researcher uses the interaction term and MINITAB to obtain the second regression output shown in Figure 6.5. This output contains x_1, x_2, and the interaction term, $x_1 x_2$. Observe the R^2, which equals .804 for this model. The introduction of the interaction term caused the R^2 to increase from 47.2% to 80.4%. In addition, the standard error of the estimate decreased from 4.570 in the first model to 2.909 in the second model. The t ratios for both the x_1 term and the interaction term are statistically significant in the second model ($t = 3.36$ with a p-value of .006 for x_1 and $t = -4.31$ with a probability of .001 for $x_1 x_2$). The inclusion of the interaction term

TABLE 6.3

Prices of Three Stocks over a 15 Month Period

Stock 1	Stock 2	Stock 3
41	36	35
39	36	35
38	38	32
45	51	41
41	52	39
43	55	55
47	57	52
49	58	54
41	62	65
35	70	77
36	72	75
39	74	74
33	83	81
28	101	92
31	107	91

FIGURE 6.5

Two MINITAB Regression Outputs—without and with Interaction

```
Regression Analysis: Stock 1 versus Stock 2, Stock 3

The regression equation is
Stock 1 = 50.9 - 0.119 Stock 2 - 0.071 Stock 3

Predictor      Coef  SE Coef       T       P
Constant     50.855    3.791   13.41   0.000
Stock 2     -0.1190   0.1931   -0.62   0.549
Stock 3     -0.0708   0.1990   -0.36   0.728

S = 4.570    R-Sq = 47.2%    R-Sq(adj) = 38.4%

Analysis of Variance

Source           DF       SS       MS       F       P
Regression        2   224.29   112.15    5.37   0.022
Residual Error   12   250.64    20.89
Total            14   474.93

Regression Analysis: Stock 1 versus Stock 2, Stock 3, Interaction

The regression equation is
Stock 1 = 12.0 + 0.879 Stock 2 + 0.220 Stock 3 - 0.00998 Interaction

Predictor        Coef   SE Coef       T       P
Constant       12.046     9.312    1.29   0.222
Stock 2        0.8788    0.2619    3.36   0.006
Stock 3        0.2205    0.1435    1.54   0.153
Interact    -0.009985  0.002314   -4.31   0.001

S = 2.909    R-Sq = 80.4% R-Sq(adj) = 75.1%

Analysis of Variance

Source           DF       SS       MS       F       P
Regression        3   381.85   127.28   15.04   0.000
Residual Error   11    93.09     8.46
Total            14   474.93
```

helped the regression model account for a substantially greater amount of the dependent variable and is a significant contributor to the model.

Figure 6.6(a) is the response surface for the first regression model presented in Figure 6.5 (the model without interaction). As you observe the response plane with stock 3 as the point of reference, you see the plane moving upward with increasing values of stock 1 as the plane moves away from you toward smaller values of stock 2. Now examine Figure 6.6(b), the response surface for the second regression model presented in Figure 6.5 (the model with interaction). Note how the response plane is twisted, with its slope changing as it moves along stock 2. This pattern is caused by the interaction effects of stock 2 prices and

---

FIGURE 6.6

Response Surfaces for the Stock Example—without and with Interaction

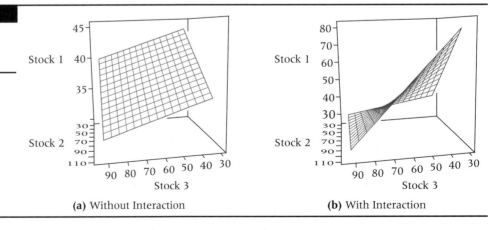

(a) Without Interaction   (b) With Interaction

stock 3 prices. A cross-section of the plane taken from left to right at any given stock 2 price produces a line that attempts to predict the price of stock 3 from the price of stock 1. As you move back through different prices of stock 2, the slope of that line changes, indicating that the relationship between stock 1 and stock 3 varies according to stock 2.

A researcher also could develop a model using two independent variables with their squares and interaction. Such a model would be a second-order model with two independent variables. The model would look like this.

$$y = \beta_0 + \beta_1 x_1 + \beta_2 x_2 + \beta_3 x_1^2 + \beta_4 x_2^2 + \beta_5 x_1 x_2 + \in$$

Model Transformation

To this point in examining polynomial and interaction models, the focus has been on recoding values of x variables. Some multiple regression situations require that the dependent variable, y, be recoded. To examine different relationships between x and y, Tukey's four-quadrant analysis and ladder of transformations can be used to explore ways to recode x or y in attempting to construct regression models with more predictability. Included on the ladder are such y transformations as log y and $1/y$.

Suppose the following data represent the annual sales and annual advertising expenditures for seven companies. Can a regression model be developed from these figures that can be used to predict annual sales by annual advertising expenditures?

Company	Sales ($ million/year)	Advertising ($ million/year)
1	2,580	1.2
2	11,942	2.6
3	9,845	2.2
4	27,800	3.2
5	18,926	2.9
6	4,800	1.5
7	14,550	2.7

One mathematical model that is a good candidate for fitting these data is an exponential model of the form

$$y = \beta_0 \beta_1^x \in$$

This model can be transformed (by taking the log of each side) so that it is in the form of the general linear equation.

$$\log y = \log \beta_0 + x \log \beta_1$$

This transformed model requires a recoding of the y data through the use of logarithms. Notice that x is not recoded but that the regression constant and coefficient are in logarithmic scale. If we let $y' = \log y$, $\beta_0' = \log \beta_0$, and $\beta_1' = \log \beta_1$, the exponential model is in the form of the general linear model.

$$y' = \beta_0' + \beta_1' x$$

The process begins by taking the log of the y values. The data used to build the regression model and the Excel regression output for these data follow.

Log Sales (y)	Advertising (x)
3.4116	1.2
4.0771	2.6
3.9932	2.2
4.4440	3.2
4.2771	2.9
3.6812	1.5
4.1629	2.7

	A	B	C	D	E	F
1	SUMMARY OUTPUT					
2	Regression Statistics					
3	Multiple R	0.990				
4	R Square	0.980				
5	Adjusted R Square	0.977				
6	Standard Error	0.0543				
7	Observations	7				
8						
9	ANOVA					
10		df	SS	MS	F	Significant F
11	Regression	1	0.739215	0.739215	250.36	0.000018
12	Residual	5	0.014763	0.002953		
13	Total	6	0.753979			
14						
15		Coefficients	Standard Error	t Stat	P-value	
16	Intercept	2.9003	0.0729	39.80	0.00000019	
17	Advertising	0.4751	0.0300	15.82	0.00001834	

A simple regression model (without the log recoding of the y variable) yields an R^2 of 87% whereas the exponential model R^2 is 98%. The t statistic for advertising is 15.82 with a p-value of 0.00001834 in the exponential model and 5.77 with a p-value of 0.00219 in the simple regression model. Thus the exponential model gives a better fit than does the simple regression model. An examination of (x^2, y) and (x^3, y) models reveals R^2 of .930 and .969, respectively, which are quite high but still not as good as the R^2 yielded by the exponential model.

The resulting equation of the exponential regression model is

$$y = 2.9003 + .4751x$$

In using this regression equation to determine predicted values of y for x, remember that the resulting predicted y value is in logarithmic form and the antilog of the predicted y must be taken to get the predicted y value in raw units. For example, to get the predicted y value (sales) for an advertising figure of 2.0 (\$ million), substitute $x = 2.0$ into the regression equation.

$$y = 2.9003 + .4751x = 2.9003 + .4751(2.0) = 3.8505$$

The log of sales is 3.8505. Taking the antilog of 3.8505 results in the predicted sales in raw units.

$$\text{antilog}(3.8505) = 7087.61 \text{ (\$ million)}$$

Thus, the exponential regression model predicts that \$2.0 million of advertising will result in \$7,087.61 million of sales.

Other ways can be used to transform mathematical models so that they can be treated like the general linear model. One example is an inverse model such as

$$y = \frac{1}{\beta_0 + \beta_1 x_1 + \beta_2 x_2 + \in}$$

Such a model can be manipulated algebraically into the form

$$\frac{1}{y} = \beta_0 + \beta_1 x_1 + \beta_2 x_2 + \in$$

Substituting $y' = 1/y$ into this equation results in an equation that is in the form of the general linear model.

$$y' = \beta_0 + \beta_1 x_1 + \beta_2 x_2 + \in$$

To use this "inverse" model, recode the data values for y by using $1/y$. The regression analysis is done on the $1/y$, x_1, and x_2 data. To get predicted values of y from this model, enter the raw values of x_1 and x_2. The resulting predicted value of y from the regression equation will be the inverse of the actual predicted y value.

DEMONSTRATION PROBLEM 6.1

In the aerospace and defense industry, some cost estimators predict the cost of new space projects by using mathematical models that take the form

$$y = \beta_0 x^{\beta_1} \in$$

These cost estimators often use the weight of the object being sent into space as the predictor (x) and the cost of the object as the dependent variable (y). Quite often β_1 turns out to be a value between 0 and 1, resulting in the predicted value of y equaling some root of x.

Use the sample cost data given here to develop a cost regression model in the form just shown to determine the equation for the predicted value of y. Use this regression equation to predict the value of y for $x = 3,000$.

y (cost in billions)	x (weight in tons)
1.2	450
9.0	20,200
4.5	9,060
3.2	3,500
13.0	75,600
0.6	175
1.8	800
2.7	2,100

Solution

The equation

$$y = \beta_0 x^{\beta_1} \in$$

is not in the form of the general linear model, but it can be transformed by using logarithms:

$$\log y = \log \beta_0 + \beta_1 \log x + \in$$

which takes on the general linear form

$$y' = \beta_0' + \beta_1 x'$$

where

$$y' = \log y$$
$$\beta_0' = \log \beta_0$$
$$x' = \log x$$

This equation requires that both x and y be recoded by taking the logarithm of each.

log y	log x
.0792	2.6532
.9542	4.3054
.6532	3.9571
.5051	3.5441
1.1139	4.8785
−.2218	2.2430
.2553	2.9031
.4314	3.3222

Using these data, the computer produces the following regression constant and coefficient:

$$b_0' = -1.25292 \qquad b_1 = .49606$$

From these values, the equation of the predicted y value is determined to be

$$\log \hat{y} = -1.25292 + .49606 \log x$$

If $x = 3{,}000$, log $x = 3.47712$, and
$$\text{log } \hat{y} = -1.25292 + .49606(3.47712) = .47194$$

then

$$\hat{y} = \text{antilog(log } \hat{y}) = \text{antilog}(.47194) = 2.9644$$

The predicted value of y is \$2.9644 billion for $x = 3{,}000$ tons of weight.

Taking the antilog of $b_0' = -1.25292$ yields $.055857$. From this and $b_1 = .49606$, the model can be written in the original form:
$$y = (.055857)x^{49606}$$

Substituting $x = 3{,}000$ into this formula also yields \$2.9645 billion for the predicted value of y.

6.1 PROBLEMS

6.1   Use the following data to develop a quadratic model to predict y from x. Develop a simple regression model from the data and compare the results of the two models. Does the quadratic model seem to provide any better predictability? Why or why not?

x	y	x	y
14	200	15	247
9	74	8	82
6	29	5	21
21	456	10	94
17	320		

6.2   Develop a multiple regression model of the form

$$y = b_0 b_1^x \in$$

using the following data to predict y from x. From a scatter plot and Tukey's ladder of transformation, explore ways to recode the data and develop an alternative regression model. Compare the results.

y	x	y	x
2,485	3.87	740	2.83
1,790	3.22	4,010	3.62
874	2.91	3,629	3.52
2,190	3.42	8,010	3.92
3,610	3.55	7,047	3.86
2,847	3.61	5,680	3.75
1,350	3.13	1,740	3.19

6.3   The Publishers Information Bureau in New York City released magazine advertising expenditure data compiled by leading national advertisers. The data were organized by product type over several years. Shown here are data on total magazine advertising expenditures and household equipment and supplies advertising expenditures. Using these data, develop a regression model to predict total magazine advertising expenditures by household equipment and supplies advertising expenditures and by (household equipment and supplies advertising expenditures)^2. Compare this model to a regression model to predict total magazine advertising expenditures by only household equipment and supplies advertising expenditures. Construct a scatter plot of the data. Does the shape of the plot suggest some alternative models in light of Tukey's four-quadrant approach? If so, develop at least one other model and compare the model to the other two previously developed.

Total Magazine Advertising Expenditures ($ millions)	Household Equipment and Supplies Expenditures ($ millions)
1,193	34
2,846	65
4,668	98
5,120	93
5,943	102
6,644	103

6.4 Dun & Bradstreet reports, among other things, information about new business incorporations and number of business failures over the years. Shown here are data on business failures since 1970 and current liabilities of the failing companies. Use these data and the following model to predict current liabilities of the failing companies by the number of business failures. Discuss the strength of the model.

$$y = b_0 b_1^x \in$$

Now develop a different regression model by recoding x. Use Tukey's four-quadrant approach as a resource. Compare your models.

Rate of Business Failures Since 1970 (10,000)	Current Liabilities of Failing Companies ($ millions)
44	1,888
43	4,380
42	4,635
61	6,955
88	15,611
110	16,073
107	29,269
115	36,937
120	44,724
102	34,724
98	39,126
65	44,261

6.5 Use the following data to develop a curvilinear model to predict y. Include both x_1 and x_2 in the model in addition to x_1^2 and x_2^2, and the interaction term $x_1 x_2$. Comment on the overall strength of the model and the significance of each predictor. Develop a regression model with the same independent variables as the first model but without the interaction variable. Compare this model to the model with interaction.

y	x_1	x_2
47.8	6	7.1
29.1	1	4.2
81.8	11	10.0
54.3	5	8.0
29.7	3	5.7
64.0	9	8.8
37.4	3	7.1
44.5	4	5.4
42.1	4	6.5
31.6	2	4.9
78.4	11	9.1
71.9	9	8.5
17.4	2	4.2
28.8	1	5.8
34.7	2	5.9
57.6	6	7.8
84.2	12	10.2
63.2	8	9.4
39.0	3	5.7
47.3	5	7.0

6.6 What follows is Excel output from a regression model to predict y using x_1, x_2, x_1^2, x_2^2, and the interaction term, $x_1 x_2$. Comment on the overall strength of the model and the significance of each predictor. The data follow the Excel output. Develop a regression model with the same independent variables as the first model but without the interaction variable. Compare this model to the model with interaction.

	A	B	C	D	E	F
1	SUMMARY OUTPUT					
2	Regression Statistics					
3	Multiple R	0.954				
4	R Square	0.910				
5	Adjusted R Square	0.878				
6	Standard Error	7.544				
7	Observations	20				
8						
9	ANOVA					
10		df	SS	MS	F	Significant F
11	Regression	5	8089.275	1617.855	28.43	0.00000073
12	Residual	14	796.725	56.909		
13	Total	19	8886			
14						
15		Coefficients	Standard Error	t Stat	P-value	
16	Intercept	464.4433	503.0955	0.92	0.3716	
17	x1	-10.5101	6.0074	-1.75	0.1021	
18	x2	-1.2212	1.9791	-0.62	0.5471	
19	x1Sq	0.0357	0.0195	1.84	0.0876	
20	x2Sq	-0.0002	0.0021	-0.08	0.9394	
21	x1*x2	0.0243	0.0107	2.28	0.0390	

y	x_1	x_2	y	x_1	x_2
34	120	190	45	96	245
56	105	240	34	79	288
78	108	238	23	66	312
90	110	250	89	88	315
23	78	255	76	80	320
34	98	230	56	73	335
45	89	266	43	69	335
67	92	270	23	75	250
78	95	272	45	63	372
65	85	288	56	74	360

6.2 INDICATOR (DUMMY) VARIABLES

Some variables are referred to as **qualitative variables** (as opposed to *quantitative* variables) because qualitative variables do not yield quantifiable outcomes. Instead, *qualitative variables yield nominal- or ordinal-level information,* which is used more to categorize items. These variables have a role in multiple regression and are referred to as **indicator,** or **dummy variables.** In this section, we will examine the role of indicator, or dummy variables as predictors or independent variables in multiple regression analysis.

Indicator variables arise in many ways in business research. Mail questionnaire or personal interview demographic questions are prime candidates because they tend to generate qualitative measures on such items as gender, geographic region, occupation, marital status, level of education, economic class, political affiliation, religion, management/non-management status, buying/leasing a home, method of transportation, or type of broker. In one business study, business researchers were attempting to develop a multiple regression model to predict the distances shoppers drive to malls in the greater Cleveland area. One independent variable was whether the mall was located on the shore of Lake Erie. In a second study, a site location model for pizza restaurants included indicator variables for (1) whether the restaurant served beer and (2) whether the restaurant had a salad bar.

These indicator variables are qualitative in that no interval or ratio level measurement is assigned to a response. For example, if a mall is located on the shore of Lake Erie, awarding it a score of 20 or 30 or 75 because of its location makes no sense. In terms of gender, what value would you assign to a man or a woman in a regression study? Yet these types of indicator, or dummy, variables are often useful in multiple regression studies and can be included if they are coded in the proper format.

Most researchers code indicator variables by using 0 or 1. For example, in the shopping mall study, malls located on the shore of Lake Erie could be assigned a 1, and all other malls would then be assigned a 0. The assignment of 0 or 1 is arbitrary, with the number merely holding a place for the category. For this reason, the coding is referred to as "dummy" coding; the number represents a category by holding a place and is not a measurement.

Many indicator, or dummy, variables are dichotomous, such as male/female, salad bar/no salad bar, employed/not employed, and rent/own. For these variables, a value of 1 is arbitrarily assigned to one category and a value of 0 is assigned to the other category. Some qualitative variables contain several categories, such as the variable "type of job," which might have the categories assembler, painter, and inspector. In this case, using a coding of 1, 2, and 3, respectively, is tempting. However, that type of coding creates problems for multiple regression analysis. For one thing, the category "inspector" would receive a value that is three times that of "painter." In addition, the values of 1, 2, and 3 indicate a hierarchy of job types: assembler < painter < inspector. The proper way to code such indicator variables is with the 0, 1 coding. Two separate independent variables should be used to code the three categories of type of job. The first variable is assembler, where a 1 is recorded if the person's job is assembler and a 0 is recorded if it is not. The second variable is painter, where a 1 is recorded if the person's job is painter and a 0 is recorded if it is not. A variable should not be assigned to inspector, because all workers in the study for whom a 1 was not recorded either for the assembler variable or the painter variable must be inspectors. Thus, coding the inspector variable would result in redundant information and is not necessary. This reasoning holds for all indicator variables with more than two categories. If an indicator variable has c categories, then $c - 1$ dummy variables must be created and inserted into the regression analysis in order to include the indicator variable in the multiple regression.*

An example of an indicator variable with more than two categories is the result of the following question taken from a typical questionnaire.

Your office is located in which region of the country?

_____ Northeast _____ Midwest _____ South _____ West

Suppose a researcher is using a multiple regression analysis to predict the cost of doing business and believes geographic location of the office is a potential predictor. How does the researcher insert this qualitative variable into the analysis? Because $c = 4$ for this question, three dummy variables are inserted into the analysis. Table 6.4 shows one possible way this process works with 13 respondents. Note that rows 2, 7, and 11 contain all zeros, which indicate that those respondents have offices in the West. Thus, a fourth dummy variable for the West region is not necessary and, indeed, should not be included because the information contained in such a fourth variable is contained in the other three variables.

A word of caution is in order. Because of degrees of freedom and interpretation considerations, it is important that a multiple regression analysis have enough observations to handle adequately the number of independent variables entered. Some researchers recommend as a rule of thumb at least three observations per independent variable. If a qualitative variable has multiple categories, resulting in several dummy independent variables, and if several qualitative variables are being included in an analysis, the number of predictors can rather quickly exceed the limit of recommended number of variables per number of observations. Nevertheless, dummy variables can be useful and are a way in which nominal or ordinal information can be recoded and incorporated into a multiple regression model.

As an example, consider the issue of gender discrimination in the salary earnings of workers in some industries. In examining this issue, suppose a random sample of 15 workers is drawn from a pool of employed laborers in a particular industry and the workers' average monthly salaries are determined, along with their age and gender. The data are shown in Table 6.5. As gender can be only male or female, this variable is a dummy variable requiring 0, 1 coding. Suppose we arbitrarily let 1 denote male and 0 denote female. Figure 6.7 is the multiple regression model developed from the data of Table 6.5 by using MINITAB to predict the dependent variable, monthly salary, by two independent variables, age and gender.

The computer output in Figure 6.7 contains the regression equation for this model.

Salary = 0.732 + 0.111 Age + 0.459 Gender

An examination of the t ratios reveals that the dummy variable "gender" has a regression coefficient that is significant at $\alpha = .001$ ($t = 8.58$, $p = .000$). The overall

TABLE 6.4

Coding for the Indicator Variable of Geographic Location for Regression Analysis

Northeast x_1	Midwest x_2	South x_3
1	0	0
0	0	0
1	0	0
0	0	1
0	1	0
0	1	0
0	0	0
0	0	1
1	0	0
1	0	0
0	0	0
0	1	0
0	0	1

* If c indicator variables are included in the analysis, no unique estimators of the regression coefficients can be found. [J. Neter, M. H. Kutner, W. Wasserman, and C. Nachtsheim. *Applied Linear Regression Models*, 3rd ed. (Chicago, Richard D. Irwin, 1996).

TABLE 6.5

Data for the Monthly
Salary Example

Monthly Salary ($1,000)	Age (10 years)	Gender (1 = male, 0 = female)
1.548	3.2	1
1.629	3.8	1
1.011	2.7	0
1.229	3.4	0
1.746	3.6	1
1.528	4.1	1
1.018	3.8	0
1.190	3.4	0
1.551	3.3	1
0.985	3.2	0
1.610	3.5	1
1.432	2.9	1
1.215	3.3	0
.990	2.8	0
1.585	3.5	1

FIGURE 6.7

MINITAB Regression Output for
the Monthly Salary Example

```
Regression Analysis: Salary versus Age, Gender

The regression equation is
Salary = 0.732 + 0.111 Age + 0.459 Gender

Predictor      Coef   SE Coef      T       P
Constant     0.7321    0.2356   3.11   0.009
Age          0.11122   0.07208  1.54   0.149
Gender       0.45868   0.05346  8.58   0.000

S = 0.09679    R-Sq = 89.0%    R-Sq(adj) = 87.2%

Analysis of Variance

Source          DF       SS        MS       F       P
Regression       2   0.90949   0.45474   48.54   0.000
Residual Error  12   0.11242   0.00937
Total           14   1.02191
```

model is significant at $\alpha = .001$ ($F = 48.54, p = .000$). The standard error of the estimate, $s_e = .09679$, indicates that approximately 68% of the errors of prediction are within $\pm$ \$96.79 (.09679 · \$1,000). The R^2 is relatively high at 89.0%, and the adjusted R^2 is 87.2%.

The t value for gender indicates that it is a significant predictor of monthly salary in this model. This significance is apparent when one looks at the effects of this dummy variable another way. Figure 6.8 shows the graph of the regression equation when gender = 1 (male) and the graph of the regression equation when gender = 0 (female). When gender = 1 (male), the regression equation becomes

$$.732 + .111(\text{Age}) + .459(1) = 1.191 + .111(\text{Age})$$

When gender = 0 (female), the regression equation becomes

$$.732 + .111(\text{Age}) + .459(0) = .732 + .111(\text{Age}).$$

The full regression model (with both predictors) has a response surface that is a plane in a three-dimensional space. However, if a value of 1 is entered for gender into the full regression model, as just shown, the regression model is reduced to a line passing through the plane formed by monthly salary and age. If a value of 0 is entered for gender, as shown, the full regression model also reduces to a line passing through the plane formed by

Predicting Export Intensity of Chinese Manufacturing Firms Using Multiple Regression Analysis

According to business researchers, Hongxin Zhao and Shaoming Zou, little research has been done on the impact of external or uncontrollable variables on the export performance of a company. These two researchers conducted a study of Chinese manufacturing firms and used multiple regression to determine whether both domestic market concentration and firm location are good predictors of a firm's export intensity. The study included 999 Chinese manufacturing firms that exported. The dependent variable was "export intensity," which was defined to be the proportion of production output that is exported and was computed by dividing the firm's export value by its production output value. The higher the proportion was, the higher the export intensity. Zhao and Zou used covariate techniques (beyond the scope of this text) to control for the fact that companies in the study varied by size, capital intensity, innovativeness, and industry. The independent variables were industry concentration and location. Industry concentration was computed as a ratio, with higher values indicating more concentration in the industry. The location variable was a composite index taking into account total freight volume, available modes of transportation, number of telephones, and size of geographic area.

The multiple regression model produced an R^2 of approximately 52%. Industry concentration was a statistically significant predictor at $\alpha = .01$, and the sign on the regression coefficient indicated that a negative relationship may exist between industry concentration and export intensity. It means export intensity is lower in highly concentrated industries and higher in lower concentrated industries. The researchers believe that in a more highly concentrated industry, the handful of firms dominating the industry will stifle the export competitiveness of firms. In the absence of dominating firms in a more fragmented setting, more competition and an increasing tendency to export are noted. The location variable was also a significant predictor at $\alpha = .01$. Firms located in coastal areas had higher export intensities than did those located in inland areas.

Source: Hongxin Zhao and Shaoming Zou, "The Impact of Industry Concentration and Firm Location on Export Propensity and Intensity: An Empirical Analysis of Chinese Manufacturing Firms," *Journal of International Marketing*, vol. 10, no. 1 (2002), pp. 52–71.

FIGURE 6.8

Regression Model for Male and Female Gender

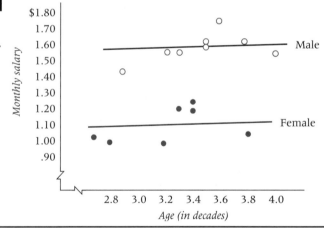

monthly salary and age. Figure 6.8 displays these two lines. Notice that the only difference in the two lines is the *y* intercept. Observe the monthly salary with male gender, as depicted by ○, versus the monthly salary with female gender, depicted by ●. The difference in the *y* intercepts of these two lines is .459, which is the value of the regression coefficient for gender. This intercept figure signifies that, on average, men earn $459 per month more than women for this population.

6.2 PROBLEMS

6.7 Analyze the following data by using a multiple regression computer software package to predict y using x_1 and x_2. Notice that x_2 is a dummy variable. Discuss the output from the regression analysis; in particular, comment on the predictability of the dummy variable.

y	x_1	x_2
16.8	27	1
13.2	16	0
14.7	13	0
15.4	11	1
11.1	17	0
16.2	19	1
14.9	24	1
13.3	21	0
17.8	16	1
17.1	23	1
14.3	18	0
13.9	16	0

6.8 Given here are the data from a dependent variable and two independent variables. The second independent variable is an indicator variable with several categories. Hence, this variable is represented by x_2, x_3, and x_4. How many categories are needed in total for this independent variable? Use a computer to perform a multiple regression analysis on this data to predict y from the x values. Discuss the output and pay particular attention to the dummy variables.

y	x_1	x_2	x_3	x_4
11	1.9	1	0	0
3	1.6	0	1	0
2	2.3	0	1	0
5	2.0	0	0	1
9	1.8	0	0	0
14	1.9	1	0	0
10	2.4	1	0	0
8	2.6	0	0	0
4	2.0	0	1	0
9	1.4	0	0	0
11	1.7	1	0	0
4	2.5	0	0	1
6	1.0	1	0	0
10	1.4	0	0	0
3	1.9	0	1	0
4	2.3	0	1	0
9	2.2	0	0	0
6	1.7	0	0	1

6.9 The MINITAB output displayed here is the result of a multiple regression analysis with three independent variables. Variable x_1 is a dummy variable. Discuss the computer output and the role x_1 plays in this regression model.

```
The regression equation is
Y = 121 + 13.4 X₁ -0.632 X₂ + 1.42 X₃

Predictor      Coef     Stdev      T       p
Constant     121.31     11.56   10.50    .000
     X₁       13.355     4.714    2.83    .014
     X₂      -0.6322    0.2270   -2.79    .015
     X₃        1.421     3.342    0.43    .678

S = 7.041    R-sq =79.5%    R-sq(adj) = 74.7%

Analysis of Variance

Source       df       SS        MS       F       p
Regression    3    2491.98   830.66   16.76    .000
Error        13     644.49    49.58
Total        16    3136.47
```

6.10 Given here is Excel output for a multiple regression model that was developed to predict y from two independent variables, x_1 and x_2. Variable x_2 is a dummy variable. Discuss the strength of the multiple regression model on the basis of the output. Focus on the contribution of the dummy variable. Plot x_1 and y with x_2 as 0, and then plot x_1 and y with x_2 as 1. Compare the two lines and discuss the differences.

	A	B	C	D	E	F
1	SUMMARY OUTPUT					
2	Regression Statistics					
3	Multiple R	0.623				
4	R Square	0.388				
5	Adjusted R Square	0.341				
6	Standard Error	11.744				
7	Observations	29				
8						
9	ANOVA					
10		df	SS	MS	F	Significant F
11	Regression	2	2270.11	1135.05	8.23	0.0017
12	Residual	26	3585.75	137.91		
13	Total	28	5855.86			
14						
15		Coefficients	Standard Error	t Stat	P-value	
16	Intercept	41.225	6.380	6.46	.00000076	
17	x1	1.081	1.353	0.80	.4316	
18	x2	-18.404	4.547	-4.05	.0004	

6.11 Falvey, Fried, and Richards[*] developed a multiple regression model to predict the average price of a meal at New Orleans restaurants. The variables explored included such indicator variables as the following: Accepts reservations, Accepts credit cards, Has its own parking lot, Has a separate bar or lounge, Has a maitre d', Has a dress code, Is candlelit, Has live entertainment, Serves alcoholic beverages, Is a steakhouse, Is in the French Quarter. Suppose a relatively simple model is developed to predict the average price of a meal at a restaurant in New Orleans from the number of hours the restaurant is open per week, the probability of being seated upon arrival, and whether the restaurant is located in the French

---

[*] *Adapted from* Rodney E. Falvey, Harold O. Fried, and Bruce Richards, "An Hedonic Guide to New Orleans Restaurants," *Quarterly Review of Economics and Finance*, vol. 32, no. 1 (Spring 1992).

Quarter. Use the following data and a computer to develop such a model. Comment on the output.

Price	Hours	Probability of Being Seated	French Quarter
$ 8.52	65	.62	0
21.45	45	.43	1
16.18	52	.58	1
6.21	66	.74	0
12.19	53	.19	1
25.62	55	.49	1
13.90	60	.80	0
18.66	72	.75	1
5.25	70	.37	0
7.98	55	.64	0
12.57	48	.51	1
14.85	60	.32	1
8.80	52	.62	0
6.27	64	.83	0

6.12 A researcher gathered 155 observations on four variables: job satisfaction, occupation, industry, and marital status. She wants to develop a multiple regression model to predict job satisfaction by the other three variables. All three predictor variables are qualitative variables with the following categories.

1. Occupation: accounting, management, marketing, finance
2. Industry: manufacturing, healthcare, transportation
3. Marital status: married, single

How many variables will be in the regression model? Delineate the number of predictors needed in each category and discuss the total number of predictors.

6.3 MODEL-BUILDING: SEARCH PROCEDURES

To this point in the chapter, we have explored various types of multiple regression models. We evaluated the strengths of regression models and learned how to understand more about the output from multiple regression computer packages. In this section we examine procedures for developing several multiple regression model options to aid in the decision-making process.

Suppose a researcher wants to develop a multiple regression model to predict the world production of crude oil. The researcher realizes that much of the world crude oil market is driven by variables related to usage and production in the United States. The researcher decides to use as predictors the following five independent variables.

1. U.S. energy consumption
2. Gross U.S. nuclear electricity generation
3. U.S. coal production
4. Total U.S. dry gas (natural gas) production
5. Fuel rate of U.S.-owned automobiles

The researcher measured data for each of these variables for the year preceding each data point of world crude oil production, figuring that the world production is driven by the previous year's activities in the United States. It would seem that as the energy consumption of the United States increases, so would world production of crude oil. In addition, it makes sense that as nuclear electricity generation, coal production, dry gas production, and fuel rates increase, world crude oil production would decrease if energy consumption stays approximately constant.

Table 6.6 shows data for the five independent variables along with the dependent variable, world crude oil production. Using the data presented in Table 6.6, the researcher attempted to develop a multiple regression model using five different independent variables. The result of this process was the MINITAB output in Figure 6.9. Examining the output, the researcher can reach some conclusions about that particular model and its variables.

The output contains an R^2 value of 92.1%, a standard error of the estimate of 1.215, and an overall significant F value of 46.62. Notice from Figure 6.9 that the t ratios indicate that the regression coefficients of four of the predictor variables, nuclear, coal, dry gas, and fuel rate, are not significant at $\alpha = .05$. If the researcher were to drop these four variables out of the regression analysis and rerun the model with the other predictor only, what would happen to the model? What if the researcher ran a regression model with only three predictors? How would these models compare to the full model with all five predictors? Are all the predictors necessary?

Developing regression models for business decision making involves at least two considerations. The first is to develop a regression model that accounts for the most variation of the dependent variable—that is, develop models that maximize the explained proportion of the deviation of the y values. At the same time, the regression model should be as parsimonious (simple and economical) as possible. The more complicated a quantitative

---

TABLE 6.6   Data for Multiple Regression Model to Predict Crude Oil Production

World Crude Oil Production (million barrels per day)	U.S. Energy Consumption (quadrillion BTUs generation per year)	U.S. Nuclear Electricity (billion kilowatt-hours)	U.S. Coal Gross Production (million short-tons)	U.S. Total Dry Gas Production (trillion cubic feet)	U.S. Fuel Rate for Automobiles (miles per gallon)
55.7	74.3	83.5	598.6	21.7	13.4
55.7	72.5	114.0	610.0	20.7	13.6
52.8	70.5	172.5	654.6	19.2	14.0
57.3	74.4	191.1	684.9	19.1	13.8
59.7	76.3	250.9	697.2	19.2	14.1
60.2	78.1	276.4	670.2	19.1	14.3
62.7	78.9	255.2	781.1	19.7	14.6
59.6	76.0	251.1	829.7	19.4	16.0
56.1	74.0	272.7	823.8	19.2	16.5
53.5	70.8	282.8	838.1	17.8	16.9
53.3	70.5	293.7	782.1	16.1	17.1
54.5	74.1	327.6	895.9	17.5	17.4
54.0	74.0	383.7	883.6	16.5	17.5
56.2	74.3	414.0	890.3	16.1	17.4
56.7	76.9	455.3	918.8	16.6	18.0
58.7	80.2	527.0	950.3	17.1	18.8
59.9	81.4	529.4	980.7	17.3	19.0
60.6	81.3	576.9	1029.1	17.8	20.3
60.2	81.1	612.6	996.0	17.7	21.2
60.2	82.2	618.8	997.5	17.8	21.0
60.2	83.9	610.3	945.4	18.1	20.6
61.0	85.6	640.4	1033.5	18.8	20.8
62.3	87.2	673.4	1033.0	18.6	21.1
64.1	90.0	674.7	1063.9	18.8	21.2
66.3	90.6	628.6	1089.9	18.9	21.5
67.0	89.7	666.8	1109.8	18.9	21.6

FIGURE 6.9	
MINITAB Output of Regression for Crude Oil Production Example	

```
Regression Analysis: CrOilPrd versus USEnCons, USNucGen, ...

The regression equation is
CrOilPrd = 2.71 + 0.836 USEnCons - 0.00654 USNucGen + 0.00983
           USCoalPr -0.143 USDryGas - 0.734 FuelRate

Predictor       Coef    SE Coef       T       P
Constant       2.708      8.909    0.30   0.764
USEnCons      0.8357     0.1802    4.64   0.000
USNucGen   -0.006544   0.009854   -0.66   0.514
USCoalPr    0.009825   0.007286    1.35   0.193
USDryGas     -0.1432     0.4484   -0.32   0.753
FuelRate     -0.7341     0.5488   -1.34   0.196

S = 1.215    R-Sq = 92.1% R-Sq(adj) = 90.1%

Analysis of Variance

Source          DF        SS       MS       F       P
Regression       5   343.916   68.783   46.62   0.000
Residual Error  20    29.510    1.476
Total           25   373.427
```

model becomes, the harder it is for managers to understand and implement the model. In addition, as more variables are included in a model, it becomes more expensive to gather historical data or update present data for the model. These two considerations (dependent variable explanation and parsimony of the model) are quite often in opposition to each other. Hence the business researcher, as the model builder, often needs to explore many model options.

In the world crude oil production regression model, if three variables explain the deviation of world crude oil production nearly as well as five variables, the simpler model is more attractive. How might researchers conduct regression analysis so that they can examine several models and then choose the most attractive one? The answer is to use search procedures.

Search Procedures

Search procedures are *processes whereby more than one multiple regression model is developed for a given database, and the models are compared and sorted by different criteria, depending on the given procedure.* Virtually all search procedures are done on a computer. Several search procedures are discussed in this section, including all possible regressions, stepwise regression, forward selection, and backward elimination.

All Possible Regressions

The **all possible regressions** search procedure *computes all possible linear multiple regression models from the data using all variables.* If a data set contains k independent variables, all possible regressions will determine $2^k - 1$ different models.

For the crude oil production example, the procedure of all possible regressions would produce $2^5 - 1 = 31$ different models from the $k = 5$ independent variables. With $k = 5$ predictors, the procedure produces all single-predictor models, all models with two predictors, all models with three predictors, all models with four predictors, and all models with five predictors, as shown in Table 6.7.

The all possible regressions procedure enables the business researcher to examine every model. In theory, this method eliminates the chance that the business researcher will never consider some models, as can be the case with other search procedures. On the other hand, the search through all possible models can be tedious, time-consuming, inefficient, and perhaps overwhelming.

	Single Predictor	Two Predictors	Three Predictors	Four Predictors	Five Predictors
TABLE 6.7	x_1	x_1, x_2	x_1, x_2, x_3	x_1, x_2, x_3, x_4	x_1, x_2, x_3, x_4, x_5
Predictors for All Possible Regressions with Five Independent Variables	x_2	x_1, x_3	x_1, x_2, x_4	x_1, x_2, x_3, x_5	
	x_3	x_1, x_4	x_1, x_2, x_5	x_1, x_2, x_4, x_5	
	x_4	x_1, x_5	x_1, x_3, x_4	x_1, x_3, x_4, x_5	
	x_5	x_2, x_3	x_1, x_3, x_5	x_2, x_3, x_4, x_5	
		x_2, x_4	x_1, x_4, x_5		
		x_2, x_5	x_2, x_3, x_4		
		x_3, x_4	x_2, x_3, x_5		
		x_3, x_5	x_2, x_4, x_5		
		x_4, x_5	x_3, x_4, x_5		

Stepwise Regression

Perhaps the most widely known and used of the search procedures is stepwise regression. **Stepwise regression** is *a step-by-step process that begins by developing a regression model with a single predictor variable and adds and deletes predictors one step at a time,* examining the fit of the model at each step until no more significant predictors remain outside the model.

STEP 1. In step 1 of a stepwise regression procedure, the k independent variables are examined one at a time by developing a simple regression model for each independent variable to predict the dependent variable. The model containing the largest absolute value of t for an independent variable is selected, and the independent variable associated with the model is selected as the "best" single predictor of y at the first step. Some computer software packages use an F value instead of a t value to make this determination. Most of these computer programs allow the researcher to predetermine critical values for t or F, but most also contain a default value as an option. If the first independent variable selected at step 1 is denoted x_1, the model appears in the form

$$\hat{y} = b_o + b_1 x_1$$

If, after examining all possible single-predictor models, it is concluded that none of the independent variables produces a t value that is significant at α, then the search procedure stops at step 1 and recommends no model.

STEP 2. In step 2, the stepwise procedure examines all possible two-predictor regression models with x_1 as one of the independent variables in the model and determines which of the other $k-1$ independent variables in conjunction with x_1 produces the highest absolute t value in the model. If this other variable selected from the remaining independent variables is denoted x_2 and is included in the model selected at step 2 along with x_1, the model appears in the form

$$\hat{y} = b_o + b_1 x_1 + b_2 x_2$$

At this point, stepwise regression pauses and examines the t value of the regression coefficient for x_1. Occasionally, the regression coefficient for x_1 will become statistically nonsignificant when x_2 is entered into the model. In that case, stepwise regression will drop x_1 out of the model and go back and examine which of the other $k-2$ independent variables, if any, will produce the largest significant absolute t value when that variable is included in the model along with x_2. If no other variables show significant t values, the procedure halts. It is worth noting that the regression coefficients are likely to change from step to step to account for the new predictor being added in the process. Thus, if x_1 stays in the model at step 2, the value of b_1 at step 1 will probably be different from the value of b_1 at step 2.

STEP 3. Step 3 begins with independent variables, x_1 and x_2 (the variables that were finally selected at step 2), in the model. At this step, a search is made to determine which of the $k - 2$ remaining independent variables in conjunction with x_1 and x_2 produces the largest significant absolute t value in the regression model. Let us denote the one that is selected as x_3. If no significant t values are acknowledged at this step, the process stops here and the model determined in step 2 is the final model. At step 3, the model appears in the form

$$\hat{y} = b_o + b_1 x_1 + b_2 x_2 + b_3 x_3$$

In a manner similar to step 2, stepwise regression now goes back and examines the t values of the regression coefficients of x_1 and x_2 in this step 3 model. If either or both of the t values are now nonsignificant, the variables are dropped out of the model and the process calls for a search through the remaining $k - 3$ independent variables to determine which, if any, in conjunction with x_3 produce the largest significant t values in this model. The stepwise regression process continues step by step until no significant independent variables remain that are not in the model.

In the crude oil production example, recall that Table 6.6 contained data that can be used to develop a regression model to predict world crude oil production from as many as five different independent variables. Figure 6.9 displayed the results of a multiple regression analysis to produce a model using all five predictors. Suppose the researcher were to use a stepwise regression search procedure on these data to find a regression model. Recall that the following independent variables were being considered.

1. U.S. energy consumption
2. U.S. nuclear generation
3. U.S. coal production
4. U.S. dry gas production
5. U.S. fuel rate

STEP 1. Each of the independent variables is examined one at a time to determine the strength of each predictor in a simple regression model. The results are reported in Table 6.8.

Note that the independent variable "energy consumption" was selected as the predictor variable, x_1, in step 1. An examination of Table 6.8 reveals that energy consumption produced the largest absolute t value (11.77) of the single predictors. By itself, energy consumption accounted for 85.2% of the variation of the y values (world crude oil production). The regression equation taken from the computer output for this model is

$$y = 13.075 + .580 x_1$$

where

y = world crude oil production
x_1 = U.S. energy consumption

STEP 2. In step 2, x_1 was retained initially in the model and a search was conducted among the four remaining independent variables to determine which of those variables in conjunction with x_1 produced the largest significant t value. Table 6.9 reports the results of this search.

The information in Table 6.9 shows that the model selected in step 2 includes the independent variables "energy consumption" and "fuel rate." Fuel rate has the largest absolute t value (−3.75), and it is significant at $\alpha = .05$. Other variables produce varying sizes of t values. The model produced at step 2 has an R^2 of 90.8%. These two variables taken together account for almost 91% of the variation of world crude oil production in this sample.

From other computer information, it is ascertained that the t value for the x_1 variable in this model is 11.91, which is even higher than in step 1.

TABLE 6.8

Step 1: Results of Simple Regression Using Each Independent Variable to Predict Oil Production

Dependent Variable	Independent Variable	t Ratio	R^2
Oil production	Energy consumption	11.77	85.2%
Oil production	Nuclear	4.43	45.0
Oil production	Coal	3.91	38.9
Oil production	Dry gas	1.08	4.6
Oil production	Fuel rate	3.54	34.2

→ Variable selected to serve as x_1

TABLE 6.9

Step 2: Regression Results with Two Predictors

Dependent Variable y	Independent Variable x_1	Independent Variable x_2	t Ratio of x_2	R^2
Oil production	Energy consumption	Nuclear	−3.60	90.6%
Oil production	Energy consumption	Coal	−2.44	88.3
Oil production	Energy consumption	Dry gas	2.23	87.9
Oil production	Energy consumption	Fuel rate	−3.75	90.8

→ Variables selected at step 2

Therefore, x_1 will not be dropped from the model by the stepwise regression procedure. The step 2 regression model from the computer output is

$$y = 7.14 + 0.772x_1 - 0.517x_2$$

where

y = world crude oil production
x_1 = U.S. energy consumption
x_2 = U.S. fuel rate

Note that the regression coefficient for x_1 changed from .580 at step 1 in the model to .772 at step 2.

The R^2 for the model in step 1 was 85.2%. Notice that none of the R^2 values produced from step 2 models is less than 85.2%. The reason is that x_1 is still in the model, so the R^2 at this step must be at least as high as it was in step 1, when only x_1 was in the model. In addition, by examining the R^2 values in Table 6.9, you can get a feel for how much the prospective new predictor adds to the model by seeing how much R^2 increases from 85.2%. For example, with x_2 (fuel rate) added to the model, the R^2 goes up to 90.8%. However, adding the variable "dry gas" to x_1 increases R^2 very little (it goes up 87.9%).

STEP 3. In step 3, the search procedure continues to look for an additional predictor variable from the three independent variables remaining out of the solution. Variables x_1 and x_2 are retained in the model. Table 6.10 reports the result of this search.

In this step, regression models are explored that contain x_1 (energy consumption) and x_2 (fuel rate) in addition to one of the three remaining variables. None of the three models produce t ratios that are significant at $\alpha = .05$. No new variables are added to the model produced in step 2. The stepwise regression process ends.

Figure 6.10 shows the MINITAB stepwise regression output for the world crude oil production example. The results printed in the table are virtually identical to the step-by-step results discussed in this section, but are in a different format.

Each column in Figure 6.10 contains information about the regression model at each step. Thus, column 1 contains data on the regression model for step 1. In each column at each step you can see the variables in the model. As an example, at step 2, energy consumption and fuel rate are in the model. The numbers above the t ratios are the

TABLE 6.10	Dependent Variable y	Independent Variable x_1	Independent Variable x_2	Independent Variable x_3	t Ratio of x_3	R^2
Step 3: Regression Results with Three Predictors	Oil production	Energy consumption	Fuel rate	Nuclear	−0.43	90.9%
	Oil production	Energy consumption	Fuel rate	Coal	1.71	91.9
	Oil production	Energy consumption	Fuel rate	Dry gas	−0.46	90.9
	No t ratio is significant at $\alpha = .05$. No new variables are added to the model.					

FIGURE 6.10

MINITAB Stepwise Regression Output for the Crude Oil Production Example

```
Stepwise Regression: CrOilPrd versus USEnCons, USNucGen, ...
Alpha-to-Enter: 0.1 Alpha-to-Remove: 0.1
Response is CrOilPrd on 5 predictors, with N =   26
Step              1       2
Constant     13.075   7.140

USEnCons      0.580   0.772
T-Value       11.77   11.91
P-Value       0.000   0.000

FuelRate             -0.52
T-Value              -3.75
P-Value               0.001

S             1.52    1.22
R-Sq         85.24   90.83
R-Sq(adj)    84.62   90.03
C-p           15.4     3.2
```

---

regression coefficients. The coefficients and the constant in column 2, for example, yield the regression model equation values for step 2.

$$\hat{y} = 7.140 + 0.772x_1 - 0.52x_2$$

The values of R^2 (R-Sq) and the standard error of the estimate (S) are displayed on the bottom row of the output along with the adjusted value of R^2 and the C_p (C-p) statistic, which is a measure of the difference between the estimated model and the true model.

Forward Selection

Another search procedure is forward selection. **Forward selection** is essentially the same as stepwise regression, but once a variable is entered into the process, it is never dropped out. Forward selection begins by finding the independent variable that will produce the largest absolute value of t (and largest R^2) in predicting y. The selected variable is denoted here as x_1 and is part of the model

$$\hat{y} = b_0 + b_1 x_1$$

Forward selection proceeds to step 2. While retaining x_1, it examines the other $k - 1$ independent variables and determines which variable in the model with x_1 produces the highest absolute value of t that is significant. To this point, forward selection is the same as stepwise regression. If this second variable is designated x_2, the model is

$$\hat{y} = b_0 + b_1 x_1 + b_2 x_2$$

At this point, forward selection does not reexamine the t value of x_1. Both x_1 and x_2 remain in the model as other variables are examined and included. When independent variables are correlated in forward selection, the overlapping of information can limit the potential predictability of two or more variables in combination. Stepwise regression takes this into account, in part, when it goes back to reexamine the t values of predictors already in the model to determine whether they are still significant predictors of y given the variables that have now entered the process. In other words, stepwise regression acknowledges that the strongest single predictor of y that is selected at step 1 may not be a significant predictor of y when taken in conjunction with other variables.

Using a forward selection procedure to develop multiple regression models for the world crude oil production example would result in the same outcome as that provided by stepwise regression because neither x_1 nor x_2 were removed from the model in that particular stepwise regression. The difference in the two procedures is more apparent in examples where variables selected at earlier steps in the process are removed during later steps in stepwise regression.

Backward Elimination

The **backward elimination** search procedure is *a step-by-step process that begins with the "full" model (all k predictors).* Using the t values, a search is made to determine whether any nonsignificant independent variables are in the model. If no nonsignificant predictors are found, the backward process ends with the full model. If nonsignificant predictors are found, the predictor with the smallest absolute value of t is eliminated and a new model is developed with $k - 1$ independent variables.

This model is then examined to determine whether it contains any independent variables with nonsignificant t values. If it does, the predictor with the smallest absolute t value is eliminated from the process and a new model is developed for the next step.

This procedure of identifying the smallest nonsignificant t value and eliminating that variable continues until all variables left in the model have significant t values. Sometimes this process yields results similar to those obtained from forward selection and other times it does not. A word of caution is in order. Backward elimination always begins with all possible predictors in the model. Sometimes the sample data do not provide enough observations to justify the use of all possible predictors at the same time in the model. In this case, backward elimination is not a suitable option with which to build regression models.

The following steps show how the backward elimination process can be used to develop multiple regression models to predict world crude oil production using the data and five predictors displayed in Table 6.6.

STEP 1. A full model is developed with all predictors. The results are shown in Table 6.11. The R^2 for this model is 92.1%. A study of Table 6.11 reveals that the predictor "dry gas" has the smallest absolute value of a nonsignificant t ($t = -.32, p = .753$). In step 2, this variable will be dropped from the model.

STEP 2. A second regression model is developed with $k - 1 = 4$ predictors. Dry gas has been eliminated from consideration. The results of this multiple regression analysis are presented in Table 6.12. The computer results in Table 6.12 indicate that the variable "nuclear" has the smallest absolute value of a nonsignificant t of the variables remaining in the model ($t = -.64, p = .528$). In step 3, this variable will be dropped from the model.

STEP 3. A third regression model is developed with $k - 2 = 3$ predictors. Both nuclear and dry gas variables have been removed from the model. The results of this multiple regression analysis are reported in Table 6.13. The computer results in Table 6.13 indicate that the variable "coal" has the smallest absolute value of a nonsignificant t of the variables remaining in the model ($t = 1.71, p = .102$). In step 4, this variable will be dropped from the model.

STEP 4. A fourth regression model is developed with $k - 3 = 2$ predictors. Nuclear, dry gas, and coal variables have been removed from the model. The results of this multiple regression analysis are reported in Table 6.14. Observe that all p-values are less than $\alpha = .05$, indicating that all t values are significant, so no

TABLE 6.11
Step 1: Backward Elimination, Full Model

Predictor	Coefficient	t Ratio	p
Energy consumption	.8357	4.64	.000
Nuclear	−.00654	−0.66	.514
Coal	.00983	1.35	.193
Dry gas	−.1432	−0.32	.753
Fuel rate	−.7341	−1.34	.196

Variable to be dropped from the model

TABLE 6.12
Step 2: Backward Elimination, Four Predictors

Predictor	Coefficient	t Ratio	p
Energy consumption	.7843	9.85	.000
Nuclear	−.004261	−0.64	.528
Coal	.010933	1.74	.096
Fuel rate	−.8253	−1.80	.086

Variable to be dropped from the model

TABLE 6.13
Step 3: Backward Elimination, Three Predictors

Predictor	Coefficient	t Ratio	p
Energy consumption	.75394	11.94	.000
Coal	.010479	1.71	.102
Fuel rate	−1.0283	−3.14	.005

Variable to be dropped from the model

TABLE 6.14
Step 4: Backward Elimination, Two Predictors

Predictor	Coefficient	t Ratio	p
Energy consumption	.77201	11.91	.000
Fuel rate	−.5173	−3.75	.001

All variables are significant at $\alpha = .05$.
No variables will be dropped from this model.
The process stops.

additional independent variables need to be removed. The backward elimination process ends with two predictors in the model. The final model obtained from this backward elimination process is the same model as that obtained by using stepwise regression.

6.3 PROBLEMS

6.13 Use a stepwise regression procedure and the following data to develop a multiple regression model to predict y. Discuss the variables that enter at each step, commenting on their t values and on the value of R^2.

y	x_1	x_2	x_3	y	x_1	x_2	x_3
21	5	108	57	22	13	105	51
17	11	135	34	20	10	111	43
14	14	113	21	16	20	140	20
13	9	160	25	13	19	150	14
19	16	122	43	18	14	126	29
15	18	142	40	12	21	175	22
24	7	93	52	23	6	98	38
17	9	128	38	18	15	129	40

6.14 Given here are data for a dependent variable and four potential predictors. Use these data and a stepwise regression procedure to develop a multiple regression model to predict y. Examine the values of t and R^2 at each step and comment on those values. How many steps did the procedure use? Why do you think the process stopped?

y	x_1	x_2	x_3	x_4
101	2	77	1.2	42
127	4	72	1.7	26
98	9	69	2.4	47
79	5	53	2.6	65
118	3	88	2.9	37
114	1	53	2.7	28
110	3	82	2.8	29
94	2	61	2.6	22
96	8	60	2.4	48
73	6	64	2.1	42
108	2	76	1.8	34
124	5	74	2.2	11
82	6	50	1.5	61
89	9	57	1.6	53
76	1	72	2.0	72
109	3	74	2.8	36
123	2	99	2.6	17
125	6	81	2.5	48

6.15 The computer output given here is the result of a stepwise multiple regression analysis to predict a dependent variable by using six predictor variables. The number of observations was 108. Study the output and discuss the results. How many predictors ended up in the model? Which predictors, if any, did not enter the model?

```
STEPWISE REGRESSION OF Y ON 6 PREDICTORS, WITH N = 108
STEP            1       2       3       4
CONSTANT     8.71    6.82    6.57    5.96

X4          -2.85   -4.92   -4.97   -5.00
T-RATIO      2.11    2.94    3.04    3.07

X2                   4.42    3.72    3.22
T-RATIO              2.64    2.20    2.05

X3                           1.91    1.78
T-RATIO                      2.07    2.02

X7                                   1.56
T-RATIO                              1.98

S            3.81    3.51    3.43    3.36
R-SQ        29.20   49.45   54.72   59.29
```

6.16 Study the output given here from a stepwise multiple regression analysis to predict y from four variables. Comment on the output at each step.

```
STEPWISE REGRESSION OF Y ON 4 PREDICTORS, WITH N = 63
STEP            1       2
CONSTANT     27.88   22.30

X3           0.89
T-RATIO      2.26

X2                   12.38
T-RATIO               2.64

X4                   0.0047
T-RATIO               2.01

S           16.52    9.47
R-SQ        42.39   68.20
```

6.17 The National Underwriter Company in Cincinnati, Ohio, publishes property and casualty insurance data. Given here is a portion of the data published. These data include information from the U.S. insurance industry about (1) net income after taxes, (2) dividends to policyholders, (3) net underwriting gain/loss, and (4) premiums earned. Use the data and stepwise regression to predict premiums earned from the other three variables.

Premiums Earned	Net Income	Dividends	Underwriting Gain/Loss
30.2	1.6	.6	.1
47.2	.6	.7	−3.6
92.8	8.4	1.8	−1.5
95.4	7.6	2.0	−4.9
100.4	6.3	2.2	−8.1
104.9	6.3	2.4	−10.8
113.2	2.2	2.3	−18.2
130.3	3.0	2.4	−21.4
161.9	13.5	2.3	−12.8
182.5	14.9	2.9	−5.9
193.3	11.7	2.9	−7.6

6.18 The U.S. Energy Information Administration releases figures in their publication, *Monthly Energy Review*, about the cost of various fuels and electricity. Shown here are the figures for four different items over a 12-year period. Use the data and stepwise regression to predict the cost of residential electricity from the cost of residential natural gas, residual fuel oil, and leaded regular gasoline. Examine the data and discuss the output.

Residential Electricity (kWh)	Residential Natural Gas (1000 ft³)	Residual Fuel Oil (gal)	Leaded Regular Gasoline (gal)
2.54	1.29	.21	.39
3.51	1.71	.31	.57
4.64	2.98	.44	.86
5.36	3.68	.61	1.19
6.20	4.29	.76	1.31
6.86	5.17	.68	1.22
7.18	6.06	.65	1.16
7.54	6.12	.69	1.13
7.79	6.12	.61	1.12
7.41	5.83	.34	.86
7.41	5.54	.42	.90
7.49	4.49	.33	.90

6.4 MULTICOLLINEARITY

One problem that can arise in multiple regression analysis is multicollinearity. **Multicollinearity** is *when two or more of the independent variables of a multiple regression model are highly correlated.* Technically, if two of the independent variables are correlated, we have collinearity; when three or more independent variables are correlated, we have multicollinearity. However, the two terms are frequently used interchangeably.

The reality of business research is that most of the time some correlation between predictors (independent variables) will be present. The problem of multicollinearity arises when the intercorrelation between predictor variables is high. This relationship causes several other problems, particularly in the interpretation of the analysis.

1. It is difficult, if not impossible, to interpret the estimates of the regression coefficients.
2. Inordinately small t values for the regression coefficients may result.
3. The standard deviations of regression coefficients are overestimated.
4. The algebraic sign of estimated regression coefficients may be the opposite of what would be expected for a particular predictor variable.

The problem of multicollinearity can arise in regression analysis in a variety of business research situations. For example, suppose a model is being developed to predict salaries in a given industry. Independent variables such as years of education, age, years in management, experience on the job, and years of tenure with the firm might be considered as predictors. It is obvious that several of these variables are correlated (virtually all of these variables have something to do with number of years, or time) and yield redundant information. Suppose a financial regression model is being developed to predict bond market rates by such independent variables as Dow Jones average, prime interest rates, GNP, producer price index, and consumer price index. Several of these predictors are likely to be intercorrelated.

In the world crude oil production example used in Section 6.3, several of the independent variables are intercorrelated, leading to the potential of multicollinearity problems. Table 6.15 gives the correlations of the predictor variables for this example. Note that r values are quite high ($r > .90$) for fuel rate and nuclear (.972), fuel rate and coal (.968), and coal and nuclear (.952).

Table 6.15 shows that fuel rate and coal production are highly correlated. Using fuel rate as a single predictor of crude oil production produces the following simple regression model.

$$\hat{y} = 44.869 + .7838(\text{fuel rate})$$

Notice that the estimate of the regression coefficient, .7838, is positive, indicating that as fuel rate increases, oil production increases. Using coal as a single predictor of crude oil production yields the following simple regression model.

$$\hat{y} = 45.072 + .0157(\text{coal})$$

The multiple regression model developed using both fuel rate and coal to predict crude oil production is

$$\hat{y} = 45.806 + .0227(\text{coal}) - .3934(\text{fuel rate})$$

Observe that this regression model indicates a *negative* relationship between fuel rate and oil production (–.3934), which is in opposition to the *positive* relationship shown in the regression equation for fuel rate as a single predictor. Because of the multicollinearity between coal and fuel rate, these two independent variables interact in the regression analysis in such a way as to produce regression coefficient estimates that are difficult to interpret. Extreme caution should be exercised before interpreting these regression coefficient estimates.

The problem of multicollinearity can also affect the t values that are used to evaluate the regression coefficients. Because the problems of multicollinearity among predictors can result in an overestimation of the standard deviation of the regression coefficients, the t values tend to be underrepresentative when multicollinearity is present. In some regression

TABLE 6.15

Correlations Among Oil Production Predictor Variables

	Energy Consumption	Nuclear	Dry Coal	Fuel Gas	Rate
Energy consumption	1	.856	.791	.057	.791
Nuclear	.856	1	.952	–.404	.972
Coal	.791	.952	1	–.448	.968
Dry gas	.057	–.404	–.448	1	–.423
Fuel rate	.796	.972	.968	–.423	1

models containing multicollinearity in which all t values are nonsignificant, the overall F value for the model is highly significant. In Section 6.1, an example was given of how including interaction when it is significant strengthens a regression model. The computer output for the regression models both with and without the interaction term was shown in Figure 6.5. The model without interaction produced a statistically significant F value but neither predictor variable was significant. Further investigation of this model reveals that the correlation between the two predictors, x_1 and x_2, is .945. This extremely high correlation indicates a strong collinearity between the two predictor variables.

This collinearity may explain the fact that the overall model is significant but neither predictor is significant. It also underscores one of the problems with multicollinearity: underrepresented t values. The t values test the strength of the predictor given the other variables in the model. If a predictor is highly correlated with other independent variables, it will appear not to add much to the explanation of y and produce a low t value. However, had the predictor not been in the presence of these other correlated variables, the predictor might have explained a high proportion of variation of y.

Many of the problems created by multicollinearity are interpretation problems. The business researcher should be alert to and aware of multicollinearity potential with the predictors in the model and view the model outcome in light of such potential.

The problem of multicollinearity is not a simple one to overcome. However, several methods offer an approach to the problem. One way is to examine a correlation matrix like the one in Table 6.15 to search for possible intercorrelations among potential predictor variables. If several variables are highly correlated, the researcher can select the variable that is most correlated to the dependent variable and use that variable to represent the others in the analysis. One problem with this idea is that correlations can be more complex than simple correlation among variables. In other words, simple correlation values do not always reveal multiple correlation between variables. In some instances, variables may not appear to be correlated as pairs, but one variable is a linear combination of several other variables. This situation is also an example of multicollinearity, and a cursory observation of the correlation matrix will probably not reveal the problem.

Stepwise regression is another way to prevent the problem of multicollinearity. The search process enters the variables one at a time and compares the new variable to those in solution. If a new variable is entered and the t values on old variables become nonsignificant, the old variables are dropped out of solution. In this manner, it is more difficult for the problem of multicollinearity to affect the regression analysis. Of course, because of multicollinearity, some important predictors may not enter in to the analysis.

Other techniques are available to attempt to control for the problem of multicollinearity. One is called a **variance inflation factor,** in which a regression analysis is conducted to predict an independent variable by the other independent variables. In this case, the independent variable being predicted becomes the dependent variable. As this process is done for each of the independent variables, it is possible to determine whether any of the independent variables are a function of the other independent variables, yielding evidence of multicollinearity. By using the results from such a model, a variance inflation factor (VIF) can be computed to determine whether the standard errors of the estimates are inflated:

$$\text{VIF} = \frac{1}{1 - R_i^2}$$

where R_i^2 is the coefficient of determination for any of the models, used to predict an independent variable by the other $k - 1$ independent variables. Some researchers follow a guideline that any variance inflation factor greater than 10 or R_i^2 value more than .90 for the largest variance inflation factors indicates a severe multicollinearity problem.[*]

---

[*]William Mendenhall and Terry Sincich, *A Second Course in Business Statistics: Regression Analysis* (San Francisco: Dellen Publishing Company, 1989); John Neter, William Wasserman, and Michael H. Kutner, *Applied Linear Regression Models*, 2nd ed. (Homewood, IL: Richard D. Irwin, 1989).

6.4 PROBLEMS

6.19 Develop a correlation matrix for the independent variables in Problem 6.13. Study the matrix and make a judgment as to whether substantial multicollinearity is present among the predictors. Why or why not?

6.20 Construct a correlation matrix for the four independent variables for Problem 6.14 and search for possible multicollinearity. What did you find and why?

6.21 In Problem 6.17, you were asked to use stepwise regression to predict premiums earned by net income, dividends, and underwriting gain or loss. Study the stepwise results, including the regression coefficients, to determine whether there may be a problem with multicollinearity. Construct a correlation matrix of the three variables to aid you in this task.

6.22 Study the three predictor variables in Problem 6.18 and attempt to determine whether substantial multicollinearity is present between the predictor variables. If there is a problem of multicollinearity, how might it affect the outcome of the multiple regression analysis?

Determining Compensation for CEOs

One statistical tool that can be used to study CEO compensation is multiple regression analysis. Regression models can be developed using predictor variables, such as age, years of experience, worth of company, or others, for analyzing CEO compensation. Search procedures such as stepwise regression can be used to sort out the more significant predictors of CEO compensation.

The researcher prepares for the multiple regression analysis by conducting a study of CEOs and gathering data on several variables. The data presented in the Decision Dilemma could be used for such an analysis. It seems reasonable to believe that CEO compensation is related to the size and worth of a company, therefore it makes sense to attempt to develop a regression model or models to predict CEO compensation by the variables company sales, number of employees in the company, and the capital investment of a company. Qualitative or dummy variables can also be used in such an analysis. In the database given in the Decision Dilemma, one variable indicates whether a company is a manufacturing company. One way to recode this variable for regression analysis is to assign a 1 to companies that are manufacturers and a 0 to others.

A stepwise regression procedure can sort out the variables that seem to be more important predictors of CEO compensation. A stepwise regression analysis was conducted on the Decision Dilemma database using sales, number of employees, capital investment, and whether a company is in manufacturing as the four independent variables. The result of this analysis follows.

```
Stepwise Regression: Cash Compen versus Sales, No. of Emp., ...
Alpha-to-Enter: 0.15 Alpha-to-Remove: 0.15
Response is Cash Com on 4 predictors, with N =   20
```

Step	1	2	3	4
Constant	243.9	232.2	223.8	223.3
No. of E	0.0696	0.1552	0.0498	
T-Value	13.67	4.97	0.98	
P-Value	0.000	0.000	0.343	
Cap. Inv		-1.66	-2.92	-3.06
T-Value		-2.77	-3.97	-4.27
P-Value		0.013	0.001	0.001
Sales			1.08	1.45
T-Value			2.46	6.10
P-Value			0.026	0.000
S	32.6	27.9	24.5	24.5
R-Sq	91.22	93.95	95.61	95.34
R-Sq(adj)	90.73	93.24	94.78	94.80
C-p	15.9	8.0	4.0	2.9

The stepwise regression analysis produces a single predictor model at step 1 with a high R^2 value of .9122. The number of employees variable used in a simple regression model accounts for over 91.2% of the variation of CEO compensation data. An examination of the regression coefficient of number of employees at the first step (.0696) indicates that a one-employee increase results in a predicted increase of (.0696 · $1,000) about $70 in the CEO's compensation.

At step 2, the company's capital investment enters the model. Notice that the R^2 increases only by .0273 and that the regression coefficient on capital investment is negative. This result seems counterintuitive because we would expect that the more capital investment a company has, the more the CEO should be compensated for the responsibility. A MINITAB simple regression analysis using only capital investment produces the following model:

The regression equation is

CashCompen = 257 + 1.29 CapInv

Notice that the regression coefficient in this model is positive as we would suppose. Multicollinearity is likely. In fact, multicollinearity is evident among sales, number of employees, and capital investment. Each is a function or determiner of company size. Examine the following correlation coefficient:

Correlations

	Sales	No. Employees
No. Employees	0.997	1
Cap. Invest	0.995	.999

Notice that these three predictors are highly interrelated. Therefore, the interpretation of the regression coefficients and the order of entry of these variables in the stepwise regression become more difficult. Nevertheless, number of employees is most highly related to CEO compensation in these data. Observe also in the stepwise regression output that number of employees actually drops out of the model at step 4. The t ratio for number of employees is not significant ($t = 0.98$) at step 3. However, the R^2 actually drops slightly when number of employees are removed. In searching for a model that is both parsimonious and explanatory, the researcher could do worse than to merely select the model at step 1.

Researchers might want to explore more complicated nonlinear models. Some of the independent variables might be related to CEO compensation but in some nonlinear manner.

A brief study of the predictor variables in the Decision Dilemma database reveals that as compensation increases, the values of the data in the independent variables do not increase at a linear rate. Scatter plots of sales, number of employees, and capital investment with CEO compensation confirm this suspicion. Shown here is a scatter plot of sales with cash compensation.

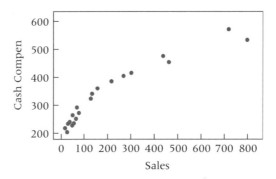

Observe that, the graph suggests more of a logarithmic fit than a linear one. We can use recoding techniques presented in the chapter to conduct a multiple regression analysis to predict compensation using the log of each of these variables. In the analysis, the compensation figures remain the same, but each of the three quantitative independent variables are recoded by taking the log of each value and entering the resultant variable in the model. A second stepwise regression analysis is undertaken with the log variables in the mix along with the original variables. The results follow:

Stepwise Regression: Cash Compen versus Sales, No. of Emp., ...

Alpha-to-Enter: 0.1 Alpha-to-Remove: 0.1

Response is Cash Com on 7 predictors, with N = 20

Step	1	2	3	4	5
Constant	−129.61	−13.23	−122.53	−147.22	−120.74
Log Sale	224.3	152.2	281.4	307.8	280.8
T-Value	22.22	8.75	11.08	32.75	26.81
P-Value	0.000	0.000	0.000	0.000	0.000
No. Emp		0.0251	0.0233	0.0903	0.0828
T-Value		4.53	6.97	13.94	15.52
P-Value		0.000	0.000	0.000	0.000
Log Cap			−106.4	−126.0	−109.8
T-Value			−5.58	−17.87	−15.56
P-Value			0.000	0.000	0.000
Sales				−0.434	−0.250
T-Value				−10.52	−4.11
P-Value				0.000	0.001
Cap. Inv					−0.37
T-Value					−3.51
P-Value					0.003
S	20.7	14.3	8.59	3.07	2.32
R-Sq	96.48	98.41	99.46	99.94	99.97
R-Sq(adj)	96.29	98.22	99.36	99.92	99.95

Note that in this stepwise regression analysis, the variable log sales has the highest single predictability of compensation producing an R^2 of .9648, which is higher than the value at step 1 in the first stepwise regression analysis. Number of employees enters at step 2 and log of capital investment at step 3. However, such a high R^2 at step 1 leaves little room for improved predictability. Our search through the variables may well end with the decision to use the log of sales as the efficient, predictable model of compensation. The final model might be:

$$\text{CEO Compensation} = -129.61 + 224.3 \text{ Log sales}$$

Human resource managers sometimes use compensation tables to assist them in determining ranges and ballparks for salary offers. Company boards of directors can use such models as the one developed here to assist them in negotiations with possible candidates for CEO positions or to aid them in determining whether a presently employed CEO is over- or undercompensated. In addition, candidates who are searching for new CEO opportunities can use models like these to determine the potential compensation for a new position and to help them be more adequately prepared for salary negotiations should they be offered a CEO position.

Some of the variables in this study will undoubtedly produce redundant information. The use of a correlation matrix and a stepwise regression process can protect the analysis from some of the problems of multicollinearity.

The use of multiple regression analysis on a large sample of CEO compensation data with many independent variables could provide some interesting and exciting results. What are the real factors in determining how much compensation a CEO receives? Multiple regression can help answer that question.

ETHICAL CONSIDERATIONS

Some business researchers misuse the results of search procedures by using the order in which variables come into a model (on stepwise and forward selection) to rank the variables in importance. They state that the variable entered at step 1 is the most important predictor of y, the variable entering at step 2 is second most important, and so on. In actuality, variables entering the analysis after step 1 are being analyzed by how much of the unaccounted-for variation (residual variation) they are explaining, not how much they are related to y by themselves. A variable that comes into the model at the fourth step is the variable that most greatly accounts for the variation of the y values leftover after the first three variables have explained the rest. However, the fourth variable taken by itself might explain more variation of y than the second or third variable when seen as single predictors.

Some people use the estimates of the regression coefficients to compare the worth of the predictor variables; the larger the coefficient is, the greater its worth. At least two problems plague this approach. The first is that most variables are measured in different units. Thus, regression coefficient weights are partly a function of the unit of measurement of the variable. Second, if multicollinearity is present, the interpretation of the regression coefficients is questionable. In addition, the presence of multicollinearity raises several issues about the interpretation of other regression output. Researchers who ignore this problem are at risk of presenting spurious results.

SUMMARY

Multiple regression analysis can handle nonlinear independent variables. One way to accommodate this issue is to recode the data and enter the variables into the analysis in the normal way. Other nonlinear regression models, such as exponential models, require that the entire model be transformed. Often the transformation involves the use of logarithms. In some cases, the resulting value of the regression model is in logarithmic form and the antilogarithm of the answer must be taken to determine the predicted value of y.

Indicator, or dummy, variables are qualitative variables used to represent categorical data in the multiple regression model. These variables are coded as 0, 1 and are often used to represent nominal or ordinal classification data that the researcher wants to include in the regression analysis. If a qualitative variable contains more than two categories, it generates multiple dummy variables. In general, if a qualitative variable contains c categories, $c - 1$ dummy variables should be created.

Search procedures are used to help sort through the independent variables as predictors in the examination of various possible models. Several search procedures are available, including all possible regressions, stepwise regression, forward selection, and backward elimination. The all possible regressions procedure computes every possible regression model for a set of data. The drawbacks of this procedure include the time and energy required to compute all possible regressions and the difficulty of deciding which models are most appropriate. The stepwise regression procedure involves selecting and adding one independent variable at a time to the regression process after beginning with a one-predictor model. Variables are added to the model at each step if they contain the most significant t value associated with the remaining variables. If no additional t value is statistically significant at any given step, the procedure stops. With stepwise regression, at each step the process examines the variables already in the model to determine whether their t values are still significant. If not, they are dropped from the model, and the process searches for other independent variables with large, significant t values to replace the variable(s) dropped. The forward selection procedure is the same as stepwise regression but does not drop variables out of the model once they have been included. The backward elimina-

tion procedure begins with a "full" model, a model that contains all the independent variables. The sample size must be large enough to justify a full model, which can be a limiting factor. Backward elimination drops out the least important predictors one at a time until only significant predictors are left in the regression model. The variable with the smallest absolute t value of the statistically nonsignificant t values is the independent variable that is dropped out of the model at each step.

One of the problems in using multiple regression is multicollinearity, or correlations among the predictor variables. This problem can cause overinflated estimates of the standard deviations of regression coefficients, misinterpretation of regression coefficients, undersized t values, and misleading signs on the regression coefficients. It can be lessened by using an intercorrelation matrix of independent variables to help recognize bivariate correlation; by using stepwise regression to sort the variables one at a time; or by using statistics such as a variance inflation factor.

KEY TERMS

all possible regressions	indicator variable	search procedures	Tukey's ladder of
backward elimination	multicollinearity	stepwise regression	transformations
dummy variable	quadratic model	Tukey's four-quadrant	variance inflation factor
forward selection	qualitative variable	approach	

FORMULAS

Variance inflation factor

$$VIF = \frac{1}{1 - R_i^2}$$

SUPPLEMENTARY PROBLEMS

CALCULATING THE STATISTICS

6.23 Given here are the data for a dependent variable, y, and independent variables. Use these data to develop a regression model to predict y. Discuss the output. Which variable is an indicator variable? Was it a significant predictor of y?

x_1	x_2	x_3	y
0	51	16.4	14
0	48	17.1	17
1	29	18.2	29
0	36	17.9	32
0	40	16.5	54
1	27	17.1	86
1	14	17.8	117
0	17	18.2	120
1	16	16.9	194
1	9	18.0	203
1	14	18.9	217
0	11	18.5	235

6.24 Use the following data and a stepwise regression analysis to predict y. In addition to the two independent variables given here, include three other predictors in your analysis: the square of each x as a predictor and an interaction predictor. Discuss the results of the process.

x_1	x_2	y	x_1	x_2	y
10	3	2002	5	12	1750
5	14	1747	6	8	1832
8	4	1980	5	18	1795
7	4	1902	7	4	1917
6	7	1842	8	5	1943
7	6	1883	6	9	1830
4	21	1697	5	12	1786
11	4	2021			

6.25 Use the x_1 values and the log of the x_1 values given here to predict the y values by using a stepwise regression procedure. Discuss the output. Were either or both of the predictors significant?

y	x_1	y	x_1
20.4	850	13.2	204
11.6	146	17.5	487
17.8	521	12.4	192
15.3	304	10.6	98
22.4	1029	19.8	703
21.9	910	17.4	394
16.4	242	19.4	647

TESTING YOUR UNDERSTANDING

6.26 The U.S. Commodities Futures Trading Commission reports on the volume of trading in the U.S. commodity futures exchanges. Shown here are the figures for grain, oilseeds, and livestock products over a period of several years. Use these data to develop a multiple regression model to predict grain futures volume of trading from oilseeds volume and livestock products volume. All figures are given in units of millions. Graph each of these predictors separately with the response variable and use Tukey's four-quadrant approach to explore possible recoding schemes for nonlinear relationships. Include any of these in the regression model. Comment on the results.

Grain	Oilseeds	Livestock
2.2	3.7	3.4
18.3	15.7	11.8
19.8	20.3	9.8
14.9	15.8	11.0
17.8	19.8	11.1
15.9	23.5	8.4
10.7	14.9	7.9
10.3	13.8	8.6
10.9	14.2	8.8
15.9	22.5	9.6
15.9	21.1	8.2

6.27 The U.S. Bureau of Mines produces data on the price of minerals. Shown here are the average prices per year for several minerals over a decade. Use these data and a stepwise regression procedure to produce a model to predict the average price of gold from the other variables. Comment on the results of the process.

Gold ($ per oz.)	Copper (cents per lb.)	Silver ($ per oz.)	Aluminum (cents per lb.)
161.1	64.2	4.4	39.8
308.0	93.3	11.1	61.0
613.0	101.3	20.6	71.6
460.0	84.2	10.5	76.0
376.0	72.8	8.0	76.0
424.0	76.5	11.4	77.8
361.0	66.8	8.1	81.0
318.0	67.0	6.1	81.0
368.0	66.1	5.5	81.0
448.0	82.5	7.0	72.3
438.0	120.5	6.5	110.1
382.6	130.9	5.5	87.8

6.28 The Shipbuilders Council of America in Washington, D.C., publishes data about private shipyards. Among the variables reported by this organization are the employment figures (per 1,000), the number of naval vessels under construction, and the number of repairs or conversions done to commercial ships (in $ millions). Shown here are the data for these three variables over a 7-year period. Use the data to develop a regression model to predict private shipyard employment from number of naval vessels under construction and repairs or conversions of commercial ships. Graph each of these predictors separately with the response variable and use Tukey's four-quadrant approach to explore possible recoding schemes for nonlinear relationships. Include any of these in the regression model. Comment on the regression model and its strengths and its weaknesses.

Employment	Naval Vessels	Commercial Ship Repairs or Conversions
133.4	108	431
177.3	99	1335
143.0	105	1419
142.0	111	1631
130.3	100	852
120.6	85	847
120.4	79	806

6.29 The U.S. Bureau of Labor Statistics produces consumer price indexes for several different categories. Shown here are the percentage changes in consumer price indexes over a period of 20 years for food, shelter, apparel, and fuel oil. Also displayed are the percentage changes in consumer price indexes for all commodities. Use these data and a stepwise regression procedure to develop a model that attempts to predict all commodities by the other four variables. Construct scatter plots of each of these variables with all commodities. Examine the graphs in light of Tukey's four-quadrant approach. Develop any other appropriate predictor variables by recoding data and include them in the analysis. Comment on the result of this analysis.

All Commodities	Food	Shelter	Apparel	Fuel Oil
.9	1.0	2.0	1.6	3.7
.6	1.3	.8	.9	2.7
.9	.7	1.6	.4	2.6
.9	1.6	1.2	1.3	2.6
1.2	1.3	1.5	.9	2.1
1.1	2.2	1.9	1.1	2.4
2.6	5.0	3.0	2.5	4.4
1.9	.9	3.6	4.1	7.2
3.5	3.5	4.5	5.3	6.0
4.7	5.1	8.3	5.8	6.7
4.5	5.7	8.9	4.2	6.6
3.6	3.1	4.2	3.2	6.2
3.0	4.2	4.6	2.0	3.3
7.4	14.5	4.7	3.7	4.0
11.9	14.3	9.6	7.4	9.3
8.8	8.5	9.9	4.5	12.0
4.3	3.0	5.5	3.7	9.5
5.8	6.3	6.6	4.5	9.6
7.2	9.9	10.2	3.6	8.4
11.3	11.0	13.9	4.3	9.2

6.30 The U.S. Department of Agriculture publishes data annually on various selected farm products. Shown here are the unit production figures for three farm products for 10 years during a 20-year period. Use these data and a stepwise regression analysis to predict corn production by the production of soybeans and wheat. Comment on the results.

Corn (million bushels)	Soybeans (million bushels)	Wheat (million bushels)
4152	1127	1352
6639	1798	2381
4175	1636	2420
7672	1861	2595
8876	2099	2424
8226	1940	2091
7131	1938	2108
4929	1549	1812
7525	1924	2037
7933	1922	2739

6.31 The American Chamber of Commerce Researchers Association compiles cost-of-living indexes for selected metropolitan areas. Shown here are cost-of-living indexes for 25 different cities on five different items for a recent year. Use the data to develop a regression model to predict the grocery cost-of-living index by the indexes of housing, utilities, transportation, and healthcare. Discuss the results, highlighting both the significant and nonsignificant predictors.

City	Grocery Items	Housing	Utilities	Transportation	Healthcare
Albany	108.3	106.8	127.4	89.1	107.5
Albuquerque	96.3	105.2	98.8	100.9	102.1
Augusta, GA	96.2	88.8	115.6	102.3	94.0
Austin	98.0	83.9	87.7	97.4	94.9
Baltimore	106.0	114.1	108.1	112.8	111.5
Buffalo	103.1	117.3	127.6	107.8	100.8
Colorado Springs	94.5	88.5	74.6	93.3	102.4
Dallas	105.4	98.9	108.9	110.0	106.8
Denver	91.5	108.3	97.2	105.9	114.3
Des Moines	94.3	95.1	111.4	105.7	96.2
El Paso	102.9	94.6	90.9	104.2	91.4
Indianapolis	96.0	99.7	92.1	102.7	97.4
Jacksonville	96.1	90.4	96.0	106.0	96.1
Kansas City	89.8	92.4	96.3	95.6	93.6
Knoxville	93.2	88.0	91.7	91.6	82.3
Los Angeles	103.3	211.3	75.6	102.1	128.5
Louisville	94.6	91.0	79.4	102.4	88.4
Memphis	99.1	86.2	91.1	101.1	85.5
Miami	100.3	123.0	125.6	104.3	137.8
Minneapolis	92.8	112.3	105.2	106.0	107.5
Mobile	99.9	81.1	104.9	102.8	92.2
Nashville	95.8	107.7	91.6	98.1	90.9
New Orleans	104.0	83.4	122.2	98.2	87.0
Oklahoma City	98.2	79.4	103.4	97.3	97.1
Phoenix	95.7	98.7	96.3	104.6	115.2

INTERPRETING THE OUTPUT

6.32 A stepwise regression procedure was used to analyze a set of 20 observations taken on four predictor variables to predict a dependent variable. The results of this procedure are given next. Discuss the results.

```
STEPWISE REGRESSION OF Y ON 4 PREDICTORS,
WITH N = 20

STEP            1       2
CONSTANT     152.2   124.5

X₁           -50.6   -43.4
T-RATIO       7.42    6.13

X₂                    1.36
T-RATIO               2.13

S            15.2    13.9
R-SQ         75.39   80.59
```

6.33 Shown here are the data for y and three predictors, x_1, x_2, and x_3. A stepwise regression procedure has been done on these data; the results are also given. Comment on the outcome of the stepwise analysis in light of the data.

y	x_1	x_2	x_3
94	21	1	204
97	25	0	198
93	22	1	184
95	27	0	200
90	29	1	182
91	20	1	159
91	18	1	147
94	25	0	196
98	26	0	228
99	24	0	242
90	28	1	162
92	23	1	180
96	25	0	219

```
STEP            1       2       3
CONSTANT     74.81   82.18   87.89

X₃           0.099   0.067   0.071
T-RATIO       6.90    3.65    5.22

X₂                   -2.26   -2.71
T-RATIO              -2.32   -3.71

X₁                          -0.256
T-RATIO                     -3.08

S            1.37    1.16    0.850
R-SQ        81.24   87.82   94.07
```

6.34 Shown below is output from two Excel regression analyses on the same problem. The first output was done on a "full" model. In the second output, the variable with the smallest absolute t value has been removed, and the regression has been rerun like a second step of a backward elimination process. Examine the two outputs. Explain what happened, what the results mean, and what might happen in a third step.

	A	B	C	D	E	F
1	FULL MODEL:					
2	Regression Statistics					
3	Multiple R	0.567				
4	R Square	0.321				
5	Adjusted R Square	0.208				
6	Standard Error	159.681				
7	Observations	29				
8						
9	ANOVA					
10		df	SS	MS	F	Significant F
11	Regression	4	289856.08	72464.02	2.84	0.046
12	Residual	24	611955.23	25498.13		
13	Total	28	901811.31			
14		Coefficients	Standard Error	Stat	P-value	
15	Intercept	336.79	124.08	2.71	0.012	
16	X₁	1.65	1.78	0.93	0.363	
17	X₂	-5.63	13.47	-0.42	0.680	
18	X₃	0.26	1.68	0.16	0.878	
19	X₄	185.50	66.22	2.80	0.010	
20						
21	SECOND MODEL:					
22	Regression Statistics					
23	Multiple R	0.566				
24	R Square	0.321				
25	Adjusted R Square	0.239				
26	Standard Error	156.534				
27	Observations	29				
28						
29	ANOVA					
30		df	SS	MS	F	Significant F
31	Regression	3	289238.1	96412.7	3.93	0.020
32	Residual	25	612573.2	24502.9		
33	Total	28	901811.3			
34		Coefficients	Standard Error	Stat	P-value	
35	Intercept	342.919	115.34	2.97	0.006	
36	X₁	1.834	1.31	1.40	0.174	
37	X₂	-5.749	13.18	-0.44	0.667	
38	X₄	181.220	59.05	3.07	0.005	

ANALYZING THE DATABASES

see www.wiley.com/college/black

1. Use the manufacturing database to develop a multiple regression model to predict Cost of Materials by Number of Employees, New Capital Expenditures, Value Added by Manufacture, Value of Industry Shipments, and End-of-Year Inventories. Create indicator variables for values of industry shipments that have been coded from 1 to 4. Use a stepwise regression procedure. Does multicollinearity appear to be a problem in this analysis? Discuss the results of the analysis.

2. Construct a correlation matrix for the hospital database variables. Are some of the variables highly correlated? Which ones and why? Perform a stepwise multiple regression analysis to predict Personnel by Control, Service, Beds, Admissions, Census, Outpatients, and Births. The variables Region, Control, and Service will need to be coded as indicator variables. Control has two subcategories, and Service has three.

3. Develop a regression model using the financial database. Use Total Revenues, Total Assets, Return on Equity, Earnings Per Share, Average Yield, and Dividends Per Share to predict the average P/E ratio for a company. How strong is the model? Use stepwise regression to help sort out the variables. Several of these variables may be measuring similar things. Construct a correlation matrix to explore the possibility of multicollinearity among the predictors.

4. Use the stock market database to develop a regression model to predict the composite index from Part of the Month, Stock Volume, Reported Trades, Dollar Value, and Warrants Volume. You will need to treat Part of the Month as a qualitative variable with three subcategories. Drop out the least significant variable if it is not significant at $\alpha = .05$ and rerun the model. How much did R^2 drop? Continue this process until only significant predictors are left. Describe the final model.

CASE: VIRGINIA SEMICONDUCTOR

Virginia Semiconductor is a producer of silicon wafers used in the manufacture of microelectronic products. The company, situated in Fredericksburg, Virginia, was founded in 1978 by two brothers, Thomas and Robert Digges. Virginia Semiconductor was growing and prospering in the early 1980s by selling a high volume of low-profit-margin wafers. However, in 1985, without notice, Virginia Semiconductor lost two major customers that represented 65% of its business. Left with only 35% of its sales base, the company desperately needed customers.

Thomas Digges, Jr., CEO of Virginia Semiconductor, decided to seek markets where his company's market share would be small but profit margin would be high because of the value of its engineering research and its expertise. This decision turned out to be a wise direction for the small, versatile company.

Virginia Semiconductor developed a silicon wafer that was two inches in diameter, 75 microns thick, and polished on both sides. Such wafers were needed by several customers, but had never been produced before. The company produced a number of these wafers and sold them for more than 10 times the price of conventional wafers.

Soon the company was making wafers from two to four microns thick (extremely thin), wafers with textured surfaces for infrared applications, and wafers with micromachined holes or shapes and selling them in specialized markets. It was able to deliver these products faster than competitors were able to deliver standard wafers.

Having made inroads at replacing lost sales, Virginia Semiconductor still had to streamline operations and control inventory and expenses. No layoffs occurred, but the average workweek dropped to 32 hours and the president took an 80% pay reduction for a time. Expenses were cut as far as seemed possible.

The company had virtually no long-term debt and fortunately was able to make it through this period without incurring any additional significant debt. The absence of large monthly debt payments enabled the company to respond quickly to new production needs.

Virginia Semiconductor improved production quality by cross-training employees. In addition, the company participated in the State of Virginia's economic development efforts to find markets in Europe, Japan, Korea, and Israel. Exports, which were 1% of the company's business in 1985, now represent 40%.

The company continues to find new customers because of new products. One new ultramachining wafer has become a key component in auto airbags. Today the company has more than 300 active customers, a significant jump from fewer than 50 in 1985.

Discussion

1. It is often useful to decision makers at a company to determine what factors enter into the size of a customer's purchase. Suppose decision makers at Virginia Semiconductor want to determine from past data what variables might be predictors of size of purchase and are able to gather some data on various customer companies. Assume the following data represent information gathered for 16 companies on five variables: the total amount of purchases

made during a one-year period (size of purchase), the size of the purchasing company (in total sales volume), the percentage of all purchases made by the customer company that were imports, the distance of the customer company from Virginia Semiconductor, and whether the customer company had a single central purchasing agent. Use these data to generate a multiple regression model to predict size of purchase by the other variables. Summarize your findings in terms of the strength of the model, significant predictor variables, and any new variables generated by recoding.

Size of Purchase ($1,000)	Company Size ($ million sales)	Percent of Customer Imports	Distance from Virginia Semiconductor	Central Purchaser?
27.9	25.6	41	18	1
89.6	109.8	16	75	0
12.8	39.4	29	14	0
34.9	16.7	31	117	0
408.6	278.4	14	209	1
173.5	98.4	8	114	1
105.2	101.6	20	75	0
510.6	139.3	17	50	1
382.7	207.4	53	35	1
84.6	26.8	27	15	1
101.4	13.9	31	19	0
27.6	6.8	22	7	0
234.8	84.7	5	89	1
464.3	180.3	27	306	1
309.8	132.6	18	73	1
294.6	118.9	16	11	1

2. Suppose that the next set of data is Virginia Semiconductor's sales figures for the past 11 years, along with the average number of hours worked per week by a full-time employee and the number of different customers the company has for its unique wafers. How do the average workweek length and number of customers relate to total sales figures? Use scatter plots to examine possible relationships between sales and hours per week and sales and number of customers. Use Tukey's four-quadrant approach for possible ways to recode the data. Use stepwise regression analysis to explore the relationships. Let the response variable be "sales" and the predictors be "average number of hours worked per week," "number of customers," and any new variables created by recoding. Explore quadratic relationships, interaction, and other relationships that seem appropriate by using stepwise regression. Summarize your findings in terms of model strength and significant predictors.

Average Sales ($ million)	Hours Worked per Week	Number of Customers
15.6	44	54
15.7	43	52
15.4	41	55
14.3	41	55
11.8	40	39
9.7	40	28
9.6	40	37
10.2	38	58
11.3	38	67
14.3	32	186
14.8	37	226

3. As Virginia Semiconductor continues to grow and prosper, the potential for slipping back into inefficient ways is always present. Suppose that after a few years the company's sales begin to level off, but it continues hiring employees. Such figures over a

10-year period of time may look like the data given here. Graph these data, using sales as the response variable and number of employees as the predictor. Study the graph in light of Tukey's four-quadrant approach. Using the information learned, develop a regression model to predict sales by the number of employees. On the basis of what you find, what would you recommend to management about the trend if it were to continue? What do you see in these data that would concern management?

Sales ($ million)	Number of Employees
20.2	120
24.3	122
28.6	127
33.7	135
35.2	142
35.9	156
36.3	155
36.2	167
36.5	183
36.6	210

Source: Adapted from "Virginia Semiconductor: A New Beginning," *Real-World Lessons for America's Small Businesses: Insights from the Blue Chip Enterprise Initiative 1994.* Published by *Nation's Business* magazine on behalf of Connecticut Mutual Life Insurance Company and the U.S. Chamber of Commerce in association with The Blue Chip Enterprise Initiative, 1994.

USING THE COMPUTER

EXCEL

The Using the Computer section at the end of Chapter 4 contains directions for doing simple regression analysis by using Excel. Multiple regression analysis can be performed by using the same commands as those used for simple regression and explained in Chapter 4. Select **Tools** on the menu bar. From the pull-down menu that appears choose **Data Analysis.** This selection will produce the **Data Analysis** dialog box. Then, select **Regression.** In the dialog box shown, input the range of the *y* values in the first slot, **Input Y Range.** In the second slot, **Input X Range,** input the range of the *x* values. The *x* value range may include several columns and Excel will determine the number of predictor variables from the number of columns entered in this box. Other options and the standard output features are presented and explained in Chapter 4. Nonlinear models can by created in Excel through data recoding using the usual cell and column operations. Excel does not have the capability of directly doing stepwise regression.

MINITAB WINDOWS

MINITAB Windows has the capability of generating multiple regression models, performing various stepwise regression procedures, along with other regression procedures. Chapter 5 contains an explanation for developing multiple regression models. Nonlinear variables can be created by recoding using the MINITAB calculator. First select **Calc** on the Menu bar. From the pull-down menu, select **Calculator.** In the **Calculator** dialog box beside **Store result in variable,** list the name of the column where the new variable is to be located. In the space beside **Expression,** perform the recoding operation on the column where the original linear data are located. After selecting **OK,** the recoded data will appear in the new column.

Stepwise regression procedures can be accessed in MINITAB Windows by selecting **Stat** on the menu bar. From the pull-down menu select **Regression.** From the second pull-down menu that appears, select **Stepwise.** A dialog box will appear. Enter the location of the *y* variable in the **Response** space. Enter all predictor variables that you want to have considered in the procedure in the **Predictors** space. You have the option of selecting which type of regression modeling you want to use by choosing the **Methods** option. In the **Methods** dialog box, you have the option of selecting **Stepwise regression, Forward selection,** or **Backward elimination.**

The output includes the α used to enter variables and the α used to remove variables, the response variable, the number of predictors, the number of observations, and a stepwise output that includes the regression constant, the partial regression weights, the *t* ratio, *s*, R^2 and adjusted R^2.

CHAPTER 7

Time-Series Forecasting and Index Numbers

LEARNING OBJECTIVES

This chapter discusses the general use of forecasting in business, several tools that are available for making business forecasts, the nature of time-series data, and the role of index numbers in business, thereby enabling you to:

1. Gain a general understanding of time-series forecasting techniques.
2. Understand the four possible components of time-series data.
3. Understand stationary forecasting techniques.
4. Understand how to use regression models for trend analysis.
5. Learn how to decompose time-series data into their various elements and to forecast by using decomposition techniques.
6. Understand the nature of autocorrelation and how to test for it.
7. Understand autoregression in forecasting.

Forecasting Air Pollution

The decade of the 1990s brought a heightened awareness of and increased concern over pollution in various forms in the United States. Air pollution is one of the main areas of environmental concern. The U.S. Environmental Protection Agency (EPA) monitors the quality of air around the country. Some of the air pollutants monitored include carbon monoxide emissions, nitrogen oxide emissions, volatile organic compounds, sulfur dioxide emissions, particulate matter, fugitive dust, and lead emissions.

Carbon monoxide is a colorless, odorless, poisonous gas caused mainly by automobile emissions. Nitrogen oxides are produced by motor vehicle exhausts and as by-products of electric utilities and industrial boilers. These oxides can result in respiratory problems. Sulfur dioxide can also cause respiratory problems and is formed when sulfur-containing fuels are burned. Particulate matter is solid or liquid airborne particles that can come from different sources including power plants and diesel trucks. These substances have the potential to cause cancer and respiratory problems. Lead emissions usually come from smelters and battery plants. Lead exposure can result in kidney disease, anemia, and reproductive problems.

Has air quality in the United States been improving or deteriorating over time? The following emission data for two air pollution variables, carbon monoxide and nitrogen oxides, come from a 15-year period and are given in thousands of short-tons.

Year	Carbon Monoxide	Nitrogen Oxides
1985	115,644	23,488
1986	110,437	23,329
1987	108,879	22,806
1988	117,169	24,526
1989	104,447	24,057
1990	96,535	23,792
1991	98,461	23,772
1992	95,123	24,137
1993	95,291	24,482
1994	99,677	24,892
1995	89,721	23,935
1996	90,611	23,391
1997	94,410	24,824
1998	89,454	24,454
1999	97,441	25,393

Managerial and Statistical Questions

1. Is it possible to forecast the emissions of carbon monoxide or nitrogen oxides for the year 2004, 2007, or 2020 using these data?

2. What techniques best forecast the emissions of carbon monoxide or nitrogen oxides in the future from these data?

Sources: Adapted from U.S. Environmental Protection Agency; information published in *The Wall Street Journal Almanac 1999*, Ronald J. Alsop, ed. (New York: Ballantine Books, 1999), p. 628; *The World Almanac 2002* (New York: World Almanac Books, 2002), p. 165; *The New York Times Almanac* 2002. John W. Wright, ed. (New York: Penguin Putnam, 2002) p. 776.

Every day, **forecasting**—*the art or science of predicting the future*—is used in the decision-making process to help businesspeople reach conclusions about buying, selling, producing, hiring, and many other actions. As an example, consider the following items:

■ Market watchers predict a resurgence of stock values next year.

■ City planners forecast a water crisis in Southern California.

■ The price of gasoline will increase sharply in the next several months.

■ Increased competition from overseas businesses will result in significant layoffs in the U.S. computer chip industry.

How are these and other conclusions reached? What forecasting techniques are used? Are the forecasts accurate? In this chapter we discuss several forecasting techniques, how to measure the error of a forecast, and some of the problems that can occur in forecasting. In addition, this chapter will focus only on data that occur over time, time-series data.

Time-series data are *data gathered on a given characteristic over a period of time at regular intervals.* Time-series forecasting techniques attempt to account for changes over time by examining patterns, cycles, or trends, or using information about previous time periods to predict the outcome for a future time period. Time-series methods include naive methods, averaging, smoothing, regression trend analysis, and the decomposition of the possible time-series factors, all of which are discussed in subsequent sections.

7.1 INTRODUCTION TO FORECASTING

Virtually all areas of business, including production, sales, employment, transportation, distribution, and inventory, produce and maintain time-series data. Table 7.1 provides an example of time-series data released by the Office of Market Finance, U.S. Department of the Treasury. The table contains the bond yield rates of three-month Treasury Bills for a 17-year period.

Why does the average yield differ from year to year? Is it possible to use these time-series data to predict average yields for year 18 or ensuing years? Figure 7.1 is a graph of these data over time. Often graphical depiction of time-series data can give a clue about any trends, cycles, or relationships that might exist there. Does the graph in Figure 7.1 show that bond yields are decreasing? Will next year's yield rate be lower or is a cycle occurring in these data that will result in an increase? To answer such questions, it is sometimes helpful to determine which of the four components of time-series data exist in the data being studied.

Time-Series Components

It is generally believed that time-series data are composed of four elements: trend, cyclicality, seasonality, and irregularity. Not all time-series data have all these elements. Consider Figure 7.2, which shows the effects of these time-series elements on data over a period of 13 years.

The long-term general direction of data is referred to as **trend.** Notice that even though the data depicted in Figure 7.2 move through upward and downward periods, the general direction or trend is increasing (denoted in Figure 7.2 by the line). **Cycles** are *patterns of highs and lows through which data move over time periods usually of more than a year.* Notice that the data in Figure 7.2 seemingly move through two periods or cycles of highs and lows over a 13-year period. Time-series data that do not extend over a long period of time may not have enough "history" to show **cyclical effects. Seasonal effects,** on the other hand, are *shorter cycles, which usually occur in time periods of less than one year.* Often seasonal effects are measured by the month, but they may occur by quarter, or may be measured in as small a time frame as a week or even a day. Note the seasonal effects shown in Figure 7.2 as up and down cycles, many of which occur during a one-year period. **Irregular fluctuations** are *rapid changes or "bleeps" in the data, which occur in even shorter time frames than seasonal effects.* Irregular fluctuations can happen as often as day to day. They are subject to momentary change and are often unexplained. Note the irregular fluctuations in the data of Figure 7.2.

TABLE 7.1

Bond Yields of Three-Month Treasury Bills

Year	Average Yield
1	14.03%
2	10.69
3	8.63
4	9.58
5	7.48
6	5.98
7	5.82
8	6.69
9	8.12
10	7.51
11	5.42
12	3.45
13	3.02
14	4.29
15	5.51
16	5.02
17	5.07

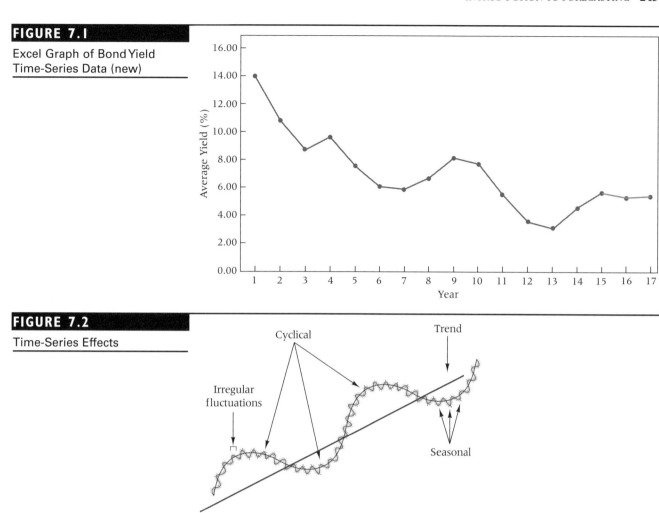

FIGURE 7.1

Excel Graph of Bond Yield
Time-Series Data (new)

FIGURE 7.2

Time-Series Effects

Observe again the bond yield data depicted in Figure 7.1. The general trend seems to move downward and contain two cycles. Each of the cycles traverses approximately five to eight years. It is possible, although not displayed here, that seasonal periods of highs and lows within each year result in seasonal bond yields. In addition, irregular daily fluctuations of bond yield rates may occur but are unexplainable.

Time-series data that contain no trend, cyclical, or seasonal effects are said to be **stationary.** Techniques used to forecast stationary data analyze only the irregular fluctuation effects.

The Measurement of Forecasting Error

In this chapter, several forecasting techniques will be introduced that typically produce different forecasts. How does a decision maker know which forecasting technique is doing the best job in predicting the future? One way is to compare forecast values with actual values and determine the amount of **forecasting error** a technique produces. An examination of individual errors gives some insight into the accuracy of the forecasts. However, this process can be tedious, especially for large data sets, and often a single measurement of overall forecasting error is needed for the entire set of data under consideration. Any of several methods can be used to compute error in forecasting. The choice depends on the forecaster's objective, the forecaster's familiarity with the technique, and the method of error measurement used by the computer forecasting software. Several techniques can be used to measure overall error, including mean error (ME), mean absolute deviation

(MAD), mean square error (MSE), mean percentage error (MPE), and mean absolute percentage error (MAPE). Here we will consider the mean absolute deviation (MAD) and the mean square error (MSE).

Error

The **error of an individual forecast** is *the difference between the actual value and the forecast of that value.*

ERROR OF AN INDIVIDUAL FORECAST	$$e_t = x_t - F_t$$ where e_t = the error of the forecast x_t = the actual value F_t = the forecast value

Mean Absolute Deviation (MAD)

One measure of overall error in forecasting is the mean absolute deviation, MAD. The **mean absolute deviation (MAD)** is *the mean, or average, of the absolute values of the errors.* Table 7.2 presents the nonfarm partnership tax returns in the United States over an 11-year period along with the forecast for each year and the error of the forecast. An examination of these data reveals that some of the forecast errors are positive and some are negative. In summing these errors in an attempt to compute an overall measure of error, the negative and positive values offset each other resulting in an underestimation of the total error. The mean absolute deviation overcomes this problem by taking the absolute value of the error measurement, thereby analyzing the magnitude of the forecast errors without regard to direction.

MEAN ABSOLUTE DEVIATION	$$MAD = \frac{\Sigma |e_i|}{\text{Number of Forecasts}}$$

The mean absolute error can be computed for the forecast errors in Table 7.2 as follows.

$$MAD = \frac{|56.0| + |111.8| + |93.5| + |91.0| + |106.3| + |83.9| + |42.2| + |14.7| + |-41.6| + |-33.5|}{10} = 67.5$$

Mean Square Error (MSE)

The **mean square error (MSE)** is another way to circumvent the problem of the canceling effects of positive and negative forecast errors. The MSE is *computed by squaring each error*

TABLE 7.2			
Nonfarm Partnership Tax Returns			

Year	Actual	Forecast	Error
1	1,402	—	—
2	1,458	1,402	56.0
3	1,553	1,441.2	111.8
4	1,613	1,519.5	93.5
5	1,676	1,585.0	91.0
6	1,755	1,648.7	106.3
7	1,807	1,723.1	83.9
8	1,824	1,781.8	42.2
9	1,826	1,811.3	14.7
10	1,780	1,821.6	−41.6
11	1,759	1,792.5	−33.5

(thus creating a positive number) and averaging the squared errors. The following formula states it more formally.

MEAN SQUARE ERROR	$$MSE = \frac{\Sigma e_i^2}{\text{Number of Forecasts}}$$

The mean square error can be computed for the errors shown in Table 7.2 as follows.

$$MSE = \frac{(56.0)^2 + (111.8)^2 + (93.5)^2 + (91.0)^2 + (106.3)^2 + (83.9)^2 + (42.2)^2 + (14.7)^2 + (-41.6)^2 + (-33.5)^2}{10} = 5,584.7$$

Selection of a particular mechanism for computing error is up to the forecaster. It is important to understand that different error techniques will yield different information. The business researcher should be informed enough about the various error measurement techniques to make an educated evaluation of the forecasting results.

7.1 PROBLEMS

7.1   Use the forecast errors given here to compute MAD and MSE. Discuss the information yielded by each type of error measurement.

Period	e
1	2.3
2	1.6
3	−1.4
4	1.1
5	.3
6	−.9
7	−1.9
8	−2.1
9	.7

7.2   Determine the error for each of the following forecasts. Compute MAD and MSE.

Period	Value	Forecast	Error
1	202	—	—
2	191	202	
3	173	192	
4	169	181	
5	171	174	
6	175	172	
7	182	174	
8	196	179	
9	204	189	
10	219	198	
11	227	211	

7.3   Using the following data, determine the values of MAD and MSE. Which of these measurements of error seems to yield the best information about the forecasts? Why?

Period	Value	Forecast
1	19.4	16.6
2	23.6	19.1
3	24.0	22.0
4	26.8	24.8
5	29.2	25.9
6	35.5	28.6

7.4 Figures for acres of tomatoes harvested in the United States from 1988 through 1998 follow. The data are published by the U.S. Department of Agriculture. With these data, forecasts have been made by using techniques presented later in this chapter. Compute MAD and MSE on these forecasts. Comment on the errors.

Year	Number of Acres	Forecast
1988	140,000	—
1989	141,730	140,000
1990	134,590	141,038
1991	131,710	137,169
1992	131,910	133,894
1993	134,250	132,704
1994	135,220	133,632
1995	131,020	134,585
1996	120,640	132,446
1997	115,190	125,362
1998	114,510	119,259

7.2 SMOOTHING TECHNIQUES

Several techniques are available to forecast time-series data that are stationary, or that include no significant trend, cyclical, or seasonal effects. These techniques are often referred to as **smoothing techniques** because they *produce forecasts based on "smoothing out" the irregular fluctuation effects in the time-series data.* Three general categories of smoothing techniques are presented here: (1) naïve forecasting models, (2) averaging models, and (3) exponential smoothing.

Naïve Forecasting Models

Naïve forecasting models are *simple models in which it is assumed that the more recent time periods of data represent the best predictions or forecasts for future outcomes.* Naïve models do not take into account data trend, cyclical effects, or seasonality. For this reason, naïve models seem to work better with data that are reported on a daily or weekly basis or in situations that show no trend or seasonality. The simplest of the naïve forecasting methods is the model in which the forecast for a given time period is the value for the previous time period.

$$F_t = x_{t-1}$$

where

F_t = the forecast value for time period t

x_{t-1} = the value for time period $t-1$

As an example, if 532 pairs of shoes were sold by a retailer last week, this naïve forecasting model would predict that the retailer will sell 532 pairs of shoes this week. With this naïve model, the actual sales for this week will be the forecast for next week.

Observe the agricultural data in Table 7.3 representing the total reported domestic rail, truck, and air shipments of bell peppers in the United States for a given year. Figure 7.3 presents an Excel graph of these shipments over the 12-month period. From these data, we can make a naïve forecast of the total number of reported shipments of bell peppers for January of the next year by using the figure for December, which is 412.

Another version of the naïve forecast might be to use the number of shipments for January of the previous year as the forecast for January of next year, because the business researcher may believe a relationship exists between bell pepper shipments and the month of the year. In this case, the naïve forecast for next January from Table 7.3 is 336 (January of the previous year). The forecaster is free to be creative with the naïve forecast model method and search for other relationships or rationales within the limits of the time-series data that would seemingly produce a valid forecast.

TABLE 7.3	Month	Shipments (millions of pounds)
Total Reported Domestic Shipments of Bell Peppers	January	336
	February	308
	March	582
	April	771
	May	935
	June	808
	July	663
	August	380
	September	333
	October	412
	November	458
	December	412

Source: *Agricultural Statistics 1999*, U.S. Department of Agriculture.

FIGURE 7.3

Excel Graph of Shipments of Bell Peppers over a 12-Month Period

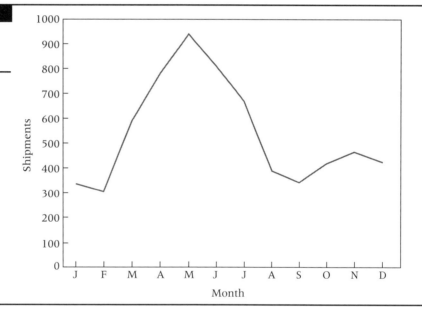

Averaging Models

Many naïve model forecasts are based on the value of one time period. Often such forecasts become a function of irregular fluctuations of the data; as a result, the forecasts are "over-steered." Using averaging models, a forecaster enters information from several time periods into the forecast and "smoothes" the data. **Averaging models** are computed by *averaging data from several time periods and using the average as the forecast for the next time period.*

Simple Averages

The most elementary of the averaging models is the **simple average model.** With this model, *the forecast for time period t is the average of the values for a given number of previous time periods,* as shown in the following equation.

$$F_t = \frac{X_{t-1} + X_{t-2} + X_{t-3} + \cdots + X_{t-n}}{n}$$

The data in Table 7.4 provide the costs of residential heating oil in the United States for three years. Figure 7.4 displays a MINITAB graph of these data.

TABLE 7.4		
Cost of Residential Heating Oil (cents per gallon)	**Time Frame**	**Cost of Heating Oil**
	January (year 1)	66.1
	February	66.1
	March	66.4
	April	64.3
	May	63.2
	June	61.6
	July	59.3
	August	58.1
	September	58.9
	October	60.9
	November	60.7
	December	59.4
	January (year 2)	61.3
	February	63.3
	March	62.1
	April	59.8
	May	58.4
	June	57.6
	July	55.7
	August	55.1
	September	55.7
	October	56.7
	November	57.2
	December	58.0
	January (year 3)	58.2
	February	58.3
	March	57.7
	April	56.7
	May	56.8
	June	55.5
	July	53.8
	August	52.8

FIGURE 7.4

MINITAB Graph of Heating Oil Cost Data

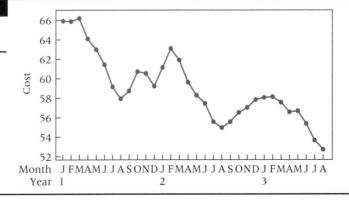

A simple 12-month average could be used to forecast the cost of residential heating oil for September of year 3 from the data in Table 7.4 by averaging the values for September of year 2 through August of year 3 (the preceding 12 months).

$$F_{\text{Sept, year 3}} = \frac{55.7 + 56.7 + 57.2 + 58.0 + 58.2 + 58.3 + 57.7 + 56.7 + 56.8 + 55.5 + 53.8 + 52.8}{12} = 56.45$$

With this **simple average,** the forecast for year 3 September heating oil cost is 56.45 cents. Note that none of the previous 12-month figures equal this value and that this average is not necessarily more closely related to values early in the period than to those late in the period. The use of the simple average over 12 months tends to smooth the variations, or fluctuations, that occur during this time.

Moving Averages

Suppose we were to attempt to forecast the heating oil cost for October of year 3 by using averages as the forecasting method. Would we still use the simple average for September of year 2 through August of year 3 as we did to forecast for September of year 3? Instead of using the same 12 months' average used to forecast September of year 3, it would seem to make sense to use the 12 months prior to October of year 3 (October of year 2 through September of year 3) to average for the new forecast. Suppose in September of year 3 the cost of heating oil is 53.3 cents. We could forecast October of year 3 with a new average that includes the same months used to forecast September of year 3, but without the value for September of year 2 and with the value of September of year 3 added.

$$F_{\text{Sept, year 3}} = \frac{56.7 + 57.2 + 58.0 + 58.2 + 58.3 + 57.7 + 56.7 + 56.8 + 55.5 + 53.8 + 52.8 + 53.3}{12} = 56.25$$

Computing an average of the values from October of year 2 through September of year 3 produces a moving average, which can be used to forecast the cost of heating oil for October of year 3. In computing this moving average, the earliest of the previous 12 values, September of year 2, is dropped and the most recent value, September of year 3, is included.

A **moving average** is *an average that is updated or recomputed for every new time period being considered.* The most recent information is utilized in each new moving average. This advantage is offset by the disadvantages that (1) it is difficult to choose the optimal length of time for which to compute the moving average, and (2) moving averages do not usually adjust for such time-series effects as trend, cycles, or seasonality. To determine the more optimal lengths for which to compute the moving averages, we would need to forecast with several different average lengths and compare the errors produced by them.

DEMONSTRATION PROBLEM 7.1	Shown here are shipments (in millions of dollars) for electric lighting and wiring equipment over a 12-month period. Use these data to compute a 4-month moving average for all available months.

Month	Shipments
January	1,056
February	1,345
March	1,381
April	1,191
May	1,259
June	1,361
July	1,110
August	1,334
September	1,416
October	1,282
November	1,341
December	1,382

Solution

The first moving average is

$$\text{4-Month Moving Average} = \frac{1,056 + 1,345 + 1,381 + 1,191}{4} = 1,243.25$$

This first 4-month moving average can be used to forecast the shipments in May. Because 1,259 shipments were actually made in May, the error of the forecast is

$$\text{Error}_{\text{May}} = 1,259 - 1,243.25 = 15.75$$

Shown next, along with the monthly shipments, are the 4-month moving averages and the errors of forecast when using the 4-month moving averages to predict the next month's shipments. The first moving average is displayed beside the month of May because it is computed by using January, February, March, and April and because it is being used to forecast the shipments for May. The rest of the 4-month moving averages and errors of forecast are as shown.

4-Month Moving Forecast

Month	Shipments	Average	Error
January	1,056	—	—
February	1,345	—	—
March	1,381	—	—
April	1,191	—	—
May	1,259	1,243.25	15.75
June	1,361	1,294.00	67.00
July	1,110	1,298.00	−188.00
August	1,334	1,230.25	103.75
September	1,416	1,266.00	150.00
October	1,282	1,305.25	−23.25
November	1,341	1,285.50	55.50
December	1,382	1,343.25	38.75

The following MINITAB graph shows the actual shipment values and the forecast shipment values based on the 4-month moving averages. Notice that the moving averages are "smoothed" in comparison with the individual data values. They appear to be less volatile and seem to be attempting to follow the general trend of the data.

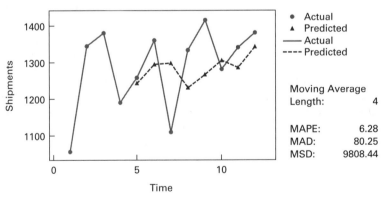

Weighted Moving Averages

A forecaster may want to place more weight on certain periods of time than on others. For example, a forecaster might believe that the previous month's value is three times as important in forecasting as other months. *A moving average in which some time periods are weighted differently than others* is called a **weighted moving average.**

As an example, suppose a 3-month weighted average is computed by weighting last month's value by 3, the value for the previous month by 2, and the value for the month before that by 1. This weighted average is computed as

$$\bar{x}_{\text{weighted}} = \frac{3(M_{t-1}) + 2(M_{t-2}) + 1(M_{t-3})}{6}$$

where

M_{t-1} = last month's value

M_{t-2} = value for the previous month

M_{t-3} = value for the month before previous month

Notice that the divisor is 6. With a weighted average, the divisor always equals the total number of weights. In this example, the value of M_{t-1} counts three times as much as the value for M_{t-3}.

DEMONSTRATION PROBLEM 7.2

Compute a 4-month weighted moving average for the electric lighting and wiring data from Demonstration Problem 7.1, using weights of 4 for last month's value, 2 for the previous month's value, and 1 for each of the values from the 2 months prior to that.

Solution

The first weighted average is

$$\frac{4(1,191) + 2(1,381) + 1(1,345) + 1(1,056)}{8} = 1,240.875$$

This moving average is recomputed for each ensuing month. Displayed next are the monthly values, the weighted moving averages, and the forecast error for the data.

Month	Shipments	4-Month Weighted Moving Average Forecast	Error
January	1,056	—	—
February	1,345	—	—
March	1,381	—	—
April	1,191	—	—
May	1,259	1,240.9	18.1
June	1,361	1,268.0	93.0
July	1,110	1,316.8	−206.8
August	1,334	1,201.5	132.5
September	1,416	1,272.0	144.0
October	1,282	1,350.4	−68.4
November	1,341	1,300.5	40.5
December	1,382	1,334.8	47.2

Note that in this problem the errors obtained by using the 4-month weighted moving average were greater than most of the errors obtained by using an unweighted 4-month moving average, as shown here.

Forecast Error, Unweighted 4-Month Moving Average	Forecast Error, Weighted 4-Month Moving Average
—	—
—	—
—	—
—	—
15.8	18.1
67.0	93.0
−188.0	−206.8
103.8	132.5
150.0	144.0
−23.3	−68.4
55.5	40.5
38.8	47.2

Smaller errors with weighted averages are not always the case. The forecaster can experiment with different weights in using the weighted moving average as a technique. Many possible weighting schemes can be used.

Exponential Smoothing

Another forecasting technique, **exponential smoothing,** is *used to weight data from previous time periods with exponentially decreasing importance in the forecast.* Exponential smoothing is accomplished by multiplying the actual value for the present time period, X_t, by a value between 0 and 1 (the exponential smoothing constant) referred to as α (not the same α used for a Type I error) and adding that result to the product of the present time period's forecast, F_t, and $(1 - \alpha)$. The following is a more formalized version.

EXPONENTIAL SMOOTHING

$$F_{t+1} = \alpha \cdot X_t + (1 - \alpha) \cdot F_t$$

where

F_{t+1} = the forecast for the next time period $(t + 1)$
F_t = the forecast for the present time period (t)
X_t = the actual value for the present time period
α = a value between 0 and 1 referred to as the exponential smoothing constant.

The value of α is determined by the forecaster. The essence of this procedure is that the new forecast is a combination of the present forecast and the present actual value. If α is chosen to be less than .5, less weight is placed on the actual value than on the forecast of that value. If α is chosen to be greater than .5, more weight is being put on the actual value than on the forecast value.

As an example, suppose the prime interest rate for a time period is 5% and the forecast of the prime interest rate for this time period was 6%. If the forecast of the prime interest rate for the next period is determined by exponential smoothing with $\alpha = .3$, the forecast is

$$F_{t+1} = (.3)(5\%) + (1.0 - .3)(6\%) = 5.7\%$$

Notice that the forecast value of 5.7% for the next period is weighted more toward the previous forecast of 6% than toward the actual value of 5% because α is .3. Suppose we use $\alpha = .7$ as the exponential smoothing constant. Then,

$$F_{t+1} = (.7)(5\%) + (1.0 - .7)(6\%) = 5.3\%$$

This value is closer to the actual value of 5% than the previous forecast of 6% because the exponential smoothing constant, α, is greater than .5.

To see why this procedure is called exponential smoothing, examine the formula for exponential smoothing again.

$$F_{t+1} = \alpha \cdot X_t + (1 - \alpha) \cdot F_t$$

If exponential smoothing has been used over a period of time, the forecast for F_t will have been obtained by

$$F_t = \alpha \cdot X_{t-1} + (1 - \alpha) \cdot F_{t-1}$$

Substituting this forecast value, F_t, into the preceding equation for F_{t+1} produces

$$F_{t+1} = \alpha \cdot X_t + (1 - \alpha)[\alpha \cdot X_{t-1} + (1 - \alpha) \cdot F_{t-1}]$$
$$= \alpha \cdot X_t + \alpha (1 - \alpha) \cdot X_{t-1} + (1 - \alpha)^2 F_{t-1}$$

but

$$F_{t-1} = \alpha \cdot X_{t-2} + (1 - \alpha)F_{t-2}$$

Substituting this value of F_{t-1} into the preceding equation for F_{t+1} produces

$$F_{t+1} = \alpha \cdot X_t + \alpha(1-\alpha) \cdot X_{t-1} + (1-\alpha)^2 F_{t-1}$$
$$= \alpha \cdot X_t + \alpha(1-\alpha) \cdot X_{t-1} + (1-\alpha)^2[\alpha \cdot X_{t-2} + (1-\alpha) F_{t-2}]$$
$$= \alpha \cdot X_t + \alpha(1-\alpha) \cdot X_{t-1} + \alpha(1-\alpha)^2 \cdot X_{t-2} + (1-\alpha)^3 F_{t-2}$$

Continuing this process shows that the weights on previous-period values and forecasts include $(1-\alpha)^n$ (exponential values). The following chart shows the values of α, $(1-\alpha)$, $(1-\alpha)^2$, and $(1-\alpha)^3$ for three different values of α. Included is the value of $\alpha(1-\alpha)^3$, which is the weight of the actual value for three time periods back. Notice the rapidly decreasing emphasis on values for earlier time periods. The impact of exponential smoothing on time-series data is to place much more emphasis on recent time periods. The choice of α determines the amount of emphasis.

α	$1-\alpha$	$(1-\alpha)^2$	$(1-\alpha)^3$	$\alpha(1-\alpha)^3$
.2	.8	.64	.512	.1024
.5	.5	.25	.125	.0625
.8	.2	.04	.008	.0064

Some forecasters use the computer to analyze time-series data for various values of α. By setting up criteria with which to judge the forecasting errors, forecasters can select the value of α that best fits the data.

The exponential smoothing formula

$$F_{t+1} = \alpha \cdot X_t + (1-\alpha) \cdot F_t$$

can be rearranged algebraically as

$$F_{t+1} = F_t + \alpha(X_t - F_t)$$

This form of the equation shows that the new forecast, F_{t+1}, equals the old forecast, F_t, plus an adjustment based on α times the error of the old forecast $(X_t - F_t)$. The smaller α is, the less impact the error has on the new forecast and the more the new forecast is like the old. It demonstrates the dampening effect of α on the forecasts.

DEMONSTRATION PROBLEM 7.3

The U.S. Census Bureau reports housing data in the publication *Current Construction Reports.* The total units of new privately owned housing started between 1984 and 1999 in the United States are given here. Use exponential smoothing to forecast the values for each ensuing time period. Work the problem using α = .2, .5, and .8.

Year	Total Units (1,000)
1984	1,750
1985	1,742
1986	1,805
1987	1,620
1988	1,488
1989	1,376
1990	1,193
1991	1,014
1992	1,200
1993	1,288
1994	1,457
1995	1,354
1996	1,477
1997	1,474
1998	1,617
1999	1,666

Solution

An Excel graph of these data is shown here.

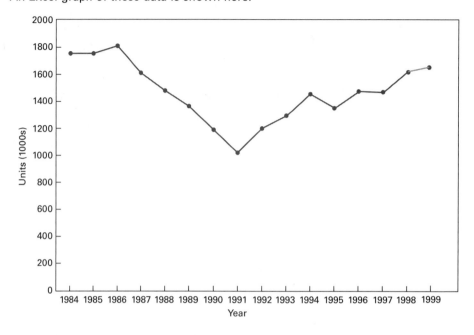

The following table provides the forecasts with each of the three values of alpha. Note that because no forecast is given for the first time period, we cannot compute a forecast based on exponential smoothing for the second period. Instead, we use the actual value for the first period as the forecast for the second period to get started. As examples, the forecasts for the third, fourth, and fifth periods are computed for $\alpha = .2$ as follows.

$$F_3 = .2(1,742) + .8(1,750) = 1,748.4$$
$$F_4 = .2(1,805) + .8(1,748.4) = 1,759.7$$
$$F_5 = .2(1,620) + .8(1,759.7) = 1,731.8$$

Year	Housing Units (1,000)	$\alpha = .2$ F	$\alpha = .2$ e	$\alpha = .5$ F	$\alpha = .5$ e	$\alpha = .8$ F	$\alpha = .8$ e
1984	1,750	—	—	—	—	—	—
1985	1,742	1,750.0	−8.0	1,750.0	−8.0	1,750.0	−8.0
1986	1,805	1,748.4	56.6	1,746.0	59.0	1,743.6	61.4
1987	1,620	1,759.7	−139.7	1,775.5	−155.5	1,792.7	−172.7
1988	1,488	1,731.8	−243.8	1,697.8	−209.8	1,654.5	−166.5
1989	1,376	1,683.0	−307.0	1,592.9	−216.9	1,521.3	−145.3
1990	1,193	1,621.6	−428.6	1,484.5	−291.5	1,405.1	−212.1
1991	1,014	1,535.9	−521.9	1,338.8	−324.8	1,235.4	−221.4
1992	1,200	1,431.5	−231.5	1,176.4	23.6	1,058.3	141.7
1993	1,288	1,385.2	−97.2	1,188.2	99.8	1,171.7	116.3
1994	1,457	1,365.8	91.2	1,238.1	218.9	1,264.7	192.3
1995	1,354	1,384.0	−30.0	1,347.6	6.4	1,418.5	−64.5
1996	1,477	1,378.0	99.0	1,350.8	126.2	1,366.9	110.1
1997	1,474	1,397.8	76.2	1,413.9	60.1	1,455.0	19.0
1998	1,617	1,413.0	204.0	1,444.0	173.0	1,470.2	146.8
1999	1,666	1,453.8	212.2	1,530.5	135.5	1,587.6	78.4

	$\alpha = .2$	$\alpha = .5$	$\alpha = .8$
MAD:	183.1	140.6	123.8
MSE:	53,803.9	29,037.1	19,428.1

Which value of alpha works best on the data? At the bottom of the preceding analysis are the values of two different measurements of error for each of the three different values of alpha. With each measurement of error, $\alpha = .8$ produces the smallest measurement of error. Observe from the Excel graph of the original data that the data vary up and down considerably. In exponential smoothing, the value of alpha is multiplied by the actual value and $1 - \alpha$ is multiplied by the forecast value to get the next forecast. Because the actual values are varying considerably, the exponential smoothing value with the largest alpha seems to be forecasting the best. By placing the greatest weight on the actual values, the new forecast seems to predict the new value better.

The MINITAB graphs shown next depict each of the exponential smoothing analyses used in this problem.

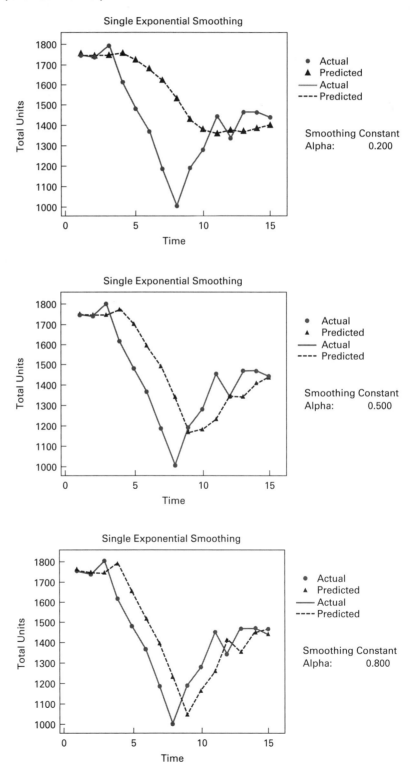

Forecasting the Economy by Scrap Metal Prices?

Economists are constantly on the lookout for valid indicators of a country's economy. Forecasters have sifted through oil indicators (for example, West Texas intermediate crude), the price of gold on the world markets, the Dow Jones averages, government-published indexes, and practically anything else that might seem related in some way to the state of the economy.

Would you believe that the price of scrap metal is a popular indicator of economic activity in the United States? Several well-known and experienced economic forecasters, including Federal Reserve chairman Alan Greenspan and the chief market analyst for Chase Manhattan, Donald Fine, believe that the price of scrap metal is a good indicator of the industrial economy.

Scrap metal is leftover copper, steel, aluminum, and other metals. Scrap metal is a good indicator of industrial activity because as manufacturing increases, the demand for scrap metals increases, as does the price of scrap metal. Donald Fine says that "scrap metal is the beginning of the production chain"; hence, an increasing demand for it is an indicator of increasing manufacturing production. Mr. Fine goes on to say that scrap metal is sometimes a better indicator of the future direction of the economy than many governmental statistics. In some cases, scrap metal correctly predicted no economic recovery when some government measures indicated that a recovery was underway.

Source: Anita Raghavan and David Wessel, "In Scraping Together Economic Data, Forecasters Turn to Scrap-Metal Prices," *The Wall Street Journal,* April 27, 1992, C1.

7.2 PROBLEMS

7.5   Use the following time-series data to answer the given questions.

Time Period	Value	Time Period	Value
1	27	6	66
2	31	7	71
3	58	8	86
4	63	9	101
5	59	10	97

  a. Develop forecasts for periods 5 through 10 using 4-month moving averages.

  b. Develop forecasts for periods 5 through 10 using 4-month weighted moving averages. Weight the most recent month by a factor of 4, the previous month by 2, and the other months by 1.

  c. Compute the errors of the forecasts in parts (a) and (b) and observe the differences in the errors forecast by the two different techniques.

7.6   Following are time-series data for eight different periods. Use exponential smoothing to forecast the values for periods 3 through 8. Use the value for the first period as the forecast for the second period. Compute forecasts using two different values of alpha, $\alpha = .1$ and $\alpha = .8$. Compute the errors for each forecast and compare the errors produced by using the two different exponential smoothing constants.

Time Period	Value	Time Period	Value
1	211	5	242
2	228	6	227
3	236	7	217
4	241	8	203

7.7   Following are time-series data for nine time periods. Use exponential smoothing with constants of .3 and .7 to forecast time periods 3 through 9. Let the value for time period 1 be the forecast for time period 2. Compute additional forecasts for time periods 4 through 9 using a 3-month moving average. Compute the errors for the forecasts and discuss the size of errors under each method.

Time Period	Value	Time Period	Value
1	9.4	6	11.0
2	8.2	7	10.3
3	7.9	8	9.5
4	9.0	9	9.1
5	9.8		

7.8 The U.S. Census Bureau publishes data on factory orders for all manufacturing, durable goods, and nondurable goods industries. Shown here are factory orders in the United States from 1987 through 1999 ($ billion).

    a. Use these data to develop forecasts for the years 1992 through 1999 using a 5-year moving average.

    b. Use these data to develop forecasts for the years 1992 through 1999 using a 5-year weighted moving average. Weight the most recent year by 6, the previous year by 4, the year before that by 2, and the other years by 1.

    c. Compute the errors of the forecasts in parts (a) and (b) and observe the differences in the errors of the forecasts.

Year	Factory Orders ($ billion)
1987	2,512.7
1988	2,739.2
1989	2,874.9
1990	2,934.1
1991	2,865.7
1992	2,978.5
1993	3,092.4
1994	3,356.8
1995	3,607.6
1996	3,749.3
1997	3,952.0
1998	3,949.0
1999	4,137.0

7.9 The following data show the number of issues from Initial Public Offerings (IPOs) for a 13-year period released by the Securities Data Company. Use these data to develop forecasts for the years 3 through 13 using exponential smoothing techniques with alpha values of .2 and .9. Let the forecast for year 2 be the value for year 1. Compare the results by examining the errors of the forecasts.

Year	Number of Issues
1	332
2	694
3	518
4	222
5	209
6	172
7	366
8	512
9	667
10	571
11	575
12	865
13	609

7.3 TREND ANALYSIS

One of the four elements of time-series data is trend. A trend is the long-run general direction of a business climate over a period of several years. Data trends can be ascertained in several ways. One particular technique is regression analysis. In time-series regression trend analysis, the response variable, Y, is the item being forecast. The independent variable, X, represents the time periods.

Many possible trend fits can be explored with time-series data. In this section we examine only the linear model and the quadratic model because they are the easiest to understand and simplest to compute. Because seasonal effects can confound trend analysis, it is assumed here that no seasonal effects occur in the data or they were removed prior to determining the trend.

Linear Regression Trend Analysis

The data in Table 7.5 represent 35 years of data on the average length of the workweek in Canada for manufacturing workers. A regression line can be fit to these data by using the time periods as the independent variable and length of work week as the dependent variable. Because the time periods are consecutive, they can be renumbered from 1 to 35 and entered along with the time-series data (Y) into a regression analysis. The linear model explored in this example is

$$Y_i = \beta_0 + \beta_1 X_{ti} + \epsilon_i$$

where

Y_i = data value for period i
X_{ti} = ith time period

Figure 7.5 shows the Excel regression output for this example. By using the coefficients of the X variable and intercept, the equation of the trend line can be determined to be

$$\hat{Y} = 37.4161 - .0614X_t$$

The slope indicates that for every unit increase in time period, X_t, a predicted decrease of .0614 occurs in the length of the average work week in manufacturing. Because the

TABLE 7.5	Time Period	Hours	Time Period	Hours
Average Hours per Week in Manufacturing by Canadian Workers	1	37.2	19	36.0
	2	37.0	20	35.7
	3	37.4	21	35.6
	4	37.5	22	35.2
	5	37.7	23	34.8
	6	37.7	24	35.3
	7	37.4	25	35.6
	8	37.2	26	35.6
	9	37.3	27	35.6
	10	37.2	28	35.9
	11	36.9	29	36.0
	12	36.7	30	35.7
	13	36.7	31	35.7
	14	36.5	32	35.5
	15	36.3	33	35.6
	16	35.9	34	36.3
	17	35.8	35	36.5
	18	35.9		

Source: Data prepared by the U.S. Bureau of Labor Statistics, Office of Productivity and Technology.

FIGURE 7.5

Excel Regression Output for Hours Worked Using Linear Trend

	A	B	C	D	E	F
1	SUMMARY OUTPUT					
2	Regression Statistics					
3	Multiple R	0.782				
4	R Square	0.611				
5	Adjusted R Square	0.600				
6	Standard Error	0.5090				
7	Observations	35				
8						
9	ANOVA					
10		df	SS	MS	F	Significance F
11	Regression	1	13.4467	13.4467	51.91	0.000000029
12	Residual	33	8.5487	0.2591		
13	Total	34	21.9954			
14						
15		Coefficients	Standard Error	t Stat	P-value	
16	Intercept	37.4161	0.1758	212.81	0.00000000	
17	Year	-0.0614	0.0085	-7.20	0.00000003	

workweek is measured in hours, the length of the average workweek decreases by an average of (.0614)(60 minutes) = 3.7 minutes each year in Canada in manufacturing. The Y intercept, 37.4161, indicates that in the year prior to the first period of these data the average workweek was 37.4161 hours.

The probability of the t ratio (.00000003) indicates that significant linear trend is present in the data. In addition, $R^2 = .611$ indicates considerable predictability in the model. Inserting the various period values (1, 2, 3, ... , 35) into the preceding regression equation produces the predicted values of Y that are the trend. For example, for period 23 the predicted value is

$$\hat{Y} = 37.4161 - .0614(23) = 36.0 \text{ hours}$$

The model was developed with 35 periods (years). From this model, the average workweek in Canada in manufacturing for period 41 (the forty-first year) can be forecast:

$$\hat{Y} = 37.4161 - .0614(41) = 34.9 \text{ hours}$$

Figure 7.6 presents an Excel scatter plot of the average workweek lengths over the 35 periods (years). In this Excel plot, the trend line has been fitted through the points. Observe the general downward trend of the data, but also note the somewhat cyclical nature of the points. Because of this pattern, a forecaster might want to determine whether a quadratic model is a better fit for trend.

FIGURE 7.6

Excel Graph of Canadian Manufacturing Data with Trend Line

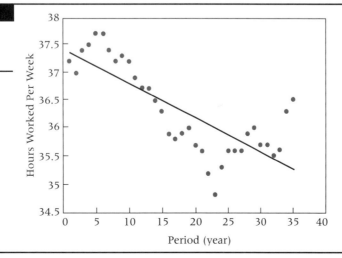

Regression Trend Analysis Using Quadratic Models

In addition to linear regression, forecasters can explore using quadratic regression models to predict data by using the time-series periods. The quadratic regression model is

$$Y_i = \beta_0 + \beta_1 X_{ti} + \beta_2 X_{ti}^2 + \epsilon_i$$

where

$Y_i =$ the time-series data value for period i

$X_{ti} =$ the ith period

$X_{ti}^2 =$ the square of the ith period

This model can be implemented in time-series trend analysis by using the time periods squared as an additional predictor. Thus, in the hours worked example, besides using $X_t = 1, 2, 3, 4, \ldots, 35$ as a predictor, we would also use $X_t^2 = 1, 4, 9, 16, \ldots, 1225$ as a predictor.

Table 7.6 provides the data needed to compute a quadratic regression trend model on the manufacturing workweek data. Note that the table includes the original data, the time periods, and the time periods squared.

The Excel computer output for this quadratic trend regression analysis is shown in Figure 7.7. We see that the quadratic regression model produces an R^2 of .761 with both X_t and X_t^2 in the model. The linear model produced an R^2 of .611 with X_t alone. The quadratic regression seems to add some predictability to the trend model.

Figure 7.8 displays an Excel scatter plot of the week work data with a second-degree polynomial fit through the data.

TABLE 7.6					
Data for Quadratic Fit of Manufacturing Workweek Example					
Time Period	**(Time Period)²**	**Hours**	**Time Period**	**(Time Period)²**	**Hours**
1	1	37.2	19	361	36.0
2	4	37.0	20	400	35.7
3	9	37.4	21	441	35.6
4	16	37.5	22	484	35.2
5	25	37.7	23	529	34.8
6	36	37.7	24	576	35.3
7	49	37.4	25	625	35.6
8	64	37.2	26	676	35.6
9	81	37.3	27	729	35.6
10	100	37.2	28	784	35.9
11	121	36.9	29	841	36.0
12	144	36.7	30	900	35.7
13	169	36.7	31	961	35.7
14	196	36.5	32	1024	35.5
15	225	36.3	33	1089	35.6
16	256	35.9	34	1156	36.3
17	289	35.8	35	1225	36.5
18	324	35.9			

Source: Data prepared by the U.S. Bureau of Labor Statistics, Office of Productivity and Technology.

FIGURE 7.7

Excel Regression Output for Canadian Manufacturing Example with Quadratic Trend

	A	B	C	D	E	F
1	SUMMARY OUTPUT					
2	Regression Statistics					
3	Multiple R	0.873				
4	R Square	0.761				
5	Adjusted R Square	0.747				
6	Standard Error	0.4049				
7	Observations	35				
8						
9	ANOVA					
10		df	SS	MS	F	Significance F
11	Regression	2	16.7483	8.3741	51.07	0.0000000001
12	Residual	32	5.2472	0.1640		
13	Total	34	21.9954			
14						
15		Coefficients	Standard Error	t Stat	P-value	
16	Intercept	38.1644	0.2177	175.34	0.0000000	
17	Year	-0.1827	0.0279	-6.55	0.0000002	
18	YearSq	0.0034	0.0008	4.49	0.0000876	

FIGURE 7.8

Excel Graph of Canadian Manufacturing Data with a Second-Degree Polynomial Fit

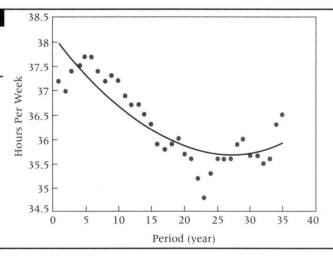

DEMONSTRATION PROBLEM 7.4

Following are data on the U.S. civilian labor force (100,000) for 1988 through 2000, obtained from the U.S. Bureau of Labor Statistics. Use regression analysis to fit a trend line through the data. Explore a quadratic regression trend also. Does either model do well? Compare the two models.

Year	Labor Force (100,000)
1988	114.968
1989	117.342
1990	118.793
1991	117.718
1992	118.492
1993	120.259
1994	123.060
1995	124.900
1996	126.708
1997	129.558
1998	131.463
1999	133.488
2000	134.337

Solution

Recode the time periods as 1 through 13 and let that be X. Run the regression analysis with the labor force members as Y, the dependent variable, and the time period as the independent variable. Now square all the X values, resulting in 1, 4, 9, ... , 121, 144, 169 and let those formulate a second predictor (X^2). Run the regression analysis to predict the number in the labor force with both the time period variable (X) and the (time period)^2 variable. The MINITAB output for each of these regression analyses follows.

LINEAR TREND ANALYSIS

Regression Analysis: Labor Force versus Year

The regression equation is
Labor Force = 112 + 1.67 Year

Predictor	Coef	SE Coef	T	P
Constant	112.229	0.808	138.93	0.000
Year	1.6715	0.1018	16.42	0.000

S = 1.373   R-Sq = 96.1%   R-Sq(adj) = 95.7%

Analysis of Variance

Source	DF	SS	MS	F	P
Regression	1	508.51	508.51	269.75	0.000
Residual Error	11	20.74	1.89		
Total	12	529.24			

QUADRATIC TREND ANALYSIS

Regression Analysis: Labor Force versus Year, YearSq

The regression equation is
Labor Force = 115 + 0.650 Year + 0.0730 YearSq

Predictor	Coef	SE Coef	T	P
Constant	114.783	0.983	116.81	0.000
Year	0.6501	0.3228	2.01	0.072
YearSq	0.07296	0.02244	3.25	0.009

S = 1.004   R-Sq = 98.1%   R-Sq(adj) = 97.7%

Analysis of Variance

Source	DF	SS	MS	F	P
Regression	2	519.16	259.58	257.54	0.000
Residual Error	10	10.08	1.01		
Total	12	529.24			

A comparison of the models shows that the linear model accounts for more than 96% of the variability in the labor force figures, but the quadratic model increases that predictability to greater than 98%. In addition, the standard error of the estimate for the linear model (1.373) is lowered to 1.004 when the quadratic model is used. In the quadratic model, the t test for the squared term is significant at $\alpha = .05$ but is not significant (p-value = .072) for the linear term, indicating that the squared term is the stronger predictor of the labor force figures. Shown next are MINITAB scatter plots of the data. First is the linear model, and then the quadratic model is presented.

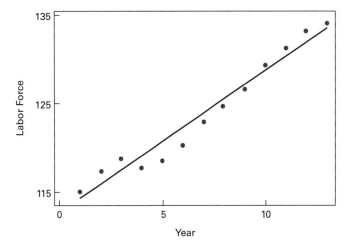

Regression Plot
Labor Force = 112.229 + 1.67152 Year
$S = 1.37299$ $R\text{-}Sq = 96.1\%$ $R\text{-}Sq(adj) = 95.7\%$

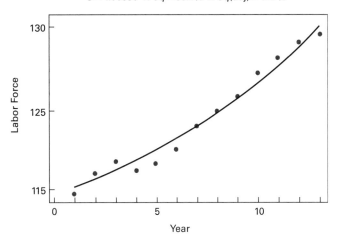

Regression Plot
Labor Force = 114.783 + 0.650088 Year
+ 0.0729595 Year**2
$S = 1.00396$ $R\text{-}Sq = 98.1\%$ $R\text{-}Sq(adj) = 97.7\%$

Holt's Two-Parameter Exponential Smoothing Method

The exponential smoothing technique presented in Section 7.2 (single exponential smoothing) is appropriate to use in forecasting stationary time-series data but is ineffective in forecasting time-series data with a trend because the forecasts will lag behind the trend. However, another exponential smoothing technique, Holt's two-parameter exponential smoothing method, can be used for trend analysis. Holt's technique uses weights (β) to smooth the trend in a manner similar to the smoothing used in single exponential smoothing (α). Using these two weights and several equations, Holt's method is able to develop forecasts that include both a smoothing value and a trend value. A more detailed explanation of Holt's two-parameter exponential smoothing method, along with examples and practice problems, is presented on the eGrade Plus Web site.

7.3 PROBLEMS

7.10 The "Economic Report to the President of the United States" included data on the amounts of manufacturers' new and unfilled orders in millions of dollars. Shown here are the figures for new orders over a 21-year period. Use a computer to develop a regression model to fit the trend effects for these data. Use a linear model and then try a quadratic model. How well does either model fit the data?

Year	Total Number of New Orders	Year	Total Number of New Orders
1	55,022	12	168,025
2	55,921	13	162,140
3	64,182	14	175,451
4	76,003	15	192,879
5	87,327	16	195,706
6	85,139	17	195,204
7	99,513	18	209,389
8	115,109	19	227,025
9	131,629	20	240,758
10	147,604	21	243,643
11	156,359		

7.11 The following data on the number of union members in the United States for the years 1984 through 2000 are provided by the U.S. Bureau of Labor Statistics. Using regression techniques discussed in this section, analyze the data for trend. Develop a scatter plot of the data and fit the trend line through the data. Discuss the strength of the model.

Year	Union Members (1,000s)	Year	Union Members (1,000s)
1984	17,340	1993	16,598
1985	16,996	1994	16,748
1986	16,975	1995	16,360
1987	16,913	1996	16,269
1988	17,002	1997	16,110
1989	16,960	1998	16,211
1990	16,740	1999	16,477
1991	16,568	2000	16,258
1992	16,390		

7.12 The following data list worldwide shipments of personal computers (1,000) according to Dataquest. Plot the data, fit a trend line, and discuss the strength of prediction of the regression model. In addition, explore a quadratic trend. Compare the results of the two models.

Year	Shipments (1,000)
1985	14,705
1986	15,064
1987	16,676
1988	18,061
1989	21,327
1990	23,738
1991	26,966
1992	32,411
1993	38,851
1994	47,894
1995	60,171
1996	71,065
1997	82,400
1998	97,321

7.4 SEASONAL EFFECTS

Earlier in the chapter, we discussed the notion that time-series data consist of four elements: trend, cyclical effects, seasonality, and irregularity. In this section, we examine techniques for identifying seasonal effects. **Seasonal effects** are *patterns of data behavior that occur in periods of time of less than one year.* How can we separate out the seasonal effects?

Decomposition

One of the main techniques for isolating the effects of seasonality is **decomposition.** The decomposition methodology presented here uses the multiplicative model as its basis. The multiplicative model is:

$$T \cdot C \cdot S \cdot I$$

where

T = trend
C = cyclicality
S = seasonality
I = irregularity

To illustrate the decomposition process, we will use the 5-year quarterly time-series data on U.S. shipments of household appliances given in Table 7.7. Figure 7.9 provides a graph of these data.

According to the multiplicative time-series model, $T \cdot C \cdot S \cdot I$, the data can contain the elements of trend, cyclical effects, seasonal effects, and irregular fluctuations. The process of isolating the seasonal effects begins by determining $T \cdot C$ for each value and dividing the time-series data $(T \cdot C \cdot S \cdot I)$ by $T \cdot C$. The result is

$$\frac{T \cdot C \cdot S \cdot I}{T \cdot C} = S \cdot I$$

TABLE 7.7

Shipments of
Household Appliances

Year	Quarter	Shipments
1	1	4,009
	2	4,321
	3	4,224
	4	3,944
2	1	4,123
	2	4,522
	3	4,657
	4	4,030
3	1	4,493
	2	4,806
	3	4,551
	4	4,485
4	1	4,595
	2	4,799
	3	4,417
	4	4,258
5	1	4,245
	2	4,900
	3	4,585
	4	4,533

FIGURE 7.9

MINITAB Time-Series Graph of Household Appliance Data

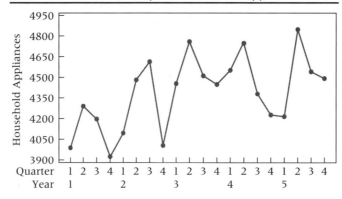

The resulting expression contains seasonal effects along with irregular fluctuations. After reducing the time-series data to the effects of *SI* (seasonality and irregularity), a method for eliminating the irregular fluctuations can be applied, leaving only the seasonal effects.

Suppose we start with time-series data that cover several years and are measured in quarterly increments. If we average the data over four quarters, we will have "dampened" the seasonal effects of the data because the rise and fall of values during the quarterly periods will have been averaged out over the year.

We begin by computing a 4-quarter moving average for quarter 1 through quarter 4 of year 1, using the data from Table 7.7.

$$4\text{-quarter average} = \frac{4,009 + 4,321 + 4,224 + 3,944}{4} = 4,124.5$$

The 4-quarter moving average for quarter 1 through quarter 4 of year 1 is 4,124.5 ($ million) worth of shipments. Because the 4-quarter average is in the middle of the four quarters, it would be placed in the decomposition table between quarter 2 and quarter 3.

Quarter 1
Quarter 2
——— 4,124.5
Quarter 3
Quarter 4

To remove seasonal effects, we need to determine a value that is "centered" with each month. To find this value, instead of using a 4-quarter moving average, we use 4-quarter moving totals and then sum two consecutive moving totals. This 8-quarter total value is divided by 8 to produce a "centered" 4-quarter moving average that lines up across from a quarter. Using this method is analogous to computing two consecutive 4-quarter moving averages and averaging them, thus producing a value that falls on line with a quarter, in between the two averages. The results of using this procedure on the data from Table 7.7 are shown in Table 7.8 in column 5.

A 4-quarter moving total can be computed on these data starting with quarter 1 of year 1 through quarter 4 of year 1 as follows:

First Moving Total = 4,009 + 4,321 + 4,224 + 3,944 = 16,498

In Table 7.8, 16,498 is between quarter 2 and quarter 3 of year 1. The 4-month moving total for quarter 2 of year 1 through quarter 1 of year 2 is

Second Moving Total = 4,321 + 4,224 + 3,944 + 4,123 = 16,612

In Table 7.8, this value is between quarter 3 and quarter 4 of year 1. The 8-quarter (2-year) moving total is computed for quarter 3 of year 1 as

8-Quarter Moving Total = 16,498 + 16,612 = 33,110

TABLE 7.8					Development of 4-Quarter Moving Averages for the Household Appliance Data

Quarter	Actual Values $(T \cdot C \cdot S \cdot I)$	4-Quarter Moving Total	4-Quarter 2-Year Moving Total	Ratios of Actual Centered Moving Average $(T \cdot C)$	Values to Moving Averages $(S \cdot I) \cdot (100)$
1 (year 1)	4,009				
2	4,321				
3	4,224	16,498	33,110	4,139	102.05
4	3,944	16,612	33,425	4,178	94.40
1 (year 2)	4,123	16,813	34,059	4,257	96.85
2	4,522	17,246	34,578	4,322	104.63
3	4,657	17,332	35,034	4,379	106.35
4	4,030	17,702	35,688	4,461	90.34
1 (year 3)	4,493	17,986	35,866	4,483	100.22
2	4,806	17,880	36,215	4,527	106.16
3	4,551	18,335	36,772	4,597	99.00
4	4,485	18,437	36,867	4,608	97.33
1 (year 4)	4,595	18,430	36,726	4,591	100.09
2	4,799	18,296	36,365	4,546	105.57
3	4,417	18,069	35,788	4,474	98.73
4	4,258	17,719	35,539	4,442	95.86
1 (year 5)	4,245	17,820	35,808	4,476	94.84
2	4,900	17,988	36,251	4,531	108.14
3	4,585	18,263			
4	4,533				

Notice that in Table 7.8 this value is centered with quarter 3 of year 1 because it is between the two adjacent 4-quarter moving totals. Dividing this total by 8 produces the 4-quarter moving average for quarter 3 of year 1 shown in column 5 of Table 7.8:

$$\frac{33,110}{8} = 4,139$$

Column 3 contains the uncentered 4-quarter moving totals, column 4 contains the 2-year centered moving totals, and column 5 contains the 4-quarter centered moving averages.

The 4-quarter centered moving averages shown in column 5 of Table 7.8 represent $T \cdot C$. Seasonal effects have been removed from the original data (actual values) by summing across the 4-quarter periods. Seasonal effects are removed when the data are summed across the time periods that include the seasonal periods and the irregular effects are smoothed, leaving only trend and cycle.

Column 2 of Table 7.8 contains the original data (actual values), which include all effects $(T \cdot C \cdot S \cdot I)$. Column 5 contains only the trend and cyclical effects, $T \cdot C$. If column 2 is divided by column 5, the result is $S \cdot I$, which is displayed in column 6 of Table 7.8.

The values in column 6, sometimes called ratios of actuals to moving average, have been multiplied by 100 to index the values. These values are thus seasonal indexes. An **index number** is *a ratio of a measure taken during one time frame to that same measure taken during another time frame, usually denoted as the time period.* Often the ratio is multiplied by 100 and expressed as a percentage. Index numbers will be discussed more fully in section 7.6. Column 6 contains the effects of seasonality and irregular fluctuations. Now we must remove the irregular effects.

TABLE 7.9

Seasonal Indexes for the Household Appliance Data

Quarter	Year 1	Year 2	Year 3	Year 4	Year 5
1	—	96.85	100.22	100.09	94.84
2	—	104.63	106.16	105.57	108.14
3	102.05	106.35	99.00	98.73	—
4	94.40	90.34	97.33	95.86	—

TABLE 7.10

Final Seasonal Indexes for the Household Appliance Data

Quarter	Index
1	98.47
2	105.87
3	100.53
4	95.13

Table 7.9 contains the values from column 6 of Table 7.8 organized by quarter and year. Each quarter in these data has four seasonal indexes. Throwing out the high and low index for each quarter eliminates the extreme values. The remaining two indexes are averaged as follows for quarter 1.

Quarter 1: 96.85   100.22   100.09   94.84
Eliminate: 94.84 and 100.22
Average the Remaining Indexes:

$$\overline{X}_{Q1\,index} = \frac{96.85 + 100.09}{2} = 98.47$$

Table 7.10 gives the final seasonal indexes for all the quarters of these data.

After the final adjusted seasonal indexes are determined, the original data can be **deseasonalized.** The deseasonalization of actual values is relatively common with data published by the government and other agencies. Data can be deseasonalized by dividing the actual values, which consist of $T \cdot C \cdot S \cdot I$, by the final adjusted seasonal effects.

$$\text{Deseasonalized Data} = \frac{T \cdot C \cdot S \cdot I}{S} = T \cdot C \cdot I$$

Because the seasonal effects are in terms of index numbers, the seasonal indexes must be divided by 100 before deseasonalization. Shown here are the computations for deseasonalizing the household appliance data from Table 7.7 for quarter 1 of year 1.

Year 1 Quarter 1 Actual = 4,009
Year 1 Quarter 1 Seasonal Index = 98.47
$$\text{Year 1 Quarter 1 Deseasonalized Value} = \frac{4,009}{.9847} = 4,071.3$$

Table 7.11 gives the deseasonalized data for this example for all years.

Figure 7.10 is a graph of the deseasonalized data.

Finding Seasonal Effects with the Computer

Through MINITAB, decomposition can be performed on the computer with relative ease. The commands for this procedure are given at the end of the chapter in the Using the Computer section. Figure 7.11 displays MINITAB output for seasonal decomposition of the household appliance example. Note that the seasonal indexes are virtually identical to those shown in Table 7.10 computed by hand.

Winters' Three-Parameter Exponential Smoothing Method

Holt's two-parameter exponential smoothing method, can be extended to include seasonal analysis. This technique, referred to as Winters' method, not only smoothes observations and trend but also smoothes the seasonal effects. In addition to the single exponential smoothing weight of α and the trend weight of β, Winters' method introduces γ, a weight for seasonality. Using these three weights and several equations, Winters' method is able to develop forecasts that include a smoothing value for observations, a trend value, and a seasonal value. A more detailed explanation of Winters' three-parameter exponential smoothing method along with examples and practice problems is presented on the eGrade Plus Web site.

TABLE 7.11

Deseasonalized Household Appliance Data

Year	Quarter	Shipments Actual Values $(T \cdot C \cdot S \cdot I)$	Seasonal Indexes S	Deseasonalized Data $T \cdot C \cdot I$
1	1	4,009	98.47	4,071
	2	4,321	105.87	4,081
	3	4,224	100.53	4,202
	4	3,944	95.13	4,146
2	1	4,123	98.47	4,187
	2	4,522	105.87	4,271
	3	4,657	100.53	4,632
	4	4,030	95.13	4,236
3	1	4,493	98.47	4,563
	2	4,806	105.87	4,540
	3	4,551	100.53	4,527
	4	4,485	95.13	4,715
4	1	4,595	98.47	4,666
	2	4,799	105.87	4,533
	3	4,417	100.53	4,394
	4	4,258	95.13	4,476
5	1	4,245	98.47	4,311
	2	4,900	105.87	4,628
	3	4,585	100.53	4,561
	4	4,533	95.13	4,765

FIGURE 7.10

Graph of the Deseasonalized Household Appliance Data

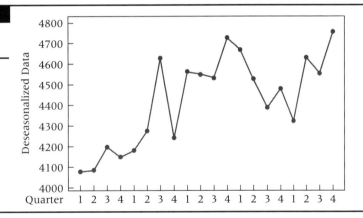

FIGURE 7.11

MINITAB Output for Seasonal Decomposition of the Household Appliance Data

```
Time-Series Decomposition
Data: House Appliances
Length: 20.0000
NMissing: 0
Seasonal Indices
Period    Index
     1  0.984691
     2   1.05871
     3   1.00536
     4  0.951239
```

7.4 PROBLEMS

7.13 The U.S. Department of Agriculture publishes statistics on the production of various types of food commodities by month. Shown here are the production figures on broccoli for January of a recent year through December of the next year. Use these data to compute 12-month centered moving averages ($T \cdot C$). Using these computed values, determine the seasonal effects ($S \cdot I$).

Month	Broccoli (million pounds)	Month	Broccoli (million pounds)
January (1st year)	132.5	January (2nd year)	104.9
February	164.8	February	99.3
March	141.2	March	102.0
April	133.8	April	122.4
May	138.4	May	112.1
June	150.9	June	108.4
July	146.6	July	119.0
August	146.9	August	119.0
September	138.7	September	114.9
October	128.0	October	106.0
November	112.4	November	111.7
December	121.0	December	112.3

7.14 The U.S. Department of Commerce publishes census information on manufacturing. Included in these figures are monthly shipment data for the paperboard container and box industry shown here for six years. The shipment figures are given in millions of dollars. Use the data to analyze the effects of seasonality, trend, and cycle. Develop the trend model with a linear model only.

Month	Shipments	Month	Shipments
January (year 1)	1,891	January (year 3)	2,183
February	1,986	February	2,230
March	1,987	March	2,222
April	1,987	April	2,319
May	2,000	May	2,369
June	2,082	June	2,529
July	1,878	July	2,267
August	2,074	August	2,457
September	2,086	September	2,524
October	2,045	October	2,502
November	1,945	November	2,314
December	1,861	December	2,277

Month	Shipments	Month	Shipments
January (year 2)	1,936	January (year 4)	2,336
February	2,104	February	2,474
March	2,126	March	2,546
April	2,131	April	2,566
May	2,163	May	2,473
June	2,346	June	2,572
July	2,109	July	2,336
August	2,211	August	2,518
September	2,268	September	2,454
October	2,285	October	2,559
November	2,107	November	2,384
December	2,077	December	2,305

Month	Shipments	Month	Shipments
January (year 5)	2,389	January (year 6)	2,377
February	2,463	February	2,381
March	2,522	March	2,268
April	2,417	April	2,407
May	2,468	May	2,367
June	2,492	June	2,446
July	2,304	July	2,341
August	2,511	August	2,491
September	2,494	September	2,452
October	2,530	October	2,561
November	2,381	November	2,377
December	2,211	December	2,277

7.5 AUTOCORRELATION AND AUTOREGRESSION

Data values gathered over time are often correlated with values from past time periods. This characteristic can cause problems in the use of regression in forecasting and at the same time can open some opportunities. One of the problems that can occur in regressing data over time is autocorrelation.

Autocorrelation

Autocorrelation, or **serial correlation,** occurs in data *when the error terms of a regression forecasting model are correlated.* The likelihood of this occurring with business data increases over time, particularly with economic variables. Autocorrelation can be a problem in using regression analysis as the forecasting method because one of the assumptions underlying regression analysis is that the error terms are independent or random (not correlated). In most business analysis situations, the correlation of error terms is likely to occur as positive autocorrelation (positive errors are associated with positive errors of comparable magnitude and negative errors are associated with negative errors of comparable magnitude).

When autocorrelation occurs in a regression analysis, several possible problems might arise. First, the estimates of the regression coefficients no longer have the minimum variance property and may be inefficient. Second, the variance of the error terms may be greatly underestimated by the mean square error value. Third, the true standard deviation of the estimated regression coefficient may be seriously underestimated. Fourth, the confidence intervals and tests using the t and F distributions are no longer strictly applicable.

First-order autocorrelation results from correlation between the error terms of adjacent time periods (as opposed to two or more previous periods). If first-order autocorrelation is present, the error for one time period, e_t, is a function of the error of the previous time period, e_{t-1}, as follows.

$$e_t = \rho e_{t-1} + v_t$$

The first-order autocorrelation coefficient, ρ, measures the correlation between the error terms. It is a value that lies between −1 and 0 and +1, as does the coefficient of correlation. v_t is a normally distributed independent error term. If positive autocorrelation is present, the value of ρ is between 0 and +1. If the value of ρ is 0, $e_t = v_t$, which means there is no autocorrelation and e_t is just a random, independent error term.

One way to *test to determine whether autocorrelation is present in a time-series regression analysis* is by using the **Durbin-Watson test** for autocorrelation. Shown next is the formula for computing a Durbin-Watson test for autocorrelation.

DURBIN-WATSON TEST

$$D = \frac{\sum_{t=2}^{n}(e_t - e_{t-1})^2}{\sum_{t=1}^{n}e_t^{\,2}}$$

where
n = the number of observations

Note from the formula that the Durbin-Watson test involves finding the difference between successive values of error $(e_t - e_{t-1})$. If errors are positively correlated, this difference will be smaller than with random or independent errors. Squaring this term eliminates the cancellation effects of positive and negative terms.

The null hypothesis for this test is that there is *no* autocorrelation. For a two-tailed test, the alternative hypothesis is that there *is* autocorrelation.

$$H_0\text{: } \rho = 0$$
$$H_a\text{: } \rho \neq 0$$

As mentioned before, most business forecasting autocorrelation is positive autocorrelation. In most cases, a one-tailed test is used.

$$H_0\text{: } \rho = 0$$
$$H_a\text{: } \rho > 0$$

In the Durbin-Watson test, D is the observed value of the Durbin-Watson statistic using the residuals from the regression analysis. A critical value for D can be obtained from the values of α, n, and k by using Table A.6 in the appendix, where α is the level of significance, n is the number of data items, and k is the number of predictors. Two Durbin-Watson tables are given in the appendix. One table contains values for $\alpha = .01$ and the other for $\alpha = .05$. The Durbin-Watson tables in Appendix A include values for d_U and d_L. These values range from 0 to 4. If the observed value of D is above d_U, we fail to reject the null hypothesis and there is no significant autocorrelation. If the observed value of D is below d_L, the null hypothesis is rejected and there is autocorrelation. Sometimes the observed statistic, D, is between the values of d_U and d_L. In this case, the Durbin-Watson test is inconclusive.

As an example, consider Table 7.12, which lists drilling data for oil wells and gas wells from 1973 through 1998 (in thousands). A regression line can be fit through these data to determine whether the number of oil wells drilled in a given year can be predicted by the number of gas wells drilled in a year. The resulting errors of prediction can be tested by the Durbin-Watson statistic for the presence of significant positive autocorrelation by using $\alpha = .05$. The hypotheses are

$$H_0\text{: } \rho = 0$$
$$H_a\text{: } \rho > 0$$

The following regression equation was obtained by means of a MINITAB computer analysis.

$$\text{Oil Wells} = -11.337 + 2.6106 \,(\text{Gas Wells})$$

With the values for the number of gas wells being drilled (X) from Table 7.12 and the regression model equation shown here, predicted values of Y (number of oil wells being drilled) can be computed. From the predicted values and the actual values, the errors of prediction for each time interval, e_t, can be calculated. Table 7.13 shows the values of $\hat{Y}$, e_t, e_t^2, $(e_t - e_{t-1})$, and $(e_t - e_{t-1})^2$ for this example. Note that the first predicted value of Y is

$$\hat{Y}_{1973} = -11.337 + 2.6106(6.933) = 6.7623$$

The error for 1973 is

$$\text{Actual}_{1973} - \text{Predicted}_{1973} = 10.167 - 6.7623 = 3.4047$$

The value of $e_t - e_{t-1}$ for 1973 and 1974 is computed by subtracting the error for 1973 from the error of 1974.

$$e_{1974} - e_{1973} = 6.3495 - 3.4047 = 2.9448$$

TABLE 7.12
U.S. Oil and Gas Well Drilling, 1973–1998

Year	Oil Wells (1,000)	Gas Wells (1,000)
1973	10.167	6.933
1974	13.647	7.138
1975	16.948	8.127
1976	17.688	9.409
1977	18.745	12.122
1978	19.181	14.413
1979	20.851	15.254
1980	32.639	17.333
1981	43.598	20.166
1982	39.199	18.979
1983	37.120	14.564
1984	42.605	17.127
1985	35.118	14.168
1986	19.097	8.516
1987	16.164	8.055
1988	13.636	8.555
1989	10.204	9.539
1990	12.198	11.044
1991	11.770	9.526
1992	8.757	8.209
1993	8.407	10.017
1994	6.721	9.538
1995	7.627	8.354
1996	8.314	9.302
1997	10.436	11.327
1998	7.118	12.106

Source: Monthly Energy Review, June 1998.

TABLE 7.13
Predicted Values and Error Terms for the Oil and Gas Well Data

Year	$\hat{Y}$	e_t	e_t^2	$e_t - e_{t-1}$	$(e_t - e_{t-1})^2$
1973	6.7623	3.4047	11.592	—	—
1974	7.2975	6.3495	40.317	2.9448	8.6718
1975	9.8793	7.0687	49.966	0.7191	0.5171
1976	13.2261	4.4619	19.908	−2.6068	6.7954
1977	20.3087	−1.5637	2.445	−6.0256	36.3078
1978	26.2896	−7.1086	50.532	−5.5449	30.7459
1979	28.4851	−7.6341	58.279	−0.5255	0.2762
1980	33.9125	−1.2735	1.622	6.3606	40.4572
1981	41.3084	2.2896	5.242	3.5632	12.6964
1982	38.2096	0.9894	0.979	−1.3002	1.6905
1983	26.6838	10.4362	108.915	9.4468	89.2420
1984	33.3747	9.2303	85.198	−1.2060	1.4544
1985	25.6500	9.4680	89.643	0.2378	0.0565
1986	10.8949	8.2021	67.275	−1.2659	1.6025
1987	9.6914	6.4726	41.895	−1.7295	2.9912
1988	10.9967	2.6393	6.966	−3.8333	14.6942
1989	13.5655	−3.3615	11.300	−6.0008	36.0100
1990	17.4945	−5.2965	28.053	−1.9350	3.7442
1991	13.5316	−1.7616	3.103	3.5349	12.4955
1992	10.0934	−1.3364	1.786	0.4252	0.1808
1993	14.8134	−6.4064	41.042	−5.0700	25.7049
1994	13.5629	−6.8419	46.812	−0.4355	0.1897
1995	10.4720	−2.8450	8.094	3.9970	15.9760
1996	12.9468	−4.6328	21.463	−1.7879	3.1966
1997	18.2333	−7.7973	60.797	−3.1645	10.0141
1998	20.2669	−13.1489	172.894	−5.3517	28.6407
	$\sum e_t = 0.0043$		$\sum e_t^2 = 1036.118$	$\sum (e_t - e_{t-1})^2 = 384.3516$	

The Durbin-Watson statistic can now be computed:

$$D = \frac{\sum_{t=2}^{n}(e_t - e_{t-1})^2}{\sum_{t=1}^{n} e_t^2} = \frac{384.3516}{1,036.118} = .371$$

Because we used a simple linear regression, the value of k is 1. The sample size, n, is 26, and $\alpha = .05$. The critical values in Table A.6 are

$$d_U = 1.46 \text{ and } d_L = 1.30$$

Because the computed D statistic, .371, is less than the value of $d_L = 1.30$, the null hypothesis is rejected. A positive autocorrelation is present in this example.

Figure 7.12 provides the graph of the residuals given in Table 7.13. Note that several "runs" of positive and negative error terms are evident instead of a random distribution of error terms, which indicates the presence of autocorrelation.

FIGURE 7.12

Excel Graph of the Residuals of the Oil and Gas Well Example

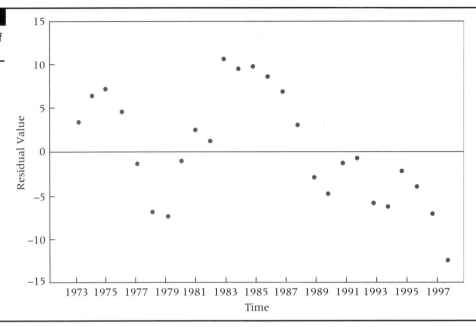

Ways to Overcome the Autocorrelation Problem

Several approaches to data analysis can be used when autocorrelation is present. One uses additional independent variables and another transforms the independent variable.

Addition of Independent Variables

Often the reason autocorrelation occurs in regression analyses is that one or more important predictor variables have been left out of the analysis. For example, suppose a researcher develops a regression forecasting model that attempts to predict sales of new homes by sales of used homes over some period of time. Such a model might contain significant autocorrelation. The exclusion of the variable "prime mortgage interest rate" might be a factor driving the autocorrelation between the other two variables. Adding this variable to the regression model might significantly reduce the autocorrelation.

Transforming Variables

When the inclusion of additional variables is not helpful in reducing autocorrelation to an acceptable level, transforming the data in the variables may help to solve the problem. One such method is the **first-differences approach.** With the first-differences approach, *each value of X is subtracted from each succeeding time period value of X;* these "differences" become the new and transformed X variable. The same process is used to transform the Y variable. The regression analysis is then computed on the transformed X and transformed Y variables to compute a new model that is hopefully free of significant autocorrelation effects.

Another way is to generate new variables by using the percentage changes from period to period and regressing these new variables. A third way is to use autoregression models.

Autoregression

A forecasting technique that takes advantage of the relationship of values (Y_t) to previous-period values (Y_{t-1}, Y_{t-2}, Y_{t-3}, ...) is called autoregression. **Autoregression** is *a multiple regression technique in which the independent variables are time-lagged versions of the dependent variable,* which means we try to predict a value of Y from values of Y from previous time periods. The independent variable can be lagged for one, two, three, or more time periods. An autoregressive model containing independent variables for three time periods looks like this:

$$\hat{Y} = b_o + b_1 Y_{t-1} + b_2 Y_{t-2} + b_3 Y_{t-3}$$

As an example, suppose we take the oil well data from Table 7.12 and attempt to predict the number of oil wells drilled by using data lagged for two time periods. The data for this analysis are displayed in Table 7.14.

Using Excel, a multiple regression model is developed to predict the values of Y_t by the values of Y_{t-1} and Y_{t-2}. The results appear in Figure 7.13.

The autoregression model is

$$Y_t = 2.3304 + 1.2822 Y_{t-1} - 0.4151 Y_{t-2}$$

The relatively high value of R^2 (83.5%) and relatively small value of S (5.1583) indicate that this regression model provides fairly strong predictability. In addition, both predictors have statistically significant t ratios ($t = 6.40$ with $p = .0000024$, and $t = -2.08$ with $p = .0504475$).

Autoregression can be a useful tool in locating seasonal or cyclical effects in time-series data. For example, if the data are given in monthly increments, autoregression using variables lagged by as much as 12 months can search for the predictability of previous monthly time periods. If data are given in quarterly time periods, autoregression of up to four periods removed can be a useful tool in locating the predictability of data from previous quarters. When the time periods are in years, lagging the data by yearly periods and using autoregression can help in locating cyclical predictability.

TABLE 7.14 Time-Lagged Oil Well Data			
Year	Oil Wells Y_t	One Period Lagged Y_{t-1} (X_1)	Two Periods Lagged Y_{t-2} (X_2)
1973	10.167		
1974	13.647	10.167	
1975	16.948	13.647	10.167
1976	17.688	16.948	13.647
1977	18.745	17.688	16.948
1978	19.181	18.745	17.688
1979	20.851	19.181	18.745
1980	32.639	20.851	19.181
1981	43.598	32.639	20.851
1982	39.199	43.598	32.639
1983	37.120	39.199	43.598
1984	42.605	37.120	39.199
1985	35.118	42.605	37.120
1986	19.097	35.118	42.605
1987	16.164	19.097	35.118
1988	13.636	16.164	19.097
1989	10.204	13.636	16.164
1990	12.198	10.204	13.636
1991	11.770	12.198	10.204
1992	8.757	11.770	12.198
1993	8.407	8.757	11.770
1994	6.721	8.407	8.757
1995	7.627	6.721	8.407
1996	8.314	7.627	6.721
1997	10.436	8.314	7.627
1998	7.118	10.436	8.314

Adapted from: Data in *Monthly Energy Review,* June 1998.

FIGURE 7.13

Excel Autoregression Results for Oil Well Data

	A	B	C	D	E	F
1	SUMMARY OUTPUT					
2	Regression Statistics					
3	Multiple R	0.914				
4	R Square	0.835				
5	Adjusted R Square	0.819				
6	Standard Error	5.1583				
7	Observations	24				
8						
9	ANOVA					
10		df	SS	MS	F	Significant F
11	Regression	2	2831.0351	1415.5176	53.20	0.000000006
12	Residual	21	558.7621	26.6077		
13	Total	23	3389.7972			
14						
15		Coefficients	Standard Error	t Stat	P-value	
16	Intercept	2.3304	2.1000	1.11	0.2796706	
17	1-lag	1.2822	0.2002	6.40	0.0000024	
18	2-lags	−0.4151	0.2001	−2.08	0.0504475	

7.5 PROBLEMS

7.15 The U.S. Bureau of Labor Statistics publishes consumer price indexes (CPIs) on many commodities. Following are the percentage changes in the CPIs for food and for shelter for 1974 through 1999. Use these data to develop a linear regression model to forecast the percentage change in food CPIs by the percentage change in shelter CPIs. Compute a Durbin-Watson statistic to determine whether significant autocorrelation is present in the model. Let $\alpha = .05$.

Year	Food	Shelter	Year	Food	Shelter
1974	14.3	9.6	1986	3.2	5.5
1975	8.5	9.9	1987	4.1	4.7
1976	3.0	5.5	1988	4.1	4.8
1977	6.3	6.6	1989	5.8	4.5
1978	9.9	10.2	1990	5.8	5.4
1979	11.0	13.9	1991	2.9	4.5
1980	8.6	17.6	1992	1.2	3.3
1981	7.8	11.7	1993	2.2	3.0
1982	4.1	7.1	1994	2.4	3.1
1983	2.1	2.3	1995	2.8	3.2
1984	3.8	4.9	1996	3.3	3.2
1985	2.3	5.6	1997	2.6	3.1
			1998	2.2	3.3
			1999	2.1	2.9

7.16 Use the data from Problem 7.15 to create a regression forecasting model using the first-differences data transformation. How do the results from this model differ from those obtained in Problem 7.15?

7.17 The Federal Deposit Insurance Corporation (FDIC) releases data on bank failures. Following are data on the number of U.S. bank failures in a given year and the total amount of bank deposits (in $ millions) involved in such failures for a given year. Use these data to develop a simple regression forecasting model that attempts to predict the failed bank assets involved in bank closings by the number of bank failures. Compute a Durbin-Watson statistic for this regression model and determine whether significant autocorrelation is present. Let $\alpha = .05$.

Year	Failures	Failed Bank Assets
1	11	8,189
2	7	104
3	34	1,862
4	45	4,137
5	79	36,394
6	118	3,034
7	144	7,609
8	201	7,538
9	221	56,620
10	206	28,507
11	159	10,739
12	108	43,552
13	100	16,915
14	42	2,588
15	11	825
16	6	753
17	5	186
18	1	27

7.18 Use the data in Problem 7.17 to compute a regression model after recoding the data by the first-differences approach. Compute a Durbin-Watson statistic to determine whether significant autocorrelation is present in this first-differences model. Compare this model with the model determined in Problem 7.17, and compare the significance of the Durbin-Watson statistics for the two problems. Let $\alpha = .05$.

7.19 *Current Construction Reports* from the U.S. Census Bureau contain data on new privately owned housing units. Data on new privately owned housing units (1,000s) built in the West between 1970 and 1997 follow. Use these time-series data to develop an autoregression model with a one-period lag. Now try an autoregression model with a two-period lag. Discuss the results and compare the two models.

Year	Housing Starts (1,000)	Year	Housing Starts (1,000)
1970	311	1984	436
1971	486	1985	468
1972	527	1986	483
1973	429	1987	420
1974	285	1988	404
1975	275	1989	396
1976	400	1990	329
1977	538	1991	254
1978	545	1992	288
1979	470	1993	302
1980	306	1994	351
1981	240	1995	331
1982	205	1996	361
1983	382	1997	364

7.20 The U.S. Department of Agriculture publishes data on the production, utilization, and value of fruits in the United States. Shown here are the amounts of noncitrus fruit processed into juice (in kilotons) for a 25-year period. Use these data to develop an autoregression forecasting model with a two-period lag. Discuss the results of this analysis.

Year	Processed Juice	Year	Processed Juice
1	598	14	1,135
2	768	15	1,893
3	863	16	1,372
4	818	17	1,547
5	841	18	1,450
6	1,140	19	1,557
7	1,285	20	1,742
8	1,418	21	1,736
9	1,235	22	1,886
10	1,255	23	1,857
11	1,445	24	1,582
12	1,336	25	1,675
13	1,226		

7.6 INDEX NUMBERS

One particular type of descriptive measure that is useful in allowing comparisons of data over time is the index number. An index number is, in part, a ratio of a measure taken during one time frame to that same measure taken during another time frame, usually denoted as the base period. Often the ratio is multiplied by 100 and is expressed as a percentage. When expressed as a percentage, index numbers serve as an alternative to comparing raw numbers. Index number users become accustomed to interpreting measures for a given time period in light of a base period on a scale in which the base period has an index of 100(%). Index numbers are used to compare phenomena from one time period to another and are especially helpful in highlighting interperiod differences.

Index numbers are widely used around the world to relate information about stock markets, inflation, sales, exports and imports, agriculture, and many other things. Some examples of specific indexes are the employment cost index, price index for construction, index of manufacturing capacity, producer price index, consumer price index, Dow Jones industrial average, index of output, and Nikkei 225 average. This section, although recognizing the importance of stock indexes and others, will focus on price indexes.

The motivation for using an index number is to reduce data to an easier-to-use, more convenient form. As an example, examine the raw data on number of business starts in the United States from 1985 through 1999 shown in Table 7.15. An analyst can describe these data by observing that, in general, the number of business starts has been decreasing since 1986. How do the number of business starts in 1995 compare to 1985? How do the number of business starts in 1997 compare to 1990 or 1991? To answer these questions without index numbers, a researcher would probably resort to subtracting the number of business starts for the years of interest and comparing the corresponding increases or decreases. This process can be tedious and frustrating for decision makers who must maximize their effort in minimal time. Using simple index numbers, the researcher can transform these data into values that are more usable. In addition, it is sometimes easier to compare other years to one particular key year.

Simple Index Numbers and Unweighted Aggregate Price Indexes

How are index numbers computed? The equation for computing a **simple index number** follows.

TABLE 7.15

Business Starts in the United States

Year	Starts
1985	249,770
1986	253,092
1987	233,710
1988	199,091
1989	181,645
1990	158,930
1991	155,672
1992	164,086
1993	166,154
1994	188,387
1995	168,158
1996	170,475
1997	166,740
1998	155,141
1999	151,016

SIMPLE INDEX NUMBER	$$I_i = \frac{X_i}{X_0}(100)$$

where
X_0 = the quantity, price, or cost in the base year
X_i = the quantity, price, or cost in the year of interest
I_i = the index number for the year of interest

Suppose cost-of-living researchers examining the data from Table 7.15 decide to compute index numbers using 1985 as the base year. The index number for the year 1997 is

$$I_{1997} = \frac{X_{1997}}{X_{1985}}(100) = \frac{166,740}{249,770}(100) = 66.8$$

Table 7.16 displays all the index numbers for the data in Table 7.15, with 1985 as the base year, along with the raw data. A cursory glance at these index numbers reveals a decrease in the number of business starts for most of the years since 1985 (because the index has been going down). In particular, the greatest drop in number seems to have occurred between 1987 and 1988—a drop of nearly 14 in the index. Because most people are easily able to understand the concept of 100%, it is likely that decision makers can make quick judgments on the number of business starts in the United States from one year relative to another by examining the index numbers over this period.

Unweighted Aggregate Price Index Numbers

The use of simple index numbers makes possible the conversion of prices, costs, quantities, and so on for different time periods into a number scale with the base year equaling 100%. One of the drawbacks of simple index numbers, however, is that each time period is represented by only one item or commodity. When multiple items are involved, multiple sets of index numbers are possible. Suppose a decision maker is interested in combining or pooling the prices of several items, creating a "market basket" in order to compare the prices for several years. Fortunately, a technique does exist for combining several items and determining index numbers for the total (aggregate). Because this technique is used mostly in determining price indexes, the focus in this section is on developing aggregate price indexes. The formula for constructing the **unweighted aggregate price index number** follows.

UNWEIGHTED AGGREGATE PRICE INDEX NUMBER	$$I_i = \frac{\Sigma P_i}{\Sigma P_0}(100)$$

where
P_i = the price of an item in the year of interest (i)
P_0 = the price of an item in the base year (0)
I_i = the index number for the year of interest (i)

Suppose a state's department of labor wants to compare the cost of family food buying over the years. Department officials decide that instead of using a single food item to do this comparison, they will use a food basket that consists of five items: eggs, milk, bananas, potatoes, and sugar. They gathered price information on these five items for the years 1990, 1995, and 2000. The items and the prices are listed in Table 7.17.

From the data in Table 7.17 and the formula, the unweighted aggregate price indexes for the years 1990, 1995, and 2000 can be computed by using 1990 as the base year. The first step is to add together, or aggregate, the prices for all the food basket items in a given year. These totals are shown in the last row of Table 7.17. The index numbers are constructed by using these totals (not individual item prices): $\Sigma P_{1990} = 2.91$, $\Sigma P_{1995} = 3.44$, and $\Sigma P_{2000} = 3.93$. From these figures, the unweighted aggregate price index for 1995 is computed as follows.

$$\text{For 1995:} \quad I_{1995} = \frac{\Sigma P_{1995}}{\Sigma P_{1990}}(100) = \frac{3.44}{2.91}(100) = 118.2$$

TABLE 7.16

Index Numbers for Business Starts in the United States

Year	Starts	Index Number
1985	249,770	100.0
1986	253,092	101.3
1987	233,710	93.6
1988	199,091	79.7
1989	181,645	72.7
1990	158,930	63.6
1991	155,672	62.3
1992	164,086	65.7
1993	166,154	66.5
1994	188,387	75.4
1995	168,158	67.3
1996	170,475	68.3
1997	166,740	66.8
1998	155,141	62.1
1999	151,016	60.5

TABLE 7.17

Prices for a Basket of Food Items

Item	Year 1990	Year 1995	Year 2000
Eggs (dozen)	.78	.86	1.06
Milk (1/2 gallon)	1.14	1.39	1.59
Bananas (per lb.)	.36	.46	.49
Potatoes (per lb.)	.28	.31	.36
Sugar (per lb.)	.35	.42	.43
Total of Items	2.91	3.44	3.93

Weighted Aggregate Price Index Numbers

A major drawback to unweighted aggregate price indexes is that they are *unweighted*—that is, equal weight is put on each item by assuming the market basket contains only one of each item. This assumption may or may not be true. For example, a household may consume 5 pounds of bananas per year but drink 50 gallons of milk. In addition, unweighted aggregate index numbers are dependent on the units selected for various items. For example, if milk is measured in quarts instead of gallons, the price of milk used in determining the index numbers is considerably lower. A class of index numbers that can be used to avoid these problems is weighted aggregate price index numbers.

Weighted aggregate price index numbers are *computed by multiplying quantity weights and item prices in determining the market basket worth for a given year.* Sometimes when price and quantity are multiplied to construct index numbers, the index numbers are referred to as *value indexes*. Thus, weighted aggregate price index numbers are also value indexes.

Including quantities eliminates the problems caused by how many of each item are consumed per time period and the units of items. If 50 gallons of milk but only 5 pounds of bananas are consumed, weighted aggregate price index numbers will reflect those weights. If the business researcher switches from gallons of milk to quarts, the prices will change downward but the quantity will increase fourfold (4 quarts in a gallon).

In general, weighted aggregate price indexes are constructed by multiplying the price of each item by its quantity and then summing these products for the market basket over a given time period (often a year). The ratio of this sum for one time period of interest (year) to a base time period of interest (base year) is multiplied by 100. The following formula reflects a weighted aggregate price index computed by using quantity weights from each time period (year).

$$I_i = \frac{\Sigma P_i Q_i}{\Sigma P_0 Q_0}(100)$$

One of the problems with this formula is the implication that new and possibly different quantities apply for each time period. However, business researchers expend much time and money ascertaining the quantities used in a market basket. Redetermining quantity weights for each year is therefore often prohibitive for most organizations (even the government). Two particular types of weighted aggregate price indexes offer a solution to the problem of which quantity weights to use. The first and most widely used is the Laspeyres price index. The second and less widely used is the Paasche price index.

Laspeyres Price Index

The **Laspeyres price index** is *a weighted aggregate price index computed by using the quantities of the base period (year) for all other years.* The advantages of this technique are that the price indexes for all years can be compared, and new quantities do not have to be determined for each year. The formula for constructing the Laspeyres price index follows.

LASPEYRES PRICE INDEX	$I_L = \dfrac{\Sigma P_i Q_0}{\Sigma P_0 Q_0}(100)$

Notice that the formula requires the base period quantities (Q_0) in both the numerator and the denominator.

In Table 7.17, a food basket is presented in which aggregate price indexes are computed. This food basket consisted of eggs, milk, bananas, potatoes, and sugar. The prices of these items were combined (aggregated) for a given year and the price indexes were computed from these aggregate figures. The unweighted aggregate price indexes computed on these data gave all items equal importance. Suppose that the business researchers realize that applying equal weight to these five items is probably not a representative way to construct this food basket and consequently ascertain quantity weights on each food item for one year's consumption. Table 7.18 lists these five items, their prices, and their quantity usage weights for the base year (1990). From these data, the business researchers can compute Laspeyres price indexes.

The Laspeyres price index for 1995 with 1990 as the base year is:

$$
\begin{aligned}
\Sigma P_i Q_0 &= \Sigma P_{1995} Q_{1990} \\
&= \Sigma\,[(.86)(45) + (1.39)(60) + (.46)(12) + (.31)(55) + (.42)(36)] \\
&= 38.70 + 83.40 + 5.52 + 17.05 + 15.12 = 159.79
\end{aligned}
$$

$$
\begin{aligned}
\Sigma P_0 Q_0 &= \Sigma P_{1990} Q_{1990} \\
&= \Sigma\,[(.78)(45) + (1.14)(60) + (.36)(12) + (.28)(55) + (.35)(36)] \\
&= 35.10 + 68.40 + 4.32 + 15.40 + 12.60 = 135.82
\end{aligned}
$$

$$
I_{1995} = \frac{\Sigma P_{1995} Q_{1990}}{\Sigma P_{1990} Q_{1990}}(100) = \frac{159.79}{135.82}(100) = 117.6
$$

Paasche Price Index

The **Paasche price index** is *a weighted aggregate price index computed by using the quantities for the year of interest in computations for a given year.* The advantage of this technique is that it incorporates current quantity figures in the calculations. One disadvantage is that ascertaining quantity figures for each time period is expensive. The formula for computing Paasche price indexes follows.

PAASCHE PRICE INDEX	$I_P = \dfrac{\Sigma P_i Q_i}{\Sigma P_0 Q_i}(100)$

Suppose the yearly quantities for the basket of food items listed in Table 7.18 are determined. The result is the quantities and prices shown in Table 7.19 for the years 1990 and 1995 that can be used to compute Paasche price index numbers.

TABLE 7.18

Food Basket Items with Quantity Weights

Item	Quantity 1990	Price 1990	Price 1995	Price 2000
Eggs (dozen)	45	.78	.86	1.06
Milk (1/2 gal.)	60	1.14	1.39	1.59
Bananas (per lb.)	12	.36	.46	.49
Potatoes (per lb.)	55	.28	.31	.36
Sugar (per lb.)	36	.35	.42	.43

TABLE 7.19

Food Basket Items with Yearly Quantity Weights for 1990 and 1995

Item	P_{1990}	Q_{1990}	P_{1995}	Q_{1995}
Eggs (dozen)	.78	45	.86	42
Milk (1/2 gal.)	1.14	60	1.39	57
Bananas (per lb.)	.36	12	.46	13
Potatoes (per lb.)	.28	55	.31	52
Sugar (per lb.)	.35	36	.42	36

The Paasche price index numbers can be determined for 1995 by using a base year of 1990 as follows.

For 1995:

$$\Sigma P_{1995}Q_{1995}= [(.86)(42) + (1.39)(57) + (.46)(13) + (.31)(52) + .42)(36)]$$
$$= 36.12 + 79.23 + 5.98 + 16.12 + 15.12$$
$$= 152.57$$

$$\Sigma P_{1990}Q_{1995}= [(.78)(42) + (1.14)(57) + (.36)(13) + (.28)(52) + (.35)(36)]$$
$$= 32.76 + 64.98 + 4.68 + 14.56 + 12.60$$
$$= 129.58$$

$$I_{1995} = \frac{\Sigma P_{1995}Q_{1995}}{\Sigma P_{1990}Q_{1995}}(100) = \frac{152.57}{129.58}(100) = 117.7$$

DEMONSTRATION PROBLEM 7.5

The Arapaho Valley Pediatrics Clinic has been in business for 18 years. The office manager noticed that prices of clinic materials and office supplies fluctuate over time. To get a handle on the price trends for running the clinic, the office manager examined prices of six items the clinic uses as part of its operation. Shown here are the items, their prices, and the quantities for the years 1999 and 2000. Use these data to develop unweighted aggregate price indexes for 2000 with a base year of 1999. Compute the Laspeyres price index for the year 2000 using 1999 as the base year. Compute the Paasche index number for 2000 using 1999 as the base year.

Item	1999		2000	
	Price	Quantity	Price	Quantity
Syringes (dozen)	6.70	150	6.95	135
Cotton swabs (box)	1.35	60	1.45	65
Patient record forms (pad)	5.10	8	6.25	12
Children's Tylenol (bottle)	4.50	25	4.95	30
Computer paper (box)	11.95	6	13.20	8
Thermometers	7.90	4	9.00	2
Totals	37.50		41.80	

Solution

Unweighted Aggregate Index for 2000:

$$I_{2000} = \frac{\Sigma P_{2000}}{\Sigma P_{1999}}(100) = \frac{41.80}{37.50}(100) = 111.5$$

Laspeyres Index for 2000:

$$\Sigma P_{2000}Q_{1999} = [(6.95)(150) + (1.45)(60) + (6.25)(8) + (4.95)(25) + (13.20)(6)$$
$$+ (9.00)(4)]$$
$$= 1{,}042.50 + 87.00 + 50.00 + 123.75 + 79.20 + 36.00$$
$$= 1{,}418.45$$

$$\Sigma P_{1999}Q_{1999} = [(6.70)(150) + (1.35)(60) + (5.10)(8) + (4.50)(25) + (11.95)(6)$$
$$+ (7.90)(4)]$$
$$= 1{,}005.00 + 81.00 + 40.80 + 112.50 + 71.70 + 31.60$$
$$= 1{,}342.6$$

$$I_{2000} = \frac{\Sigma P_{2000}Q_{1999}}{\Sigma P_{1999}Q_{1999}}(100) = \frac{1418.45}{1342.6}(100) = 105.6$$

Paasche Index for 2000:

$$\Sigma P_{2000}Q_{2000} = [(6.95)(135) + (1.45)(65) + (6.25)(12) + (4.95)(30) + (13.20)(8)$$
$$+ (9.00)(2)]$$
$$= 938.25 + 94.25 + 75.00 + 148.50 + 105.60 + 18.00$$
$$= 1,379.60$$

$$\Sigma P_{1999}Q_{2000} = [(6.70)(135) + (1.35)(65) + (5.10)(12) + (4.50)(30) + (11.95)(8)$$
$$+ (7.90)(2)]$$
$$= 904.50 + 87.75 + 61.20 + 135.00 + 95.60 + 15.80$$
$$= 1,299.85$$

$$I_{2000} = \frac{\Sigma P_{2000}Q_{2000}}{\Sigma P_{1999}Q_{2000}}(100) = \frac{1,379.60}{1,299.85}(100) = 106.1$$

7.6 PROBLEMS

7.21 Suppose the following data represent the price of 20 reams of office paper over a 50-year time frame. Find the simple index numbers for the data.

  a. Let 1950 be the base year.

  b. Let 1980 be the base year.

Year	Price	Year	Price
1950	$22.45	1980	$69.75
1955	31.40	1985	73.44
1960	32.33	1990	80.05
1965	36.50	1995	84.61
1970	44.90	2000	87.28
1975	61.24		

7.22 The U.S. Patent and Trademark Office reports fiscal year figures for patents issued in the United States. Following are the numbers of patents issued for the years 1980 through 1997. Using these data and a base year of 1990, determine the simple index numbers for each year.

Year	Number of Patents (1,000s)
1980	66.0
1981	70.8
1982	63.1
1983	61.7
1984	72.5
1985	77.1
1986	76.7
1987	89.3
1988	84.2
1989	102.4
1990	98.9
1991	106.8
1992	107.7
1993	110.1
1994	124.1
1995	114.4
1996	122.6
1997	125.5
1998	163.1

7.23 Using the U.S. Bureau of Labor Statistics data that follow, compute the aggregate index numbers for the four types of meat. Let 1987 be the base year for this market basket of goods.

	Year		
Items	1987	1992	1997
Ground beef (per lb.)	1.31	1.53	1.40
Sausage (per lb.)	1.99	2.21	2.15
Bacon (per lb.)	2.14	1.92	2.68
Round steak (per lb.)	2.89	3.38	3.10

7.24 Suppose the following data are prices of market goods involved in household transportation for the years 1994 through 2002. Using 1998 as a base year, compute aggregate transportation price indexes for this data.

	Year								
Items	1994	1995	1996	1997	1998	1999	2000	2001	2002
Gasoline (per gal.)	1.06	1.21	1.09	1.13	1.10	1.16	1.23	1.23	1.08
Oil (per qt.)	1.47	1.65	1.60	1.62	1.58	1.61	1.78	1.77	1.61
Transmission fluid (per qt.)	1.70	1.70	1.80	1.85	1.80	1.82	1.98	1.96	1.94
Radiator coolant (per gal.)	6.65	6.90	7.50	8.10	7.95	7.96	8.24	8.21	8.19

7.25 Calculate Laspeyres price indexes for 2000–2002 from the following data. Use 1995 as the base year.

	Quantity	Price			
Item	1995	1995	2000	2001	2002
1	21	$0.50	$0.67	$0.68	$0.71
2	6	1.23	1.85	1.90	1.91
3	17	0.84	.75	.75	.80
4	43	0.15	.21	.25	.25

7.26 Calculate Paasche price indexes for 2001 and 2002 using the following data and 1997 as the base year.

		2001		2002	
Item	1997 Price	Price	Quantity	Price	Quantity
1	$22.50	$27.80	13	$28.11	12
2	10.90	13.10	5	13.25	8
3	1.85	2.25	41	2.35	44

Forecasting Air Pollution

In searching for the most effective forecasting technique to use to forecast either the carbon monoxide emission or the nitrogen oxide, it is useful to determine whether a trend is evident in either set of time-series data. MINITAB's trend analysis output is presented on the next page for each of the variables.

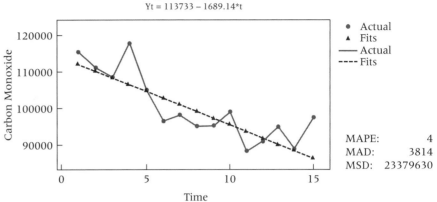

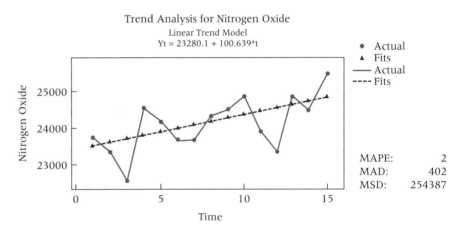

Regression trend analysis produces an R^2 of 69.5% for carbon monoxide and 41.8% for nitrogen oxide. It appears, based on the trend analysis graphs, and the R^2 values that more trend is evident in the carbon monoxide data than in the nitrogen oxide data. Is a quadratic trend present in either of these variables? The output for a MINITAB quadratic trend analysis for carbon monoxide is shown next. Notice the error, MAD, has been reduced from 3814 with a linear trend to 2961 with a quadratic trend. Using multiple regression to determine trend with a quadratic model (results not shown here) for carbon monoxide produces an R^2 of 79.8%, an increase of 10.3% over the linear regression trend model. This same analysis on the nitrogen oxide data produces no improvement in the trend fit using a quadratic model.

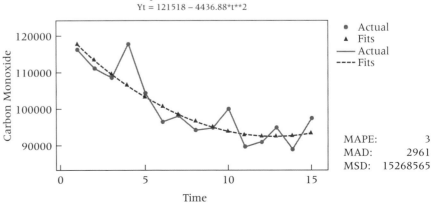

Smoothing techniques can be used to forecast time-series data when no significant trend characterizes the data. A MINITAB moving average graphical analysis of the nitrogen oxide data and the carbon monoxide data using a 5-year moving average are provided here.

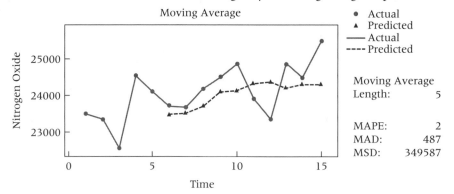

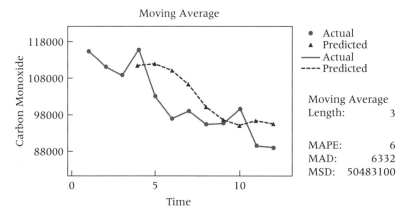

Observe the fit of the moving averages to the data. The moving average forecasts seem to be somewhat linear while the actual data are moving up and down. Also of concern might be that the moving average forecast is in a slightly downward trend on the last data point whereas the data are rapidly increasing.

MINITAB has the capability of administering exponential smoothing to time-series data in such a way as to determine the optimum value of alpha by comparing error values. Shown here is MINITAB output from exponential smoothing analysis on the nitrogen oxide data. The optimum value of alpha for this analysis is .322.

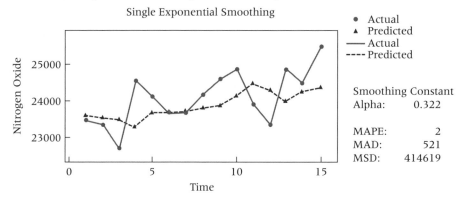

Note that single exponential smoothing seems to be responding better to the rapid rise in the final data point even though the overall MAD is greater than that of the moving average model. It does not make sense to explore seasonal effects with these data since the time period is years.

ETHICAL CONSIDERATIONS

The true test of a forecast is the accuracy of the prediction. Until the actual value is obtained for a given time period, the accuracy of the forecast is unknown. Many forecasters make predictions in society, including card readers, religious leaders, and self-proclaimed prophets. The proof of the forecast is in the outcome. The same holds true in the business world. Forecasts are made about everything from market share to interest rates to number of international air travelers. Many businesses fail because of faulty forecasts.

Forecasting is perhaps as much an art as a science. To keep forecasting ethical, the consumer of the forecast should be given the caveats and limitations of the forecast. The forecaster should be honestly cautious in selling the predictions to a client. In addition, the forecaster should be constantly on the lookout for changes in the business setting being modeled and quickly translate and incorporate those changes into the forecasting model.

Unethical behavior can occur in forecasting when particular data are selected to develop a model that has been predetermined to produce certain results. As mentioned previously, statistics can be used to "prove" almost anything. The ethical forecaster lets the data drive the model and is constantly seeking honest input from new variables to revise the forecast. He or she strives to communicate the limitations of both the forecasts and the models to clients.

SUMMARY

Time-series data are data that have been gathered at regular intervals over a period of time. It is generally believed that time-series data are composed of four elements—trend, cyclical effects, seasonality, and irregularity. Trend is the long-term general direction of the time-series data. Cyclical effects are the business and economic cycles that occur over periods of more than one year. Seasonal effects are patterns or cycles of data behavior that occur over time periods of less than one year. Irregular fluctuations are unaccounted-for "bleeps" or variations that occur over short periods of time.

One way to establish the validity of a forecast is to examine the forecasting error. The error of a forecast is the difference between the actual value and the forecast value. Computing a value to measure forecasting error can be done in several different ways. This chapter presents mean absolute deviation and mean square error for this task.

Regression analysis with either linear or quadratic models can be used to explore trend. Regression trend analysis is a special case of regression analysis in which the dependent variable is the data to be forecast and the independent variable is the time periods numbered consecutively from 1 to k, where k is the number of time periods. For the quadratic model, a second independent variable is constructed by squaring the values in the first independent variable, and both independent variables are included in the analysis.

One group of time-series forecasting methods contains smoothing techniques. Among these techniques are naïve models, averaging techniques, and simple exponential smoothing. These techniques do much better if the time-series data are stationary or show no significant trend or seasonal effects. Naïve forecasting models are models in which it is assumed that the more recent time periods of data represent the best predictions or forecasts for future outcomes.

Simple averages use the average value for some given length of previous time periods to forecast the value for the next period. Moving averages are time period averages that are revised for each time period by including the most recent value(s)in the computation of the average and deleting the value or values that are farthest away from the present time period. A special case of the moving average is the weighted moving average, in which different weights are placed on the values from different time periods.

Simple (single) exponential smoothing is a technique in which data from previous time periods are weighted exponentially to forecast the value for the present time period. The forecaster has the option of selecting how much to weight more recent values versus those of previous time periods.

Decomposition is a method for isolating the four possible effects in time-series data, trend, cyclical effects, seasonality, and irregular fluctuations.

Autocorrelation or serial correlation occurs when the error terms from forecasts are correlated over time. In regression analysis, this effect is particularly disturbing because one of the assumptions is that the error terms are independent. One way to test for autocorrelation is to use the Durbin-Watson test.

A number of methods attempt to overcome the effects of autocorrelation on the data. One way is to determine whether at least one independent variable is missing and, if so, include it or them in the model. Another way is to transform the variables. One transformation technique is the first-differences approach, in which each value of X is subtracted from the succeeding time period value of X and the differences are used as the values of the X variable. The same approach is used to transform the Y variable. The forecasting model is then developed from the transformed variables.

Autoregression is a forecasting technique in which time-series data are predicted by independent variables that are lagged versions of the original dependent variable data. A variable that is lagged one period is derived from values of the previous time period. Other variables can be lagged two or more periods.

Index numbers can be used to translate raw data into numbers that are more readily comparable. Simple index numbers are constructed by creating the ratio of the raw data value for a given time period to the raw data value for the base period and multiplying the ratio by 100. The index number for the base time period is designated to be 100.

Unweighted aggregate price index numbers are constructed by summing the prices of several items for a time period and comparing that sum to the sum of the prices of the same items during a base time period and multiplying the ratio by 100. Weighted aggregate price indexes are index numbers utilizing the prices of several items, and the items are weighted by their quantity usage.

The Laspeyres price index uses the quantity weights from the base year in all calculations. The Paasche price index uses the quantity weights for the current time period for both the current time period and the base time period in calculations.

KEY TERMS

autocorrelation	exponential smoothing	mean square error (MSE)	smoothing techniques
autoregression	first-differences approach	moving average	stationary
averaging models	forecasting	naïve forecasting models	time-series data
cycles	forecasting error	Paasche price index	trend
cyclical effects	index number	seasonal effects	unweighted aggregate price index number
decomposition	irregular fluctuations	serial correlation	
deseasonalized data	Laspeyres price index	simple average	weighted aggregate price index numbers
Durbin-Watson test	mean absolute deviation (MAD)	simple average model	
error of an individual forecast		simple index number	weighted moving average

FORMULAS

Individual forecast error

$$e_t = X_t - F_t$$

Mean absolute deviation

$$\text{MAD} = \frac{\Sigma |e_i|}{\text{Number of Forecasts}}$$

Mean square error

$$\text{MSE} = \frac{\Sigma e_i^2}{\text{Number of Forecasts}}$$

Exponential smoothing

$$F_{t+1} = \alpha \cdot X_t + (1 - \alpha) \cdot F_t$$

Durbin-Watson test

$$D = \frac{\sum_{t=2}^{n} (e_t - e_{t-1})^2}{\sum_{t=1}^{n} e_t^2}$$

CALCULATING THE STATISTICS

7.27 Following are the average yields of long-term new corporate bonds over a several-month period published by the Office of Market Finance of the U.S. Department of the Treasury.

Month	Yield	Month	Yield
1	10.08	13	7.91
2	10.05	14	7.73
3	9.24	15	7.39
4	9.23	16	7.48
5	9.69	17	7.52
6	9.55	18	7.48
7	9.37	19	7.35
8	8.55	20	7.04
9	8.36	21	6.88
10	8.59	22	6.88
11	7.99	23	7.17
12	8.12	24	7.22

a. Explore trends in these data by using regression trend analysis. How strong are the models? Is the quadratic model significantly stronger than the linear trend model?

b. Use a 4-month moving average to forecast values for each of the ensuing months.

c. Use simple exponential smoothing to forecast values for each of the ensuing months. Let $\alpha = .3$ and then let $\alpha = .7$. Which weight produces better forecasts?

d. Compute MAD for the forecasts obtained in parts (b) and (c) and compare the results.

e. Determine seasonal effects using decomposition on these data. Let the seasonal effects have four periods. After determining the seasonal indexes, deseasonalize the data.

7.28 Compute index numbers for the following data using 1988 as the base year.

Year	Quantity	Year	Quantity
1988	2,073	1996	2,520
1989	2,290	1997	2,529
1990	2,349	1998	2,483
1991	2,313	1999	2,467
1992	2,456	2000	2,397
1993	2,508	2001	2,351
1994	2,463	2002	2,308
1995	2,499		

7.29 Compute unweighted aggregate price index numbers for each of the given years using 1998 as the base year.

Item	1998	1999	2000	2001	2002
1	3.21	3.37	3.80	3.73	3.65
2	.51	.55	.68	.62	.59
3	.83	.90	.91	1.02	1.06
4	1.30	1.32	1.33	1.32	1.30
5	1.67	1.72	1.90	1.99	1.98
6	.62	.67	.70	.72	.71

7.30 Using the following data and 1999 as the base year, compute the Laspeyres price index for 2002 and the Paasche price index for 2001.

	1999		2000	
Item	Price	Quantity	Price	Quantity
1	$2.75	12	$2.98	9
2	0.85	47	0.89	52
3	1.33	20	1.32	28

	2001		2002	
Item	Price	Quantity	Price	Quantity
1	$3.10	9	$3.21	11
2	0.95	61	0.98	66
3	1.36	25	1.40	32

TESTING YOUR UNDERSTANDING

7.31 Following are data on the quantity (million pounds) of the U.S. domestic fishing catch for human food from 1980 through 2000. The data are published by the U.S. National Oceanic and Atmospheric Administration.

a. Use a 3-year moving average to forecast the quantity of fish for the years 1983 through 2000 for these data. Compute the error of each forecast and then determine the mean absolute deviation of error for the forecast.

b. Use exponential smoothing and $\alpha = .2$ to forecast the data from 1983 through 2000. Let the forecast for 1981 equal the actual value for 1980. Compute the error of each forecast and then determine the mean absolute deviation of error for the forecast.

c. Compare the results obtained in parts (a) and (b) using MAD. Which technique seems to perform better? Why?

Year	Quantity	Year	Quantity
1980	3,654	1989	6,204
1981	3,547	1990	7,041
1982	3,285	1991	7,031
1983	3,238	1992	7,618
1984	3,320	1993	8,214
1985	3,294	1994	7,936
1986	3,393	1995	7,667
1987	3,946	1996	7,474
1988	4,588	1997	7,244
		1998	7,173
		1999	6,832
		2000	6,912

7.32 The U.S. Department of Commerce publishes a series of census documents referred to as *Current Industrial Reports*. Included in these documents are the Manufacturers' Shipments, Inventories, and Orders over a five-year period. Displayed here is a portion of these data representing the shipments of chemicals and allied products from January of year 1 through December of year 5. Use time-series decomposition methods to develop the seasonal indexes for these data.

Time Period	Chemicals and Allied Products ($ billion)	Time Period	Chemicals and Allied Products ($ billion)
January (year1)	23.701	January (year 2)	23.347
February	24.189	February	24.122
March	24.200	March	25.282
April	24.971	April	25.426
May	24.560	May	25.185
June	24.992	June	26.486
July	22.566	July	24.088
August	24.037	August	24.672
September	25.047	September	26.072
October	24.115	October	24.328
November	23.034	November	23.826
December	22.590	December	24.373
January (year 3)	24.207	January (year 4)	25.316
February	25.772	February	26.435
March	27.591	March	29.346
April	26.958	April	28.983
May	25.920	May	28.424
June	28.460	June	30.149
July	24.821	July	26.746
August	25.560	August	28.966
September	27.218	September	30.783
October	25.650	October	28.594
November	25.589	November	28.762
December	25.370	December	29.018

Time Period	Chemicals and Allied Products ($ billion)
January (year 5)	28.931
February	30.456
March	32.372
April	30.905
May	30.743
June	32.794
July	29.342
August	30.765
September	31.637
October	30.206
November	30.842
December	31.090

7.33 Use the seasonal indexes computed to deseasonalize the data in Problem 7.32.

7.34 Determine the trend for the data in Problem 7.32 using the deseasonalized data from Problem 7.33. Explore both a linear and a quadratic model in an attempt to develop the better trend model.

7.35 The U.S. Department of Labor reports the prices of some food commodities. Shown here are the average retail price figures for five different food commodities over three years. In addition, quantity estimates are included. Use these data and a base year of 1999 to compute unweighted aggregate price indexes for this market basket of food. Using a base year of 1999, calculate Laspeyres price indexes and Paasche price indexes for 2000 and 2001.

Item	1999		2000	
	Price	Quantity	Price	Quantity
Margarine (lb.)	.83	21	.81	23
Shortening (lb.)	.89	5	.87	3
Milk (1/2 gal.)	1.43	70	1.56	68
Cola (2 l)	1.05	12	1.02	13
Potato chips (16 oz.)	3.01	27	3.06	29

Item	2001	
	Price	Quantity
Margarine (lb.)	.83	22
Shortening (lb.)	.87	4
Milk (1/2 gal.)	1.59	65
Cola (2 l)	1.01	11
Potato chips (16 oz.)	3.13	28

7.36 The National Cable Television Association publishes data on the cable television market. Shown here are "the number of basic cable subscribers" and "as percentage of household with TVs" for the years 1976 to 2001. Develop a regression model to predict the number of basic cable subscribers from the variable "as percentage of households with TVs" using these data. Use this model to predict the number of basic cable subscribers if the value of the variable "as percentage of households with TVs" is 55%. Discuss the strength of the regression model. Use the data and the regression model to compute a Durbin-Watson test to determine whether significant autocorrelation is present. Let $\alpha = .05$.

Year	Basic Cable Subscribers	As Percentage of Households with TVS
1976	10,787,970	15.1
1977	12,168,450	16.6
1978	13,391,910	17.9
1979	14,814,380	19.4
1980	17,671,490	22.6
1981	23,219,200	28.3
1982	29,340,570	35.0
1983	34,113,790	40.5
1984	37,290,870	43.7
1985	39,872,520	46.2
1986	42,237,140	48.1
1987	44,970,880	50.5
1988	48,636,520	53.8
1989	52,564,470	57.1
1990	54,871,330	59.0
1991	55,786,390	60.6
1992	57,211,600	61.5
1993	58,834,440	62.5
1994	60,483,600	63.4
1995	62,956,470	65.7
1996	64,654,180	66.7
1997	65,929,420	67.3
1998	67,011,180	67.4
1999	68,537,980	68.0
2000	69,368,920	67.9
2001	69,501,440	68.0

7.37 The U.S. Bureau of Labor Statistics releases consumer price indexes (CPIs) for selected items in the publication *Monthly Labor Review*. Shown here are the CPIs for apparel and upkeep for the years 1983 through 2000. Use the data to answer the following questions.

  a. Compute a 4-year moving average to forecast the CPIs from 1987 through 2000.

  b. Compute a 4-year weighted moving average to forecast the CPIs from 1987 through 2000. Weight the most recent year by 4, the next most recent year by 3, and the next year by 2, and the last year of the four by 1.

  c. Determine the errors for parts (a) and (b). Compute MSE for parts (a) and (b). Compare the MSE values

and comment on the effectiveness of the moving average versus the weighted moving average for these data.

Year	Apparel and Upkeep
1983	100.2
1984	102.1
1985	105.0
1986	105.9
1987	110.6
1988	115.4
1989	118.6
1990	124.1
1991	128.7
1992	131.9
1993	133.7
1994	133.4
1995	132.0
1996	131.7
1997	132.9
1998	133.0
1999	131.3
2000	129.6

7.38 In the *Survey of Current Business*, the U.S. Department of Commerce publishes data on farm commodity prices. Given are the cotton prices from November of year 1 through February of year 4. The prices are indexes with a base of 100 from the period of 1910 through 1914. Use these data to develop autoregression models for a 1-month lag and a 4-month lag. Compare the results of these two models. Which model seems to yield better predictions? Why?

Time Period	Cotton Prices	Time Period	Cotton Prices
November (year 1)	552	January (year 3)	571
December	519	February	573
		March	582
January (year 2)	505	April	587
February	512	May	592
March	541	June	570
April	549	July	560
May	552	August	565
June	526	September	547
July	531	October	529
August	545	November	514
September	549	December	469
October	570		
November	576	January (year 4)	436
December	568	February	419

7.39 The U.S. Department of Commerce publishes data on industrial machinery and equipment. Shown here are the shipments (in $ billions) of industrial machinery and equipment from the first quarter of year 1 through the fourth quarter of year 6. Use these data to determine the seasonal indexes for the data through time-series decomposition methods. Use the four-quarter centered moving average in the computations.

Time Period	Industrial Machinery and Equipment Shipments
1st quarter (year 1)	54.019
2nd quarter	56.495
3rd quarter	50.169
4th quarter	52.891
1st quarter (year 2)	51.915
2nd quarter	55.101
3rd quarter	53.419
4th quarter	57.236
1st quarter (year 3)	57.063
2nd quarter	62.488
3rd quarter	60.373
4th quarter	63.334
1st quarter (year 4)	62.723
2nd quarter	68.380
3rd quarter	63.256
4th quarter	66.446
1st quarter (year 5)	65.445
2nd quarter	68.011
3rd quarter	63.245
4th quarter	66.872
1st quarter (year 6)	59.714
2nd quarter	63.590
3rd quarter	58.088
4th quarter	61.443

7.40 Use the seasonal indexes computed to deseasonalize the data in Problem 7.39.

7.41 Use both a linear and quadratic model to explore trends in the deseasonalized data from Problem 7.40. Which model seems to produce a better fit of the data?

7.42 The Board of Governors of the Federal Reserve System publishes data on mortgage debt outstanding by type of property and holder. The following data give the amounts of residential nonfarm debt (in $ billions) held by savings institutions in the United States over a 10-year period. Use these data to develop an autoregression model with a 1-period lag. Discuss the strength of the model.

Year	Debt
1	529
2	554
3	559
4	602
5	672
6	669
7	600
8	538
9	490
10	470

7.43 The data shown here, from the Investment Company Institute, show that the equity fund assets of mutual funds have been growing since 1981. At the same time, the assets of mutual funds in taxable money markets have been increasing since 1980. Use these data to develop a regression model to forecast the equity fund assets by the taxable money market assets. All figures are given in billion-dollar units. Conduct a Durbin-Watson test on the data and the regression model to determine whether significant autocorrelation is present. Let $\alpha = .01$.

Year	Equity Funds	Taxable Money Markets
1980	44.4	74.5
1981	41.2	181.9
1982	53.7	206.6
1983	77.0	162.5
1984	83.1	209.7
1985	116.9	207.5
1986	161.5	228.3
1987	180.7	254.7
1988	194.8	272.3
1989	249.0	358.7
1990	245.8	414.7
1991	411.6	452.6
1992	522.8	451.4
1993	749.0	461.9
1994	866.4	500.4
1995	1,269.0	629.7
1996	1,750.9	761.8
1997	2,399.3	898.1
1998	2,978.2	1,163.2
1999	4,041.9	1,408.7
2000	3,962.3	1,607.2

7.44 The purchasing-power value figures for the minimum wage in 1997 dollars for the years 1980 through 1997 are shown here. Use these data and exponential smoothing to develop forecasts for the years 1981 through 1997. Try α = .1, .5, and .8, and compare the results using MAD. Discuss your findings. Select the value of alpha that worked best and use your exponential smoothing results to predict the figure for 1998.

Year	Purchasing Power	Year	Purchasing Power
1980	$6.04	1989	$4.34
1981	5.92	1990	4.67
1982	5.57	1991	5.01
1983	5.40	1992	4.86
1984	5.17	1993	4.72
1985	5.00	1994	4.60
1986	4.91	1995	4.48
1987	4.73	1996	4.86
1988	4.55	1997	5.15

INTERPRETING THE OUTPUT

7.45 Shown below is the Excel output for a regression analysis to predict the number of business bankruptcy filings over a 16-year period by the number of consumer bankruptcy filings. How strong is the model? Note the residuals. Compute a Durbin-Watson statistic from the data and discuss the presence of autocorrelation in this model.

	A	B	C	D	E	F
1	SUMMARY OUTPUT					
2	Regression Statistics					
3	Multiple R	0.529				
4	R Square	0.280				
5	Adjusted R Square	0.228				
6	Standard Error	8179.84				
7	Observations	16				
8						
9	ANOVA					
10		df	SS	MS	F	Significant F
11	Regression	1	364069877.4	364069877.4	5.44	0.0351
12	Residual	14	936737379.6	66909812.8		
13	Total	15	1300807257			
14						
15		Coefficients	Standard Error	t Stat	P-value	
16	Intercept	75532.43621	4980.08791	15.17	0.0000	
17	Consumer Bankrupcies	–0.01574	0.00675	–2.33	0.0351	
18						
19	RESIDUAL OUTPUT					
20	Observation	Predicted Bus. Bankruptcies	Residuals			
21	1	70638.58	–1338.6			
22	2	71024.28	–8588.3			
23	3	71054.61	–7050.6			
24	4	70161.99	1115.0			
25	5	68462.72	12772.3			
26	6	67733.25	14712.8			
27	7	66882.45	–3029.4			
28	8	65834.05	–2599.1			
29	9	64230.61	622.4			
30	10	61801.70	9747.3			
31	11	61354.16	9288.8			
32	12	62738.76	–434.8			
33	13	63249.36	–10875.4			
34	14	61767.01	–9808.0			
35	15	57826.69	–4277.7			
36	16	54283.80	–256.8			

ANALYZING THE DATABASES
see www.wiley.com/college/black

1. Use the agricultural time-series database and the variable Green Beans to forecast the number of green beans for period 169 by using the following techniques.
   a. Five-period moving average
   b. Simple exponential smoothing with $\alpha = .6$
   c. Time-series linear trend model
   d. Decomposition

2. Use decomposition on Carrots in the agricultural database to determine the seasonal indexes? These data actually represent 14 years of 12-month data. Do the seasonal indexes indicate the presence of some seasonal effects? Run an autoregression model to predict Carrots by a 1-month lag and another by a 12-month lag. Compare the two models. Because vegetables are somewhat seasonal, is the 12-month lag model significant?

3. Use the energy database to forecast 1999 U.S. Coal Production by using simple exponential smoothing of previous U.S. Coal Production data. Let $\alpha = .2$ and $\alpha = .8$. Compare the forecast with the actual figure. Which of the two models produces the forecast with the least error?

4. Use the international labor database to develop a regression model to predict the Unemployment Rate for Germany by the Unemployment Rate of Italy. Test for autocorrelation and discuss its presence or absence in this regression analysis.

CASE: DEBOURGH MANUFACTURING COMPANY

The DeBourgh Manufacturing Company was founded in 1909 as a metal-fabricating company in Minnesota by the four Berg brothers. In the 1980s, the company ran into hard times, as did the rest of the metal-fabricating industry. Among the problems that DeBourgh faced were declining sales, deteriorating labor relations, and increasing costs. Labor unions had resisted cost-cutting measures. Losses were piling up in the heavy job-shop fabrication division, which was the largest of the company's three divisions. A division that made pedestrian steel bridges closed in 1990. The remaining company division, producer of All-American lockers, had to move to a lower-cost environment.

In 1990, with the company's survival at stake, the firm made a risky decision and moved everything from its high-cost location in Minnesota to a lower-cost area in La Junta, Colorado. Eighty semitrailer trucks were used to move equipment and inventory 1,000 miles at a cost of $1.2 million. The company was relocated to a building in La Junta that had stood vacant for three years. Only 10 of the Minnesota workers transferred with the company, which quickly hired and trained 80 more workers in La Junta. By moving to La Junta, the company was able to go nonunion.

DeBourgh also faced a financial crisis. A bank that had been loaning the company money for 35 years would no longer do so. In addition, a costly severance package was worked out with Minnesota workers to keep production going during the move. An internal stock-purchase "earnout" was arranged between company president Steven C. Berg and his three aunts, who were the other principal owners.

The roof of the building that was to be the new home of DeBourgh Manufacturing in La Junta was badly in need of repair. During the first few weeks of production, heavy rains fell on the area and production was all but halted. However, DeBourgh was able to overcome these obstacles. One year later, locker sales achieved record-high sales levels each month. The company is now more profitable than ever with sales topping $6 million. Much credit has been given to the positive spirit of teamwork fostered among its approximately 80 employees. Emphasis shifted to employee involvement in decision making, quality, teamwork, employee participation in compensation action, and shared profits. In addition, DeBourgh became a more socially responsible company by doing more for the town in which it is located and by using paints that are more environmentally friendly.

Discussion

1. After its move in 1990 to La Junta, Colorado, and its new initiatives, the DeBourgh Manufacturing Company began an upward climb of record sales. Suppose the figures shown here are the DeBourgh monthly sales figures from January 1993 through December 2001 (in $1,000s). Are any trends evident in the data? Does DeBourgh have a seasonal component to its sales? Shown after the sales figures is MINITAB output from a decomposition analysis of the sales figures using 12-month seasonality. Next an Excel graph displays the data with a trend line. Examine the data, the output, and any additional analysis you feel is helpful, and write a short report on DeBourgh sales. Include a discussion of the general direction of sales and any seasonal tendencies that might be occurring.

Month	1993	1994	1995	1996	1997	1998	1999	2000	2001
January	139.7	165.1	177.8	228.6	266.7	431.8	381.0	431.8	495.3
February	114.3	177.8	203.2	254.0	317.5	457.2	406.4	444.5	533.4
March	101.6	177.8	228.6	266.7	368.3	457.2	431.8	495.3	635.0
April	152.4	203.2	279.4	342.9	431.8	482.6	457.2	533.4	673.1
May	215.9	241.3	317.5	355.6	457.2	533.4	495.3	558.8	749.3
June	228.6	279.4	330.2	406.4	571.5	622.3	584.2	647.7	812.8
July	215.9	292.1	368.3	444.5	546.1	660.4	609.6	673.1	800.1
August	190.5	317.5	355.6	431.8	482.6	520.7	558.8	660.4	736.6
September	177.8	203.2	241.3	330.2	431.8	508.0	508.0	609.6	685.8
October	139.7	177.8	215.9	330.2	406.4	482.6	495.3	584.2	635.0
November	139.7	165.1	215.9	304.8	393.7	457.2	444.5	520.7	622.3
December	152.4	177.8	203.2	292.1	406.4	431.8	419.1	482.6	622.3

Time-series Decomposition
Data: DeBourgh
Length: 108.000
NMissing: 0
Seasonal Indices
Period   Index
   1   0.794869
   2   0.851250
   3   0.926003
   4   1.02227
   5   1.11591
   6   1.24281
   7   1.31791
   8   1.16422
   9   0.992014
  10   0.915239
  11   0.850714
  12   0.806788
Accuracy of Model
MAPE: 48.1
MAD: 141.1
MSD: 26153.6

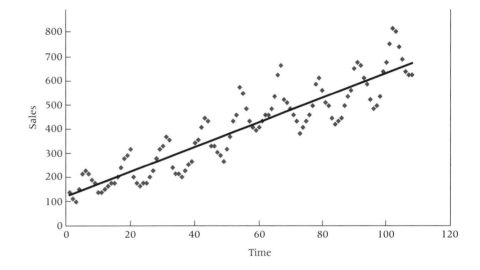

2. Suppose DeBourgh accountants computed a per-unit cost of lockers for each year since 1988, as reported here. Use techniques in this chapter to analyze the data. Forecast the per-unit labor costs through the year 2002. Use smoothing techniques, moving averages, trend analysis, and any others that seem appropriate. Calculate the error of the forecasts and determine which forecasting method seems to do the best job of minimizing error. Study the data and explain the behavior of the per-unit labor cost since 1988. Think about the company history and objectives since 1988.

Year	Per-Unit Labor Cost
1988	$80.15
1989	85.29
1990	85.75
1991	64.23
1992	63.70
1993	62.54
1994	60.19
1995	59.84
1996	57.29
1997	58.74
1998	55.01
1999	56.20
2000	55.93
2001	55.60

Source: Adapted from "DeBourgh Manufacturing Company: A Move That Saved a Company," *Real-World Lessons for America's Small Businesses: Insights from the Blue Chip Enterprise Initiative.* Published by *Nation's Business* magazine on behalf of Connecticut Mutual Life Insurance Company and the U.S. Chamber of Commerce in association with the Blue Chip Enterprise Initiative, 1992. See also DeBourgh, available at http://www.debourgh.com: and the Web site containing Colorado Springs top business stories, available at http://www.csbj.com/1998/981113/top_stor.htm.

USING THE COMPUTER

EXCEL

Excel has the capability of doing several of the forecasting techniques presented in this chapter. Two of the techniques, exponential smoothing and moving averages, are accessed by using the **Data Analysis** selection. Begin the process by selecting **Tools** on the menu bar. A pull-down menu will appear. Select **Data Analysis** from this menu to produce the **Data Analysis** dialog box.

Exponential Smoothing

From the **Data Analysis** dialog box, select **Exponential Smoothing**. A dialog box will appear. Input the location of the data to be smoothed in the **Input Range** space. Place the value of the dampening factor in the **Damping Factor** space. The default value is .3. In the **Output Range** space, place the location of the upper left cell of the output table. The output consists of forecast values of the data using the smoothing constant. If the **Standard Errors** slot is checked, a second column of output will be given with the standard errors.

Moving Average

From the **Data Analysis** dialog box, select **Moving Average.** A dialog box will appear. Place the location of the data in the **Input Range** space. In the **Interval** space, record how many data values you want to include in the moving average. The default is three values. In the **Output Range** space, place the location of the upper left cell for the moving averages. The output consists of the moving averages. If the **Standard Errors** slot is checked, a second column of output will be given with the standard errors.

Two other forecasting techniques can be accessed in Excel by using the Paste Function. Begin the process by clicking on the Paste Function key, f_x, on the standard tool bar. The Paste Function dialog box will appear. From the left side menu, select **Statistical.** From the choices on the right side, select **FORECAST** to compute forecasts and **TREND** to fit trend to the data.

Forecast

From the Paste Function box, select **FORECAST.** This feature enables you to forecast a value by using linear regression. A dialog box will appear. Place in the space on the first line the value of X for which you want a predicted value. You must place an entry here. Place in the space on the second line the location of X values to be used in development of the regression model; and in the space on the third line, place the location of the Y values. The output consists of the predicted value.

Trend

This Paste Function selection fits a straight line (by using least squares analysis) to the arrays of X and Y. It returns the Y values along the line for the array of new Xs that you specify.

From the Paste Function box, select **TREND.** A dialog box will appear. In the space on the first line, place the location of the known Y values; in the space on the second line, place the location of the known X values. The X values can consist of more than one column if you want to fit a polynomial curve. Merely place squared values of X, cubed values of X, and so on as desired in other columns and include those columns in the **known X** space. In the **new X's** box, place the values for which you want to return corresponding Y values. If you want to compute linear trend based on Y values for consecutive periods, you can choose to omit the known X values and Excel will default to $(1, 2, 3, 4, \ldots)$. Then under **new X's** place the period (e.g., 15) or periods for which you want to forecast using trend. The space on the fourth line in the dialog box is **Const,** which is a logical value specifying whether to force the regression constant to be zero. If you place **TRUE** in the box, you will get a value for the constant as usual (default option). If you place **FALSE** in the box, b_0 will be set to zero.

MINITAB

MINITAB Windows offers much in the way of forecasting analysis. Begin by selecting **Stat** on the menu bar. A pull-down menu will appear. Select **Time-Series** from the menu. Another pull-down menu will appear. From this pull-down menu, you can make your forecasting analysis selections. The appropriate dialog box will appear.

Time-Series Plot

A time-series plot can be obtained by using the command, **Time-Series Plot.** Enter the column containing the Y values under **Graph variables.** Under **Time Scale,** you can define what scale you want to use for X. You have the option of checking whether you want to use an **Index** (scale of 1 to n consecutive numbers), a **Calender** (with various options and combinations of days, weeks, months, quarters, years, etc.), or some **Clock** scales such as day, hour, or minute. The output is a time-series plot with time on the X axis.

Trend Analysis

The **Trend Analysis** option on the pull-down menu enables you to fit a trend through the data. Place the location of the time-series data in the **Variable** slot. Under **Model Type,** you have four options: linear, quadratic, exponential growth, or S-curve. Select the model desired. You have the option of generating forecasts.

Decomposition

Select the **Decomposition** option to perform classical decomposition on time-series data. Under **Variable,** place the location of the time-series data. Under **Seasonal Length,** enter a positive integer greater than or equal to 2. Under **Model Type,** select either the multiplicative model (the one presented in the chapter) or the additive model. Under **Model**

Components, select either seasonal only or trend plus seasonal. Select an initial seasonal period (the default is 1). The output is a summary table and a set of plots. The summary table includes the trend equation, the seasonal indexes, and three measures of error. The plots include a time-series plot, a component analysis, and a seasonal analysis.

Moving Average

The **Moving Average** choice produces moving averages. Enter the location of the data under **Variable.** Under M̲A Length, enter the number of values to be averaged. Check whether you want to center the moving averages. If you check this, MINITAB will compute the moving average values at the period that is at the center of the range rather than at the end of it. The default output consists of a time-series plot displaying the data and one-period-ahead forecasts along with three measures of forecast error.

Single Exponential Smoothing

The selection of **Single Exp Smoothing** allows you to smooth time-series data with a single exponential smoothing weight. Enter the location of the data under **Variable.** You can attempt to optimize the smoothing process by checking Optimize. This option allows MINITAB to attempt to minimize the sum of squares errors. If you choose to enter your own weight, select **U̲se** and enter the value. You have the option of generating forecasts, selecting the number of forecasts, and/or selecting the starting point (**Starting from origin).** The output is a time-series plot displaying the data and one-period-ahead forecasts. Also displayed are the smoothing weight used and three measures of error.

Double Exponential Smoothing

The **Double Exp Smoothing** option enables you to smooth the data and smooth for trend. Enter the location of the data under **Variable.** Check whether you want MINITAB to optimize the model or whether you want to enter your own weights. If you choose **U̲se,** you will enter a smoothing constant (weight) for both leveling and trend. The output is similar to that obtained under Single Exponential Smoothing, but includes the trend component.

Winters' Method

The selection of **W̲inters' Method** produces an exponential smoothing using both seasonality and trend. Enter the location of the data in **V̲ariable;** the seasonal length (greater than or equal to 2) under **Seasonal length;** and the smoothing weights (constants between 0 and 1) for leveling, trend, and seasonality. By default, all three smoothing weights will be set at .2. The output is a time-series plot similar to that of Single Exponential Smoothing but includes the smoothing weights used.

Differences

The **Differences** command enables you to compute the differences between the data elements in a column. Under **Series,** select the column containing the data for which you want to compute the differences. Under **Store differences in,** enter the location of a storage column for the differences. Using the **Lag** slot, specify the value for the lag. MINITAB subtracts from each value the element k rows above, where k is the lag specified, and stores the resulting values in a new column.

Lag

The **Lag** command moves data values in a column down a specified number of rows. MINITAB stores the results in a new column of the same length. Enter the column containing the data in **Series.** Enter the column location for the results under **Store lags in.** Specify the value for the lag under **Lag.**

Autocorrelation Function

The **Autocorrelation** command computes and plots the autocorrelation of a set of time-series data. In the **Series** slot, enter the column location of the data. If you check **Default number of lags,** MINITAB will default to $n/4$ if there are less than 240 observations and to $\sqrt{n} + 45$ for more than 240 observations. If you check **Number of lags,** you can specify the number of lags. Check either **Graphical ACF** or **Nongraphical ACF,** depending on the output you desire.

CHAPTER 8

Linear and Integer Programming Models

San Miguel Corporation

With assets totaling over $4.4 billion, San Miguel Corporation (http://www.sanmiguel .com.ph), the most diversified company in the Philippines, generates over 4% of that country's gross national product. Beverage production and distribution is a major component of the company's operations. San Miguel produces six brands of beer and bottles three wine and spirit brands at three different sites. It also bottles five brands of soft drinks for Coca-Cola Bottlers Philippines at 18 bottling plants.

Among its other endeavors are the manufacturing of packaging materials, such as glass containers, plastic crates, polybags, and cardboard boxes, and the development and manufacturing of animal feeds for its chicken, hog, and cattle interests. Other sources of profit are the manufacture and distribution of ice cream, butter, cheese, and other dairy and nondairy products, the raising of prawns for export, and the processing and trading of coconut oil.

Since 1971, management science, in general, and linear models, in particular, have had a significant impact on the company's bottom line. Projects in which linear models have played a major role include blending problems for determining animal feed mixes and ice cream base composition, distribution problems for determining allocations among its 68 production facilities and 230 sales offices, and marketing problems, such as minimizing the cost of television advertising.

Over the course of several years, use of these models has saved the company millions of dollars, allowing it to expand at a vigorous rate. By 1995, San Miguel had become the first non-Japanese and non-Australian firm to rank in the top 20 Asian food and beverage companies. As it looks to the future, San Miguel will continue to refine and develop integrative linear models in order to enhance its growth and financial strength.

8.1 INTRODUCTION TO LINEAR PROGRAMMING

Mathematical programming is the branch of management science that deals with solving optimization problems, in which we want to maximize a function (such as profit, expected return, or efficiency) or minimize a function (such as cost, time, or distance), usually in a constrained environment. The recommended course of action is known as a *program;* hence, the term **mathematical programming** is used to describe such problems.

A constrained mathematical programming model consists of three components: (1) a set of *decision variables* that can be controlled or determined by the decision maker; (2) an *objective function* that is to be maximized or minimized; and (3) a set of *constraints* that describe the restrictive set of conditions that must be satisfied by any solution to the model. The most widely used mathematical programming models are **linear programming (LP) models:**

Linear Programming Models

A **linear programming model** is a model that seeks to maximize or minimize a *linear* objective function subject to a set of *linear* constraints.

That's a mouthful! But all that means is that the objective function and constraints contain only mathematical terms involving variables (X_1, X_2, X_3, etc.) that are raised to the first power (e.g., $5X_1$, $-2X_2$, or $0X_3$). Models with terms such as X_1^2, X_1X_2, X_1/X_2, e^{X_2} and $\sqrt{X_1}$ are classified as **nonlinear programming (NLP) models.** Linear models in which at least one of the variables is required to be integer-valued are called **integer linear programming (ILP) models.**

Large companies such as the San Miguel Corporation, Texaco, American Airlines, and General Motors have used linear models to affect efficiency and improve the bottom line. But linear models can also be applied in smaller venues. In fact a wide variety of cases lend themselves to linear modeling, including problems from such diverse areas as manufacturing, marketing, investing, advertising, trucking, shipping, agriculture, nutrition, e-commerce, restaurant operations, and the travel industry.

Why Linear Programming Models Are Important

Linear programming models are important for three basic reasons.

Why Linear Programming Models Are Important

1. Many problems lend themselves to a linear programming formulation, and many other problems can be closely approximated by models with this structure.

2. Efficient solution techniques exist for solving models of this type.

3. The output generated from linear programming packages provides useful "what-if" information concerning the sensitivity of the optimal solution to changes in the model's coefficients.

Assumptions of Linear Models

Because linear models are solved so efficiently, linear programming formulations have proven quite valuable for solving numerous problems in business and government. As with all mathematical models, however, certain inherent assumptions must be made in order to use the linear programming approach. The modeler must be keenly aware of the impact of these assumptions on the real-life situation being modeled; if the assumptions are deemed unacceptable, the model must be modified or another model developed.

All linear models satisfy three assumptions.

**Assumptions for Linear Programming
and Integer Linear Programming Models**

1. The parameter values are known with *certainty*.

2. The above function and constraints exhibit *constant returns to scale*.

3. There are *no interactions* between the decision variables.

The **certainty assumption** asserts that all parameters of the problem are known, fixed constants. Although this assumption is crucial for solving a linear model, as we show in Section 8.4, the "optimal solution" to a linear model may be valid within a range of the parameter values. Hence, in some cases, when a model includes a parameter whose value is not known precisely, the model may still successfully be solved by approximating this parameter value and assuming it to be constant.

The **constant returns to scale (proportionality) assumption** implies that, if for instance, one unit of an item adds $4 to profit and requires three hours to produce, then 500 units will contribute $4(500) = $2000 to profit and require 3(500) = 1500 hours to produce. This assumption is frequently violated in practice. For example, a good deal of time and expense might go into setting up a production run for a given set of products. Thus, if only one item were produced, the unit production cost would be quite high. As more and more of the products are made, however, production costs per unit tend to stabilize, yielding a relatively fixed unit profit. Then, as even more are produced, from a supply and demand perspective, selling prices may have to be reduced, resulting in a decrease in the unit profits. When using a linear model, we must assume the constant returns to scale assumption is reasonable within the range of possible values of the decision variables.

The **additivity assumption** implies that the total value of some function can be found by simply adding the linear terms. Suppose in the model above that X_1, X_2, and X_3 were the amounts of three different but similar items produced during a production run. In this case, it might be argued that since the expertise and materials required to produce all three items are similar, a cost saving would result from producing all three types of items. However, in linear models, the additivity assumption implies no such cost saving would result.

In addition to these three assumptions, *linear programming models* also require the assumption that the variables are continuous. This **continuity assumption** implies that the decision variables can take on any value within the limits of the functional constraints. In *integer linear programming models*, for those variables restricted only to integer values, this assumption is replaced by an **integer assumption.**

Although these assumptions might appear to be overly restrictive, they frequently provide "close enough" approximations for many practical problems. As a result, linear programming techniques have been applied successfully in many diverse areas including those in Table 8.1. Several of these applications are illustrated in examples and end-of-chapter exercises in this and ensuing chapters.

	Application Area	Objective	Constraints
TABLE 8.1 Applications of Linear Programming	Manufacturing	Determine production quantities that maximize profit	■ Labor availability ■ Resource availability
	Finance	Allocate funds to maximize expected return	■ Diversification ■ Acceptable risk levels
	Advertising	Select a media mix that maximizes exposure to a target population	■ Budget ■ Length of advertising campaign
	Worker Training	Assign workers to production and training activities to maximize profit while building a workforce	■ Production quotas ■ Number of qualified instructors and trainees available
	Construction	Plan tasks and assign labor to meet a production schedule	■ Ordering of tasks ■ Project deadline
	Oil Refining	Blend raw crude oils into different grades of gasolines	■ Supply of raw crude oil and demand for different grades of gasolines ■ Required characteristics of the different grades of gasolines
	Transportation	Assign delivery of resources to minimize transportation costs	■ Supply/demand of product ■ Shipping capacities
	Agriculture	Determine a plant rotation plan to maximize long-term profit	■ Anticipated demand for crops ■ Rotation restrictions
	Military Operations	Assign troops and material to accomplish a military mission	■ Troop availability/training ■ Transportation of resources

8.2 A LINEAR PROGRAMMING MODEL—A PROTOTYPE EXAMPLE

In this section we illustrate the procedure used to construct linear programming models by considering the situation faced by Galaxy Industries. Although this prototype model requires only two decision variables, it will be used to develop the concepts that hold true for linear programming models with any number of decision variables.

GALAXY INDUSTRIES

Galaxy Industries is an emerging toy manufacturing company that produces two "space age" water guns that are marketed nationwide, primarily to discount toy stores. Although many parents object to the potentially violent implications of these products, the products have proven very popular and are in such demand that Galaxy has had no problem selling all the items it manufactures.

The two models, the Space Ray and the Zapper, are produced in lots of one-dozen each and are made exclusively from a special plastic compound. Two of the

Barnes.xls
Galaxy.xls

limiting resources are the 1000 pounds of the special plastic compound and the 40 hours of production time that are available each week.

Galaxy's marketing department is more concerned with building a strong customer demand base for the fledgling company's products than with meeting high production quotas. Two of its recommendations, which Galaxy's management has already accepted, are to limit total weekly production to at most 700 dozen units and to prevent weekly production of Space Rays from exceeding that of Zappers by more then 350 dozen. Table 8.2 summarizes the per dozen resource requirements and profit values (calculated by subtracting variable production costs from their wholesale selling prices).

Table 8.2   Galaxy's Resource Requirements and Profit Values

Product	Profit per Dozen	Plastic (lb.) per Dozen	Production Time (min.) per Dozen
Space Ray	$8	2	3
Zapper	$5	1	4

Figure 8.1 shows a simple Excel spreadsheet which Hal Barnes, Galaxy's production manager, built to calculate the total profit and keep track of the usage of plastic and production time for assigned production quantities. Hal reasoned that since the $8 profit per dozen Space Rays exceeds the $5 profit per dozen Zappers by 60%, the company would maximize its profits by producing as many Space Rays as possible, while still remaining within the marketing guidelines. That is, if the resources were sufficient, Space Ray production should exceed Zapper production by 350 dozen, with the combined total production not exceeding 700 dozen.

Hal entered formulas into cells B5, B6, and B7 as shown to keep track of the total products produced, the total amount of plastic, and the total production minutes, respectively, given the number of dozen Space Rays and Zappers produced (cells B2 and C2). To ensure that Space Ray production (cell B2) exceeded Zapper production (cell C2) by 350 dozen, Hal entered the formula = C2 + 350 into cell B2.

He then used a trial-and-error approach of entering increasingly larger values into cell C2. With each change he observed the values in cells B5, B6, and B7 to ensure that these values did not exceed the weekly limits 700, 1000, and 2400 (in cells C5, C6, and C7), respectively.

In Figure 8.1 we see the result of Hal entering 100 for the weekly production of Zappers (in dozens) in cell C2. At this value, all available plastic would be used. Thus, Hal ordered a production schedule of 450 dozen Space Rays and 100 dozen Zappers weekly, giving Galaxy a profit of $4100 per week or 52($4100) = $213,200 per year.

Although this was considered a good profit, upper management began to question whether a different production schedule might increase company profits.

SOLUTION

We begin our analysis by building a mathematical model of the situation.

FIGURE 8.1

Hal Barnes's Spread Solution for Galaxy Industries

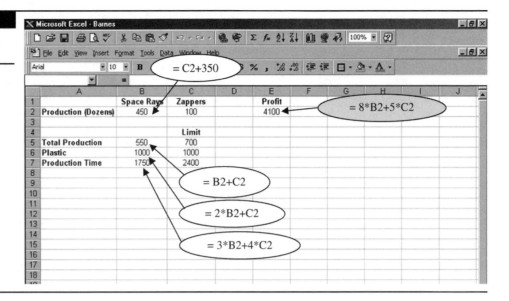

Formulation of the Galaxy Industries Model

Recall that a mathematical model consists of three parts:

1. A well-defined set of decision variables
2. An overall objective to be maximized or minimized
3. A set of constraints

A helpful starting point for determining each of these components is to briefly summarize the details of the problem statement.

From the problem statement for Galaxy Industries we can make a number of observations:

- Production is to be in terms of dozens and scheduled on a weekly basis.
- The overall objective is to maximize weekly profit.
- Production must be scheduled so that the weekly supply of plastic and the availability of production time are not exceeded.
- The two marketing department guidelines concerning maximum total production and the product mix must be met.

Using this brief overview, we can now construct a mathematical model which management at Galaxy Industries can use to determine the most profitable product mix.

Decision Variables

The decision maker can control the production levels of Space Rays and Zappers. Noting that the production units are in terms of *dozens* and production is done on a *weekly* basis, we observe that the appropriate decision variables are:

$$X_1 = \text{number of dozen Space Rays produced weekly}$$
$$X_2 = \text{number of dozen Zappers produced weekly}$$

Objective Function

The objective of maximizing total weekly profit is obtained by summing the weekly profits of each of the two types of items produced. For each product the weekly profit is:

$$\text{(Profit per Dozen Units Produced)} \times$$
$$\text{(Number of Dozen Units Produced Weekly)}$$

Thus, the objective is to:

$$\text{MAXIMIZE } 8X_1 + 5X_2$$

Constraints

In addition to the nonnegativity constraints for the decision variables, there are four functional constraints:

1. The availability of plastic
2. The weekly limit for production time
3. The maximum production limit of total units
4. The mix of Space Rays and Zappers

Our approach to formulating these constraints is first to express, in words, a restriction of the form:

$$\text{(Some quantity)} \langle \text{has some relation to} \rangle \text{(Another quantity)}$$

We can then substitute mathematical functions or constants for the appropriate "quantities." Finally, if necessary, we can rewrite the expression so that all terms involving the decision variables are on the left side of the constraint and the constant term is on the right side.

Plastic

$$\text{(The total amount of plastic used weekly) cannot exceed}$$
$$\text{(The amount of plastic available weekly)}$$

Since each dozen Space Rays requires two pounds of plastic and each dozen Zappers requires one pound, the total amount of plastic used in a week is $2X_1 + 1X_2$. Because this amount cannot exceed the limit of 1000 pounds weekly, the constraint is:

$$2X_1 + 1X_2 \leq 1000$$

Production Time

$$\text{(The amount of production minutes used weekly) cannot exceed}$$
$$\text{(The total number of production minutes available weekly)}$$

Because each dozen Space Rays requires three minutes of labor and each dozen Zappers requires four minutes of labor, the total number of labor minutes used weekly is $3X_1 + 4X_2$. This number cannot exceed the number of labor *minutes* available weekly. Since 40 *hours* are available, the number of available minutes is $(40)(60) = 2400$. Thus, the production time constraint is:

$$3X_1 + 4X_2 \leq 2400$$

Total Production Limit

(The total number of dozen units produced weekly) cannot exceed
(The marketing limit)

The total number of dozens of units produced is simply the sum of the number of dozen Space Rays produced and the number of dozen Zappers produced. Since this is not to exceed 700 dozen, the constraint is:

$$X_1 + X_2 \leq 700$$

Balanced Product Mix

(The number of dozen Space Rays produced weekly) cannot exceed
(The number of dozen Zappers) plus 350

The number of dozen Space Rays produced weekly is X_1, and the number of dozen Zappers produced weekly is X_2. So the appropriate constraint is:

$$X_1 \leq X_2 + 350$$

Rewriting the equation so that X_2 is on the left side yields:

$$X_1 - X_2 \leq 350$$

Nonnegativity of Decision Variables   Negative production of Space Rays and Zappers is impossible. Thus,

$$X_1, X_2 \geq 0$$

The Mathematical Model

The complete mathematical model for Galaxy Industries is:

$$
\begin{array}{lll}
\text{MAX} & 8X_1 + 5X_2 & \text{(Total weekly profit)} \\
\text{ST} & 2X_1 + X_2 \leq 1000 & \text{(Plastic)} \\
& 3X_1 + 4X_2 \leq 2400 & \text{(Production time)} \\
& X_1 + X_2 \leq 700 & \text{(Total production)} \\
& X_1 - X_2 \leq 350 & \text{(Mix)} \\
& X_1, X_2 \geq 0 & \text{(Nonnegativity)}
\end{array}
$$

This model is expressed using the standard mathematical programming conventions of grouping all the nonnegativity constraints together and putting them at the end of the model and using the abbreviations "MAX" for "Maximize" and "ST" for "subject to" or "such that." Note that the objective function and the expressions on the left side of the constraints are all linear functions. Hence this mathematical model is a linear program.

In Section 8.5 we discuss how we can use the Solver function in Excel to obtain an optimal solution to this model. First, however, we shall use a graphical approach to illustrate many of the important properties of linear programming models.

8.3 A GRAPHICAL ANALYSIS OF LINEAR PROGRAMMING

Exactly what production combinations of Space Rays and Zappers are possible for Galaxy Industries? And, of these possible production values, which maximizes the objective function? A graphical representation of the model will help answer both questions.

To determine the set of possible production combinations, we graph one constraint and determine all the points that satisfy that constraint. Then we add a second constraint. Some points that satisfy this second constraint also satisfy the first; others do not, and we eliminate them from consideration. We repeat this process until all the constraints, including the nonnegativity constraints, have been considered. The reader may wish to refer to the PowerPoint slides for an animated presentation of this process.

Here, we begin with the nonnegativity constraints. Because both variables must be nonnegative, we consider points in the first quadrant. This is illustrated in Figure 8.2a. Next, we graph the plastic constraint: $2X_1 + 1X_2 \leq 1000$.[1] The shaded region in Figure 8.2b shows all the points satisfying the nonnegativity constraints and the plastic constraint.

Repeating this process for the production time constraint, $3X_1 + 4X_2 \leq 2400$, yields Figure 8.2c. The shaded region now contains all the points satisfying the nonnegativity constraints, the plastic constraint, and the production time constraint. Note that some of the points that satisfied only the plastic constraint and the nonnegativity constraints have been eliminated.

Figure 8.2d illustrates what happens when we add the constraint on total production, $X_1 + X_2 \leq 700$. As you can see, adding this constraint does not eliminate any additional points from consideration. Constraints with this characteristic are called **redundant constraints.**

Redundant Constraints

A redundant constraint is one that, if removed, will not affect the feasible region.

Figure 8.3 shows the completed graph for this problem, which is formed by adding the mix constraint, $X_1 - X_2 \leq 350$, to the previously graphed constraints.[2] The shaded region of Figure 8.3, which consists of all the "possible" or "feasible" points satisfying all of the model's functional and variable constraints, is known as the **feasible region.**

Feasible Region

The set of all points that satisfy all the constraints of the model is called the **feasible region.**

---

[1] In cases in which both the coefficients of X_1 and X_2 are positive, first set $X_1 = 0$ and solve for X_2 (in this case $X_2 = 1000$), yielding one point on the line. Then set $X_2 = 0$ and solve for X_1 (in this case $X_1 = 500$). We can now draw $2X_1 + X_2 = 1000$ by connecting these two points. The "<" part consists of all points below the line.

[2] The line $X_1 - X_2 = 350$ is generated differently since the coefficient of X_2 is negative. One point (350,0) is determined as usual by setting X_2 to zero and solving for X_1. To find a second point on the line that is in the first quadrant, we set X_1 to any number greater than 350 (say 750) and solve for X_2. This yields $X_2 = 400$. Connecting the point (350,0) with the point (750,400) gives the required line segment. Note that the point (0,0) is on the "<" side of the line. Hence, values to the left of the line represent the points with $X_1 - X_2 < 350$.

FIGURE 8.2a

Nonnegativity Constraints

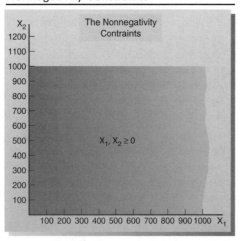

FIGURE 8.2b

Plastic Constraint Added

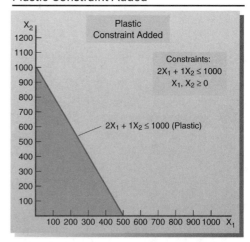

FIGURE 8.2c

Production Time Constraint Added

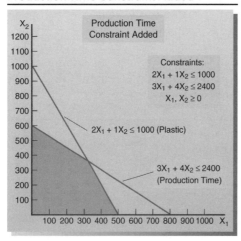

FIGURE 8.2d

Total Production Constraint Added

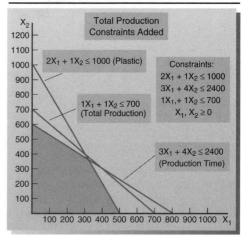

FIGURE 8.3

Mix Constraint Added—The Result Is the Feasible Region

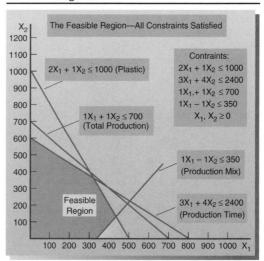

Infeasible and Feasible Points

Infeasible points—those lying outside the feasible region—violate one or more of the function or variable constraints. In Figure 8.4, you can see that the infeasible point (300,500) violates both the plastic constraint and the mix constraint. Figure 8.4 also illustrates three types of **feasible points** that satisfy all the constraints of the model, as defined in Table 8.3.

The characterization of these points is quite important. As we will show in the next section, an optimal solution to a linear programming model *must* occur at an extreme point, *may* occur at a boundary point, but can *never* occur at an interior point.

Extreme Points

Because extreme points play a crucial role in determining the optimal solution to linear programming models, we should discuss them in a little more detail. Extreme points are the "corner points" of the feasible region, occurring at the intersection of two of the boundary constraints. The X_1 and X_2 values for extreme points can be found by solving the two equations in two unknowns that determine the point.

For example, to find the point at the intersection of boundaries of the plastic and the mix constraint, in Figure 8.4 we solve the following two equations in two unknowns:

$$2X_1 + X_2 = 1000$$
$$X_1 - X_2 = 350$$

FIGURE 8.4

Feasible Region—Interior Points, Boundary Points, Extreme Points, and Infeasible Points

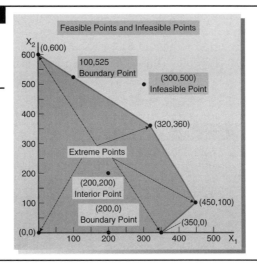

TABLE 8.3 Types of Feasible/Infeasible Points

Point	Characteristic	Example(s)
Feasible Points		
Interior point	Satisfies all constraints, but none with equality	(200,200)
Boundary point	Satisfies all constraints, at least one with equality	(100,525), (200,0)
Extreme point	Satisfies all constraints, two with equality	(0,0), (350,0), (450,100), (320,360), (0,600)
Infeasible Point	Violates at least one constraint	(300,500)

Adding these two equations gives us $3X_1 = 1350$, or $X_1 = 450$. Substituting $X_1 = 450$ into the second equation gives $450 - X_2 = 350$, or $X_2 = 100$. Thus, this extreme point is $X_1 = 450$, $X_2 = 100$. Similarly, the extreme point at the intersection of the production time constraint and the X_2 axis is $(0,600)$, which is found by solving the equations $3X_1 + 4X_2 = 2400$ and $X_1 = 0$ (the equation of the X_2 axis).

For models requiring three dimensions, an extreme point is a feasible point that lies at the intersection of three boundary constraints. Thus, we would have to solve *three* equations in *three* unknowns to determine these extreme points. This notion extends naturally to problems with any number of dimensions.

Solving Graphically for an Optimal Solution

All but the simplest linear programming models (those with only a few variables and constraints) make use of computer software such as Microsoft Excel to perform the voluminous (though straightforward) mathematical operations required in the solution process. Here, however, we present a graphical solution approach that can be used to solve problems with two variables, such as the Galaxy Industries model.

In Figure 8.4, we see that there are an *infinite number of points* in the feasible region. The question is, "Which one gives the maximum profit?" That is, "Which one maximizes the objective function $8X_1 + 5X_2$?" If there were only five or ten feasible points; we could substitute simply the X_1 and X_2 values for each of these points into the objective function, and the point with the largest value would be the optimal solution. However, since the feasible region consists of an infinite number of points, we must take a different approach.

Suppose we ask, "Are there any solutions that would yield a $5000 weekly profit?" This is equivalent to saying, "Are there any feasible points that satisfy the following equation $8X_1 + 5X_2 = 5000$?" When this line is graphed, as illustrated in Figure 8.5a, we see that it lies entirely above the feasible region. Thus, to our dismay, we find that no point in the feasible region gives a value of the objective function as large as $5000.

So let's set our sights lower. Let's see whether any solutions yield a $2000 weekly profit. Figure 8.5b shows us that when we draw the line, $8X_1 + 5X_2 = 2000$, many solutions (the points on the line, $8X_1 + 5X_2 = 2000$, that are in the feasible region) give us a $2000 weekly profit. Thus, Galaxy can do no worse than a $2000 weekly profit.

FIGURE 8.5a	FIGURE 8.5b
No Feasible Points with Objective Function Value of 5000	There Are Feasible Points with Objective Function Value of 2000

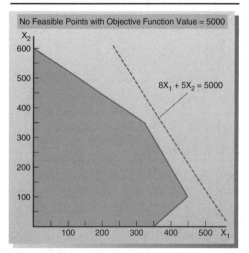

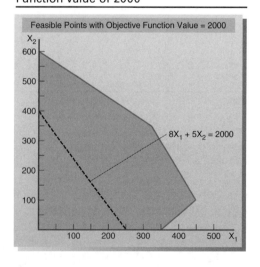

If a $2000 profit can be made, perhaps even larger profits are possible. Are there any combinations of the decision variables that could yield, say, a $3000 profit or even a $4000 profit? To determine whether Galaxy could attain such profits, we add the lines $8X_1 + 5X_2 = 3000$ and $8X_1 + 5X_2 = 4000$ to the graph. As shown in Figure 8.6, both lines intersect the feasible region.

Because the profit lines have the same slope, they are parallel; the lines yielding higher profits lie above those with lower profits. Therefore, if the objective function line is moved parallel to itself upward through the feasible region, the optimal feasible point is found when the objective function line touches the last point of the feasible region.

The last point of the feasible region that is touched by the objective function is the **extreme point** at the intersection of the limit for the availability of plastic ($2X_1 + 1X_2 = 1000$) and the limit on production time ($3X_1 + 4X_2 = 2400$). These constraints, known as the **binding constraints** of the model because they are satisfied with equality. The two other functional constraints and the nonnegativity constraints are the *nonbinding constraints,* which are not satisfied with equality at the optimal point.

To determine the values for X_1 and X_2 at the optimal point, the two equations of the binding constraints that must be solved are:

$$2X_1 + 1X_2 = 1000$$
$$3X_1 + 4X_2 = 2400$$

Multiplying the first equation by 4 gives us:

$$8X_1 + 4X_2 = 4000$$
$$3X_1 + 4X_2 = 2400$$

Subtracting the bottom equation from the top equation gives us $5X_1 = 1600$, or $X_1 = 320$. Substituting $X_1 = 320$ into the original first equation gives us $2(320) + 1X_2 = 1000$, or $X_2 = 360$. Thus, the optimal solution is:

$$X_1 = 320$$
$$X_2 = 360$$

To determine the optimal profit, we substitute these values into the objective function:

$$8X_1 + 5X_2 = 8(320) + 5(360) = \$4360$$

FIGURE 8.6

Determining the Optimal Point

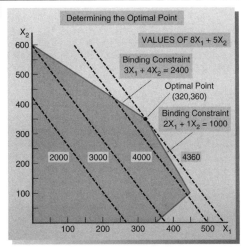

Thus, Hal Barnes should recommend to management at Galaxy Industries a weekly production of 320 dozen Space Rays and 360 dozen Zappers. This would give the company an increase of $260 (=$4360 − $4100), or over a 6.3% increase in weekly profit over Hal's "intuitive" weekly policy of producing 450 dozen Space Rays and 100 dozen Zappers. On a yearly basis, this will net the company 52(260) = $13,520 in increased profits.

Slack

This solution utilizes all the plastic and production time (there is no **slack** for these constraints). There is, however, slack on both of the other functional constraints. Since $X_1 + X_2 = 320 + 360 = 680$, there is a slack of $700 − 680 = 20$ for the total production limit constraint. And since $X_1 − X_2 = 320 − 360 = −40$, there is a slack of $350 − (−40) = 390$ for the product mix constraint.

Summary of the Graphical Solution Approach

To summarize, the following steps are used to find the optimal solution to a two-variable linear programming model graphically.

Graphical Solution Procedure for Two-Variable Linear Programs

1. Graph the constraints to find the feasible region.
2. Set the objective function equal to an arbitrary value so that the line passes through the feasible region.
3. Move the objective function line parallel to itself in the direction of improvement until it touches the last point of the feasible region.
4. Solve for X_1 and X_2 by solving the two equations that intersect to determine this point.
5. Substitute these values into the objective function to determine its optimal value.

Extreme Points and Optimal Solutions

It is useful to recognize where the optimal solution for a linear program can occur. Consider problems that have the same feasible region as Galaxy Industries but different objective functions, as shown in Figures 8.7a–d. Table 8.4 presents the optimal solution for various objective functions,[3] including the original objective function for Galaxy Industries (MAXIMIZE $8X_1 + 5X_2$).

TABLE 8.4 Optimal Solutions	Figure	Objective Function	Optimal Extreme Point
	8.6	MAXIMIZE $8X_1 + 5X_2$	(320,360)
	8.7a	MINIMIZE $8X_1 + 5X_2$	(0,0)
	8.7b	MAXIMIZE $8X_1 + 1X_2$	(450,100)
	8.7c	MAXIMIZE $8X_1 + 20X_2$	(0,600)
	8.7d	MAXIMIZE $8X_1 − 20X_2$	(350,0)

---

[3] For minimization problems, the objective function line is moved in the direction opposite to that for a maximization problem.

FIGURE 8.7a

Objective Function: MIN $8X_1 + 5X_2$ OPTIMAL: (0,0)

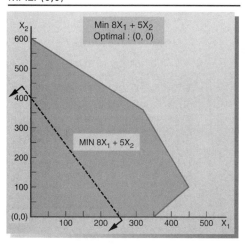

FIGURE 8.7b

Objective Function: MAX $8X_1 + 1X_2$ OPTIMAL: (450,100)

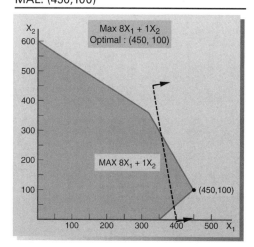

FIGURE 8.7c

Objective Function: MAX $8X_1 + 20X_2$ OPTIMAL: (0,600)

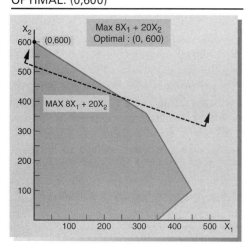

FIGURE 8.7d

Objective Function: MAX $8X_1 - 20X_2$ OPTIMAL: (350,0)

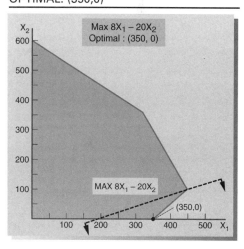

It is not coincidental that, in each case, the optimal solution occurs at an extreme point; rather, it is a fundamental property of linear programming.

Extreme Point Property of Optimality

If a linear programming problem has an optimal solution, an extreme point is optimal.

Alternate Optimal Solutions

In some cases, a linear programming model may have more than one optimal solution, as when the objective function line is parallel to one of the constraints; that is, the slope of the objective function line is the same as the slope of one of the constraints. Recall that the slope of a line = $-(X_1$ coefficient$)/(X_2$ coefficient$)$.

For example, suppose, as shown in Figure 8.8, that the objective function is:

$$\text{MAXIMIZE } 8X_1 + 4X_2$$

FIGURE 8.8

Multiple Optimal Solutions:
Objective Function: MAX $8X_1 +$ $4X_2$ Is Parallel to Plastic
Constraint: $2X_1 + 1X_2 = 1000$

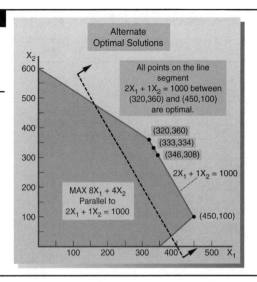

In this case, when we move the objective function line parallel through the feasible region, the slope of the objective function line ($-8/4 = -2$) is the same as the slope of the boundary of the plastic constraint ($-2/1 = -2$), and the last "point" that is touched is actually a set of points, namely, all those on the line $2X_1 + X_2 = 1000$ between the extreme points (320,360) and (450,100). Since at least one optimal solution is an extreme point, the fact that some optimal points are not extreme points does not violate the extreme point property of optimality.

Note, however, that if the objective function would have been MINIMIZE $8X_1 + 4X_2$, even though the slope is still parallel to the boundary of the plastic constraint, there is now a unique optimal solution, $X_1 = 0$, $X_2 = 0$. Thus, the slope of the objective function line being parallel to a boundary constraint is a necessary but not a *sufficient* condition for a model to have multiple optimal solutions.

As Figure 8.8 illustrates, there will never be just two optimal solutions. Any point on the line segment connecting two optimal points is also optimal. The coordinates of points on this line segment can be found by taking any weighted average of the two optimal points.

For example, $X_1 = 320$, $X_2 = 360$ is one optimal solution in Figure 8.8, and $X_1 = 450$, $X_2 = 100$ is another. Each gives an optimal objective function value of $8(320) + 4(360) = 8(450) + 4(100) = 3800$. Then another optimal solution on the line segment $2X_1 + 1X_2 = 1000$ that puts a weight of .8 on the first point and .2 on the second is:

$$X_1 = .8(320) + .2(450) = 346$$
$$X_2 = .8(360) + .2(100) = 308$$

Note that the objective function value is still 3800 (=$8(346) + 4(308)$).

Similarly, we can show that using weights of .9 and .1 gives $X_1 = 333$, $X_2 = 334$ and using weights of .5 and .5 gives $X_1 = 385$, $X_2 = 230$. You can verify that each of these also gives an objective function value equal to $3800. In fact, any combination of weights of the form w, (1 − w) with $0 \leq w \leq 1$, will also give an optimal solution.

Alternate Optimal Solutions

1. For alternate optimal solutions to exist, the objective function must be parallel to a part of the boundary of the feasible region.

2. Any weighted average of optimal solutions is also an optimal solution.

Having more than one optimal solution allows the decision maker to consider secondary criteria in selecting an optimal strategy. For example, one optimal solution may have more of the decision variables equal to 0. In some cases, management might consider this a plus—fewer product types may mean more attention and better quality for the products that are produced. In other cases, this may be a minus—the greater the variety of products produced, perhaps the greater the likelihood of attracting more customers. Another optimal solution may have a more equal product mix than another, which, under some conditions, might be more appealing. In any event, having multiple optimal solutions affords management the luxury of being able to select that solution most to its liking from the set of optimal solutions.

Why "< Constraints" and "> Constraints" Are Not Part of a Linear Programming Model

The constraints of a linear programming model must consist of "$\leq$" constraints, "$\geq$" constraints, and "$=$" constraints. The "$<$" and "$>$" constraints are not allowed because, using them, there would be no "last" point touched by moving the objective function line parallel to itself through the feasible region.

For example, if both the plastic and production time constraints were the strict inequalities $2X_1 + X_2 < 1000$ and $3X_1 + 4X_2 < 2400$, respectively, the point (320,360) would not be feasible. The point (319.99,359.99) would be feasible, but the feasible point (319.999,359.999) gives a higher objective function value and the point (319.9999,359.9999) an even higher value. Thus, there would be no "best value" because, no matter what solution was proposed, adding a "9" in the next decimal place would yield another feasible solution with an even better objective function value.

If a strict inequality is part of a formulation, the constraint should be approximated using a nonstrict inequality. For example, if Galaxy Industries required that less than 1000 pounds of plastic be used weekly ($2X_1 + X_2 < 1000$), in order to use linear programming solution methods, the mathematical modeler might approximate the constraint by $2X_1 + X_2 \leq 999.99999$.

8.4 THE ROLE OF SENSITIVITY ANALYSIS OF THE OPTIMAL SOLUTION

Inevitably, once an optimal solution has been determined, questions arise about how sensitive the optimal solution is to changes in one or more of the input parameters or to other changes, such as the addition or elimination of constraints or variables. The effect of these changes is known as **sensitivity** or **post-optimality analysis.** Decision makers at Galaxy Industries might be interested in sensitivity analyses for the following reasons.

1. *Some of the input parameters may not have been known with certainty but are approximations or best estimates.*

   - The profit coefficients might have been based solely on estimates of the production costs for Space Rays and Zappers.

   - The 40 production hours might have assumed no vacations, illnesses, power failures, and so on.

   - The production times to produce Space Rays and Zappers may have been approximations or averages.

2. *The model may have been formulated in a dynamic environment in which some of the parameters are subject to change.*

   ■ The availability of specially treated plastic might be disrupted by, among other factors, weather or manufacturer stockouts.

   ■ The price of labor and materials could change.

   ■ Higher or lower interest rates could change the profitability of each product.

3. *The manager may simply wish to perform a "what-if" analysis resulting from changes to some of the input parameters.*

   ■ "What-if" overtime is scheduled?

   ■ "What-if" the marketing department modifies its recommendations?

   ■ "What-if" another item is added to the product line?

Of course, if a change is made to a linear programming model, the problem can simply be re-solved. This can be a time-consuming process, however, that in many cases may not even be necessary. Rather, sensitivity reports generated by linear programming software packages can tell us at a glance the ramifications of certain changes to the objective function and the right-hand side coefficients of the model.

Sensitivity Analysis of Objective Function Coefficients

Once the optimal solution to a linear programming model has been found, the decision maker may be concerned about how changes to any one of the objective function coefficients affect the optimal solution. As shown in Section 8.3, the optimal solution may change depending on the values of the objective function coefficients.

Range of Optimality

Sensitivity analysis of an objective function coefficient focuses on answering the following question: "Keeping *all* other factors the same, how much can an objective function coefficient change without changing the optimal solution?"

Let us see what happens when the objective function coefficient per dozen Space Rays (which we designate as C_1) changes from the current value of $8. Figure 8.9 illustrates the effect of increasing and decreasing this coefficient. As C_1 is decreased from $8, the objective function line, $C_1X_1 + 5X_2$, becomes more horizontal. The optimal point, however, remains (320,360) until the line becomes parallel to (has the same slope as) the production time constraint, $3X_1 + 4X_2 = 2400$. Recall that the slope of a straight line is expressed by (–Coefficient of X_1/Coefficient of X_2). Thus, the slope of the production time constraint is –3/4, and the slope of the objective function line is $-C_1/5$. These slopes are equal when $C_1/5 = -3/4$ or $C_1 = 3.75$.

As C_1 is increased from $8, the objective function line, $C_1X_1 + 5X_2$ becomes more vertical, but the optimal point remains (320,360) until the line becomes parallel to (has the same slope as) the plastic constraint, $2X_1 + 1X_2 = 1000$. Since the slope of the plastic constraint is –2/1 and the slope of the objective function line is $-C_1/5$, the slopes are equal when $C_1/5 = -2/1$ or $C_1 = 10$.

This range of values for C_1 from $3.75 to $10.00 is called the **range of optimality** for C_1, the objective function coefficient of Space Rays. This is an *Allowable Increase* of $10 – $8 = $2 and an *Allowable Decrease* of $8 – $3.75 = $4.25 from the original objective function coefficient value of $C_1 = $8. (We shall see in the next section that Excel expresses the range of optimality in terms of an Allowable Increase and an

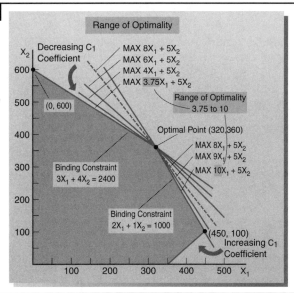

FIGURE 8.9

Range of Optimality—Obtained by Rotating the Objective Function Line Through the Optimal Point Until It Becomes Parallel to a Binding Constraint

Allowable Decrease.) We further observe in Figure 8.9 that if C_1 falls below \$3.75, the point $(0,600)$ becomes the new optimal solution, whereas if C_1 is increased above \$10.00, the point $(450,100)$ becomes optimal.

Note that in this range of optimality, although the optimal solution remains $X_1 = 320$, $X_2 = 360$, the value of the objective function will change with changes to C_1. For example, if the profit per dozen Space Rays were decreased from \$8 to \$6, the optimal profit would now be \$6(320) + \$5(360) = \$3720. It is important to note that this analysis is predicated on the assumption that no other changes occur, other than that to C_1.

Range of Optimality

Assuming that there are no other changes to the input parameters:

1. The **range of optimality** is the range of values for an objective function coefficient in which the optimal solution remains unchanged.

2. The value of the objective function will change if this coefficient multiplies a variable whose value is positive.

The range of optimality for C_2, the objective function coefficient of Zappers, is similarly calculated. This time the equation of the objective function line is $8X_1 + C_2X_2$, whose slope is $-8/C_2$. The range of optimality for C_2 is again bounded by the slopes of the binding constraints of $-3/4$ for the production time constraint and -2 for the plastic constraint. Thus, we get the limits for its range of optimality by: $-8/C_2 = -3/4$ or $C_2 = 10.67$ and $-8/C_2 = -2/1$ or $C_2 = 4$.

Thus the range of optimality for C_2, the objective function coefficient of Zappers, is then between \$4.00 and \$10.67 (an Allowable Increase of \$5.67 and an Allowable Decrease of \$1.00).

Reduced Costs

The optimal solution to the Galaxy Industries model has positive values for both of the decision variables. But as we just argued from Figure 8.9, if the profit coefficient for Space Rays is below \$3.75, the optimal solution is $X_1 = 0$, $X_2 = 600$. So let us suppose that the objective function had been MAX $2X_1 + 5X_2$. Since the optimal solution will be $X_1 = 0$, $X_2 = 600$, the optimal objective function value is $2(0) + \$5(600) = \$3000$.

In this case, $X_1 = 0$ (no Space Rays are produced) because the \$2 profit for the coefficient of X_1 is not large enough to justify the production of Space Rays. It is then reasonable to ask, "How much will the profit coefficient for X_1 have to increase before X_1 can be positive (i.e., to justify the production of some Space Rays) in the optimal solution?" The answer is expressed by the **reduced cost** for this profit coefficient.

We see from Figure 8.9, that the point (0,600) is the optimal solution until the profit per dozen Space Rays increases to more than $C_1 = \$3.75$. Beyond this value, the optimal solution changes to (320,360). Thus, C_1 must increase by \$1.75 from \$2 to \$3.75 before it becomes economically feasible to produce Space Rays. Increasing the profit by \$1.75 is equivalent to reducing the cost component of the coefficient by \$1.75; hence, we say that the reduced cost of this coefficient is -1.75.

Another question that might arise is, "Although it is not economically feasible to produce Space Rays at this value of \$2 per dozen ($X_1 = 0$), how much would the optimal profit decrease if we were forced to produce at least one dozen Space Rays ($X_1 \geq 1$)?" Again the answer is expressed by the reduced cost. As shown in Figure 8.10, with the addition of the constraint $X_1 \geq 1$, the optimal solution is now $X_1 = 1$, $X_2 = 599.25$, giving an objective function value of \$2998.25. This represents a \$1.75 reduction in profit from \$3000.

Reduced Cost

Assuming that there are no other changes to the input parameters:

1. The reduced cost for a variable that has a solution value of 0 is the negative of the objective function coefficient increase necessary for the variable to be positive in the optimal solution.

2. The reduced cost is also the amount the objective function will change per unit increase in this variable.

Note that if a variable is already positive, its reduced cost is 0. Thus, either the value of a variable is 0 or its reduced cost is 0. This property is known as the **complementary slackness** property for objective function coefficients.

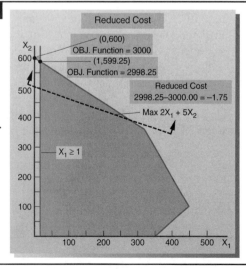

FIGURE 8.10

Reduced Cost for X_1 When Objective Function is $2X_1 + 5X_2$. Add $X_1 \geq 1$ and compare optimal objective function values. Reduced Cost = Value after Constraint Is Added—Original Value

FIGURE 8.11

Shadow Price: Calculated by the Difference in Objective Function Values When the Right-Hand Side of a Constraint Is Increased by 1

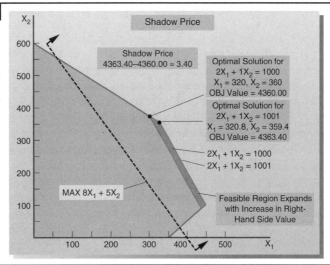

Sensitivity Analysis of Right-Hand Side Coefficients

Any change to a right-hand side value of a binding constraint will change the optimal solution. For example, as shown in Figure 8.11, if the amount of available plastic is increased from 1000 to 1001 pounds, the new optimal solution is found by solving:

$$2X_1 + 1X_2 = 1001$$
$$3X_1 + 4X_2 = 2400$$

You can verify that the solution to this pair of equations is $X_1 = 320.8$, $X_2 = 359.4$.

Shadow Prices

When the optimal solution changes to $X_1 = 320.8$, $X_2 = 359.4$, the optimal objective function value also changes to $\$8(320.8) + \$5(359.4) = \$4363.40$. This is a difference of $\$4363.40 - \$4360.00 = \$3.40$.

If 1002 pounds (two additional pounds) of plastic are available, the optimal solution is found by solving:

$$2X_1 + 1X_2 = 1002$$
$$3X_1 + 4X_2 = 2400$$

The solution to this pair of equations, $X_1 = 321.6$, $X_2 = 358.8$, gives an optimal objective function value of $\$8(321.6) + \$5(358.8) = \$4366.80$. This is a $\$6.80$ increase, or a $\$6.80/2 = \$3.40$ per pound increase, over the original objective function value. Similarly, it can be shown that if there are only 999 pounds of plastic available (one less pound), the resulting optimal solution of $X_1 = 319.2$, $X_2 = 360.6$, gives an optimal objective function value of $\$8(319.2) + \$5(360.6) = \$4356.60$, a decrease of $\$3.40$ per pound! It is this $\$3.40$ change to the optimal value per unit change in the amount of plastic that is called the **shadow price** for a pound of plastic.

Shadow Price

Assuming that there are no other changes to the input parameters, the **shadow price** for a constraint is the change to the objective function value per unit increase to its right-hand side coefficient.

Range of Feasibility

This $3.40 shadow price is valid only over a certain range of values for the availability of plastic, however. If we continued to change the right-hand side value for plastic, we would still get changes of $3.40 per unit in the objective function value as long as the plastic constraint and the production time constraint determine the optimal extreme point. But if the change to the amount of plastic is too great, whether it is too large an increase or too large a decrease, there can come a point when different constraints determine the optimal point.

The **range of feasibility** for plastic gives the limits on the right-hand side values for plastic between which these two constraints, the plastic constraint and the production time constraint, continue to determine the optimal point. It is given this name because, over its range of values, the solution to the current set of binding constraint equations is a *feasible* solution.

Figures 8.12a and 8.12b illustrate how the range of feasibility for plastic can be determined. Notice that increasing the right-hand side value for plastic from 1000 expands the feasible region, while the feasible region contracts when its value is decreased. In each case, the slope of the plastic constraint remains the same; however, its X_2-intercept changes. Thus, changing its right-hand side value creates a new constraint line that is *parallel* to the original constraint line for plastic.

Figure 8.12a shows what happens as the availability of plastic increases. The plastic and the production constraints continue to determine the optimal point until the plastic constraint line passes through the intersection of the production time and the total production constraints at (400,300). This point is determined by solving $3X_1 + 4X_2 = 2400$ and $X_1 + X_2 = 700$. At (400,300), the right-hand side of the plastic constraint is $2(400) + 1(300) = 1100$. For values above 1100 the production time constraint and the total mix constraint will now determine the optimal point, while the intersection of the plastic and production time lines yields an *infeasible* point outside the new feasible region. Thus, the upper limit of the range of feasibility for plastic is 1100. This is an **Allowable Increase** of $1100 - 1000 = 100$ pounds.

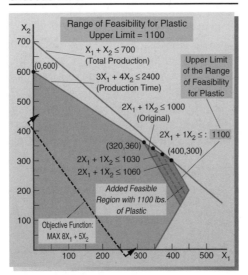

FIGURE 8.12a

Upper Limit of the Range of Feasibility for Plastic. The plastic constraint *and* the production time constraint continue to determine the optimal solution until the RHS exceeds 1100.

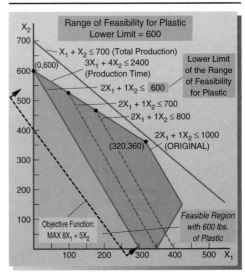

FIGURE 8.12b

Lower Limit of the Range of Feasibility for Plastic. The plastic constraint *and* the production time constraint continue to determine the optimal solution until the RHS is less than 600.

Similarly, Figure 8.12b, shows that as the availability of plastic decreases, the plastic and the production time constraints continue to determine the optimal point until the plastic constraint passes through the intersection of the production time boundary and the X_2 axis at (0,600). At (0,600) the right-hand side of the plastic constraint is $2(0) + 1(600) = 600$. For values of plastic below 600, the optimal solution is determined by the plastic constraint and X_2 axis, while the intersection of the plastic and production time lines yields an *infeasible* point outside the new feasible region. Thus, the lower limit of the range of feasibility for plastic is 600, an **Allowable Decrease** of $1000 - 600 = 400$ pounds.

The range of feasibility of plastic, that is, the range of values for which the $3.40 shadow price for plastic is valid, is between 600 and 1100 pounds. In this range, the value of the objective function will change by $3.40 for each unit change to the availability of plastic.

Range of Feasibility

Assuming that there are no other changes to the input parameters:

1. The **range of feasibility** is the range of values for a right-hand side value in which the shadow prices for the constraints remain unchanged.

2. In the range of feasibility, the value of the objective function will change by the amount of the shadow price times the change to the right-hand side value.

Shadow Prices and Ranges of Feasibility for the Other Constraints

The shadow price for production minutes can be found in a similar fashion by solving:

$$2X_1 + X_2 = 1000$$
$$3X_1 + 4X_2 = 2401$$

The solution to this set of equations is: $X_1 = 319.8$, $X_2 = 360.4$. This solution gives a profit of $4360.40, a $0.40 increase over the original optimal value of the objective function. Thus, the shadow price for production minutes is $0.40 or $60(\$0.40) = \$24$ per hour.

You can verify that, as the availability of the production minutes increases, the plastic and production time constraints continue to determine the optimal point until the production time constraint passes through the intersection of the plastic constraint and the total production constraint at $X_1 = 300$, $X_2 = 400$. At that point, the value of the right-hand side of the production time constraint is $3(300) + 4(400) = 2500$, an allowable increase of $2500 - 2400 = 100$.

As the availability of the production minutes decreases, the plastic and production time constraints continue to determine the optimal point until the production time constraint passes through the intersection of the plastic constraint and the product mix constraint at $X_1 = 450$, $X_2 = 100$. At that point, the value of the right-hand side of the production time constraint is $3(450) + 4(100) = 1750$, an Allowable Decrease of $2400 - 1750 = 650$.

Since the constraints $X_1 + X_2 \leq 700$ and $X_1 - X_2 \leq 350$ do not determine the optimal point (i.e., there is slack on each of these constraints), these are said to be **nonbinding constraints.** Their shadow prices will both be 0, since for at least small changes in these coefficients, all that changes in the optimal solution is the amount of slack on these constraints; the optimal point remains the same at $X_1 = 320$, $X_2 = 360$. Increasing the right-hand side values of either of these two constraints will not change the optimal solution.

The optimal point will not change until the right-hand side coefficient of a non-binding constraint is decreased sufficiently so that it passes through the optimal point! Thus, the lower bound of the range of feasibility for the total production constraint is 1(320) + 1(360) = 680 (an Allowable Decrease of 700 − 680 = 20), and the lower bound for the product mix constraint is 1(320) − 1(360) = −40 (an Allowable Decrease of 350 −(−40) = 390.) This leads to the **complementary slackness** property for right-hand side values: The shadow price for a resource is 0 if there is slack on the constraint; if the shadow price is not 0, there is no slack.

The Correct Interpretation of Shadow Prices

Since the shadow price for plastic is $3.40 per pound, it would seem, then, that management should be willing to pay up to, but no more than, $3.40 for each additional pound of plastic. However, as we show below, this would be true *only if the cost of plastic were not included in the calculation of the profit coefficients of the decision variables.* Let us now consider two cases.

Case 1: Sunk Costs Suppose the 1000 pounds of plastic were automatically delivered to Galaxy each week at a cost of $3 per pound or $3000 per week, and that production time is scheduled for 40 hours per week at $20 per hour ($0.3333 per minute), for a total cost of $800. Because the $3000 for plastic and the $800 for production time must be paid regardless of the amount of plastic and production time actually used during the week, they are **sunk costs.** Thus, we would not include the cost of plastic or production time in determining the objective function coefficients for Space Rays and Zappers.

The net profit for the problem can be obtained by subtracting the total sunk costs of $3000 + $800 = $3800 from the optimal objective function value of the model. Because additional pounds of plastic add $3.40, and additional minutes of production time add $0.40 to the optimal objective function value, these shadow prices do, in fact, represent an upper limit that management would be willing to pay for additional pounds of plastic and additional minutes of production time, respectively.

Case 2: Included Costs Suppose, instead, that management could order any amount of plastic it wanted to, up to 1000 pounds per week at $3 per pound, and it could schedule any amount of production time, up to 2400 minutes. Management would then order only enough plastic and schedule only enough production time needed for the optimal solution.

In this case, the costs of the required plastic and production time (and perhaps other resources) should be *included* in the derivation of the profit coefficients of Space Rays and Zappers. For instance, suppose that the selling price was $17 per dozen Space Rays and $11 per dozen Zappers and that other production costs amounted to $2 per

TABLE 8.5		Space Rays (per dozen)	Zappers (per dozen)
Objective Function Coefficients	Revenue		
	Selling price	$17.00	$11.00
	Costs		
	Plastic (@ $3/lb.)	$ 6.00 (2 lbs.)	$ 3.00 (1 lb.)
	Production time (@ $20/hr.)	$ 1.00 (3 min.)	$ 1.33 (4 min.)
	Other	$ 2.00	$ 1.67
	Total Costs	$ 9.00	$ 6.00
	Unit Profit	$ 8.00	$ 5.00

dozen Space Rays and $1.67 per dozen Zappers. Table 8.5 shows the calculations required to determine the respective $8 and $5 objective function coefficients per dozen Space Rays and Zappers.

The optimal solution of 320 dozen Space Rays and 360 dozen Zappers uses all 1000 pounds of plastic and all 2400 minutes of production time. The objective function value of $4360 is the net profit, which includes $3000 (=$3/lb. × (1000 lbs.)) spent for plastic and $800 (=$20/hr. × (40 hours), or $0.3333/min. × (2400 min.)) spent for production time.

If 1001 pounds of plastic are available, the optimal objective function value will increase by $3.40 to $4363.40; this includes $3003 (=$3/lb. × (1001 lbs.)) spent for plastic. Thus, the shadow price of $3.40 represents a premium above $3.00 which management should be willing to pay for extra pounds of plastic; that is, Galaxy should be willing to pay up to $6.40 (=$3.40 + $3.00) for an extra pound of plastic. Similarly, Galaxy would be willing to pay up to $0.7333 (=$0.40 + $0.3333) for an extra minute of production.

Sunk and Included Costs

Sunk costs—the cost of the resource is not included in the calculation of objective function coefficients—the shadow price is the value of an extra unit of the resource.

Included costs—the cost of the resource is included in the calculation of objective function coefficients—the shadow price is the premium value above the existing unit value for the resource.

Other Post-Optimality Changes

The addition or deletion of constraints, the addition or deletion of variables, and changes to the left-hand side coefficients of a linear programming model are additional post-optimality analyses that may be of interest to the decision maker. Typically, such changes are made directly to the model formulation, and the problem is simply resolved. However, there are some observations worth considering in these cases.

Addition of a Constraint

When a constraint is added to a linear programming model, the first step is to determine whether this constraint is satisfied by the current optimal solution. If it is, it is not necessary to re-solve the problem; the current solution will remain optimal.

If the new constraint is violated, however, the problem must be re-solved. Of course, the optimal objective function value will not be better than the original optimal value (smaller for maximization problems; larger for minimization problems) because the problem is now more constrained.

Deletion of a Constraint

If the constraint to be deleted from the model is nonbinding, the current optimal solution will not change. If it is binding, however, the problem must be re-solved. Since the problem is less restrictive, the new optimal solution will generate optimal objective function at least as good as that to the original model.

Deletion of a Variable

If the variable to be deleted is zero in the optimal solution, deleting it will not affect the optimal solution. If the value of the variable is not zero in the optimal solution, the problem must be re-solved. Deleting a variable that was nonzero in the original optimal solution will result in a worse objective function value or one that is at best no better than the original objective function value.

Addition of a Variable

When a variable is added, in most cases, the problem must be re-solved. There is, however, a **net marginal profit** procedure that can determine whether the addition of the new variable will have any effect on the optimal solution. Net marginal profit is the difference between the objective function coefficient and the total marginal cost of the resources (calculated using the current values of the shadow prices).

To illustrate, suppose that a new product, Big Squirts, requiring three pounds of plastic and five minutes of production time, can be produced, yielding a profit of $10 per dozen. The new model is:

$$
\begin{array}{lllll}
\text{MAXIMIZE} & 8X_1 + 5X_2 + 10X_3 & & \\
\text{ST} & 2X_1 + X_2 + 3X_3 & \leq & 1000 & \text{(Plastic)} \\
& 3X_1 + 4X_2 + 5X_3 & \leq & 2400 & \text{(Production time)} \\
& X_1 + X_2 + X_3 & \leq & 700 & \text{(Total units)} \\
& X_1 - X_2 + & \leq & 350 & \text{(Space Ray/Zapper mix)} \\
& X_1, X_2, X_3 & \geq & 0 &
\end{array}
$$

The shadow prices for the constraints turn out to be $3.40, $0.40, $0, and $0, respectively. Thus, the net marginal profit for the production of a dozen Big Squirts is:

$$\$10 - ((\$3.40)(3) + (\$0.40)(5) + (\$0)(1) + (\$0)(0)) = -\$2.20$$

Hence, it would not be profitable to produce Big Squirts, and the current solution of producing 320 dozen Space Rays and 360 dozen Zappers remains optimal. If the profit per dozen Big Squirts had been $15, however, the net marginal profit would have been $2.80. This would indicate that there is a new optimal solution, which includes the production of Big Squirts, yielding a higher optimal profit.

Changes in the Left-Hand Side Coefficients

When a left-hand side coefficient is changed, the entire feasible region is reshaped. If the change is made to a coefficient in a nonbinding constraint, the first step is to ascertain whether the current optimal solution satisfies the modified constraint. If it does, it remains the optimal solution to the revised model; if it does not, or if the change is made in a coefficient of a binding constraint, both the optimal solution and the shadow prices change in ways that are more complex to calculate than changes resulting from modifications to objective function coefficients or right-hand side values. In this case, the model must be re-solved.

8.5 USING EXCEL SOLVER TO FIND AN OPTIMAL SOLUTION AND ANALYZE RESULTS

In this section, we illustrate the use of Excel's Solver to determine an optimal solution for the Galaxy Industries model and discuss the information generated by its sensitivity reports. The step-by-step procedure outlined here is very valuable, for it can be used to solve any linear model with any number of decision variables.

Solver is an option found in the Tools menu. If you do not see Solver listed, you must check the Solver Add-In box of the Add-Ins option under the Tools menu. If you do not see this option listed, you may have to re-install part or all of Excel using the disks that include the Solver option.

To use Solver, designate cells to contain:

- The values of the decision variables (known as **changing** or **adjustable cells**)
- The value of the objective function (known as the **target cell**)
- The total value of the left-hand side of the constraints

The cells for the objective function value and the left hand side values contain formulas that can be written as the sum of several terms. While the complete formulas can be entered explicitly, using Excel's SUM and SUMPRODUCT functions usually simplifies the input.

We shall use the spreadsheet developed in Figure 8.13 to solve the Galaxy Industries model. Although color coding and boxing cells can have an impact on the effect of the presentation of the spreadsheet (we discuss this in more detail in Chapter 9), here we concentrate on the basics of Solver.

Begin by entering the data for the model as shown. Designate cells B4 and C4 as the adjustable cells that will contain the values of the decision variables for Space Rays and Zappers. Cell D6 will be "programmed" to contain the value of the objective function, and cells D7 to D10 (written as D7:D10) will be programmed to contain the left-hand side of the constraints.

Entering Formulas for the Objective Function and Left-Hand Side Values

The formula for the total profit in cell D6 could be written as B4*B6 + C4*C6. This is fine when there are only two variables. But when there are many variables, this is more easily done using the SUMPRODUCT function of Excel. This function has the form 5SUMPRODUCT(*array1*, *array2*). Here array 1 and array 2 are rows or columns of

---

FIGURE 8.13   Excel Spreadsheets for Galaxy Industries

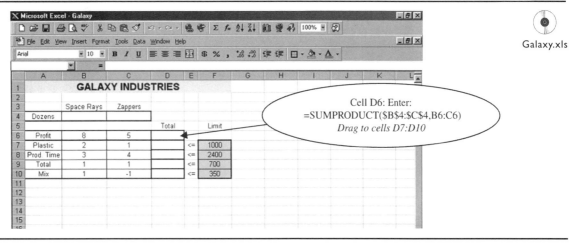

equal length.[4] The arrays can be entered by highlighting the appropriate cells (cells B4 and C4 and cells B6 and C6 in this case) using the left mouse key. Thus, as shown in Figure 8.13, for cell D6, we enter:

$$=\text{SUMPRODUCT}(\textbf{B4:C4,B6:C6})$$

Cells D7, D8, D9, and D10 will contain the total on the left side for the plastic, production time, total production, and mix constraints, respectively, resulting from a given solution. Each has a formula similar to that in cell D6 with the same first array (B4:C4) and a second array that is relative to the row. To easily enter these formulas, return to cell D6. Highlight only the first array (B4:C4) of the formula in the formula bar and press the F4 function key at the top of the keyboard. This makes these cell references absolute by inserting $ signs. After pressing Enter, the formula in cell D6 is now:

$$=\text{SUMPRODUCT}(\textbf{\$B\$4:\$C\$4,B6:C6})$$

When we drag this formula to cells D7, D8, D9, and D10, the resulting respective formulas in those cells give the total left-hand side for each of the constraints. The formulas in these cells are shown in Table 8.6.[5]

We now call Solver from the Tools menu. This gives the dialogue box shown in Figure 8.14.

TABLE 8.6 Cell Formulas in Figure 8.13

Cell	Quantity	Formula	Excel Formula
D6	Total Weekly Profit	$8X_1 + 5X_2$	=SUMPRODUCT($B$4:$C$4,B6:C6)
D7	Total Plastic Used Weekly	$2X_1 + 1X_2$	=SUMPRODUCT($B$4:$C$4,B7:C7)
D8	Total Production Minutes Used Weekly	$3X_1 + 4X_2$	=SUMPRODUCT($B$4:$C$4,B8:C8)
D9	Total Weekly Production	$1X_1 + 1X_2$	=SUMPRODUCT($B$4:$C$4,B9:C9)
D10	Amount Space Ray Production Exceeds Zapper Production Each Week	$1X_1 - 1X_2$	=SUMPRODUCT($B$4:$C$4,B10:C10)

FIGURE 8.14

Solver Dialogue Box

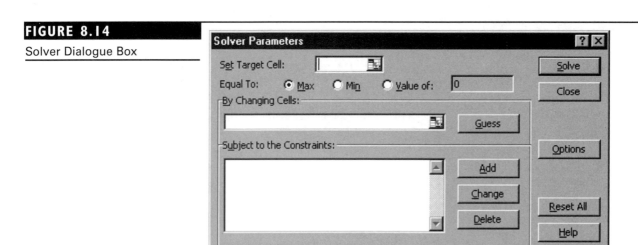

---

[4] If one of the arrays is a row and the other is a column, the equivalent formula is =MMULT(array1, array2), where array 1 is the *row* and array 2 is the *column*.

[5] Alternatively, we could have *defined* the word **Dozens** to be cells B4:C4 by highlighting these cells and then going to **Insert** menu and selecting **Name**, then **Define** and click OK. The formula in cell D6 would now be programmed as =SUMPRODUCT(Dozens,B6:C6) which would be dragged to cells D7, D8, D9, and D10.

Filling In the Solver Dialogue Box

Step 1: Set Target Cell

The target cell is the cell containing the value of the objective function. This cell must have a formula in it. For this model, this is cell D6 since it will contain the total weekly profit.

With the cursor in the Set Target Cell box: Click on Cell D6.

Step 2: Equal To

This tells Solver whether you want to find a solution that maximizes or minimizes the value of the objective function or find a solution that gives a particular value for the objective function. In linear programming we are always seeking to maximize or minimize the objective function value. For this model, we wish to maximize cell D6.

Leave the button for Max highlighted.

Step 3: By Changing Cells

Changing cells are the cells that contain the decision variables. Solver will return values to these cells that optimize the objective function subject to the constraints entered below.[6] For this model the decision variables are in cells B4 and C4.

**With the cursor in the By Changing Cells box:
Highlight Cells B4 and C4.**

Step 4: Subject to the Constraints

To enter constraints we click the Add button. This brings up the Add Constraint dialogue box shown in Figure 8.15.

Note that the default direction for a constraint is "≤," but this can be changed by clicking on the arrow of the drop down box. Options include "≤," "=," "≥," "int," and "bin." The last two options allow us to restrict a Cell Reference to be integer-valued or binary (0 or 1), respectively.

In the Cell Reference box, designate the cell containing the value for the left side of the constraint. In the Constraint box, input a number, a formula, or a cell containing the right side of the constraint. Several constraints can be entered at one time as long as they have the same direction. For our model, all the constraints are "≤," and thus we input them all at once.

FIGURE 8.15

The Add Constraint Dialogue Box

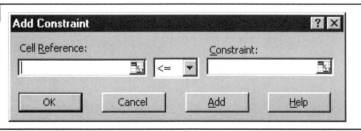

---

[6] Note that if formulas are entered in any of the cells designated as Changing Cells, Solver will simply ignore these formulas.

> **With the cursor in the Cell Reference box: Highlight cells D7 through D10. Leave the direction as "≤." With the cursor in the Constraint box: Highlight cells F7 through F10.**

If more constraints were to be added, we would click **Add** and follow the same procedure. When we are done entering constraints in the Add Constraint dialogue box and click [OK].

Step 5: Options

Clicking Options brings up the dialogue box shown in Figure 8.16.

This dialogue box allows us to reset several parameters of a technical nature that are beyond the scope of our discussion here. However, it is important that we designate that the variables are restricted to be "≥0" (Assume Non-Negative) and that the problem be solved specifically as a linear program rather than a general mathematical programming model (Assume Linear). Doing these two things allows relevant "what-if" sensitivity analyses to be generated. Check these boxes and click [OK].

Step 6: Solve

Figure 8.17 shows the completed Solver dialogue box for the Galaxy Industries model.

FIGURE 8.16   The Solver Options Dialogue Box

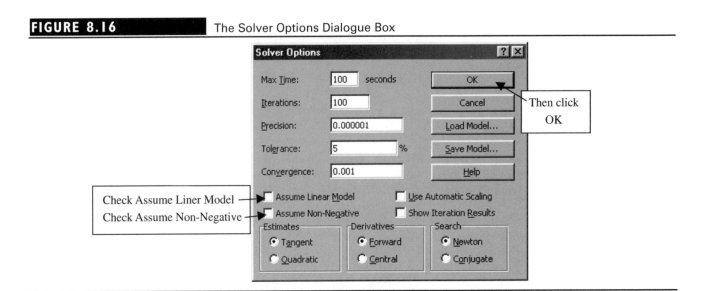

FIGURE 8.17

Completed Solver Dialogue Box for Galaxy Industries

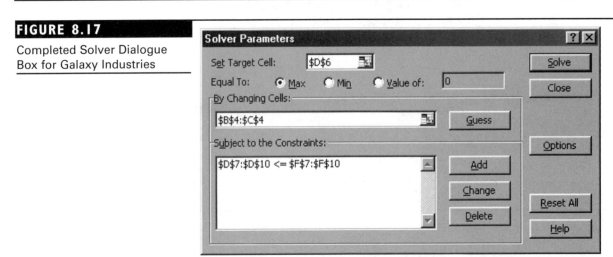

To solve for the optimal solution, click  .

The values in the spreadsheet are changed to reflect the optimal solution, the optimal value of the objective function, and the total left-hand side values in their respective cells.

Step 7: Reports

On top of the spreadsheet is the Solver Results dialogue box shown in Figure 8.18.

This indicates that an optimal solution was found, it also asks which reports we wish to have generated. The two reports that are of interest to us are the Answer Report and the Sensitivity Report. Highlight them and click 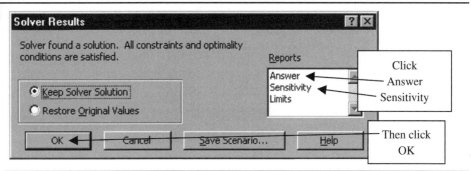 .

We are finally done! Now let us analyze the results.

Analyzing the Excel Spreadsheet

Figure 8.19 shows the optimal Excel spreadsheet for the Galaxy Industries model.

FIGURE 8.18

Solver Results Dialogue Box

FIGURE 8.19   Optimal Excel Spreadsheet for Galaxy Industries

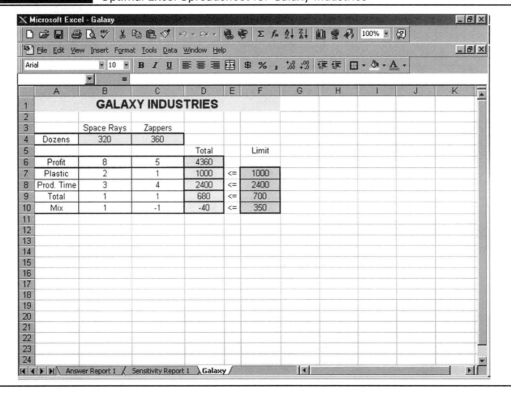

From this spreadsheet we can see that the optimal solution for this model is:

■ Produce 320 dozen Space Rays (cell B4) and 360 dozen Zappers (cell C4) weekly

■ Total weekly profit = $4360 (cell D6)

From column D, we see that this solution uses all 1000 pounds of plastic (cell D7) and all 2400 production minutes (cell D8). Since these two constraints hold as *equalities* at the optimal solution, they are said to have *no slack* and they are the *binding constraints*. The left side of the total production constraint is 680 (cell D9), and it indicates that there is a *slack* of 20 for the total production constraint (calculated by subtracting the left-side value (680) from right-side limit for the constraint (700)). Similarly, the slack for the mix constraint is 350 –(–40) = 390.

The Answer Report

The above information is summarized in the Answer Report. Clicking on the Answer Report tab at the bottom of the spreadsheet gives the window shown in Figure 8.20.

The Answer Report is divided into three sections: the Target Cell section, the Adjustable Cells section, and the Constraints section. What appears in the **Name** column of each of these sections is a combination of the last nonnumeric cell to the left and the last nonnumeric cell above the corresponding cell entry.

In the **Target Cell** Section, the optimal value of the objective function is given in the column labeled **Final Value**. Similarly, the optimal values for the decision variables are found in the **Final Value** column of the **Adjustable Cells** section.

In the **Constraints** section, the **Cell Value** column gives the total values of the left side of the constraints (i.e., the values in cells D7, D8, D9, and D10). The information entered in the Constraint Dialogue Box of Solver is given in the **Formula** column. The **Slack** column shows the amount of slack for each constraint. Note that if the slack is

---

FIGURE 8.20   Galaxy Industries Answer Report

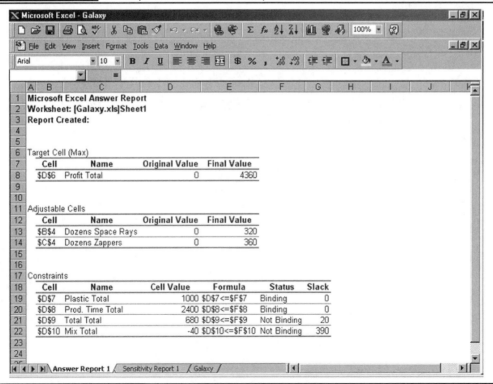

0, the word "Binding" is printed in the **Status** column; "Not Binding" is printed when the slack is positive.

The Sensitivity Report

The Sensitivity Report shown in Figure 8.21 contains the relevant information concerning the effects of changes to either an objective function coefficient or a right-hand side value as discussed in Section 8.4. The Adjustable Cells section includes the reduced costs and ranges of optimality for objective function coefficients (expressed in terms of Allowable Increases and Allowable Decreases). The Constraints section details the shadow prices and ranges of feasibility for right-hand side values (again expressed in terms of Allowable Increases and Allowable Decreases). This report can be thought of as the linear programming equivalent of a *marginal analysis* in economics, as the results deal with the effects of making *one and only one parameter value change* to the model.

Note that in Figure 8.21 there is a value of "1E+30" for the Allowable Increase for the total production and mix constraints. "1E+30" is Excel's way of saying "infinity." That is, the range of feasibility for the total production is from $700 - 20 = 680$ to infinity, and the range of feasibility for the mix constraint is from $350 - 390 = -40$ to infinity.

8.6 USING COMPUTER OUTPUT TO GENERATE A MANAGEMENT REPORT

Given the computer solution to the problem faced by Galaxy Industries, the following report can be prepared for Hal Barnes, Galaxy's production manager. This report compares the results of the recommended policy to those of the current policy at Galaxy Industries. It not only summarizes the results but also details the distribution of the resources as well as sensitivity issues that might be of interest to management. The statements made about the shadow price for plastic and production hours outside their ranges of feasibility are based on completely re-solving the problem.

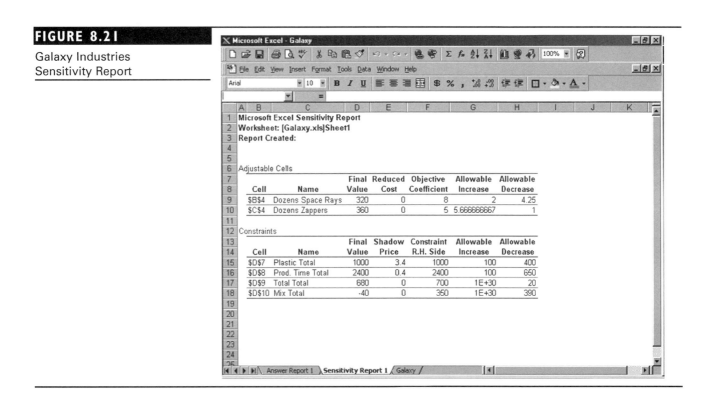

FIGURE 8.21

Galaxy Industries
Sensitivity Report

·SCG·

STUDENT CONSULTING GROUP

MEMORANDUM

To: Hal Barnes, Production Manager
Galaxy Industries

From: Student Consulting Group

Subj: Optimal Production Quantities for Space Rays and Zappers

Galaxy Industries wishes to determine production levels for its Space Ray and Zapper water guns, which will maximize the company's weekly profit. It is our understanding that production of these products occurs in batches of one dozen each; however, any batch not completed in a given week is considered "work in progress" and will be finished as the beginning of the following week.

Physical production limitations include the amount of plastic (1000 pounds) and available production time (40 hours) to the company on a weekly basis. In addition, the company wishes to adhere to marketing recommendations that limit total production to 700 dozen units weekly and restrict weekly production of Space Rays to a maximum of 350 dozen more than the number of Zappers produced. Current weekly production levels of 450 dozen Space Rays and 100 dozen Zappers result in a $4100 weekly profit for Galaxy.

We have had the opportunity to determine the plastic and production time requirements for these products and to analyze Galaxy's situation. By assuming profit and production requirements are fixed and constant, we were able to solve this as a linear programming model using Excel.

Analysis and Recommendation

Based on the results of our model, we recommend that Galaxy change its production levels to the following:

Space Rays	320 dozen
Zappers	360
Weekly profit	$4360

The current and proposed policies are compared in Table I.

Table I. Current vs. Proposed Policies—Galaxy Industries

	Production (doz.)	Plastic (lb.)	Production Time (hr.)	Profit ($)
Current Policy (Weekly basis)				
Space Rays	450	900	22.50	$3,600
Zappers	100	100	6.67	$ 500
Total	550	1000	29.17	$4,100
Unused		0	10.83	
Proposed Policy (Weekly basis)				
Space Rays	320	640	16.00	$2,560
Zappers	360	360	24.00	$1,800
Total	680	1000	40.00	$4,360
Unused		0	0	

As this table indicates, both policies produce less than the limit of 700 dozen suggested by the marketing department. The proposed policy has a more balanced production of Space Rays and Zappers than the present production policy. Under the current policy, weekly production of Space Rays exceeds that of Zappers by the maximum limit of 350 dozen. Under the proposed plan, production of Zappers actually exceeds that of Space Rays by 40 dozen per week.

The $4360 weekly profit corresponding to the recommended production schedule represents a 6.34% (or $260) increase in weekly profit, or $13,520 annually. This amount could be used to increase marketing of the current products, fund production of the new Big Squirt model under development, or lease more efficient machines to improve product profit contributions.

Although this model is based on profit projections of $8 per dozen Space Ray units and $5 per dozen Zapper units, our analysis reveals that our recommendation would reman unchanged unless the Space Ray profit is higher than $10.00 or lower than $3.75 (a 25% underestimation or a 59% overestimation), or the Zapper profit is higher than $10.67 or lower than $4.00 (a 113% underestimation or a 20% overestimation). We are confident that our profit projections fall well within this margin of error.

If Galaxy has the opportunity to purchase additional plastic from its vendor, our analysis shows that it will prove profitable to purchase up to 100 additional pounds of plastic, as long as the cost does not exceed $3.40 per pound over its normal cost. If the additional 100 pounds of plastic are purchased, giving a total of 1100 pounds of plastic, our recommendation is to produce 400 dozen Space Rays and 300 dozen Zappers.

If more than 1100 pounds of plastic were available, it would be profitable to purchase up to an additional 125 pounds of plastic (for a total of 1225 pounds) as long as the cost of these additional 125 pounds does not exceed $3.00 per pound. If a total of 1225 pounds of plastic were available, we recommend a production schedule of 525 dozen Space Rays and 175 dozen Zappers.

There is insufficient production time to use more than 1225 pounds of plastic while still adhering to to the marketing department recommendation that Space Ray production not exceed Zapper production by more than 350 dozen.

In lieu of purchasing plastic, if Galaxy considers scheduling overtime, we recommend that scheduling up to 1 2/3 hours of overtime weekly will be profitable if total overtime costs do not exceed $24 over the normal hourly wage rate. Using this overtime, the company should produce 300 dozen Space Rays and 400 Zappers weekly.

Production Recommendations with Additional Resources

Additional Resource	Space Rays (doz.)	Zappers (doz.)	Weekly Profit
150 pounds of plastic	400	300	$4700
225 pounds of plastic	525	175	$5075
1 2/3 overtime hours	300	400	$4400

These recommendations are based on changes in only one resource—plastic or overtime. The Student Consulting Group is available to analyze any combination of changes in plastic availability and overtime, changes in the marketing department's restrictions, or any other changes in the company's position. Please do not hesitate to call on us again for such analyses.

8.7 MODELS WITHOUT UNIQUE OPTIMAL SOLUTIONS—INFEASIBILITY, UNBOUNDEDNESS, AND ALTERNATE OPTIMAL SOLUTIONS

Not every linear programming model possesses a unique optimal solution. We already saw in Section 8.3 that when the objective function is parallel to a constraint, the problem can have more than one optimal solution. Under certain conditions, linear programming models may also have no feasible solutions at all, or they may have unbounded feasible regions giving the possibility of theoretically generating infinite profits. We now examine such situations.

Infeasibility

In some cases, a linear program possesses no feasible solutions whatsoever. For example, suppose that, in addition to the other constraints, management at Galaxy Industries wishes to produce at least 500 dozen Space Rays per week. This constraint is expressed as $X_1 \geq 500$ and is illustrated in Figure 8.22. As you can see, there are no feasible points satisfying all the constraints.

When infeasible models are detected by Excel Solver, the dialogue box shown in Figure 8.23 appears on the spreadsheet stating a feasible solution could not be found.

On the one hand, **infeasibility** can occur because the problem has been misformulated at either the modeling or the data input stage, or, as was the case above, the problem may be modeled correctly but is overconstrained; management has simply given the modeler a situation to which there is no solution. If infeasibility is detected,

---

FIGURE 8.22

Infeasibility—No Points Satisfy All Constraints

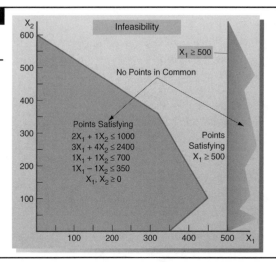

FIGURE 8.23

Infeasible Solution Dialogue Box

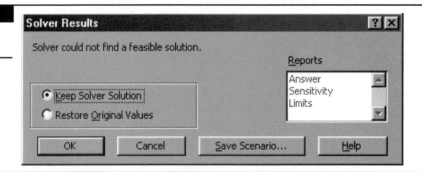

some of the constraints must be relaxed in order to obtain a feasible solution. Note that changing the objective function will never make an infeasible problem feasible.

Infeasibility

A model that has no feasible points is an *infeasible* model.

Unboundedness

Consider the model for Galaxy Industries depicted in Figure 8.24. The model is constrained only by the nonnegativity constraints and the marketing constraint that Space Ray production should not exceed Zapper production by more than 350 dozen per week ($X_1 - X_2 \leq 350$). In this situation, the feasible region extends indefinitely, bounded only by the X_1 axis, the X_2 axis, and the functional constraint $X_1 - X_2 \leq 350$. Such a feasible region, which extends "forever" in a particular direction, is called an **unbounded feasible region**.

Problems with unbounded feasible regions may or may not possess optimal solutions. In Figure 8.24, we see that when the objective function line, MAXIMIZE $8X_1 + 5X_2$, is moved parallel outwardly through the feasible region, this gives ever-increasing objective function values. This is an example of a linear program with an **unbounded solution**.

When Excel's Solver detects that the model has an unbounded solution, the dialogue box shown in Figure 8.25 appears on the spreadsheet.

FIGURE 8.24

Unbounded Feasible Region for $X_1 - X_2 \leq 350$, $X_1 \geq 0$, $X_2 \geq 0$. Problem is unbounded if objective function is MAX $8X_1 + 5X_2$; problem has an optimal solution (0,0) if objective functions is MIN $8X_1 + 5X_2$

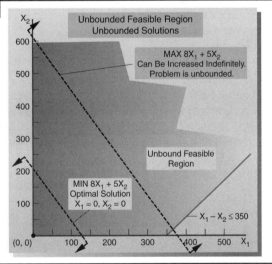

FIGURE 8.25

Unbounded Solution Dialogue Box

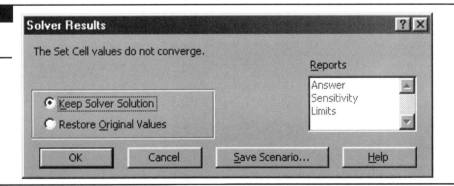

"The Set Cell values do not converge" is Excel's way of stating that the problem has an unbounded solution.

Unbounded Solutions

A linear program with an unbounded solution is one in which feasible solutions exist but there is no bound for the value of the objective function.

For a linear program to have an unbounded solution, the feasible region must be unbounded. But the fact that the feasible region is unbounded does not necessarily imply that the linear program has an unbounded solution. We see in Figure 8.24 that if the objective function were MINIMIZE $8X_1 + 5X_2$, although the feasible region is unbounded, (0,0) is the optimal point.

Linear programs with unbounded solutions are theoretically possible, but they do not occur in business situations. A business cannot make an infinite profit, or, in the case of a minimization problem, have an infinitely negative cost. If we determine that a linear programming formulation of a "real" business problem has an unbounded solution, a data entry error must have occurred or some constraint has been omitted from the formulation.

Alternate Optimal Solutions

In Section 8.3 we pointed out that alternate optimal solutions to a linear programming model can exist when the objective function line is parallel to a constraint. When alternate optimal solutions exist, many software packages alert the user to this event and assist the user in determining some, if not all, additional optimal extreme points. Unfortunately, Solver does not explicitly indicate when alternate optimal solutions exist.

However, when the Allowable Increase (or Allowable Decrease) for an objective function coefficient is 0, this usually indicates the existence of alternative optima.[7] This condition indicates that if the objective function coefficient were increased (decreased) even slightly, Excel would generate a new optimal solution. Because of the change to the objective function coefficient, this new solution would have a slightly higher (lower) value of the objective function. The trick is to get Excel to generate this solution without increasing (decreasing) the value of an objective function coefficient. This can be done as follows.

Generating Alternate Optimal Solutions with Excel

1. Observe that an Allowable Increase or Allowable Decrease for the objective function coefficient of some variable X_j is 0.

2. Add a constraint that sets the value of the objective function cell to the printed optimal value in that cell.

3. If the Allowable Increase = 0, change the objective to MAXIMIZE X_j by changing the target cell to the cell containing the value of X_j and setting the Equal To bullet to Max.

    If the Allowable Decrease = 0, change the objective to MINIMIZE X_j by changing the target cell to the cell containing the value of X_j and setting the Equal To bullet to Min.

---

[7] There are special cases in which these conditions hold, but there are no alternate optimal solutions.

We illustrate the procedure for the Galaxy Industries model in which the objective function has been changed to MAXIMIZE $8X_1 + 4X_2$. Using this objective function, Solver generates the worksheet shown in Figure 8.26. Note that these show an optimal solution of 450 dozen Space Rays and 100 dozen Zappers, yielding an optimal profit of $4000.

Step 1: We note in the Sensitivity Report in Figure 8.27, that there is an Allowable Decrease of 0 for the profit coefficient of Space Rays and an Allowable Increase of 0 for the profit coefficient for Zappers. Thus, we could choose MIN X_1 or MAX X_2 to generate an alternate optimal solution. We shall use the latter.

Step 2: Add the constraint that the value of the objective function (in cell D6) must equal 4000 to the Solver dialogue box. Go to Solver: Click ADD, enter the constraint as in Figure 8.28, and click OK.

FIGURE 8.26

An Optimal Solution with Objective Function: MAX $8X_1 + 4X_2$

Galaxy Alt1.xls

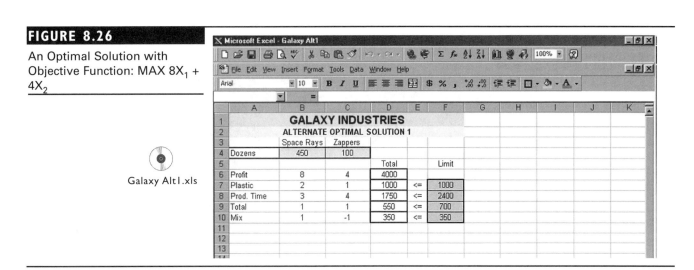

FIGURE 8.27

Sensitivity Report for Model with Objective Function: MAX $8X_1 + 4X_2$

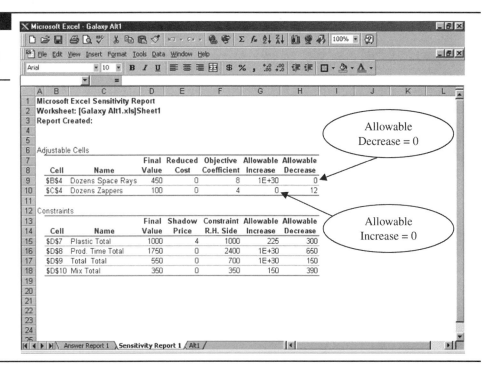

FIGURE 8.28

Adding the Constraint That the Objective Function Value Must Remain 4000

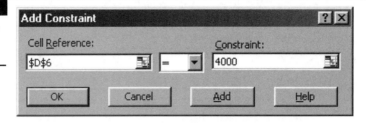

Step 3: Change the objective function to MAX X_2. Since X_2 is in cell C4, position the cursor in Set Target Cell and click on cell C4 as shown in Figure 8.29.

Clicking Solve gives the spreadsheet shown in Figure 8.30, reflecting a second optimal solution. This alternate optimal solution requires the production of 320 dozen Space Rays and 360 dozen Zappers. Notice that the solution has the same objective function value of $4000.

FIGURE 8.29

Resetting the Target Cell to MAX X_2

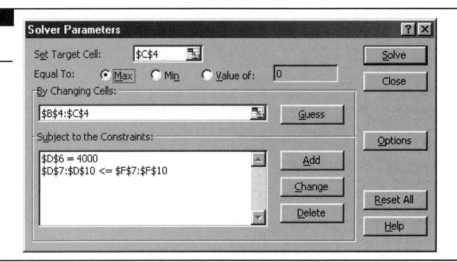

FIGURE 8.30

An Alternate Optimal Solution with Objective Function MAX $8X_1 + 4X_2$

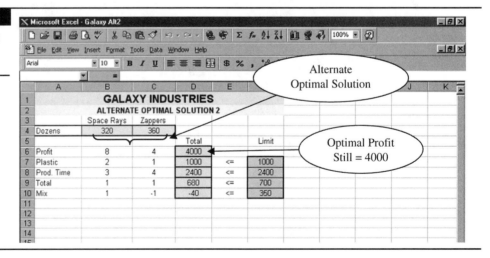

8.8 A MINIMIZATION PROBLEM

The Galaxy Industries problem is a typical example of a common linear programming model known as a product mix problem. In its simplest form, this type of problem has a maximization objective function and all "$\leq$" functional constraints. That is, management is trying to maximize something, but limited amounts of resources are restricting it or holding it back.

The inverse of this type of problem is one in which the objective function is to be minimized and the constraints are of the "$\geq$" variety. Problems with this structure have come to be known as diet problems. This is because finding a least cost diet that meets minimum nutritional standards was one of the earliest applications of linear programming, dating back to the World War II era. The following Navy sea ration problem is a simplified version of a diet problem.

NAVY SEA RATIONS

Navy Sea Rations.xls

The Department of the Navy has been downsizing and is looking for cost savings opportunities to meet mandated congressional budget cuts. One suggestion under consideration is to change the makeup of the content of Navy sea rations, the canned food supplies containing certain minimum daily requirement (MDR) of Vitamin A, Vitamin D, iron, and other nutrients, which combat troops carry into battle.

According to Texfoods, the current supplier of sea rations for the Navy, each two-ounce portion of its product supplies 20% of the required amount of Vitamin A, 25% of the MDR of Vitamin D, and 50% of the required amount of iron. Each portion costs the Navy $0.60. Because all minimum standards must be met in each serving, the current sea ration container must contain 10 ounces of the Texfoods product (to meet the MDR of Vitamin A). This costs the Navy $3.00 (=5 × $0.60) per serving.

The Navy is considering switching to another product from a different supplier, Calration. A two-ounce portion of Calration costs $0.50 and provides 50% of the MDR of Vitamin A and 25% of the requirement of Vitamin D, but only 10% of the MDR for iron. Substituting the Calration product, the sea ration container would have to contain 20 ounces in order to meet the MDR for iron, costing the Navy $5.00 (=10 × $0.50) per serving.

One bright Navy lieutenant has suggested that a mixture of the two products might meet the overall standards at a lower cost than the current $3 per serving. The Navy has never worried about the taste of sea rations; hence, mixing them, either by combining them or by packing a portion of each, is an acceptable alternative. The lieutenant has been given permission to evaluate the data.

SOLUTION

The following is a brief synopsis of the problem posed by the lieutenant:

- Determine the amount of 2-ounce portions of each sea ration product in the mix.
- Minimize the total cost of the sea rations.
- Meet the MDR for Vitamin A, Vitamin D, and iron.

Decision Variables

The following decision variables must be included in the problem:

X_1 = number of 2-ounce portions of Texfoods product used in a serving of sea rations

X_2 = number of 2-ounce portions of Calration product used in a serving of sea rations

Objective Function

The objective is to minimize the total cost of a serving of sea rations. Since each 2-ounce serving of Texfoods costs \$0.60 and each 2-ounce serving of Calration costs \$0.50, the objective function is:

$$\text{MINIMIZE } .60X_1 + .50X_2$$

Constraints

Each 2-ounce portion of Texfoods product provides 20% of the MDR for Vitamin A; each 2-ounce portion of the Calration product provides 50%. If X_1 2-ounce portions of Texfoods and X_2 2-ounce portions of Calration are included in the sea rations, this would give $20X_1 + 50X_2$ percent of the MDR for Vitamin A. The constraint that at least 100% of the MDR of Vitamin A must be met can then be written as

$$\text{(The total percent of Vitamin A)} \geq (100\%)$$
$$20X_1 + 50X_2 \geq 100$$

Similar constraints for Vitamin D and iron, respectively, are:

$$25X_1 + 25X_2 \geq 100$$

and

$$50X_1 + 10X_2 \geq 100$$

Together with the nonnegativity constraints, this gives us the following linear programming model:

$$
\begin{aligned}
\text{MINIMIZE} \quad & .60X_1 + .50X_2 \\
\text{ST} \quad & \\
& 20X_1 + 50X_2 \geq 100 \\
& 25X_1 + 25X_2 \geq 100 \\
& 50X_1 + 10X_2 \geq 100 \\
& X_1, X_2 \geq 0
\end{aligned}
$$

This problem is illustrated in Figure 8.31. Note that the feasible region is unbounded. Since the objective is to minimize the objective function, however, the objective function line is moved downward toward the origin, and the optimal point is (1.5,2.5).

FIGURE 8.31

Navy Sea Rations—Graphical Solution

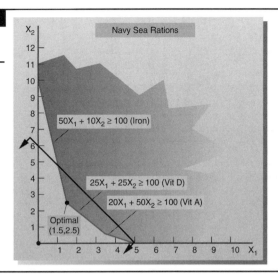

The Excel Spreadsheet

Figure 8.32 shows the Excel Spreadsheet and Solver Dialogue box for this model.

The only cell programmed is the target cell D7 giving the total cost. Its formula is dragged to cells D8, D9, and D10 to give the total Vitamin A, Vitamin D, and iron, respectively, in a serving.

In the Solver dialogue box we highlighted the MIN button, and in the Options box we checked, Assume Linear Model and Assume Non-Negative. Figure 8.33 gives the optimal spreadsheet for the model.

FIGURE 8.32

Spreadsheets for Navy Sea Rations

Navy Sea Rations.xls

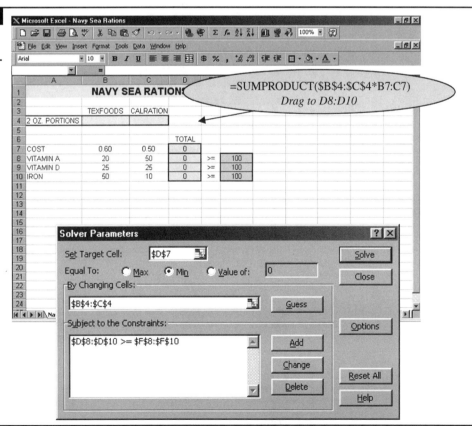

Optimal Spreadsheet for Navy
Sea Rations

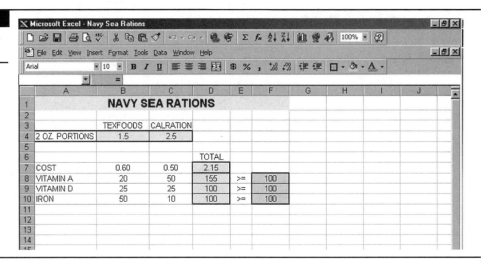

Analysis of Excel Output

The Optimal Solution

From the spreadsheet in Figure 8.33 we see that the optimal solution is to mix 1.5 portions (=3 ounces) of Texfoods product with 2.5 portions (=5 ounces) of Calration product. This 8-ounce mixture meets the MDR's for Vitamin D and iron (the binding constraints). The percentage of Vitamin A in the mixture is $20(1.5) + 50(2.5) = 155\%$, a *surplus* of $155\% - 100\% = 55\%$ above the MDR for Vitamin A. The total cost per serving is $2.15, an $0.85, or 28.33% (=$0.85/$3.00), reduction in the cost of sea rations from the current $3 level.

An additional benefit of this solution is the reduced quantity of sea rations a sailor must carry—from 10 ounces to 8 ounces per serving. This reduction in weight means a significant reduction in the fuel consumption required to transport the sea rations to the sailors. Given the large supply of sea rations purchased by the Navy, this adds up to a considerable cost savings.

Let us now analyze the output given on the Sensitivity Report shown in Figure 8.34.

Sensitivity Report for Navy Sea
Rations

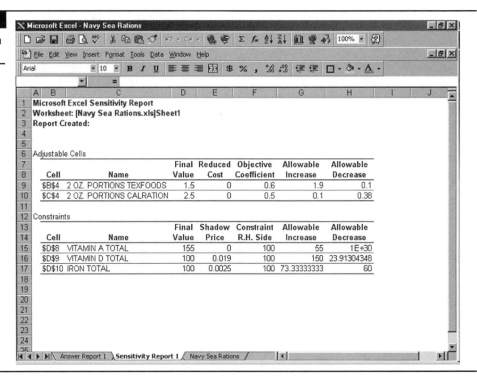

Reduced Costs

Because both decision variables are positive in the optimal solution, the reduced costs are zero. If one of the variables had been zero, then, for a minimization problem, increasing its value by one unit would increase the minimized value of the objective function; that is, the reduced cost for a minimization problem would be positive.

Ranges of Optimality

From Figure 8.34, we can make the following observations regarding the ranges of optimality for 2-ounce portions of the Texfoods and Calrations products. These are summarized in Table 8.7.

Shadow Prices and Ranges of Feasibility

Figure 8.34 also gives us information about the effect of the required percentages of Vitamin A, Vitamin D, and iron on the total cost of the mixture. These are summarized in Table 8.8.

TABLE 8.7   Ranges of Optimality

Unit Cost for 2 oz. of	Current Value	Allowable Increase	Allowable Decrease	Range of Optimality	Interpretation (if no other changes are made)
Texfoods	$0.60	$1.90	$0.10	$0.50 ↔ $2.50	If the cost of 2 oz. of Texfoods is between $0.50 and $2.50, it is optimal to blend 1.5 portions (3 oz.) of Texfoods with 2.5 portions (5 oz.) of Calrations.
Calration	$0.50	$0.10	$0.38	$0.12 ↔ $0.60	If the cost of 2 oz. of Calration is between $0.12 and $0.60, it is optimal to blend 1.5 portions (3 oz.) of Texfoods with 2.5 portions (5 oz.) of Calrations.

TABLE 8.8   Shadow Prices and Ranges of Feasibility

Nutrient	Shadow Price	Current Requirement	Allowable Increase	Allowable Decrease	Range of Feasibility	Interpretation (if no other changes are made)
Vitamin A	$0.000	100%	55%	Infinite	−∞ ↔ 155%	As long as the mixture must contain less than 155% of the MDR for Vitamin A, the optimal total cost will remain $2.15.
Vitamin D	$0.019	100%	150%	23.91%	76.09% ↔ 250%	As long as the mixture must contain between 76.09% and 250% of the MDR for Vitamin D, the total cost of $2.15 will increase (decrease) by $0.019 for each 1% increase (decrease) in the required percent of MDR for Vitamin D from 100%
Iron	$0.0025	100%	73.33%	60%	40% ↔ 173.33%	As long as the mixture must contain between 60% and 173.33% of the MDR for Iron, the total cost of $2.15 will increase (decrease) by $0.0025 for each 1% increase (decrease) in the required percent of MDR for Iron from 100%.

8.9 INTEGER LINEAR PROGRAMMING (ILP) MODELS

Thus far we have focused on the formulation and analysis of linear programming problems that allow decision variables to take on a continuous range of values within the confines of the other constraints. For many models, however, some or all of the decision variables make sense only if they are restricted to integer values. These are known as **integer linear programming (ILP)** models. The number of aircraft United Airlines will purchase this year from McDonnell-Douglas; the number of machines needed for production at Galaxy Industries; the number of trips a company president will take to potential new markets in the Pacific Rim; the number of police personnel to be assigned to the night shift in Portland, Oregon—these are all examples of integer decision variables.

When Are Integer Variables Required?

It is easy to reason that decision variables expressed in pounds, inches, hours, acres, and the like, need not be restricted to integers. But even if a decision variable represents airplanes, televisions, or desks, depending on the context of the problem, it still may not be necessary to require that these variables take on integer values.

For example, an integer requirement would be essential for the number of MD-11 aircraft McDonnell-Douglas sells to United Airlines. However, the number of MD-11s McDonnell-Douglas produces in a year need not necessarily be an integer. If McDonnell-Douglas's optimal annual production of MD-11s were 24.37, the .37 or an aircraft would be considered work in progress to be completed at a later date. Thus, when determining whether or not a variable should be integer-valued, we should ask, "Does the model represent a one-time decision or an ongoing operation?"

Designating Integer Variables in Excel

It is easy to designate variables as "Integer" when using Excel Solver by using the Add Constraint dialogue box. In the Cell Reference section we denote the cells containing the variables that must be integer. Then we use the pull down menu in the middle input area and select "int." Solver will then print "integer" in the Constraint side of the box (see Figure 8.35).

The integer constraints will appear in the Subject to the Constraints section of the Solver dialogue box. To generate the optimal integer solution we click Solve.

You may notice, particularly for larger problems, that it takes Solver longer to generate the optimal solution when there are integer variables than it would if no integer variables were present. More computation time is required when integer variables are

FIGURE 8.35

Defining Variables to Be Integer

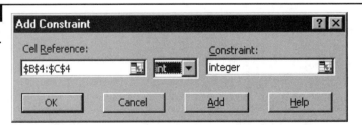

present because the solution procedure Solver uses actually solves many linear programming models just to generate the one optimal integer solution. Furthermore, when we select the Sensitivity Report option, once Solver has determined the optimal solution the box shown in Figure 8.36 appears.

Rounding

Because of the longer computation times and the lack of sensitivity analyses, it may be worthwhile to solve the model as a linear programming model and round the noninteger solution. However, the rounded solution may be infeasible. Even if the rounded solution is feasible, there is no way of telling whether it is the optimal integer solution.

Difficulties with Models Requiring Integer Variables

Why is it important to designate whether or not a variable is required to be integer-valued? It might seem that restricting variables to integers would actually simplify the solution process, since a finite[8] number of integer points exist, compared to an infinite number for linear programming models.

But, alas, much is lost when integer requirements are imposed. Compared to linear programming solution methods, unless the problem has some special structure, algorithms for solving models with integer-valued decision variables are more complex, require much more computation time, and as we have seen, do not yield valuable sensitivity analysis information. Hence, if an integer programming formulation is not essential, it may be worthwhile to keep a linear programming structure. Thus when rounding is done, one of three situations will occur.

Possible Outcomes from Rounding to Integer Values

1. The rounded point may be infeasible.
2. The rounded point may be feasible but not optimal.
3. The rounded point may be the optimal point.

So is rounding ever done? The answer to this question is an emphatic, "yes," particularly if the values of the positive decision variables are relatively large and the values of the objective function coefficients are relatively small. For example, suppose a producer of multiple vitamins used linear programming to determine the production quantities of 50-tablet, 100-tablet, and 500-tablet bottles to be produced

FIGURE 8.36

Dialogue Box Indicating No Sensitivity Information for Integer Models

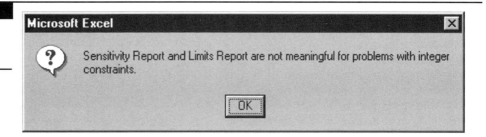

---

[8] If the feasible region is unbounded, at least the number of feasible solutions is countably infinite, as opposed to continuously infinite.

during a production run. If the unit profits for these items are $1.20, $1.75, and $4.80, respectively, and the linear program indicates that 12,253.43, 34,876.90, and 22,623.47 bottles, respectively, should be produced, then rounding these quantities will have little effect on either the value of the objective function or the viability of the constraints.

Of course, the feasibility of any rounded solution should be checked. If the rounded solution does, in fact, violate some constraints, we need to determine whether the violations are significant. For instance, in the vitamin example, suppose one constraint is a marketing restriction requiring that no product is to account for more than 50% of production. If the above solution were rounded to 12,253 50-tablet bottles, 34,877 100-tablet bottles, and 22,623 500-tablet bottles, the proportion of 100-tablet bottles would now be 50.001%—is this so terrible?

On the other hand, if rounding yields a solution that is simply not possible (there is just not enough of a particular resource to achieve this solution), the rounded solution would have to be altered. In this case, a trial-and-error approach might be used.

Although rounding and using trial and error is not guaranteed to produce the true optimal integer solution, it frequently yields a "pretty good" solution. It is important to check the difference between the objective function values of the optimal LP solution and the result of rounding using trial and error. If the difference is small, it may not be worthwhile to use an integer programming optimization procedure that could tie up computer resources for long periods with no guarantee that the optimal result would be better or even different.

An ILP Model

To illustrate these concepts, consider the problem faced by Boxcar Burger Restaurants.

BOXCAR BURGER RESTAURANTS

Boxcar.xls

Boxcar Burger is a new chain of fast-food establishments planning to expand to locations in and around the Washington, D.C., area. Although the food is of high quality and geared to today's health concerns, the main attraction is the boxcar motif. In downtown locations, the interiors of former office buildings are decorated to resemble the inside of a boxcar, while at suburban locations, fast-food sites are remodeled into Boxcar Burger restaurants by using actual boxcars.

The company has $27 million available for the expansion. Each suburban location requires a $2 million investment, and each downtown location a $6 million investment. It is projected that, after expenses, the net weekly profit generated by suburban locations open 24 hours per day will average $12,000. The downtown locations will be open only 12 hours per day, but because of the extremely high customer volume during the workweek, projections indicate that net weekly profits will average $20,000. The company wishes to open at least two restaurants downtown.

Boxcar Burger currently employs 19 managers to run the restaurants. Each suburban location will require three managers for its 24-hour per day operation, whereas the company feels it can get by with just one manager for each downtown location.

Boxcar Burger would like to determine how many restaurants it should open in suburban and downtown Washington, D.C., locations in order to maximize its total net weekly profit.

SOLUTION

The following is a brief synopsis of the problem facing Boxcar Burger:

- Boxcar Burger must decide how many suburban and downtown locations to open in the Washington, D.C., area.
- It wishes to maximize its total average net weekly profits.
- Boxcar Burger's total investment cannot exceed $27 million.
- At least two downtown restaurants are to be opened.
- No more than the current 19 managers can be assigned.

Decision Variables

Let,

X_1 = number of suburban Boxcar Burger restaurants to be opened
X_2 = number of downtown Boxcar Burger restaurants to be opened

Objective Function

The objective is to maximize total average net weekly profits:

$$\text{MAX } 12{,}000X_1 + 20{,}000X_2$$

Constraints

The following constraints apply:

1. The total investment cannot exceed $27 million. In $1,000,000's this can be written as

$$2X_1 + 6X_2 \leq 27$$

2. The number of downtown restaurants is at least 2:

$$X_2 \geq 2$$

3. The number of managers needed cannot exceed 19:

$$3X_1 + X_2 \leq 19$$

The Mathematical Model

Clearly, the number of restaurants opened must be an integer. Thus, the complete mathematical programming formulation for the Boxcar Burger problem is:

$$
\begin{aligned}
\text{MAX} \quad & 12{,}000X_1 + 20{,}000X_2 \\
\text{ST} \quad & \\
& 2X_1 + 6X_2 \leq 27 \\
& \qquad\quad X_2 \geq 2 \\
& 3X_1 + \;\; X_2 \leq 19 \\
& X_1, X_2 \geq 0 \text{ and integer}
\end{aligned}
$$

To solve this model we shall use the spreadsheet shown in Figure 8.37.

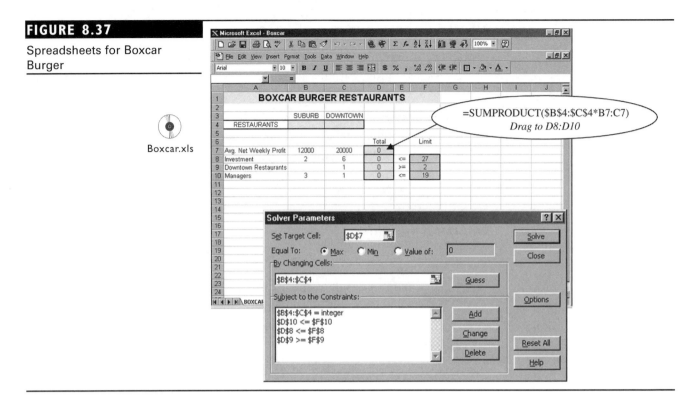

The target cell (D7), is programmed to give the total average net weekly profit as shown in Figure 8.37. We then drag this formula to cells D8, D9, and D10 to give the total investment (in $1,000,000's), the total number of downtown restaurants, and the total number of managers required, respectively. Note that since the constraints are not ordered by type (i.e., the two "$\leq$" do not follow one another), we add them one at a time, each time clicking the Add button in the Solver dialogue box.

We also click in the Options box and check, Assume Linear Model and Assume Non-Negative.

Clicking Solve in the Solver dialogue box results in the spreadsheet in Figure 8.38, showing that it is optimal to open four suburban restaurants and three downtown restaurants, netting the company a total average weekly profit of $108,000.

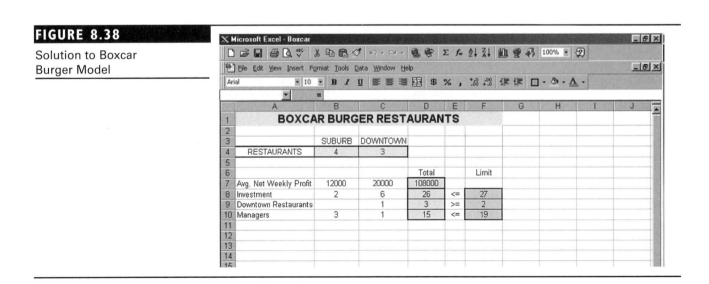

A Graphical Analysis

Figure 8.39 shows that the feasible region for the integer model is the set of 13 integer points that fall within the linear programming feasible region. Thus, the objective is to determine which of these 13 feasible points gives the highest value for the objective function. For a small problem like this one, we could simply enumerate all 13 points shown on the graph, substitute their values into the objective function, and select the one giving the highest value. However, for larger problems, the number of feasible points can be in the thousands, millions, or even billions, and simply identifying all feasible points is itself quite a task. Thus, a total enumeration approach is impractical.

Let us consider the rounding approach. If the model is solved as a linear programming model, ignoring the integer constraints, the optimal solution is $X_1 = 5\ 7/16$, $X_2 = 2\ 11/16$, giving an optimal weekly profit of $12,000(5\ 7/16) + 20,000(2\ 11/16) = \$119,000$. If both fractions are *rounded up*, the integer solution attained is $X_1 = 6$, $X_2 = 3$. If the solution is *rounded off* to the nearest whole number, the integer solution generated is $X_1 = 5$, $X_2 = 3$. From Figure 8.39, we see that neither of these points is in the linear programming feasible region; that is, each violates at least one of the functional constraints. If, however, both fractions are *rounded down*, the resulting integer solution is $X_1 = 5$, $X_2 = 2$. While this solution gives a "relatively good" objective function value of $12,000(5) + 20,000(2) = \$100,000$, this falls \$8000 short of the \$108,000 generated by the optimal integer point of $X_1 = 4$, $X_2 = 3$.

We note two things from this discussion. First, in this case, no form of rounding gave the optimal integer solution. Second, the profit generated by the optimal integer solution is less than that of the optimal solution to the linear model. This is because although the integer linear program (ILP) model has the same functional constraints as the LP, it is more constrained by the addition of the two integer constraints: $X_1 = $ integer and $X_2 = $ integer.

Lack of Sensitivity Analysis

As we have mentioned, one of the ILP's biggest drawbacks is its lack of sensitivity analyses. For example, suppose we wished to find the range of values for the profit of suburban restaurants (currently \$12,000) which keeps the optimal ILP solution the same ($X_1 = 4$, and $X_2 = 3$). If we connect the feasible integer points that are "farthest

FIGURE 8.39

Integer Points in the Linear Programming Feasible Region. The optimal ILP solution is *not* one of the rounded solutions.

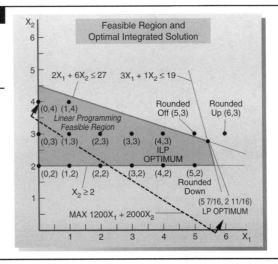

out" in all possible directions,[9] we can then attempt to apply the graphical techniques discussed in Section 8.5 to find the ranges of optimality for the objective function coefficients.

From Figure 8.40, we can reason that the point (4,3) will remain the optimal point as long as the objective function coefficients yield a slope between −1/3 (the slope of the line between (1,4) and (4,3)) and −1 (the slope of the line between (4,3) and (5,2)). You can verify that this implies that the range of optimality for the average weekly profit for suburban restaurants is between $6333.33 and $20,000 and that for downtown restaurants it is between $12,000 and $36,000.

The difficulty with this analysis is that we would have to know the "farthest-out" integer points, which itself is a computationally complex problem. Furthermore, the slope of the lines connecting these points usually has no relationship to the slopes of the lines formed by the functional constraints. In this model, for example, the slope of one of the lines restraining the objective function is −1. No functional constraint has this slope. The other restraining line has a slope of −1/3, which is only coincidentally the slope of the first functional constraint line.

Integer linear programming offers no parallel to shadow price analysis. In *linear programming*, a shadow price of $10 for a resource implies that the marginal improvement for each extra unit of the resource is $10, as long as the change occurs within the resource's range of feasibility. Two extra units of the resource would improve the objective function $20, and half an extra unit would improve it by $5. This is not the case for integer models, however. For example, in the Boxcar Burger model, consider the constraint for investment:

$$2X_1 + 6X_2 \leq 27 \ (\$1,000,000\text{'s})$$

Figure 8.41 shows that increasing the amount of investment will have no effect on the optimal solution until the investment equals $28 (million), an increase of $1 (million). Thus, if an extra $999,999.99 is invested, the optimal solution is still $X_1 = 4$, $X_2 = 3$, with a total average weekly profit of $108,000. Then with the next penny, the right-hand side of the investment constraint increases to $28 (million) and the optimal ILP solution becomes $X_1 = 5$, $X_2 = 3$. This results in a total average weekly profit of $12,000(5) + 20,000(3) = \$120,000$. Thus, for the first $999,999.99

FIGURE 8.40

Boxcar Burger—Connecting the "Farthest Out" Points

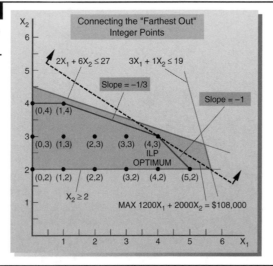

FIGURE 8.41

Boxcar Burger Investment
Constraint Changed to:
$2X_1 + 6X_2 \leq 28$

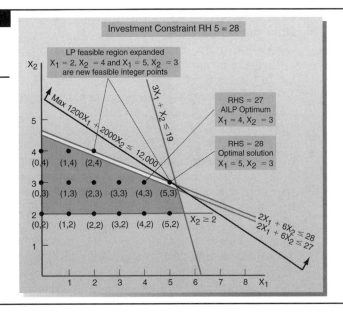

of additional investment, no additional profit is made; then with the next penny, there is an increase in profit of $12,000 per week!

This example points out that there is no pattern to the disjoint effects of changes to the objective function and right-hand side coefficients. When do changes occur, they occur in big "steps," rather than the smooth, marginal changes experienced in linear programming. Thus, unfortunately, when we contemplate changes in either objective function coefficients or right-hand side values, re-solving the problem is usually the only viable means for determining the resulting effect.

8.10 ALGEBRAIC SOLUTION APPROACHES FOR SOLVING LINEAR MODELS

In this chapter we have presented examples with only two decision variables so that we could motivate the discussion of linear and integer programming concepts graphically. However, Excel, as well as all other linear programming packages, can be used to solve problems with any number of variables and constraints, limited only by the capacity of the program and your computer.

But, of course, these packages do not solve the problems by drawing graphs and moving objective function lines until the last point of the feasible region is touched. Instead, these problems are solved algebraically. The most common solution procedure for linear programming models is the simplex method, first proposed by Dr. George Dantzig, circa 1947. In this approach, an extreme point is generated and evaluated for optimality. If it is found not to be optimal, using a simple but tedious procedure of adding multiples of one constraint equation to the others, an *adjacent* extreme point is generated with an improved value of the objective function. This process is repeated until it is determined that the last extreme point generated is optimal. The simplex method is the one used by Excel Solver to solve linear programming models. The details of this approach are outlined in Supplement CD3 on the accompanying CD-ROM.

Another method, proposed by Narendra Karmarkar circa 1985, first generates an interior point and then makes a series of movements to other interior points closer to the boundary. Ultimately, it approaches the optimal extreme point of the feasible region. This method is far more complex than the simplex method, but for many larger models, it has been shown to generate optimal solutions in a fraction of the time of the simplex method.

Various approaches may also be used to solve linear models with integer variables. Virtually all involve adding more and more linear constraints to the original set of functional constraints. Each time a new constraint is added, the problem is re-solved as a linear program and the optimal solution is checked for integrality. If it is not integer-valued, more constraints are added.

In one method, known as the cutting plane approach, each added constraint is guaranteed to be satisfied by all integer points in the original feasible region. A more popular solution method, however, is the branch and bound approach which is discussed in detail in Supplement CD4 on the accompanying CD-ROM. In this approach, when an optimal solution to a linear programming model has one or more noninteger variables, two new "branches" of the model are explored. In each branch a new constraint dealing with one of the noninteger variables is added, making the last optimal solution infeasible.

For example, in the Boxcar Burger model, the optimal solution to the linear model without integer constraints was $X_1 = 5\ 7/16$, $X_2 = 2\ 11/16$. We could now concentrate on X_1 and generate two new linear programming models. One would add $X_1 \geq 6$ to the current set of constraints, and the other would add $X_1 \leq =$ to the current set of constraints. Both of these new models would then be solved as linear programs with their optimal solutions checked for integer values. If the optimal solution to either or both still had noninteger values, the process would then be repeated.

SUMMARY

In this chapter we have introduced the concepts of building simple linear models (both with and without integer restrictions for the decision variables) and have shown how to solve linear models using the Solver feature from the Tools menu of Excel. We have pointed out that the linear approach can be used to model a variety of business situations. Additional examples having greater complexity are discussed in detail in Chapter 9.

For models without integer restrictions we have discussed the value of the information generated from Solver's Sensitivity Report, including:

Reduced Cost

The amount a variable's objective function coefficient must change in order for it to become positive in the optimal solution. It is also the amount the objective function value will be affected by increasing this variable by one unit.

Range of Optimality

The range of values for an objective function coefficient such that the optimal solution does not change.

Shadow Price

The per unit change to the optimal objective function value when a right-hand side value changes within its range of feasibility. If the resource's cost is included in the calculation of the objective function coefficients, the shadow price will represent a "premium" value beyond the current price of the resource.

Range of Feasibility

The range of values for a right-hand side coefficient within which the shadow prices are valid.

No sensitivity information is generated from the solution to integer models.

An important theoretical concept in linear programming is that of complementary slackness. For objective function coefficients, this principle states that, at optimality, either the value of a variable is 0 or its reduced cost is 0. For right-hand side coefficients, the complementary slackness principle states that, at optimality, either there is no slack (or surplus) on a given constraint or the value of the shadow price is 0.

For linear models with integer variables, the optimal integer solution is not always the one generated by rounding the optimal solution to the linear programming model. In fact, the rounded solution may not even be feasible. Instead, methods for solving integer models usually involve repeatedly solving linear models. Because of the time and complexity involved to solve integer models, it is often advantageous to solve the models as linear programming models absent the integer restrictions. Rounding and using trial error usually leads to a good, if not optimal, integer solution.

ON THE CD-ROM

- Excel spreadsheet for a trial-and-error approach to solving linear programming models — **Barnes.xls**
- Excel spreadsheets for solving basic linear programming models — **Galaxy.xls** / **Navy Sea Rations.xls**
- Excel spreadsheet for determining alternate optimal solutions — **Galaxy Alt1.xls**
- Excel spreadsheet for solving integer linear programming models — **Boxcar.xls**
- Duality — **Supplement CD2**
- The Simplex Method — **Supplement CD3**
- Branch and Bound Algorithms for Integer Linear Programming Models — **Supplement CD4**
- Problem Motivations — **Problem Motivations**
- Problems 41–50 — **Additional Problems/Cases**

PROBLEMS

Problems 1–30 can be formulated as linear programming models.

Problems 31–40 require the use of integer variables.

Most problems in these exercises require only two decision variables so that they may be solved graphically or using Excel. In Chapter 9 we focus on more complex problems requiring more than two decision variables.

1. PRODUCT PRODUCTION. Kite 'N String manufactures old-fashioned diagonal and box kites from high-strength paper and wood. Each diagonal kite, which nets the company a $3 profit, requires 8 square feet of paper and 5 linear feet of wood (including waste). Box kites net a $5 profit and, including waste, require 6 square feet of paper and 10 linear feet of wood. Each is packaged in similar boxes. This week Kite 'N String has 1500 boxes and capacity to tailor 10,000 square feet of paper and 12,000 linear feet of wood for kite production. How many of each type of kite do you recommend Kite 'N String produce this week?

2. MANUFACTURING. Golden Electronics manufactures several products, including 45-inch GE45 and 60-inch GE60 televisions. It makes a profit of $50 on each GE45 and $75 on each GE60 television produced. During each shift, Golden allocates up to 300 man-hours in its production area and 240 man-hours in its assembly area to manufacture the televisions. Each GE45 requires two man-hours in the production area and one man-hour in the assembly area, whereas each GE60 requires two man-hours in the production area and three man-hours in the assembly area.

a. What production levels of GE45 and GE60 television sets optimize the expected profit per shift? What is the optimal expected profit per shift?

b. What is the shadow price for extra assembly hours? Interpret.

c. Would the optimal solution change if the unit profit for GE60 televisions were increased to (i) $135? (ii) $300?

3. MANUFACTURING. Suppose that management at Golden Electronics (see problem 2) has decided to do extensive testing on every television manufactured to ensure its quality standards. Each GE45 television will require inspection time of 30 minutes and each GE60 television 45 minutes.

a. Reformulate the linear program for television production for Golden Electronics if management made available 80 hours for quality control inspections during each production run.

b. Give an optimal solution that manufactures as many GE60 television sets as possible.

c. Give an optimal solution that manufactures exactly three times as many GE45 television sets as GE60 television sets during a shift.

4. MANUFACTURING. Compaids, Inc. manufactures two types of slide-out keyboard trays for use with personal computers. Model C15 is designed for desktop use. It can stand alone, or it can fit under a desktop CPU or monitor. Model UN8 is designed to be mounted underneath a desk with screws. Both units are manufactured from laminated particle board supplied by SSS

Industries and use two slide assemblies purchased from Corrigation, Inc. The following table summarizes the wholesale selling price and requirements for each keyboard tray.

Model	Selling Price	Cost of Screws	Particle Board	Production Time
C15	$11.10	$0.40	8 sq. ft.	4 min.
UN8	$12.40	$0.90	5 sq. ft.	6 min.

Each week, SSS can sell Compaids up to 15,000 square feet of laminated particle at $0.40 per square foot, and Compaids can purchase up to 4500 slide assemblies from Corrigation at $0.75 each. Screws are in abundant supply and do not restrict production. Up to five Compaids workers, working eight hours a day, five days a week, can be assigned to the production of the keyboard trays; however, their labor costs are considered sunk costs.

a. Show that the net unit profit for the model C15 and UN8, excluding the sunk labor costs, are $6 and $8, respectively.

b. Solve for the optimal weekly production quantities, given the limits on laminated particle board, slide assemblies, and production time.

c. If 200 additional slide assemblies were made available each week, what is the most Compaids should consider paying for the 200 slide assemblies?

d. If one additional worker were made available, explain why the shadow prices would change.

e. What is the maximum selling price for the model C15 units for which the optimal weekly production schedule, found in part (b), remains unchanged?

5. MANUFACTURING. Anderson & Blount (A&B) Woodworks makes tables and chairs from 30-inch wide mahogany sheets that it purchases by the linear foot. It can purchase whatever mahogany it desires for $10 per linear foot up to 2250 linear feet per week. Each table requires 9 linear feet and each chair 3 linear feet (including waste). Each chair also utilizes a soft cushion. Up to 500 cushions can be purchased each week for $25 each. Other required hardware (supports, braces, nuts, bolts, etc.) averages $45 for each table and $25 for each chair. A&B sells the tables to retailers for $300 each and each chair for $150 each.

The 10 craftsmen employed by A&B are salaried workers. Their wages of $800 each per week as well as the $5000 per week in rent, insurance and utility costs are all considered fixed costs. To produce a table requires 1 hour of a craftsmen's time, whereas each chair requires only 36 minutes. Each craftsman averages 37.5 productive work-hours per week. Company policy mandates that the ratio of chairs to tables must be between 4 to 1 and 6 to 1.

a. Develop a linear programming model for A&B. The objective function should maximize its gross weekly profit (gross revenue less the variable costs of wood, cushions and other materials). Express the feasible region by the nonnegativity constraints and a set of five functional constraints (wood and cushion availability, the minimum and maximum chair to table ratios, and the maximum weekly production time).

b. Solve for A&B's optimal weekly production schedule of tables and chairs. What is the optimal gross weekly profit? What is the optimal net weekly profit (gross weekly profit less the fixed labor, rent, insurance and utility costs)?

c. Determine and interpret the shadow prices for:

   i. linear feet of mahogany

   ii. cushions

   iii. production hours

6. ADVERTISING. Print Media Advertising (PMA) has been given a contract to market Buzz Cola via newspaper ads in a major Southern newspaper. Full-page ads in the weekday editions (Monday through Saturday) cost $2000, whereas on Sunday a full-page ad costs $8000. Daily circulation of the newspaper is 30,000 on weekdays and 80,000 on Sunday.

PMA has been given a $40,000 advertising budget for the month of August. The experienced advertising executives at PMA feel that both weekday and Sunday newspaper ads are important; hence, they wish to run the equivalent of at least eight weekday and at least two Sunday ads during August. (Assume that a fractional ad would simply mean that a smaller ad is placed on one of the days; that is, 3.5 ads would mean three full-page ads and one one-half page ad. Also assume that smaller ads reduce exposure and costs proportionately.) This August has 26 weekdays and 5 Sundays.

a. If the objective is to maximize cumulative total exposure (as measured by circulation) for the month of August, formulate and solve a linear program to determine the optimal placement of ads by PMA in the newspaper during August. Comment on the validity of the "no interaction" assumption of linear programming for this model.

b. Explain why the constraints on the maximum number of weekday ads and the maximum number of Sunday ads are both redundant.

c. Suppose the minimum restriction for Sunday ads were eliminated. What would be the new optimal solution? What would be the reduced cost for Sunday ads?

7. PRODUCTION. Wilson Manufacturing produces both baseballs and softballs, which it wholesales to vendors around the country. Its facilities permit the manufacture of a maximum of 500 dozen baseballs and a maxi-

mum of 500 dozen softballs each day. The cowhide covers for each ball are cut from the same processed cowhide sheets. Each dozen baseballs require 5 square feet of cowhide, including waste, whereas each dozen softballs require 6 square feet. Wilson has 3600 square feet of cowhide sheets available each day.

Production of baseballs and softballs includes making the inside core, cutting and sewing the cover, and packaging. It takes about one minute to manufacture a dozen baseballs and two minutes to manufacture a dozen softballs. A total of 960 minutes is available for production daily.

a. Formulate a set of linear constraints that characterize the production process at Wilson Manufacturing and draw a graph of the feasible region.

b. Wilson is considering manufacturing either 300 dozen baseballs and 300 dozen softballs or 350 dozen baseballs and 350 dozen softballs. Characterize each of these solutions as an interior point, extreme point, or infeasible point and explain why, regardless of Wilson Manufacturing's objective, neither could be an optimal solution.

c. If Wilson estimates that its profit is $7 per dozen baseballs and $10 per dozen softballs, determine a production schedule that maximizes Wilson's daily profit.

8. **MATERIAL BLENDING.** Missouri Mineral Products (MMP) purchases two unprocessed ores from Bolivia Mining, which it uses in the production of various compounds. Its current needs are for 800 pounds of copper, 600 pounds of zinc, and 500 pounds of iron. The amount of each mineral found in *each* 100 *pounds* of the unprocessed ores and MMP's cost *per* 100 *pounds* are given in the following table.

Ore	Copper	Zinc	Iron	Waste	Cost
La Paz ore	20	20	20	40	$100
Sucre ore	40	25	10	25	$140

a. Formulate and solve a linear program to determine the amount of each ore that should be purchased in order to minimize total purchasing costs.

b. Calculate and interpret the range of optimality for the cost of 100 pounds of each unprocessed ore.

c. Suppose the cost of Sucre ore was $250 per 100 pounds. Why would the solution in part (a) not be optimal? What is the reduced cost for Sucre ore in this case? Explain.

d. Calculate and interpret the shadow prices and the range of feasibility for the requirements for copper, zinc, and iron.

e. Suppose a constraint were added that required that waste be limited to a maximum of 1000 pounds. Characterize this revised problem.

9. **BLENDING.** Ocean Juice produces both a cranberry juice cocktail and a raspberry-cranberry blend. Each day Ocean Juice can receive up to 1000 gallons of a raspberry concentrate that costs $2.00 per gallon and up to 4000 gallons of a cranberry concentrate that costs $1.20 per gallon. Purified water, which is in unlimited supply, costs Ocean Juice $0.08 per gallon. The cranberry juice cocktail is 25% cranberry concentrate and 75% water. The raspberry-cranberry blend is 20% raspberry concentrate, 15% cranberry concentrate, and 65% water.

The juices are bottled in glass quart containers costing $0.05 each. Other costs including labor and packaging amount to $0.15 per quart for the cranberry juice cocktail and $0.18 per quart for the raspberry-cranberry blend. The minimum daily required production is 10,000 quarts of cranberry juice cocktail and 8000 quarts of the raspberry-cranberry blend. The total daily production capacity is 50,000 quarts. Ocean Juice sells the cranberry juice cocktail to stores for $0.75 per quart and the raspberry cranberry blend for $0.95 per quart.

a. What is its optimal daily production schedule and daily profit?

b. How much should Ocean Juice be willing to pay for:

  i.   An extra quart of production capacity?

  ii. Extra gallons of raspberry concentrate?

  iii. Extra gallons of cranberry concentrate?

10. **DIET PROBLEM.** Charley Judd is a salesman for Futura Farm Foods, which is currently marketing a feed for dairy cattle called Moo Town Buffet. On a recent visit to Norfolk, Nebraska, Charley called on Dan Preston, a successful dairy farmer with a herd of 100 dairy cattle.

Dan's success is due in part to a rigid diet he feeds his cattle. In particular, each cow receives a daily minimum of 100 units of calcium, 20,000 calories, and 1500 units of protein. To accomplish this regimen, Dan has been giving his cattle Cow Chow Feed. Each ounce costs $0.015 and supplies 1 unit of calcium, 400 calories, and 20 units of protein. In contrast, each ounce of the Moo Town Buffet Feed would cost Dan $0.020 and supply 2 units of calcium, 250 calories, and 20 units of protein.

a. How much is Dan Preston currently spending to feed a dairy cow each day using Cow Chow?

b. Why would Charley Judd not be successful in persuading Dan Preston to abandon his use of Cow Chow and switch exclusively to Moo Town Buffet?

c. Charley is a resourceful salesman, and he has offered Dan a plan to mix Cow Chow and Moo Town Buffet. The result would be a lower overall cost to Dan for a feed mixture that meets the minimum calcium, calorie, and protein requirements, and a sale for Charley. What overall mix should Charley recommend to minimize Dan's overall feeding cost per cow? How much would Dan Preston save daily by feeding his

100 cattle the mixture recommended by Charley Judd?

11. TOY PRODUCTION. J&J Toy Company produces two dolls that are popular with young girls, the male Jack doll and the female Jill doll. Both dolls are made from plastic and come with a variety of outfits in standard packages. The Jack doll is slightly larger requiring 4 ounces of plastic as compared to 3.5 ounces for the Jill doll. Because the Jill doll is packaged with more clothes, it uses 2 linear feet of cloth as compared to only 1 linear foot of cloth for the clothes packaged with the Jack doll. Due to the popularity of the Jill doll, it is priced to net a unit profit of $7 on each doll while each Jack doll only nets a profit of $5. In a typical week J&J will have the following resources:

- 4200 square feet of cloth for clothes
- 600 pounds of plastic
- production time to make at most 3000 dolls

What production quantities do you recommend for weekly production of Jack and Jill dolls? What is the expected weekly profit?

12. AGRICULTURE. Frank Hurley is a farmer with 250 acres on which he wishes to plant wheat and corn to maximize his expected return for the season. For crop rotation purposes he must plant at least 50 acres of each crop. He can participate in a federal program that will require him to produce at least as much wheat as corn. Under this program, he is guaranteed to earn $150 per acre of wheat planted and $200 per acre of corn planted. Alternatively, he can opt not to participate in the program, in which case he projects he would make only $125 per acre of wheat planted and $184 per acre of corn planted. What would you recommend to Frank?

13. RECYCLING. Alpine Attic is the charity sponsored by local Episcopal churches in Denver, Colorado. Literally thousands of items, including televisions and stereos, are donated each year, most in need of repair. When Alpine Attic receives either a television or a stereo, it determines whether it can be sold "as is" or should be scrapped for parts. Those not sold "as is" are sent directly to JKL Electronics, whose owner, John K. Lucas, is a deacon at St. Paul's Episcopal Church. In addition to his primary business, each month John donates 45 hours of an electrician's time and 30 hours of a technician's time to rebuild and test televisions and stereos for Alpine Attic. In addition to a tax write-off, he feels rewarded by helping out his church.

The recycled televisions and stereos typically sell for $50 and $30 each at the Alpine Attic Thrift Store. Each recycled television averages 90 minutes of an electrician's time to rebuild and 30 minutes of a technician's time to test, whereas each stereo averages 30 minutes of an electrician's time to rebuild and 60 minutes of a technician's time to test. What is the best use of the elec-

trician's and technician's time to help Alpine Attic realize its optimal profit each month?

14. POLITICAL CAMPAIGNING. Bob Gray is running for a seat in the House of Representatives from a very competitive district in Atlanta, Georgia. With six days to go in the campaign, he has 250 volunteers who can be assigned to either phone banks or door-to-door canvassing. The average time he expects a volunteer to spend on the campaign is 25 hours.

The campaign manager can staff 20 telephones from 8:00 A.M. to 10:00 P.M. each day. On the average, 30 voters can be reached by phone contact each hour, whereas only 18 voters can be reached each hour by door-to-door canvassing. However, Bob wants at least one-third of the remaining volunteer hours to be used for personal door-to-door contacts and at least 15 phones to be used on a continuous basis during the remaining days of the campaign.

a. How many volunteer hours should be allocated to phone contacts and how many to door-to-door canvassing if Bob wishes the maximum number of voters to be contacted during the final six days of the campaign?

b. Suppose Bob's campaign manager feels that door-to-door contacts are twice as valuable in terms of swaying voter opinion as phone contacts. How many volunteer hours should be allocated to phone contacts and how many to door-to-door canvassing if Bob wishes to maximize the "value" of the contacts during the final six days of the campaign?

15. ADVERTISING. Intronix uses copy editors, computer graphics specialists, and Java programmers to produce ads for magazines and the Internet. The average new ad for magazines typically requires 180 hours of a copy editor's time and 135 hours of a computer graphics specialist's time, whereas ads produced for the Internet require 35 hours of copy editor time, 195 hours of computer graphics time, and 60 hours of a Java programmer's time.

Lassie Foods, a dog food manufacturer, has hired Intronix to produce ads in the next four weeks. Although currently it considers magazine ads 3 times more valuable than Internet ads, it still wishes to have at least 2 of each produced within the next four weeks. Intronix has assigned up to 3 copy editors, 4 computer graphics specialists, and 1 Java programmer, each committed to work up to 70 hours per week on the project. How many of each type of ad should be produced to maximize the overall value to Lassie Foods?

16. MERCHANDISE DISPLAYS. The upscale toy store August Kids has a picture window with 100 linear feet of display space. The theme this month is bicycles and tricycles. At least ten tricycles and eight bicycles are to be displayed. Each tricycle needs three linear feet of

space in the window display, and each bicycle requires five linear feet. August Kids makes a profit of $40 on each tricycle and $80 on each bicycle it sells. The probability that, on a given day, a displayed tricycle will be sold is .10 and that a displayed bicycle will be sold is .12. Solve for the optimal number of tricycles and bicycles August Kids should display in its picture window daily under each of the following objectives:

a. Maximize total expected daily profit.

b. Maximize the total expected number of daily sales of tricycles and bicycles.

c. Minimize the total number of tricycles and bicycles displayed.

17. PERSONAL INVESTMENTS. George Rifkin is considering investing some or all of a $60,000 inheritance in a one-year certificate of deposit paying a fixed 6% or a venture capital group project with a guaranteed 3% return but the potential of earning 10%. George would like to invest the minimum amount of month necessary to achieve a potential return of at least $4000 and a guaranteed return of at least $2000.

Formulate a mathematical model and recommend an investment strategy for George. How much of his $60,000 can he keep for his personal use during the year and still meet his investment criteria?

18. PERSONAL INVESTMENTS. Consider the situation faced by George Rifkin in problem 17. He has decided to invest the entire $60,000 inheritance. Besides the certificate of deposit paying 6% and the venture capital group paying a minimum of 3% (but with a potential maximum return of 10%), he is considering investing in an oil exploration company. Although this investment could yield a 100% one-year return, George could also lose his entire investment in the company. (*Note:* This is not a 0% return but a loss of 100%.)

a. Formulate and solve a three-variable mathematical model for George that will maximize the potential value of his inheritance after one year, given the following investment criteria:

- At most $30,000 is to be invested in the oil exploration company.

- At least $20,000 is to be invested in the certificate of deposit.

- The value of the portfolio must be at least $40,000 at the start of next year.

- All $60,000 is to be invested.

b. What is the maximum potential return? Thus what is the maximum potential value of the portfolio at the beginning of next year? What is the minimum value of the portfolio at the beginning of next year?

19. AGRICULTURE. Gilroy Farms of California owns 200 acres of land on which it plants garlic (for which the region is famous) and onions. It estimates that it makes

$550 per acre of garlic and $400 per acre of onions planted. During the growing season each acre of garlic requires the use of 4 tons of fertilizer and 2 acre feet of water, whereas each acre of onions requires 3 tons of fertilizer and 1.5 acre-feet of water. Gilroy has contracted for at most 750 tons of fertilizer and 400 acre-feet of water.

a. How many acres of land should be devoted to each crop to maximize its profit for the season? Is there any land left unfarmed?

b. What is the minimum profit per acre for onions that would make it economically feasible for Gilroy Farms to grow onions.

c. If the profit per acre of onion were $450, how many acres of land should Gilroy plant of each crop to maximize its profit for the season?

d. Gilroy Farms is considering leasing another 200-acre parcel adjoining its current property on which it would expand its planting of garlic and onions. If Gilroy can lease this site for $1000, how much additional profit would it make during the growing season if it could not increase its fertilizer and water allocation?

20. BLENDING. Corless Chemical Company can purchase up to 1000 gallons of each of three pesticide compounds, which it blends to make two different commercial products: Bugoff, a plant pesticide, and Weedaway, a lawn pesticide. Bugoff sells for $5 per *quart* and Weedaway for $4 per *quart*. The number of gallons of each of the pesticides required to make a gallon of each commercial product and the cost per gallon are summarized in the following table.

Pesticide	Requirements per Gallon		
	Xylothon	Diazon	Sulferious
Bugoff	.25	.50	.25
Weedaway	.60	.10	.30
Cost per gallon	$12.00	$8.00	$9.00

Corless wants to produce at least 1000 quarts of each product. The cost of the quart bottle container for Bugoff is $0.20; for Weedaway it is $0.30.

a. How many gallons of each commercial product should be blended to yield the maximum net profit to Corless?

b. How much of the 1000 gallons of each of the pesticides will be used? How much of each will Corless *not* purchase?

21. LEASE/BUY. Schick Industries needs to replace some of its aging equipment that produces molded frames for its best-selling Schick racing cycle. Schick can lease machines with a rated capacity of 2000 frames per month for $3000 monthly. Alternatively, it can purchase smaller machines with a rated capacity of 800 frames per month for $10,000 down and $1000 monthly.

Schick only has $50,000 available to purchase machines now, which limits the number of machines that it could purchase to five. Schick must produce at least 10,000 frames per month to keep up with customer demand.

a. Formulate and solve a linear program for Schick to minimize its total monthly payments for machines.

b. Suppose that instead of minimizing total monthly payments, Schick wished to maximize total production capacity. Solve the problem with this objective and comment.

c. Comment on the validity of the linear programming assumptions for this model.

22. INTERNATIONAL SHIPPING. The Takahashi Transport Company (TTC) leases excess space on commercial vessels to the United States at a reduced rate of $10 per square foot. The only condition is that goods must be packaged in standard 30-inch-high crates.

TTC ships items in two standard 30-inch-high crates, one 8-square-foot crate (2 feet by 4 feet) and one 4-square-foot (2 feet by 2 feet) specially insulated crate. It charges customers $160 to ship an 8-square-foot crate and $100 to ship the insulated 4-square-foot crate. Thus, allowing for the $10 per square foot cost, TTC makes a profit of $80 per standard 8-foot crate and $60 on the 4-foot crate.

TTC stores the crates until space becomes available on a cargo ship, at which time TTC receives payment from its customers.

TTC has been able to lease 1200 square feet of cargo space on the *Formosa Frigate* cargo ship, which leaves for the United States in two days. As of this date, TTC has 140 8-square-foot crates and 100 insulated 4-square-foot crates awaiting shipment to the United States. It has 48 hours to finish loading the crates, and it estimates the average loading time to be 12 minutes (0.2 hour) per 8-square-foot crate and 24 minutes (0.4 hour) per 4-square-foot crate (owing to the special handling of the insulated crates).

a. Formulate and solve a *linear* program for TTC to optimize its profit on the upcoming sailing of the *Formosa Frigate*. What are the optimal values of the slack on each constraint in the optimal solution? Express this result in words.

b. Determine the shadow price and the range of feasibility for the number of square feet available. What problem would you have interpreting the shadow prices and the range of feasibility? (*Hint:* Consider what would happen if there were one more square foot of space available. What would be the new optimal solution? Would this make sense?)

c. Suppose that, at the last second, the *Formosa Frigate* decided to raise its charge per square foot from $10 to $12. Note how this change would affect the objective function coefficients. Show that the optimal solution would not change. How does this $2 per square foot increase in leasing charges to TTC affect the shadow price for a square foot of space? Does this make sense?

23. STOCK INVESTMENTS. Idaho investments is a small, newly formed investment group that will invest exclusively in local stocks. The group is planning its initial investment of $100,000, which it will allocate between two stocks—Tater, Inc. and Lakeside Resorts. If the group is successful with these investments, it plans to expand its portfolio further into other Idaho-based stocks. For each of the stocks, the group has estimated three numbers:

- The projected annual return per share with reinvested dividends

- A "potential" index—a number between 0 and 1 that measures the likelihood of high returns in a one-year period

- A "risk" index—a number between 0 and 1 that measures the likelihood of a substantial loss in a one-year period.

The portfolio potential factor is obtained by summing the products of the potential factor for an investment times the fraction of the total investment *dollars* in that investment. For example, if X_1 is the amount invested in Tater and X_2 is the amount invested in Lakeside Resorts, the portfolio potential would be:

$$(X_1/100000)(\text{potential index for Tater}) +$$
$$(X_2/100000)(\text{potential index for Lakeside})$$

The portfolio risk factor is obtained in a similar manner. The current share price and the group estimates for these factors are summarized in the following table.

Stock	Share Price	Estimated Annual Return	Potential Index	Risk Index
Tater, Inc.	$40	10%	.20	.30
Lakeside Resorts	$50	12%	.40	.80

Formulate and solve for the optimal investment strategy in order to maximize overall expected annual return for Idaho investments if it wishes to:

- Invest all $100,000.

- Keep the portfolio potential at .25 or higher.

- Restrict the portfolio risk to .5 or lower.

24. MANUFACTURING. Lawn Master produces 19-inch and 21-inch lawn mowers, which it sells to membership warehouses and discount stores nationwide. Each lawn mower is powered by a Briggs and Stratton 3.5-horse-

power engine. The 19-inch model is a "side-bagger" and requires 40 minutes (2/3 hour) to assemble, test, and package. The 21-inch model is a "rear-bagger" with a variable speed assembly and requires one hour to perform the same operations.

Each week Lawn Master can receive up to 200 Briggs and Stratton engines and has production facilities to manufacture up to 100 variable-speed assemblies. There are four production lines, each working eight hours a day, five days a week, for assembly, testing, and packaging. Each 19-inch model nets Lawn Master a $50 profit, whereas each 21-inch model nets a $60 profit.

a. Formulate and solve a linear programming problem for Lawn Master to determine an optimal weekly production schedule of 19-inch and 21-inch lawn mowers. What is the optimal weekly profit?

b. Determine and interpret the range of feasibility for (i) engines; (ii) variable speed assemblies; (iii) production hours.

c. If an emergency developed so that the amount of production time fell just below the lower limit determined in part (b), what would be the new optimal production schedule?

25. TRUCKING. Bay City Movers is a local company that specializes in intercity moves. In the business plan submitted to its backers, Bay City has committed itself to a total trucking capacity of at least 42 tons.

The company is in the process of replacing its entire fleet of trucks with 1-ton pickup trucks and -ton moving van-type trucks. The 1-ton pickup trucks will be manned by one worker, whereas the large vans will utilize a total of four workers for larger moves.

Bay City Movers currently employs 63 workers and has facilities for at most 50 trucks. Pickup trucks cost the company $24,000 each; the moving vans cost $60,000 each. The company wishes to make a minimum investment of capital that will provide a trucking capacity of at least 42 tons while not requiring any additional workers or trucking facilities.

a. Use a linear programming model to determine the optimal number of pickup trucks and moving vans Bay City Movers should purchase.

b. There are alternate optimal solutions to this model. Determine the one that:

  i. Purchases only one type of truck

  ii. Purchases the same number of pickup trucks as moving vans

  iii. Purchases the minimum number of trucks

26. BAKERY. Mary Custard's is a pie shop that specializes in custard and fruit pies. It makes delicious pies and sells them at reasonable prices so that it can sell all the pies it makes in a day. Every *dozen* custard pies nets Mary Custard's $15 and requires 12 pounds of flour, 50 eggs,

5 pounds of sugar and no fruit mixture. Every dozen fruit pies nets a $25 profit and uses 10 pounds of flour, 40 eggs, 10 pounds of sugar, and 15 pounds of fruit mixture.

On a given day, the bakers at Mary Custard's found that they had 150 pounds of flour, 500 eggs, 90 pounds of sugar, and 120 pounds of fruit mixture with which to make pies.

a. Formulate and solve a linear program that will give the optimal production schedule of pies for the day.

b. If Mary Custard's could double its profit on custard pies, should more custard pies be produced? Explain.

c. If Mary Custard's raised the price (and hence the profit) on all pies by $0.25 ($3.00 per dozen), would the optimal production schedule for the day change? Would the profit change?

d. Suppose Mary Custard's found that 10% of its fruit mixture had been stored in containers that were not air-tight. For quality and health reasons, it decided that it would be unwise to use any of this portion of the fruit mixture. How would this affect the optimal production schedule? Explain.

e. Mary Custard's currently pays $2.50 for a five-pound bag of sugar from its bakery supply vendor. (The $0.50 per pound price of sugar is included in the unit profits given earlier.) Its vendor has already made its deliveries for the day. If Mary Custard's wishes to purchase additional sugar, it must buy it from Donatelli's Market, a small, local independent grocery store that sells sugar in one-pound boxes for $2.25 a box. Should Mary Custard's purchase any boxes of sugar from Donatelli's Market? Explain.

27. BAKERY. For the problem faced by Mary Custard's in problem 26:

a. Each pie is baked and sold in an aluminum pie tin. Suppose at the start of the day Mary Custard's had 200 pie tins available. Would the production schedule change from that determined in part (a) of problem 29?

b. Answer part (a) assuming that there were only 100 pie tins.

c. Mary Custard's has, in the past, made a third type of pie—a chocolate pie. Given the current prices of ingredients, Mary Custard's estimates that it would net a profit of $27 per dozen chocolate pies. Each dozen chocolate pies requires 15 pounds of flour, 30 eggs, 12 pounds of sugar and no fruit mixture. Show that it would not be profitable to bake any chocolate pies this day even if Mary Custard's had an abundant supply of chocolate. What is the minimum profit for a dozen chocolate pies which would justify their production?

28. MANUFACTURING. Klone Computers manufactures two models of its current line of personal computers: the KCU and the KCP. The KCU, which is purchased primarily by universities and other businesses that network their computers, is equipped with two floppy drives and no hard disk drive. The KCP is designed for home and personal use and is equipped with one floppy drive and one hard disk drive. Each model is housed in a tower case. During the current production run, Klone must manufacture at least 300 KCU computers to satisfy a contract to Texas State University. The following table summarizes the resource requirements and unit profits for each computer model and the resources available for the current production run.

Model	Floppy Drives	Hard Drives	Tower Cases	Production Hours	Unit Profit
KCU	2	0	1	0.4	$100
KCP	1	1	1	0.6	$250
Available	1800	700	1000	480	

Formulate and solve a linear program for Klone to determine its optimal production schedule for this production cycle. How many of the current inventory of floppy drives, hard disk drives, and tower cases will be used in the production cycle? How many are unused? Is all the available production time utilized?

29. MANUFACTURING. For the Klone Computer problem (problem 28):

a. Suppose the unit profit for the KCU model were increased to $150 per unit. Does the optimal solution change? Does the total profit change? Suppose the profit for the KCU model could be increased to $200 per unit. Does the optimal solution change? Does the total profit change?

b. The unit profit coefficients took into account the $50 per unit cost to Klone of the floppy disk drives. Klone has negotiated a deal with another company to purchase floppy disk drives at $35 each. Will the optimal solution change? If so, what will be the new optimal profit?

c. Suppose the constraint requiring the production of at least 300 KCU models were eliminated. Determine the new optimal solution.

30. PRODUCTION. Klone Computer (see problems 28, 29) is making one last production run of its KCU and KCP computers before introducing its new line of models, which includes CD-ROM drives, utilizes faster CPUs and floppy disk drives, and has larger hard disk drives. Because this is the last run of "old technology" machines, Klone's net profit per computer has been reduced from $100 and $250 to $75 and $105 for KCU and KCP models, respectively. The following table summarizes the resource requirements and unit profits for each computer model and the resources available for this *final* production run of these models.

Model	Floppy Drives	Hard Drives	Tower Cases	Production Hours	Unit Profit
KCU	2	0	1	0.4	$ 75
KCP	1	1	1	0.6	$105
Available	2800	1400	2000	960	

Formulate this problem and solve it as a linear program. Note that the optimal solution to the linear program gives integer values. Why is this also the optimal solution to the ILP model?

31. ROUNDING PRODUCTION. Suppose in problem 30 there were 970 production hours available.

a. Solve the model as a *linear* programming model, ignoring the integer restrictions, and show that the optimal solution is attained with fractional values for the decision variables.

b. Round your solution in part (a) by (i) rounding off, (ii) rounding up, and (iii) rounding down. In each instance state whether or not the solution is feasible. Determine the profit for any feasible results.

c. Solve for the optimal integer solution. Did you get any of the rounded answers in part (b)? What is the difference in the optimal profit between the true optimal integer solution and the best feasible rounded linear programming solution? *Note:* This illustrates that when large quantities are involved, rounding the optimal linear programming solution usually gives a "good enough answer."

32. PHYSICAL FITNESS. Sarah Stone measures her performance in the gym as follows: 10 points for every Nautilus machine used, and 1 point for every minute on the treadmill. Including preparation time and transition time between machines, Sarah spends an average of 6.5 minutes on each Nautilus machine. Formulate a model with both an integer and a continuous variable to determine the optimal number of Nautilus machines she should use and the number of minutes she should spend on the treadmill if:

- The total time of the workout is not to exceed 1 hour.
- At least 20 minutes must be spent on the treadmill.
- At least 5 different Nautilus machines should be used.

33. MANUFACTURING. Plant Equipment Corporation (PEC) manufactures two large industrial machines—a metal compactor and a drill press. Next month PEC will convert its production facilities to produce new machine designs and will cease producing the current models. PEC must determine its production schedule for this month, however.

PEC could sell up to three compactors and two drill presses to customers who are not anxious to pay the increased price PEC will charge for the new models.

Current models net PEC a $24,000 profit for metal compactors and $30,000 for drill presses. Each metal compactor requires 50 hours to produce, whereas each drill press requires 60 hours to produce; 160 production hours are available during the current month.

a. Formulate and solve this problem as an integer linear programming problem.

b. Solve the problem as a linear program and note that when the optimal solution is rounded (up, down, or off), the result is *not* the optimal integer solution.

c. Why would a linear programming model be a correct model if the production process were to continue indefinitely?

34. RESTAURANT OPERATION. Jackson's Sports Bar and Grill would like to minimize the cost of installing television sets throughout the restaurant so that it can accommodate a potential viewership of at least 750 patrons. It is considering purchasing two models of Sony televisions. The large-screen 60-inch model costs $3500 and, with proper placement, could be viewed by 150 customers. The 27-inch models cost $800 each and can be seen by 35 customers. Jackson's wishes to have at least one 60-inch television and no more than 20 27-inch models.

a. Formulate the model for the problem faced by Jackson's.

b. Solve for the optimal linear programming solution. Round the solution to integer values. What is the total cost of the rounded solution?

c. Solve for the optimal solution for the integer programming model. Did you get the rounded solution of part (b)? What is the total cost of the optimal integer solution?

35. AIRCRAFT LEASING. Des Moines Airlines (DMA) is a small new commuter airline that will locate its hub in Des Moines, Iowa. DMA plans to have 11 mechanics, 15 pilots, and 21 flight attendants available daily.

DMA will be leasing two types of aircraft—the DM4 and the B77. The Federal Aviation Association's (FAA's) mandatory requirements for these aircraft are summarized in the following table. DMA's objective is to maximize its total passenger capacity.

	Mechanics Required	Pilots Required	Flight Attendants Required
DM4	1	1	1
B77	1	2	3

a. Formulate and graph a feasible region for this problem. Without knowing the seat capacity on each aircraft, why can we say for certain that the optimal solution to the linear programming model would also be the optimal solution to the integer linear pro-

gramming model? (*Hint:* What are the possible optimal points for a linear programming model?)

b. The seat capacity is 25 for the DM4 and 70 for the B77. What is the optimal leasing plan for DMA?

c. If DMA must make do with one less worker to operate its fleet, should it be a mechanic, a pilot, or a flight attendant?

d. Excluding certain fixed costs (including pilot costs), each seat of fleet capacity gives DMA a net yearly profit of $25,000. If DMA plans to pay its pilots $110,000 per year, including benefits, should it hire an additional pilot?

e. DMA is considering redesigning the interior of the B77 to increase its seat capacity beyond 70. What is the maximum seating capacity for which the leasing plan found in part (a) remains optimal?

f. Suppose DMA could squeeze one more row of three seats into each of the two types of aircraft, increasing the seating capacity of the DM4 to 28 and the B77 to 73. Given no other changes in the assumptions of the problem, would the optimal leasing decision change? What practical considerations might you consider before implementing such a change?

36. AIRCRAFT LEASING. Consider the problem faced by Des Moines Airlines (DMA) in problem 35. Now suppose that the B77 aircraft actually requires 4 flight attendants rather than three.

a. Solve for the optimal solution to the (i) linear programming model and (ii) integer programming model.

b. Explain why the optimal solution in (ii) gives a smaller total seat capacity than that in (i).

37. AIRCRAFT LEASING (*continued*). Consider the Des Moines Airlines (DMA) problem referred to in problem 35. Now suppose DMA is considering leasing a third aircraft, the L-200. The L-200, as currently configured, has a seating capacity of 110 and requires two mechanics, three pilots, and five flight attendants.

a. Solve the DMA problem as a *linear* program and show that the solution found in 35(b) remains optimal; that is, no L-200 aircraft should be leased.

b. According to the sensitivity analysis for the linear program in part (a), what is the minimum seating capacity for the L-200 that would justify DMA leasing them?

c. Suppose the seating arrangement of the L-200 could be reconfigured so that the capacity is increased to 120. Solve for the optimal leasing plan for DMA.

38. HELICOPTER SERVICE. Wolfe Helicopters is to begin flying passengers from a helicopter pad in Berkeley, California, to the two large airports in the area, Oakland and San Francisco. Wolfe will operate two models—the

HG30 and the WH10. The characteristics for each air-craft are given in the following table.

	Estimated Monthly Profit	Purchase Cost	Required Monthly Maintenance (Hours)	Capacity
HG30	$3000	$600,000	20	20
WH10	$2000	$200,000	60	8

Wolfe has $1,800,000 available to purchase helicopters, and it wishes to have a total fleet capacity of at least 25. It also has a service contract with HMC, a helicopter maintenance company, for up to 140 hours of maintenance per month. (Additional hours would require a complete renegotiation of the service contract at a much higher cost; thus, Wolfe wishes not to exceed the 140 hours of the contract.)

a. Formulate and solve for the mix of helicopters that would bring Wolfe its maximum monthly profit.

b. Show graphically that there are only five feasible integer solutions. Evaluate the profit of each and verify that the answer to part (a) is correct.

c. What would be Wolfe's optimal mix of helicopters if it had only $1,799,999 available to purchase helicopters? If Wolfe had only $1,799,999 for the purchase of helicopters, would you "invest" a dollar with Wolfe for a small percentage of the increased profits?

39. INVESTMENTS. Carol Klein has $10,000 she wishes to invest in a particular stock and a bond. The stock has the potential to earn a 15% annual return whereas the bond will yield only a 6% annual return. However, due to the volatility in the stock market, she wishes to invest no more than $5000 in the stock.

a. Determine Carol's optimal allocation of the $10,000 between the stock and the bond and her maximum potential return if:

i. There are no other restrictions on her investment decisions

ii. Carol must purchase whole shares of the stock at $165 per share. *Note:* Solver *may* incorrectly

state that this problem is infeasible; but the solution it generates is feasible and optimal.

iii. Carol must purchase whole shares of the stock at $165 per share and the bond must be purchased in multiples of $100 each.

b. Discuss why each of the above scenarios yielded a different optimal solution and why the maximum potential return was lower in case (ii) than in case (i) and lower still in case (iii).

40. E-COMMERCE. Designdotcom.com is a company that designs websites for clients. Much of the work is done in-house, but it finds that it must subcontract some work to graduate students at a local university when the demand is great. It charges clients $2500 to build a typical website. Designdotcom pays the graduate students $1500 for their services in building a website, thus reducing its profit to $1000. In March, it would like to design at least 200 websites, with no more than 100 subcontracted to graduate students.

Designdotcom would like to determine how many websites it should design in-house and how many should be subcontracted in the month of March.

a. Formulate this problem as a linear problem and solve. Explain the result.

b. Designdotcom failed to mention that it takes approximately 40 man-hours to design a website in-house and approximately 20 man-hours to supervise and monitor a website design by the graduate students. Workers at Designdotcom average 12-hour workdays. During March there are 26 workdays. Formulate, solve, and explain the revised model if Designdotcom has:

i. 15 employees

ii. 20 employees

PROBLEMS 41–50 ARE ON THE CD

CASE 1: FRANKLIN FURNITURE

This case can be solved by splitting it into three small cases, two of which can be analyzed using only two decision variables.

Franklin Furniture produces tables and chairs at its Eastside plant for use in university classrooms. The unit profit for tables is $70, while that for chairs is $30.

Tables and chairs are manufactured using finished pressed wood and polished aluminum fittings. Including scrap, each table uses 20 square feet of pressed wood, whereas each chair uses 12.5 square feet of the pressed wood. Franklin has 6000 square feet of the pressed wood available for the Eastside plant weekly. The aluminum fittings that reinforce the legs of both the tables and chairs are purchased from an outside supplier. Franklin can purchase up to 400 boxes of fittings weekly; one box is required for each table or chair manufactured.

Production time is 72 minutes (1.2 hours) per table and 18 minutes (.3 hour) per chair. Franklin has eight employees, each of whom works an average of 7.5 hours per day. Thus, in an average five-day work week, the company has available 8(7.5)(5) = 300 production hours.

Franklin Furniture also produces desks and computer workstations at its Westside plant. Each desk nets the company a profit of $100, while each computer workstation nets $125. These products are also produced from finished pressed wood and aluminum. The amount of each, as well as the labor time needed to produce a desk or computer workstation, is given in the following table.

	Pressed Wood	Aluminum Fittings	Labor
Desks	20 sq. ft.	1 box	1.5 hours
Workstations	30 sq. ft.	1 box	2.0 hours
Available	6000 sq. ft.	400 boxes	300 hours

Franklin is considering combining operations of both plants into a single plant. This consolidation will combine the weekly available resources so that 12,000 square feet of pressed wood, 800 boxes of aluminum fittings, and 600 production hours will be available weekly. However, the accounting department estimates the cost of renovating the plant will be $5000 per week, on an amortized basis.

Prepare a business report for Franklin Furniture giving optimal weekly production schedules for each of its plants operating separately. Then include an analysis and a recommendation to Franklin for combining operations at both plants into a single plant.

CASE 2: RINALDO'S HATCH 'N AX

Rinaldo's Hatch 'N Ax is the manufacturer of the store brand of hatchets and axes sold by Home Supply Hardware (HSH) Stores. Each item consists of a hickory handle produced in Rinaldo's processing facility and a steel blade forged and polished in its machine shop. These items are then transported to an assembly area where the blade is attached to the handle and the item is packaged for shipment. Because of its exclusive contract with HSH, Rinaldo's can sell all the hatchets and axes it produces. The accompanying spreadsheet is an Excel spreadsheet giving the following details for each item. (This information is also available in file RINALDO.xls in the Excel files folder on the accompanying CD-ROM.)

- The contract selling price to HSH
- The amount of hickory required for its handle
- The amount of steel required for its blade
- The number of minutes required to produce the handle in its processing facility
- The number of minutes required to produce the blade in the machine shop
- The number of minutes required for assembly and packaging

		A	B	C	D	E	F	G	H	I	J	K	L	M
1						Rinaldo's Hatch 'N Ax Production Schedule								
2						Quarter II								
3														
4			Hatchets	Axes								April	May	June
5										Contracted Minimum Production				
6		Selling Price to HSH	$16.00	$29.50						Hatchets – Min. Production		400	300	200
7						Resources Used			Quarter	Axes – Min. Production		175	300	350
8					April	May	June		Totals					
9		Hickory Required (Ft./Unit)	1.6	3.1						Costs				
10		Steel Required (Lbs./Unit)	1.8	4.2						Skilled Labor Costs ($/hr.)		$12.00	$12.00	$12.84
11										Unskilled Labor Costs ($/hr.)		$7.00	$7.00	$7.35
12	Skilled Labor Required Per Unit									Hickory ($/ft.)		$1.00	$1.20	$1.05
13		Handle Production (Min/Unit)	5.0	2.6						Steel ($/lb.)		$1.18	$1.06	$0.98
14		Blade Production (Min/Unit)	11.0	9.4										
15		Total Skilled Labor (Min/Unit)								Unit Profits				
16										Hatchets				
17	Unskilled Labor Required Per Unit									Axes				
18		Assembly (Min/Unit)	4.0	5.5										
19		Packaging (Min/Unit)	2.0	2.5						Resource Availability				
20		Total Unskilled Labor (Min/Unit)								Skilled Labor (Hours)		220	250	200
21										Unskilled Labor (Hours)		120	100	140
22										Hickory (Feet)		2000	2200	1500
23		Production Schedule			Total Profit					Steel (Pounds)		2000	2000	2000
24		April												
25		May												
26		June												
27		Quarter Totals												
28														
29														
30														
31														

The file also gives the current hourly cost and availability for the skilled and unskilled labor of Rinaldo's workforce. Skilled laborers produce the handles and blades, whereas unskilled laborers assemble and package the items. Also given is the information on contracts negotiated with HSH for minimum shipments for the next three months of each item as well as details of contracts Rinaldo's has made for the purchase price and availability of the hickory and steel for the same time period.

Given this data, program the following cells and use Excel Solver three times (once for each month) to determine the production schedule for the quarter:

Cells	Quantities
E9-G10	Hickory/Steel Used Each Month
E13-G14	Handle/Blade Production Time Used Each Month
C15-D15	Total Skilled Labor per Unit
E15-G15	Total Skilled Labor Used Each Month
E18-G19	Assembly/Packaging Time Used Each Month
C20-D20	Total Unskilled Labor per Unit
E20-G20	Total Unskilled Labor Used Each Month
Column H	Quarter Totals
K16-M17	Unit Profits for Hatchets/Axes Each Month
E24-E26	Total Profit Each Month
C27-E27	Total Production/Profit for the Quarter

Prepare a report detailing your production recommendations for the quarter. Include quarter totals of relevant quantities of interest to management at Rinaldo's. Discuss the following in the report:

- An interpretation of the shadow prices and the range of feasibility for the binding constraints of this model for each month
- How the accuracy in the estimates of the profit coefficients affects your analyses

CASE 3: KOOTENAY STRAW BROOM COMPANY

The Kootenay Straw Broom Company, located in British Columbia, Canada, is a small, family-run business that hand-makes two models of straw brooms, the Pioneer and the Heritage models, which are sold in "country stores" throughout Canada and the northwestern United States. Given its current production capacity and selling price, Kootenay is able to sell all the brooms it produces.

The Pioneer model is the company's basic model. It consists of a plain wooden handle, utilizes one pound of straw, and takes an average of 15 minutes (.25 hour) to make. Kootenay sells them for $12.75 each. The Heritage model is the company's deluxe model. Although the same wooden handles are used, they are run through a decorative lathe and attached to a larger base consisting of 1.5 pounds of straw. These two factors increase the production time of the Heritage broom to 24 minutes (.40 hour), and Kootenay sells them for $18 each.

Kootenay receives daily deliveries of straw that is specially treated for their brooms from Tyler Farms. Tyler can supply Kootenay with up to 350 pounds daily of the specially treated straw. This straw costs Kootenay $1.50 per pound.

Kootenay purchases its handles from Adhor Mills, which manufactures the handles according to Kootenay's specifications. Adhor Mills is a two-hour drive from Kootenay. It currently makes only one daily delivery to Kootenay in a truck capable of hauling 30 boxes of 10 handles each (or 300 handles). Adhor charges Kootenay $7.50 per box of 10 for manufacture and delivery of the handles.

Adhor also makes a major delivery of products to a town 45 miles from Kootenay and has offered to swing by Kootenay with one additional box of 10 handles. However, the added expense for making this detour means that Kootenay would have to pay Adhor $25 for this extra box of 10 handles.

Kootenay averages 80 production hours per day. Since Kootenay is a family-run business, it considers the daily cost of $2800 for its overhead and "family labor" of its 10 members as sunk costs required for the business. Kootenay is ready to consider several options that could increase the daily profit:

1. Seeking additional sources for treated straw
2. Taking Adhor Mills up on its offer to deliver an extra box of handles (for $25)
3. Adding a half-time worker (four hours per day) for $50 per day

Prepare a report for the Kootenay Straw Broom Company that evaluates the option or set of options it should implement. The report should:

1. Recommend an optimal production under current conditions.

2. Include a summary of the determination of unit profits of $10.50 and $15.00, respectively, for the Pioneer and Heritage broom models, showing that the costs of both treated straw and broom handles are included in these calculations.

3. Show that after subtracting fixed costs, the business nets $500 per day.

4. Give a brief analysis of the sensitivity of the objective function coefficients.

5. Analyze the options using the correct interpretation of the shadow prices considering which costs are included and which costs are sunk. (*Remember:* Do not call them shadow prices in the report.)

CHAPTER 9

Applications of Linear and Integer Programming Models

FedEx Corporation

With approximately $20 billion in revenues, FedEx Corporation (http://www.fedex
.com) has become a world leader in providing integrated transportation, information,
and logistics solutions. As the company has expanded, it has created a high-level management science group to provide senior management with recommendations on a
wide variety of issues. This group uses state-of-the-art computer-based mathematical
models to analyze a broad range of complex corporate problems with an overall goal
of maintaining and increasing company profits while continuing to provide a consis-
tently high level of service to its customers.

One of the models developed by this group is its Global Supply Chain Model,
built to redesign its supply chain for revenue packaging. The model has helped management answer the following questions:

- Should FedEx pursue offshore production of packaging? If so, which items
  and where?

- Should FedEx consolidate nearby warehouses and pick centers into a new
  form of distribution center?

- Should FedEx pursue expansion of distribution center locations?

- What transportation modes on each link would most reliably get packaging
  from suppliers to stations while reducing costs?

- What should the service area boundaries be for each distribution center?

The Global Supply Chain Model uses, among other techniques, a large-scale
mixed integer programming approach. This model has already resulted in a cost savings to FedEx of over $10 million.

9.1 THE EVOLUTION OF LINEAR PROGRAMMING MODELS IN BUSINESS AND GOVERNMENT

Following World War II, the U.S. Air Force sponsored research for solving military planning and distribution models. In 1947, the simplex algorithm was developed for solving these types of linear models. Not long after, the first commercial uses of linear programming were reported in "large" businesses that had access to digital computers. Seemingly unrelated industries, such as agriculture, petroleum, steel, transportation, and communications, saved millions of dollars by successfully developing and solving linear models for complex problems.

As computing power has become more accessible, the realm of businesses and government entities using linear models has expanded exponentially. In this chapter we present numerous "small" examples selected from a wide variety of applications areas, designed to accomplish four goals:

1. To examine potential applications areas where linear models may be useful

2. To develop good modeling skills

3. To demonstrate how to develop use of the power of spreadsheets to effectively represent the model in unambiguous terms and generate results

4. To gain confidence in interpreting and analyzing results from spreadsheet reports

Although the examples illustrated in this chapter represent "scaled-down" versions of potential real-life situations, today linear and integer programming models proliferate in a wide variety of actual business and government applications. Banking models, large economic/financial models, marketing strategy models, production scheduling and labor force planning models, computer design and networking models, and health care and medical models are but a few notable examples of successful linear programming applications. Below is just a sampling of the thousands of actual documented uses of linear programming models.

- Aircraft fleet assignments
- Telecommunications network expansion
- Air pollution control
- Health care
- Bank portfolio selection
- Agriculture
- Fire protection
- Defense/aerospace contracting
- Land use planning
- Dairy production
- Military deployment

An example of each of the above is detailed in Appendix 3.1 on the accompanying CD-ROM. The reader is encouraged to reference this subfolder for details.

These are but a few of the numerous applications areas of linear optimization models. Additional applications include traffic analysis, fast-food operations, transportation, assignment of medical personnel, coal, steel, gas, chemical, and paper production, recycling, educational assignments, worker evaluations, awarding of contracts, manufacturing, railroads, forestry, school desegregation, government planning, tourism, and sports scheduling. Each year hundreds of new applications appear in the professional literature. Add to that the numerous unreported models that are regularly utilized in business and government, and you can see that linear programming continues to play a significant role in today's world.

9.2 BUILDING GOOD LINEAR AND INTEGER PROGRAMMING MODELS

Given the widespread use of linear models today, it has become increasingly important for practitioners to be able to develop good, efficient models to aid the manager in the decision-making process. Three factors—familiarity, simplification, and clarity—are important considerations when developing such models.

The greater the modeler's *familiarity* with the relationships between competing activities, the limitations of the resources, and the overall objective, the greater the likelihood of generating a usable model. Viewing the problem from as many perspectives as possible (e.g., those of various management levels, front-line workers, and accounting) helps in this regard.

Linear models are always *simplifications* of real-life situations. Usually, some or all of the required linear programming assumptions discussed in Chapter 8 are violated by an actual situation. Because of the efficiency with which they are solved and the associated sensitivity analysis reports generated, however, linear models are generally preferable to more complicated forms of mathematical models.

When developing a model, it is important to address the following question: "Is a very sophisticated model needed, or will a less sophisticated model that gives fairly good results suffice?" The answer, of course, will guide the level of detail required in the model.

Although a model should reflect the real-life situation, one should not try to model every aspect or contingency of the situation. This could get us bogged down in minutiae, adding little, if any, real value to the model while unnecessarily complicating the solution procedure, delaying solution time, and compromising the usefulness of the model. As George Dantzig, the developer of the simplex algorithm for solving linear programming models, points out, however, "What constitutes the proper simplification, is subject to individual judgment and experience. People often disagree on the adequacy of a certain model to describe the situation."[1] In other words, although experience is the best teacher, you should be aware that even experienced management scientists may disagree as to what level of simplification is realistic or warranted in a model.

Finally, a linear programming model should be *clear*; that is, it should be easy to follow and as transparent as possible to the layperson. From a practitioner's point of view, the model should also be easy to input and yield accurate results in a timely manner.

Summation Variables and Constraints

In an effort to make the model easier to understand and debug, we can introduce **summation variables** and corresponding **summation constraints** into the formulation. A summation variable is the sum of two or more of the decision variables. It is particularly useful when there are constraints involving maximum or minimum percentages for the value of one or more of the decision variables.

To illustrate the use of a summation variable, consider the situation in which X_1, X_2, and X_3 represent the production quantities of three television models to be produced during a production run in which 7000 pounds of plastic are available. The unit

---

[1] George B. Dantzig, *Linear Programming and Extensions* (Princeton, NJ: Princeton University Press, 1963).

profits are \$23, \$34, and \$45, and the amount of plastic required to produce each is 2 pounds, 3 pounds, and 4 pounds, respectively. In addition, management does not want any model to exceed 40% of total production ($X_1 + X_2 + X_3$).

First, we note that although the proportion of model 1 televisions produced during the production run is $X_1/(X_1 + X_2 + X_3)$. However a constraint of the form: $X_1/(X_1 + X_2 + X_3) \leq .4$ is not a linear constraint. But, because we know that the total production, $X_1 + X_2 + X_3$ is positive, we could multiply both sides of this constraint by the denominator to obtain the equivalent linear constraint: $X_1 \leq .4(X_1 + X_2 + X_3)$. The constraints $X_2 \leq .4(X_1 + X_2 + X_3)$ and $X_3 \leq .4(X_1 + X_2 + X_3)$ require that models 2 and 3 represent no more than 40% of the total production. Thus, the model could be written as:

$$
\begin{aligned}
\text{MAX} \quad & 23X_1 + 34X_2 + 45X_3 \\
\text{ST} \quad & 2X_1 + 3X_2 + 4X_3 \leq 7000 \\
& X_1 \leq .4(X_1 + X_2 + X_3) \\
& X_2 \leq .4(X_1 + X_2 + X_3) \\
& X_3 \leq .4(X_1 + X_2 + X_3) \\
& X_1, X_2, X_3 \geq 0
\end{aligned}
$$

or,

$$
\begin{aligned}
\text{MAX} \quad & 23X_1 + 34X_2 + 45X_3 \\
\text{ST} \quad & 2X_1 + 3X_2 + 4X_3 \leq 7000 \\
& .6X_1 - .4X_2 - .4X_3 \leq 0 \\
& -.4X_1 + .6X_2 - .4X_3 \leq 0 \\
& -.4X_1 - .4X_2 + .6X_3 \leq 0 \\
& X_1, X_2, X_3 \geq 0
\end{aligned}
$$

Written in this form, not only are the coefficients cumbersome to input into a spreadsheet, but the last three constraints do not immediately convey the fact that each television model is not to exceed 40% of the total production.

To clarify the above formulation, a *summation variable* representing the total production and a *summation constraint* expressing this relationship may be introduced into the model as follows:

- Define the summation variable:

    X_4 = the total production of televisions during a production run.

- Add the following summation constraint:

    $X_1 + X_2 + X_3 = X_4$ or equivalently $X_1 + X_2 + X_3 - X_4 = 0$ to the model formulation.

- The 40% production limit constraints can now be written as:

    $X_1 \leq .4X_4$, $X_2 \leq .4X_4$, and $X_3 \leq .4X_4$ respectively.

By subtracting $.4X_4$ from both sides of each of the above production limit constraints, the complete set of constraints can now be written as:

$$
\begin{aligned}
\text{MAX} \quad & 23X_1 + 34X_2 + 45X_3 \\
\text{ST} \quad & 2X_1 + 3X_2 + 4X_3 \leq 7000 \\
& X_1 + X_2 + X_3 - X_4 = 0 \ (\text{Summation Constraint}) \\
& X_1 - .4X_4 \leq 0 \\
& X_2 - .4X_4 \leq 0 \\
& X_3 - .4X_4 \leq 0 \\
& \text{All X's} \geq 0
\end{aligned}
$$

Although by adding the summation variable and the summation constraint we have increased the number of constraints and number of variables each by one, the new set of constraints is easier to input and easier to read and interpret when checking the model.[2]

When using spreadsheets, a convenient way of modeling this situation without listing all the percentage constraints explicitly is shown in Figure 9.1. In this figure, cells B2, C2, and D2 are used for the decision variables, while another cell (H2) is set aside to represent total production. The formula in cell H2 is =SUM(B2:D2). Note that summation variable cell H2 is not considered a "Changing Cell." As shown in the accompanying Solver dialogue box, the percentage constraints can be included by $B$2:$D$2 <= .4*$H$2.

Binary Variables

In Chapter 8 we saw that sometimes one or more of the decision variables in a linear model are required to be integer-valued. Some models may also contain **binary variables**, variables that can only assume values of 0 or 1. Any situation that can be modeled by "yes/no," "good/bad," "right/wrong," and so on, can be considered a binary variable. Such situations include whether or not a plant is built, whether or not a particular highway is used when traveling between two cities, and whether or not a worker is assigned to perform a job.

A Modeling Checklist

Mathematical modeling is an art that improves with experience. To this point we have suggested several modeling tips that can aid your development of mathematical models. For your convenience we offer a summary of many of these tips in the form of a checklist.

FIGURE 9.1   Solver Spreadsheet for Television Production Model

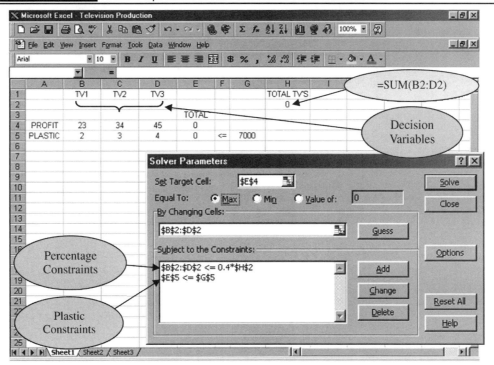

A checklist for Building Linear Models

1. Begin by listing the details of the problem in short expressions. (We have done this in Chapter 8 using "bullets.")

2. Determine the objective in general terms and then determine what is within the control of the decision maker to accomplish this goal. These controllable inputs are *decision variables*.

3. If, during the course of the formulation, you find that another decision variable is needed, add it to the list at that time and include it in the formulation.

4. Define the decision variables precisely using an appropriate time frame (i.e., cars per month, tons of steel per production run, etc.)

5. When writing a constraint or a function, first formulate it in words in the form: (some expression) ⟨has some relation to⟩ (another expression or constant); then convert the words to the appropriate mathematical symbols.

6. Keep the units in the expressions on both sides of the relation consistent (e.g., one side should not be in hours, the other in minutes).

7. If the right-hand side is an expression rather than a constant, do the appropriate algebra so that the end result is of the form:

    (mathematical function) ⟨has a relation to⟩ (a constant)

8. Use *summation variables* when appropriate, particularly when many constraints involve percentages.

9. Indicate which variables are restricted to be nonnegative, which are restricted to be integer valued, and which are binary.

9.3 BUILDING GOOD SPREADSHEET MODELS

When we employed spreadsheets to solve linear programming models in Chapter 8, the models were written in a rectangular fashion with columns used for the variables and rows used for constraints. This approach, which is used in many nonspreadsheet software packages, presents a structured approach for inputting the coefficients of the model. Any linear or integer programming model can be represented and solved in this manner.

But with spreadsheets, you are not burdened with such a restrictive format. You can present the data and results in such a way that they do not even look like a linear programming model. This can be very valuable, particularly when information is shared with nonquantitative end-users. With spreadsheets you can:

- Embed formulas that represent required values or subsets of values into individual cells
- Express coefficients as mathematical expressions rather than specific numbers
- Designate various cells scattered throughout the spreadsheet to contain left-hand side and right-hand side values of the constraints without confining them to be in a single column or row

Solver even allows the right-hand side of constraints to be mathematical expressions instead of constants or cell references. Add to this the use of color, various border designs, and other formatting techniques, and this flexibility allows the user to present a spreadsheet in a way that conveys the requisite information in a visually pleasing manner. For instance, the modeler can:

- Group certain types of constraints together
- Designate certain cells for the left sides and right sides of these constraints at positions on the spreadsheet disjoint from the left-hand coefficients

- Highlight the information by using a thick or colored border
- Use a different color background for cells containing the left-hand side values as opposed to the cells that contain the right-hand side restrictions
- Create entries on the spreadsheet that give other relevant information such as subtotals or proportions
- Use various formulas in cells representing the total left-hand side values. This can simply be a cell representing the value of a decision variable, a formula, or the result of a function such as SUMPRODUCT, SUM, and SUMIF

Another option that one might take advantage of is Excel's ability to name cells or sets of cells. Cells can be named by following these steps:

- Highlight the cell(s) to be named.
- Click on the Name box (the far left box immediately above column A) and type in what you wish to call the cells. (The name must start with a letter, and no spaces are allowed.)
- Press Enter.

Then when these cells are referenced in a Solver dialogue box, for instance, the name appears rather than the cell references. This can make it easier to follow the logic of the model. For instance, in the television production model in Section 9.2 which was illustrated in Figure 9.1, we could have assigned the following names:

Cells	*NAME*
B2:D2	SetsProduced
H2	TotalSets
E4	TotalProfit
E5	PlasticUsed
G5	AvailablePlastic

Then by highlighting the same cells as before, the dialogue box would appear as in Figure 9.2. Note that when we input a formula (such as .4*$H$2) for the right side of a constraint, the name does not appear.

Although we could do this throughout our illustrations of linear models, we leave cell references as they are so that they can be easily referenced on the spreadsheet itself. But for large models, naming cells certainly has its advantages. In short, a spreadsheet

---

FIGURE 9.2

Dialogue Box Using
Named Cells

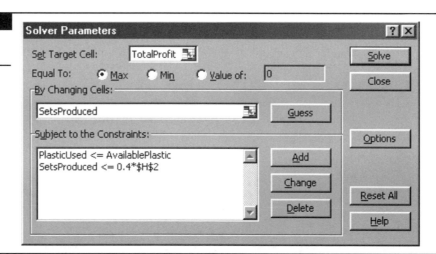

offers a variety of ways other than a matrix format to convey the input coefficients. Solver is still used, but the results will be placed on spreadsheets that make them ripe for discussion or inclusion into business reports or PowerPoint presentations.

In Sections 9.4 and 9.5, the mathematical and spreadsheet modeling tips discussed in the last two sections are illustrated in various formulations of linear and integer models from the private and public sectors. In these models we shall:

- Show how linear models can be applied to different situations arising from the functional areas of business and government
- Illustrate the modeling approach, including some of the problems that might arise in the modeling process
- Employ effective spreadsheet modeling techniques
- Interpret, analyze, and extend the output generated from Excel Solver

In the process we shall illustrate a number of concepts, including how to:

- Choose an appropriate objective function
- Define an inclusive set of decision variables
- Write accurate expressions to model the constraints
- Interpret sensitivity outputs for both maximization and minimization models
- Recognize and address unboundedness
- Recognize and address infeasibility
- Recognize and address alternate optimal solutions

To simplify matters, we identify the applications area and the concepts illustrated for each model introduced in this chapter.

9.4 APPLICATIONS OF LINEAR PROGRAMMING MODELS

In Chapter 8, we introduced the basic concepts of linear programming through the use of two-variable models. These concepts included modeling, using Excel's Solver to generate an optimal solution (or determine that the model is unbounded or infeasible), and interpretation of the output on the Answer and Sensitivity Reports. In this section we illustrate how to model more realistic problems requiring more than two decision variables. However, the concepts developed for two-variable models apply equally as well to these more complex ones.

The models in this section represent small versions of problems one might find in such diverse areas as production, purchasing, finance, and cash flow accounting. Besides spanning a range of applications areas, each model was constructed to illustrate at least one new linear programming concept. Thus, for each model take note of its application area, the model development, the spreadsheet design, and the analysis and interpretation of the output.

9.4.1 Production Scheduling Models

Assisting manufacturing managers in making production decisions that efficiently utilize scarce resources is an area in which a variety of linear programming models have been applied. Determining production levels, scheduling shift workers and overtime, and determining the cost effectiveness of purchasing additional resources for the manufacturing process are just some of the key decisions that these managers must make. The Galaxy Industries model introduced in Chapter 8 is a simplified version of a production scheduling situation. Here, in a slightly larger version of that model, we illustrate how linear programming can help make some of these management decisions.

GALAXY INDUSTRIES— AN EXPANSION PLAN

Galaxy Expansion.xls

Concepts: Maximization
Sensitivity Analysis (All constraint types)
Both Signs in Objective Function
Unit Conversion
Summation Variables, Percentage Constraints

Galaxy Industries has been very successful during its first six months of operation and is already looking toward product expansion and possible relocation within the year to a facility in Juarez, Mexico, where both labor and material costs are considerably lower. The availability of the cheaper labor and a contract with a local distributor to supply up to 3000 pounds of plastic at a substantially reduced cost will effectively double the profit for Space Rays to $16 per dozen and triple the profit for Zappers to $15 per dozen.

The new facility will be equipped with machinery and staffed with workers to facilitate a 40-hour regular time work schedule. In addition, up to 32 hours of overtime can be scheduled. Accounting for wages, benefits, and additional plant operating expenses, each scheduled overtime hour will cost the company $180 more than regular time hours.

Galaxy has been test marketing two additional products, tentatively named the Big Squirt and the Soaker, which appear to be as popular as the Space Ray and Zapper. Table 9.1 summarizes the profit and requirements for each product line.

Galaxy has a signed contract with Jaycee Toys, Inc. to supply it with 200 dozen Zappers weekly once the relocation has taken place. The marketing department has revised its strategy for the post-relocation period. It has concluded that, to keep total demand at its peak, Galaxy's most popular model, the Space Ray, should account for exactly 50% of total production, while no other product line should account for more than 40%. But now, instead of limiting production to at most 700 dozen weekly, the department wishes to ensure that production will total at least 1000 dozen units weekly.

Management would like to determine the weekly production schedule (including any overtime hours, if necessary) that will maximize its net weekly profit.

TABLE 9.1

Profit and Requirements Per Dozen

Product	Profit	Plastic (lb.)	Production Time (min.)
Space Rays	$16	2	3
Zappers	$15	1	4
Big Squirts	$20	3	5
Soakers	$22	4	6
Available		3000	40 hrs. (Reg.)
			32 hrs. (O/T)

SOLUTION

The following is a brief synopsis of the problem.

- Galaxy wants to maximize its Net Weekly Profit = (Weekly Profit from Sales) − (Extra Cost of Overtime).

- A weekly production schedule, including the amount of overtime to schedule, must be determined.

- The following restrictions exist:
    1. Plastic availability (3000 pounds)
    2. Regular time labor (2400 minutes)
    3. Overtime availability (32 hours)
    4. Minimum production of Zappers (200 dozen)
    5. Appropriate product mix

        (Space Rays = 50% of total production)
        (Zappers, Big Squirts, Soakers ≤ 40% of total production)

    6. Minimum total production (1000 dozen)

Decision Variables

Galaxy must not only decide on the weekly production rates but also determine the number of overtime hours to utilize each week. Thus, we define five decision variables:

X_1 = number of *dozen* Space Rays to be produced each week
X_2 = number of *dozen* Zappers to be produced each week
X_3 = number of *dozen* Big Squirts to be produced each week
X_4 = number of *dozen* Soakers to be produced each week
X_5 = number of *hours* of overtime to be scheduled each week

Objective Function

The total net weekly profit will be the profit from the sale of each product less the cost of overtime. Since each overtime hour costs the company an extra $180, the objective function is:

$$\text{MAXIMIZE } 16X_1 + 15X_2 + 20X_3 + 22X_4 - 180X_5$$

Constraints

The following constraints exist in the Galaxy problem:

- *Plastic*: (Amount of plastic used weekly) ≤ 3000 lbs.
$$2X_1 + X_2 + 3X_3 + 4X_4 \leq 3000$$

- *Production Time*: (Number of production *minutes* used weekly) ≤ (Number of regular *minutes* available) + (Overtime *minutes* used)

Here,

Number of regular time *minutes* available = 60(40) = 2400
Number of overtime *minutes* used is 60(O/T hours used) = $60X_5$

Thus, the production time constraint is:

$$3X_1 + 4X_2 + 5X_3 + 6X_4 \leq 2400 + 60X_5, \text{ or}$$
$$3X_1 + 4X_2 + 5X_3 + 6X_4 - 60X_5 \leq 2400$$

- *Overtime Hours*: (Number of overtime *hours* used) ≤ 32

$$X_5 \leq 32$$

- *Zapper Contract*: (Number of zappers produced weekly) ≥ 200 doz.

$$X_2 \geq 200$$

- *Product Mix*: Since each of the product mix restrictions is expressed as a percentage of the total production, to clarify the model we introduce the following summation *variable*:

$$X_6 = \text{Total weekly production (in dozens of units)}$$

- *Summation Constraint*: Before expressing the product mix constraints, we introduce the *summation constraint* showing that the total weekly production, X_6, is the sum of the weekly production of Space Rays, Zappers, Big Squirts, and Soakers: $X_6 = X_1 + X_2 + X_3 + X_4$, or

$$X_1 + X_2 + X_3 + X_4 - X_6 = 0$$

Now the product mix constraints can be written as

(Weekly production of Space Rays)	$= $ (50% of total production)
X_1	$= .5X_6$
(Weekly production of Zappers)	$\leq$ (40% of total production)
X_2	$\leq .4X_6$
(Weekly production of Big Squirts)	$\leq$ (40% of total production)
X_3	$\leq .4X_6$
(Weekly production of Soakers)	$\leq$ (40% of total production)
X_4	$\leq .4X_6$

or

$$
\begin{aligned}
X_1 \quad\quad\quad\quad\quad\quad &- .5X_6 = 0 \\
X_2 \quad\quad\quad\quad &- .4X_6 \leq 0 \\
X_3 \quad\quad &- .4X_6 \leq 0 \\
X_4 &- .4X_6 \leq 0
\end{aligned}
$$

- Total Production: (Total weekly production) ≥ 1000 dozen.

$$X_6 \geq 1000$$

- Nonnegativity: All decision variables ≥ 0

$$X_1, X_2, X_3, X_4, X_5, X_6 \geq 0$$

The Mathematical Model

Thus, the complete mathematical model for the Galaxy Industries expansion problem is:

$$
\begin{array}{lll}
\text{MAXIMIZE} & 16X_1 + 15X_2 + 20X_3 + 22X_4 - 180X_5 & \text{(Weekly profit)} \\
\text{ST} & & \\
& 2X_1 + X_2 + 3X_3 + 4X_4 & \leq 3000 \text{ (Plastic)} \\
& 3X_1 + 4X_2 + 5X_3 + 6X_4 - 60X_5 & \leq 2400 \text{ (Production time)} \\
& X_5 & \leq 32 \text{ (Overtime)} \\
& X_2 & \geq 200 \text{ (Contract)} \\
& X_1 + X_2 + X_3 + X_4 - X_6 & = 0 \text{ (Definition)} \\
& X_1 - .5X_6 & = 0 \text{ (Space Rays)} \\
& X_2 - .4X_6 & \leq 0 \text{ (Zappers)} \\
& X_3 - .4X_6 & \leq 0 \text{ (Big Squirts)} \\
& X_4 - .4X_6 & \leq 0 \text{ (Soakers)} \\
& X_6 & \geq 1000 \text{ (Total)} \\
& \text{All X's} \geq 0 & \text{(Nonnegativity)}
\end{array}
$$

Excel Solver Input/Output

There are many ways we could set up a spreadsheet to represent the model. Although we use more sophisticated spreadsheets that generate a great deal of additional information in later models in this chapter, at this point, the one we show in Figure 9.3a is only a slight extension of that in Chapter 8. Note that the numbers in row 4 giving the production quantities and scheduled overtime and the numbers in column G giving the total production, the total profit, and the resources used, are the results of executing Solver. The model is constructed as follows:

■ Row 4 is set aside for the values of the decision variables.

■ Input data for the profit and the first four functional constraints are entered into rows 6 through 10. The SUMPRODUCT function is used to get the total left-hand side values.

■ Cell G4 is programmed to be the sum of the other variables. This represents the summation constraint, and since it will be determined by the other variables, it is NOT a changing cell.

■ The percentage constraints of exactly 50% for Space Rays and at most 40% for the other models and the restriction of a minimum production of 1000 dozen units are reflected in the Solver dialogue box. Note that the right-hand side of these constraints is not a cell. For the percentage constraints, it is an expression, and for the minimum production constraint, it is a constant.

Clicking Solve gives the result shown in Figure 9.3a. Figure 9.3b is the corresponding Sensitivity Report.

FIGURE 9.3a   Spreadsheet for the Expansion of Galaxy Industries

Galaxy Expansion.xls

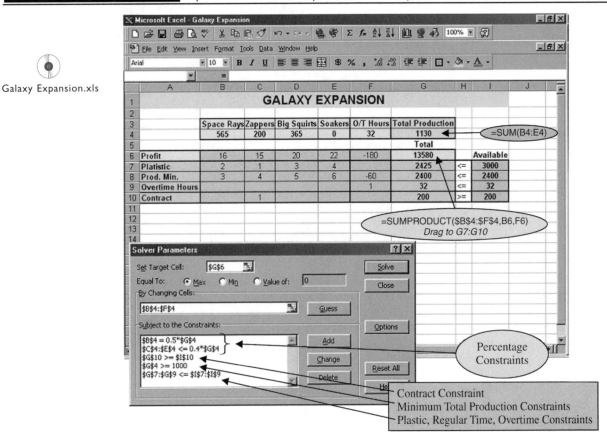

FIGURE 9.3b

Sensitivity Report for the
Expansion of Galaxy Industries

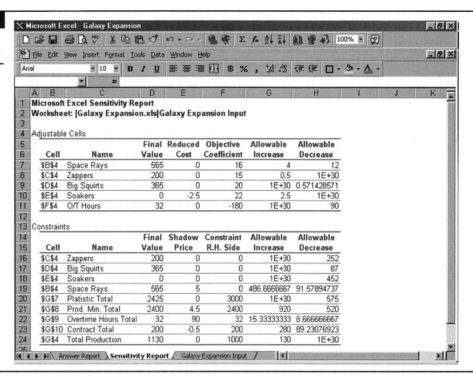

Analysis

From Figure 9.3a we can determine the gross profit for each model by multiplying the unit profit per dozen times the number of dozens produced. The cost of overtime is $32(\$180) = \$5760$. This gives the following results.[3]

Model	Dozens Produced	Total Gross Profit	Percent of Total
Space Rays	565	$ 9,040	50.0%
Zappers	200	$ 3,000	17.7%
Big Squirts	365	$ 7,300	32.3%
Soakers	0	$ 0	0%
Total	1130	$19,340	
	Cost of Overtime	$ 5,760	
	NET PROFIT	$13,580	

Furthermore, we note that:

- The total production of 1130 dozen exceeds the minimum requirement by 130 dozen.

- All 2400 minutes of regular time and all 32 hours of overtime will be used.

- Only 2425 of the 3000 pounds of available plastic will be used.

From the Sensitivity Report information shown in Figure 9.3b, we subtract the Allowable Decrease from and add the Allowable Increase to the profit coefficients to

---

[3] In a more elaborate spreadsheet design, such as several of those given in the remainder of this chapter, we could have programmed various cells to generate this information automatically.

determine the following ranges of optimality for which the above solution will remain optimal. Recall that the range of optimality is the range of values for an objective function coefficient within which the optimal solution remains valid, as long as no other changes are made.

Model	Profit Per Dozen	Minimum Profit Per Dozen	Maximum Profit Per Dozen
Space Rays	$16.00	$ 4.00	$20.00
Zappers	$15.00	No Minimum	$15.50
Big Squirts	$20.00	$19.43	No Maximum
Soakers	$22.00	No Minimum	$24.50

We further note from Figure 9.3b that:

- The above solution will remain optimal as long as the cost of overtime hours is less than $270 (Allowable Decrease from −180 is 90 (cell H11)).

- The profit per dozen Soakers must increase by $2.50 (cell E10) to $24.50 before they will be profitable to produce.

- Additional regular time minutes will add $4.50 per minute or $270 per hour to the total profit (cell E21). This holds true for up to an additional 920 minutes or 15 1/3 hours (cell G21).

- Additional (or fewer) overtime hours above or below the 32 scheduled overtime hours will add (or subtract) $90 to the total profit (cell E22). This holds true as long as the total number of overtime hours is between 23 1/3 hours and 47 1/3 hours (obtained from 32 − 8 2/3 (cell H22) and 32 + 15 1/3 (cell G22)).

- Each additional dozen Zappers added to the contract with Jaycee Toys will subtract $0.50 (cell E23) from the total profit (up to an additional 280 dozen (cell G23)). A reduction in the contract amount will save $0.50 per dozen for a reduction not to exceed 89.23 dozen (cell H23). If the contract requirement was outside this range, we would have to re-solve the problem to determine a new shadow price.

- Each dozen Space Rays that are allowed to be produced *above 50% of the total* will add $5.00 (cell E19) to the total profit (up to 486 2/3 dozen more than 50% (cell G19)). Again the problem must be re-solved if the change is outside this range.

Based on this information, the manager might ask for permission to schedule additional overtime hours, increase the percentage of Space Rays produced, reduce the contract with Jaycee Toys, or find ways to increase the profit for Soakers. However, if any changes are made, before proceeding management should first determine if the changes would affect any of the other parameters or basic assumptions underlying the model.

9.4.2 Portfolio Models

Numerous mathematical models have been developed for a variety of financial/portfolio models. These models take into account return projections, measures of risk and volatility, liquidity, and long- and short-term investment goals. Some of these models are nonlinear in nature. However, here we present a situation that could be modeled as a linear program.

JONES INVESTMENT SERVICE

Jones Investment.xls

Concepts: Minimization
                Sensitivity Analysis (All constraint types)

Charles Jones is a financial advisor who specializes in making recommendations to investors who have recently come into unexpected sums of money from inheritances, lottery winnings, and the like. He discusses investment goals with his clients, taking into account each client's attitude toward risk and liquidity.

After an initial consultation with a client, Charles selects a group of stocks, bonds, mutual funds, savings plans, and other investments that he feels may be appropriate for consideration in the portfolio. He then secures information on each investment and determines his own rating. With this information he develops a chart giving the risk factors (numbers between 0 and 100, based on his evaluation), expected returns based on current and projected company operations, and liquidity information. At the second meeting Charles defines the client's goals more specifically. The responses are entered into a linear programming model, and a recommendation is made to the client based on the results of the model.

Frank Baklarz has just inherited $100,000. Based on their initial meeting, Charles has found Frank to be quite risk-averse. Charles, therefore, suggests the following potential investments that can offer good returns with small risk.

Potential Investment	Expected Return	Jones's Rating	Liquidity Analysis	Risk Factor
Savings account	4.0%	A	Immediate	0
Certificate of deposit	5.2%	A	5-year	0
Atlantic Lighting	7.1%	B+	Immediate	25
Arkansas REIT	10.0%	B	Immediate	30
Bedrock Insurance annuity	8.2%	A	1-year	20
Nocal Mining bond	6.5%	B+	1-year	15
Minicomp Systems	20.0%	A	Immediate	65
Antony Hotels	12.5%	C	Immediate	40

Based on their second meeting, Charles has been able to help Frank develop the following portfolio goals.

1. An expected annual return of at least 7.5%

2. At least 50% of the inheritance in A-rated investments

3. At least 40% of the inheritance in immediately liquid investments

4. No more than $30,000 in savings accounts and certificates of deposit

Given that Frank is risk-averse, Charles would like to make a final recommendation that will minimize total risk while meeting these goals. As part of his service, Charles would also like to inform Frank of potential what-if scenarios associated with this recommendation.

SOLUTION

The following is a brief summary of the problem.

■   Determine the amount to be placed in each investment.

■   Minimize total overall risk.

■   Invest all $100,000.

■   Meet the goals developed with Frank Baklarz.

The Mathematical Model

Defining the X's as the amount Frank should allot to each investment, the following linear model represents the situation:

$$\text{MINIMIZE} \quad 25X_3 + 30X_4 + 20X_5 + 15X_6 + 65X_7 + 40X_8 \quad \text{(Risk)}$$

ST

$$
\begin{aligned}
X_1 + X_2 + X_3 + X_4 + X_5 + X_6 + X_7 + X_8 &= 100{,}000 \text{ (Total)} \\
.04X_1 + .052X_2 + .071X_3 + .1X_4 + .082X_5 + .065X_6 + .2X_7 + .125X_8 &\geq 7500 \text{ (Return)} \\
X_1 + X_2 + X_5 + X_7 &\geq 50{,}000 \text{ (A-Rated)} \\
X_1 + X_3 + X_4 + X_7 + X_8 &\geq 40{,}000 \text{ (Liquid)} \\
X_1 + X_2 &\leq 30{,}000 \text{ (Savings/CD)}
\end{aligned}
$$

$$\text{All X's} \geq 0$$

Since Jones Investment Service shares its findings directly with its clients, Charles wants to have a spreadsheet designed with his client in mind. Thus, the spreadsheet should convey all the requisite information without looking like a linear programming model. Accordingly, Charles used the "user-friendly" spreadsheet shown in Figure 9.4a. Here the right-hand sides of the constraints are in cells C2, F16, F17, F18, and F19, respectively, and cells C14, B13, D16, D17, D18, and D19 have been programmed as shown to give the quantity designated in the cells to their left. Note that SUMIF formulas in cells D17 and D18 sum only the values that meet the criteria of "A" rating and "Immediate" liquidity, respectively. Cells B5:B12 are reserved for the values of the decision variables.

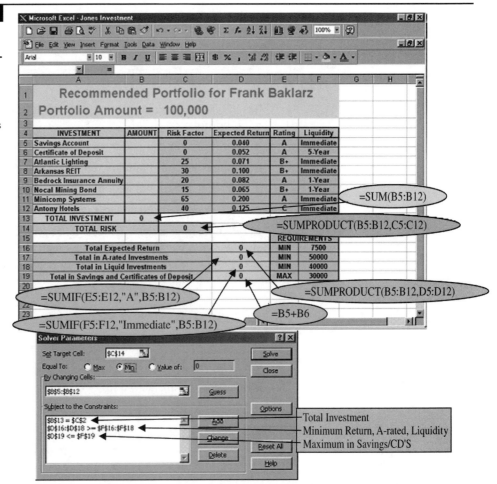

FIGURE 9.4a

Excel Spreadsheet and Dialogue Box for Frank Baklarz

Jones Investment.xls

FIGURE 9.4b

Optimal Portfolio for Frank Baklarz

Recommended Portfolio for Frank Baklarz

Portfolio Amount = 100,000

INVESTMENT	AMOUNT	Risk Factor	Expected Return	Rating	Liquidity
Savings Account	17333.33	0	0.040	A	Immediate
Certificate of Deposit	12666.67	0	0.052	A	5-Year
Atlantic Lighting	0	25	0.071	B+	Immediate
Arkansas REIT	22666.67	30	0.100	B+	Immediate
Bedrock Insurance Annuity	47333.33	20	0.082	A	1-Year
Nocal Mining Bond	0	15	0.065	B+	1-Year
Minicomp Systems	0	65	0.200	A	Immediate
Antony Hotels	0	40	0.125	C	Immediate
TOTAL INVESTMENT	100000				
TOTAL RISK		1626666.667			

		REQUIREMENTS	
Total Expected Return	7500	MIN	7500
Total in A-rated Investments	77333.33333	MIN	50000
Total in Liquid Investments	40000	MIN	40000
Total in Savings and Certificates of Deposit	30000	MAX	30000

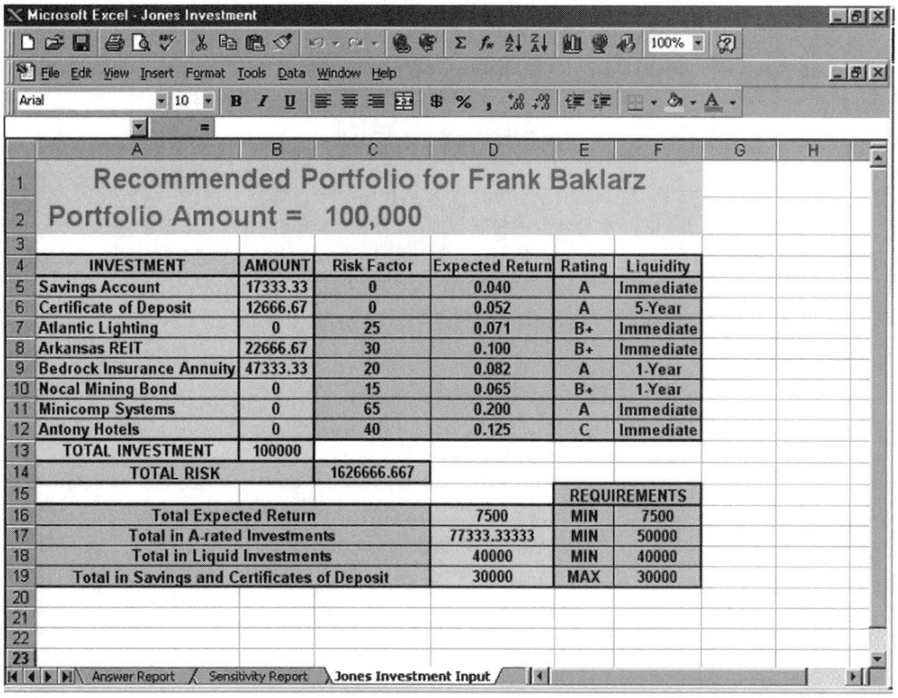

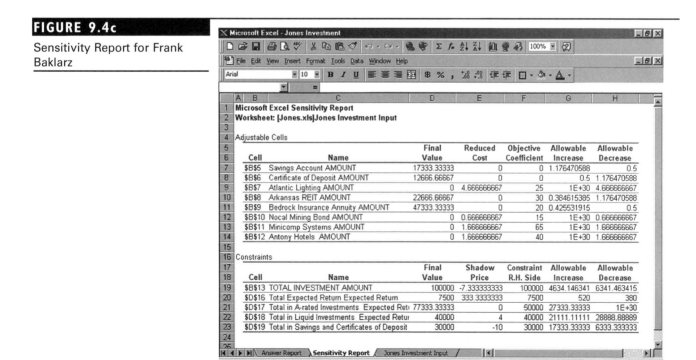

After verifying all requirements with Frank Baklarz, Charles clicked on Excel Solver giving the results and Sensitivity Report in Figures 9.4b and 9.4c, respectively.

Analysis

The spreadsheet is designed for easy reading and interpretation. In addition to the optimal solution, it is easy to see that the binding constraints are those requiring an expected annual return of at least $7500, a minimum amount of $40,000 in immediately liquid

FIGURE 9.4c

Sensitivity Report for Frank Baklarz

Microsoft Excel Sensitivity Report
Worksheet: [Jones.xls]Jones Investment Input

Adjustable Cells

Cell	Name	Final Value	Reduced Cost	Objective Coefficient	Allowable Increase	Allowable Decrease
$B$5	Savings Account AMOUNT	17333.33333	0	0	1.176470588	0.5
$B$6	Certificate of Deposit AMOUNT	12666.66667	0	0	0.5	1.176470588
$B$7	Atlantic Lighting AMOUNT	0	4.666666667	25	1E+30	4.666666667
$B$8	Arkansas REIT AMOUNT	22666.66667	0	30	0.384615385	1.176470588
$B$9	Bedrock Insurance Annuity AMOUNT	47333.33333	0	20	0.425531915	0.5
$B$10	Nocal Mining Bond AMOUNT	0	0.666666667	15	1E+30	0.666666667
$B$11	Minicomp Systems AMOUNT	0	1.666666667	65	1E+30	1.666666667
$B$12	Antony Hotels AMOUNT	0	1.666666667	40	1E+30	1.666666667

Constraints

Cell	Name	Final Value	Shadow Price	Constraint R.H. Side	Allowable Increase	Allowable Decrease
$B$13	TOTAL INVESTMENT AMOUNT	100000	-7.333333333	100000	4634.146341	6341.463415
$D$16	Total Expected Return Expected Return	7500	333.3333333	7500	520	380
$D$17	Total in A-rated Investments Expected Ret	77333.33333	0	50000	27333.33333	1E+30
$D$18	Total in Liquid Investments Expected Retur	40000	4	40000	21111.11111	28888.88889
$D$19	Total in Savings and Certificates of Deposit	30000	-10	30000	17333.33333	6333.333333

investments, and a maximum amount of $30,000 in the savings account and the certificate of deposit. This portfolio exceeds Frank's minimum requirement of at least $50,000 in A-rated investments by $27,333.

Recommendation

According to the spreadsheet in Figure 9.4b, Charles should recommend to Frank that he invest $17,333 in a savings account, $12,667 in a certificate of deposit, $22,667 in Arkansas REIT, and $47,333 in the Bedrock Insurance Annuity. This gives an overall risk value of 1,626,667 (an average risk factor of 16.27 per dollar invested). Any other combination of investments will give a higher risk value.

Reduced Costs

According to the Sensitivity Report in Figure 9.4c, for Atlantic Lighting to be included in the portfolio, its risk factor would have to be lowered by 4.67 to 20.33. Similarly, to include Nocal Mining, Minicomp Systems, or Antony Hotels requires a reduction in their risk factors of 0.67, 1.67, and 1.67, respectively.

Range of Optimality

For each investment, the "Allowable Increase" and "Allowable Decrease" columns in the Sensitivity Report give the minimum and maximum amounts that the risk factors can change without altering Charles's recommendation. For example, the range of optimality of the risk factor for the Bedrock Insurance annuity is between 19.5(=20 − 0.5) and 20.43(=20 + 0.43). Recall that the range of optimality applies to changing one investment at a time. Since negative risk factors do not make sense, the minimum risk factors for the savings account and certificate of deposit would be 0.

Shadow Prices

The shadow prices in the Sensitivity Report give us the following information:

- If an extra dollar were invested above the $100,000, the risk value would improve (decrease) by 7.33.
- For every extra dollar increase to the minimum expected annual return, the overall risk value would increase by 333.33.
- For every extra dollar that must be made immediately liquid, the overall risk value would increase by 4.
- For every extra dollar that is allowed to be invested in a savings account or a certificate of deposit, the risk value would decrease by 10.
- No change in total risk value would result from requiring that additional dollars be invested in A-rated investments.

Range of Feasibility

The Allowable Increase and Allowable Decrease to the original right-hand side coefficients give the range of feasibility of individual changes to the right-hand side within which the shadow prices remain constant. For example, the range of feasibility corresponding to the $7500 minimum return is ($7500 − $380) to ($7500 + $520) or from $7120 to $8020. An Allowable Decrease of 1E+30 is effectively infinity; thus, −∞ is the minimum right-hand side value in the range of feasibility for the amount invested in A-rated investments.

9.4.3 Public Sector Models

National, state, and local governments and agencies are charged with distributing resources for the public good. Frequently, political pressures and conflicts cause these entities to try to do more than the available resources will allow. When that happens, several remedies are possible. One is to try to meet a subset, but not all, of a perceived set of constraints, as is the case of one of the homework exercises in this chapter. A second approach is to treat several of the constraints as "goals" and to prioritize and weight these goals. This is called a "goal programming" approach, which is discussed in Chapter 13 on the accompanying CD-ROM. A third approach, and the one illustrated here, is simply to scale back and try to "live within one's means."

ST. JOSEPH PUBLIC UTILITY COMMISSION

Saint Joseph.xls
Saint Joseph (Revised).xls

Concepts: Ignoring Integer Restrictions
                    Summation Variable
                    Infeasibility
                    Multiple Optimal Solutions

The St. Joseph Public Utilities Commission has been charged with inspecting and reporting utility problems that have resulted from recent floods in the area. Concerns have been raised about the damage done to electrical wiring, gas lines, and insulation. The Commission has one week to carry out its inspections. It has been assigned three electrical inspectors and two gas inspectors, each available for 40 hours, to analyze structures in their respective areas of expertise. In addition, the Commission has allocated $10,000 for up to 100 hours (at $100 per hour) of consulting time from Weathertight Insulation, a local expert in home and industrial insulation.

These experts are assigned to inspect private homes, businesses (office complexes), and industrial plants in the area. The goal is to thoroughly inspect as many structures as possible during the allotted time in order to gather the requisite information. However, the minimum requirements are to inspect at least eight office buildings and eight industrial plants, and to make sure that at least 60% of the inspections are of private homes.

Once the total number of each type of structure to be inspected has been determined, the actual inspections will be done by choosing a random sample from those that are served by the St. Joseph Public Utility Commission. The Commission has mandated the following approximate inspection hours for each type of inspection:

	Electrical	Gas	Insulation
Homes	2	1	3
Offices	4	3	2
Plants	6	3	1

A team of management science consultants has been hired to suggest how many homes, office buildings, and plants should be inspected.

SOLUTION

The following is a brief summary of the problem faced by the St. Joseph Public Utilities Commission.

- St. Joseph must determine the number of homes, office complexes, and plants to be inspected.
- It wishes to maximize the total number of structures inspected.
- At least eight offices and eight plants are to be inspected.
- At least 60% of the inspections should involve private homes.
- At most, 120 hours (3×40) can be allocated for electrical inspections, 80 hours (2×40) for gas inspections, and 100 consulting hours for insulation inspection

The management science team has decided to formulate the problem as a linear program, although the results should be integer-valued. If the linear program does not generate an integer solution, another method such as integer programming or dynamic programming (which is discussed in Chapter 13 on the accompanying CD-ROM) must be used, or St. Joseph could accept a feasible rounded solution.

Decision Variables

The team defined the following variables:

$$X_1 = \text{number of homes to be inspected}$$
$$X_2 = \text{number of office complexes to be inspected}$$
$$X_3 = \text{number of industrial plants to be inspected}$$

and they used the following summation variable

$$X_4 = \text{total number of structures to be inspected}$$

Objective Function

The problem is to determine the maximum number of structures that can be inspected, subject to the constraints. Thus, the objective function of the model is simply:

$$\text{MAXIMIZE } X_4$$

Constraints

The summation constraint for X_4 is:

$$X_1 + X_2 + X_3 - X_4 = 0$$

The minimum number of office complexes and plants to be inspected are simply modeled as

$$X_2 \geq 8$$
$$X_3 \geq 8$$

The fact that at least 60% of the inspections must be of homes is modeled as

$$X_1 \geq 0.6X_4$$

or

$$X_1 - 0.6X_4 \geq 0$$

Finally, the constraints on the time limits for electrical, gas, and insulation inspections are:

$$2X_1 + 4X_2 + 6X_3 \leq 120 \text{ (Electrical)}$$
$$1X_1 + 3X_2 + 3X_3 \leq 80 \text{ (Gas)}$$
$$3X_1 + 2X_2 + 1X_3 \leq 100 \text{ (Insulation)}$$

The Linear Programming Model

The complete linear programming model for the St. Joseph Public Utility Commission is:

$$
\begin{array}{lrl}
\text{MAXIMIZE} & X_4 & \text{(Total structures)} \\
\text{ST} & & \\
X_1 + X_2 + X_3 - X_4 = & 0 & \text{(Summation)} \\
X_2 \geq & 8 & \text{(Minimum offices)} \\
X_3 \geq & 8 & \text{(Minimum plants)} \\
X_1 - 0.6X_4 \geq & 0 & (\geq 60\% \text{ Homes)} \\
2X_1 + 4X_2 + 6X_3 \leq & 120 & \text{(Electrical)} \\
X_1 + 3X_2 + 3X_3 \leq & 80 & \text{(Gas)} \\
3X_1 + 2X_2 + 1X_3 \leq & 100 & \text{(Insulation)} \\
\text{All } X\text{'s} \geq & 0 &
\end{array}
$$

Excel Solver Input/Output and Analysis

Figure 9.5a shows the Excel spreadsheet and Solver dialogue box used by management science consultants. Note that the summation constraint is included in cell B9. The constraint requiring a minimum limit of 60% of the inspections to be houses can be expressed as $X_1 \geq .6X_4$. By entering the formula 5.6*B9 into cell C5, this constraint requires (cell B5) $\geq$ (cell C5), which is part of the first set of constraints in the dialogue box.

FIGURE 9.5a   Input for the St. Joseph Public Utility Commission

Saint Joseph.xls

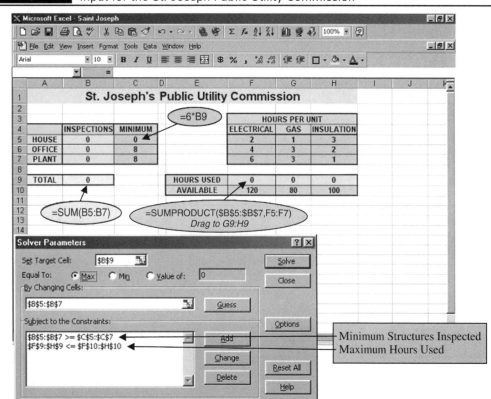

But when Solve was clicked, instead of an optimal solution, Solver returned the dialogue box shown in Figure 9.5b. Needless to say, the Commission was not too pleased with this analysis. In fact, it was beginning to conclude that the management science consultants (and perhaps management science itself) could not be trusted to give the desired results.

When the consultants were asked to explain this result, they pointed out the reason for infeasibility. Even if only the minimum eight offices and eight plants were inspected, 80 of the 120 electrical hours [4(8) + 6(8)] would be used, leaving only 40 hours to inspect homes. At two hours per home, a maximum of 20 homes could be inspected. Thus, a total of 36 structures would be inspected, only 20 of which would be homes. This represents only 55.56% of the total homes (=20/36), not the minimum 60% the Commission desired.

In other words, the problem had been formulated correctly by the management science team, but the Commission had simply given them a set of constraints that were impossible to meet. Given this situation, after much debate the Commission decided that it could get by with inspecting a minimum of six office buildings and six plants. This would use up 60 electrical hours, leaving 60 electrical hours to inspect 30 homes, which far exceeds the 60% minimum limit on homes.

The Commission was about to initiate this action when it was pointed out that inspecting 30 homes, six office buildings, and six plants would use up 108 hours for insulation inspection [3(30) + 2(6) + 1(6)], exceeding the 100 available inspection hours. What to do?

The Commission asked the management science consultants to reconsider their problem in light of these relaxed constraints and offer a recommendation. The consultants changed the values in cells C6 and C7 of their spreadsheet from 8 to 6 and again called Solver to determine an optimal solution. The resulting spreadsheet and the Sensitivity Report are shown in Figures 9.6a and 9.6b, respectively.

The optimal solution turned out to have integer values, and thus the consultants could now report that a maximum of 40 structures (27 houses, 6 office buildings, and 7 plants) could be inspected; 67.5% (=27/40) of the inspected structures would be houses. All 120 electrical inspection hours and all 100 insulation inspection hours would be used. A total of 12 hours of gas inspection time would remain unused.

An Alternate Optimal Solution

But the consultants noted from the Sensitivity Report in Figure 9.6b that the Allowable Increase of Office Inspections and the Allowable Decrease for both House Inspections and Plant Inspections were all 0. From our discussion in Chapter 8, recall that this is an indication that there may be alternate optimal solutions. Following the

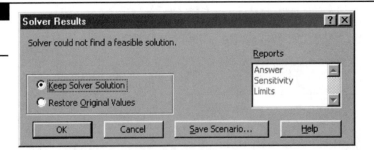

FIGURE 9.5b

Solver Found the St. Joseph Utility Model to Be Infeasible

FIGURE 9.6a

Optimal Solution for the St. Joseph Public Utility Commission

Saint Joseph (Revised).xls

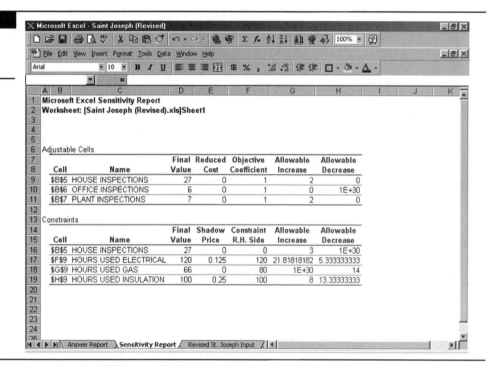

FIGURE 9.6b

Sensitivity Report for the St. Joseph Public Utility Commission

procedure for generating alternate optimal solutions outlined in Chapter 8, the consultants:

- Added a constraint requiring the total number of inspections to be 40
- Changed the objective function to MAX X_2 (cell B6), since the Allowable Increase for office building inspections is 0. (Alternatively, they could have chosen to *minimize* either cell B5 or B7 since the Allowable *Decrease* for house inspections or plant inspections is also 0.)

Figure 9.7 shows the dialogue box and the resulting spreadsheet.

This spreadsheet shows that inspecting 26 houses, 8 office buildings, and 6 plants would be an alternative way of inspecting 40 structures while staying within the constraints of the model. In this solution, 65% (=26/40) of the structures inspected would be houses.

FIGURE 9.7

Alternate Optimal Solution for St. Joseph's Public Utility Commission

Saint Joseph (Revised).xls
(Alternative Solution Worksheet)

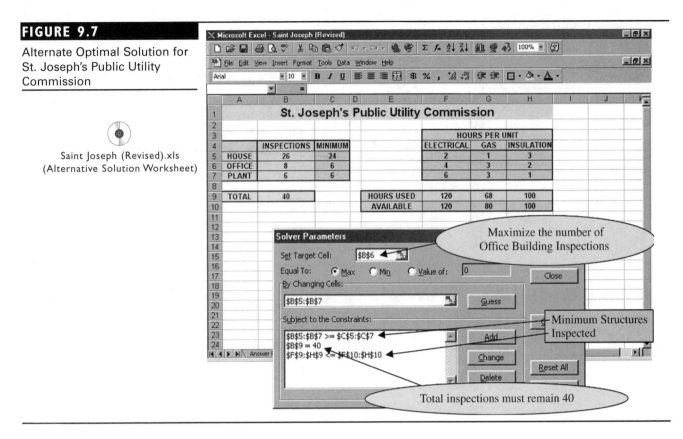

Although any weighted average of these two solutions would also be optimal, since the first solution calls for inspecting 26 homes and the second 27 homes, any weighted average of the two solutions would yield a *fractional* solution of between 26 and 27 homes to be inspected. Thus, the consultants reported that these two solutions are the only optimal solutions that yield integers for the number of homes, office complexes, and plants to be inspected.

Faced with two feasible alternatives, the Commission had the opportunity to inject some political preferences into the decision process while still inspecting 40 structures.

9.4.4 Purchasing Models

Purchasing models can take into account customer demand, budgets, cash flow, advertising, and inventory restrictions. In today's global economy, purchasing models play a key role in balancing customer satisfaction levels within the limited resources of the business enterprise. In the following application we present a very simplified model that takes only a few of these factors into account. We have purposely presented this problem in such a way as to illustrate another situation that can arise when building mathematical models—that of failing to consider all (or at least not enough) of the limiting factors in the original formulation.

EUROMERICA LIQUORS	*Concepts*:	Choosing an Objective

Concepts:
Choosing an Objective
Lower Bound Constraints
Unboundedness
"Slightly" Violated Constraints
Interpretation of Reduced Costs for Bounded Variables

Euromerica Liquors.xls
Euromerica Liquors (Revised).xls

Euromerica Liquors of Jersey City, New Jersey purchases and distributes a number of wines to retailers. See Table 9.2. Purchasing manager Maria Arias has been asked to order at least 800 bottles of each wine during the next purchase cycle. The only other direction Maria has been given is that, in accordance with a long-standing company policy, she is to order at least twice as many domestic (U.S.) bottles as imported bottles in any cycle. Management believes that this policy promotes a steady sales flow that keeps inventory costs at a minimum. Maria must decide exactly how many bottles of each type of wine the company is to purchase during this ordering cycle.

SOLUTION

To summarize, Maria must:

- determine the number of bottles of each type of wine to purchase
- order at least 800 of each type
- order at least twice as many domestic bottles as imported bottles
- select an appropriate objective function

Decision Variables

The four decision variables can be defined as:

X_1 = bottles of Napa Gold purchased in this purchase cycle
X_2 = bottles of Cayuga Lake purchased in this purchase cycle
X_3 = bottles of Seine Soir purchased in this purchase cycle
X_4 = bottles of Bella Bella purchased in this purchase cycle

Objective Function

At first, Maria reasoned that since Euromerica Liquors' goal is to make good profits, her objective should be to maximize the profit from the purchases made during this purchase cycle. Because inventory costs are assumed to be small due to the company's ordering policy, she defined the profit coefficients in terms of the selling price minus the purchase cost per bottle. Thus, the unit profits for the respective decision variables are $1.75, $1.50, $3, and $2, and the objective function is:

$$\text{MAX } 1.75X_1 + 1.50X_2 + 3X3 + 2X_4$$

TABLE 9.2			
Euromerica Liquors' Wine Purchases and Distribution			
Wine	**Country**	**Cost**	**Selling Price**
Napa Gold	U.S.	$2.50	$4.25
Cayuga Lake	U.S.	$3.00	$4.50
Seine Soir	France	$5.00	$8.00
Bella Bella	Italy	$4.00	$6.00

Constraints

The following constraints must be considered

Minimum Production: At least 800 bottles of each of the wines are to be purchased:

$$X_1 \geq 800$$
$$X_2 \geq 800$$
$$X_3 \geq 800$$
$$X_4 \geq 800$$

These constraints could be entered in linear programming software either as functional constraints or as lower bound constraints that would replace the nonnegativity constraints for the variables.

Mix Constraint: (The number of bottles of domestic wine purchased) should be at least (twice the number of bottles of imported wine purchased):

$$X_1 + X_2 \geq 2(X_3 + X_4)$$

or

$$X_1 + X_2 - 2X_3 - 2X_4 \geq 0$$

The Mathematical Model

The complete model can now be formulated as

$$
\begin{array}{lllllll}
\text{MAXIMIZE} & 1.75X_1 + & 1.50X_2 + & 3X_3 + & 2X_4 & & \\
\text{ST} & X_1 & & & & \geq & 800 \\
& & X_2 & & & \geq & 800 \\
& & & X_3 & & \geq & 800 \\
& & & & X_4 & \geq & 800 \\
& X_1 + & X_2 - & 2X_3 - & 2X_4 & \geq & 0
\end{array}
$$

Excel Input/Output and Analysis

Maria created the Excel spreadsheet and Solver dialogue box shown in Figure 9.8a, with cells C4:C7 set aside for the number of bottles to order.

When she clicked Solve, however, she got the result shown in Figure 9.8b. Recall that the message "The Set Cell values do not converge" is Excel's way of stating that the problem is unbounded.

But Euromerica cannot make an infinite profit! When Maria examined the model, she realized that she had ignored the following considerations when building the model:

- Euromerica has a finite budget for the procurement of bottles of wine during the purchase cycle.
- The suppliers have a finite amount of product available.
- There is a limit on demand from the wine-buying public.

Undaunted, Maria discussed the situation with management and discovered that they wished to commit no more than $28,000 to purchase wine during this cycle. She then contacted the wine producers and found that there were ample supplies of Cayuga Lake and Bella Bella, but that only 300 cases of Napa Gold and 200 cases of

FIGURE 9.8a

Spreadsheet and Dialogue Box for Euromerica Liquors

Euromerica Liquors.xls

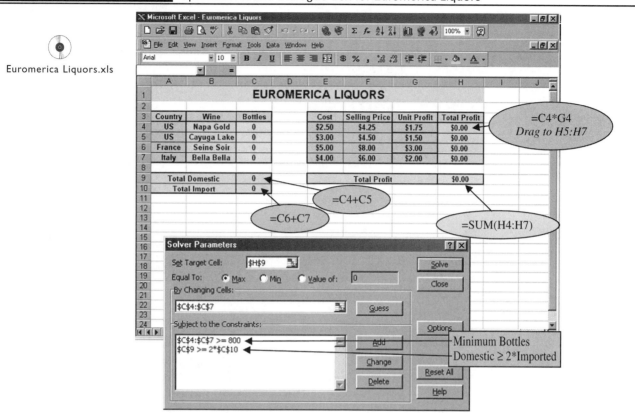

FIGURE 9.8b

Solver Results for Euromerica Liquors—Unbounded Solution

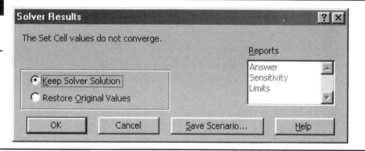

Seine Soir were available (each case contains 12 bottles). Finally, she performed a market survey and, based on the results, concluded that no more than 10,000 total bottles should be purchased. Thus, the revised model is:

$$
\begin{array}{llr}
\text{MAXIMIZE} & 1.75X_1 + 1.50X_2 + 3X_3 + 2X_4 & \\
\text{ST} & X_1 & \geq 800 \\
& X_2 & \geq 800 \\
& X_3 & \geq 800 \\
& X_4 & \geq 800 \\
& X_1 + X_2 - 2X_3 - 2X_4 & \geq 0 \\
& 2.50X_1 + 3.00X_2 + 5X_3 + 4X_4 & \leq 28{,}000 \text{ (Budget)} \\
& X_1 & \leq 3600 \text{ (Napa)} \\
& X_3 & \leq 2400 \text{ (Seine)} \\
& X_1 + X_2 + X_3 + X_4 & \leq 10{,}000 \text{ (Total)}
\end{array}
$$

Maria revised her spreadsheet to reflect these changes by adding cells C11 and C13 to reflect the total number of bottles purchased and the amount of budget spent and cells G11 and G13 to reflect the limits on the maximum number of bottles purchased and the cycle budget. When the constraints for the maximum number of bottles purchased and the maximum budget expenditure along with limits on the availability of Napa Gold and Seine Soire were added to the Solver dialogue box, clicking Solve generated the optimal spreadsheet and Sensitivity Report shown in Figures 9.9a and 9.9b.

Maria rounded off the solution to *full cases* and placed them in the order shown in Table 9.3. Note that this proposal is $20 over the budget limit of $28,000. Although the $28,000 limit was a restriction, it was probably a strong guideline rather than a hard and fast value. Hence, Maria had no qualms about recommending this solution.

FIGURE 9.9a   Revised Spreadsheet for Euromerica Liquors

Euromerica Revised.xls

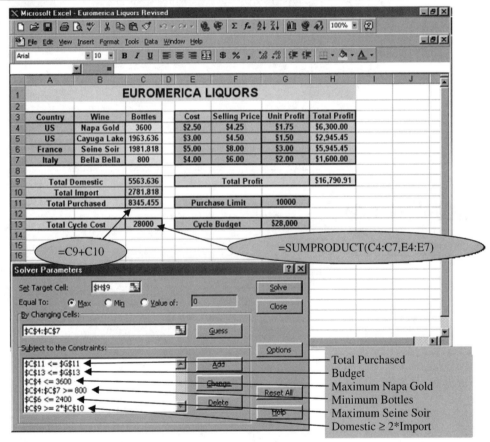

TABLE 9.3	Wine	Bottles	Cases	Cost	Profit
Euromerica Liquors' Solution	Napa Gold	3600	300	$ 9,000	$ 6,300
	Cayuga Lake	1968	164	$ 5,904	$ 2,952
	Seine Soir	1980	165	$ 9,900	$ 1,608
	Bella Bella	804	67	$ 3,216	$ 1,608
	Total	8352	696	$28,020	$16,800

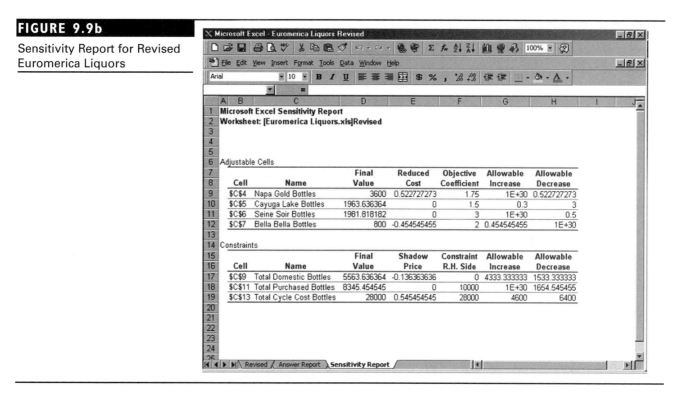

FIGURE 9.9b

Sensitivity Report for Revised
Euromerica Liquors

Reduced Cost for Bounded Variables

In Chapter 8 we defined the reduced cost for a variable as the amount the objective function would change if the value of that variable were increased from 0 to 1. There we implicitly assumed that the lower bound for the variable was 0 and that there was no upper bound. When a variable is defined to be a **bounded variable** by restricting its cell value in the spreadsheet to be at least or at most some nonzero constant, the reduced cost indicates the change in the objective function value if that bound were changed by 1.

In Figure 9.9b Maria noticed that the number of Napa Gold bottles purchased would be its upper bound of 3600. She also noticed that the number of Bella Bella bottles purchased would be at its lower bound of 800. Thus, she reported to management that if she were allowed to *increase* the number of bottles of Napa Gold (above 3600), overall profit would increase by slightly more than $0.52 per bottle, whereas if she were allowed to *decrease* the number of bottles of Bella Bella ordered (below 800), profit would increase by slightly more than $0.45 per bottle.

9.4.5 Blending Models

One of the early successful applications of linear programming models was that of aiding executives in the oil industry in determining how much raw crude oil to purchase from various sources and how to blend these oils into useful gasoline and other byproducts. Each of these products has certain specifications that must be met such as a minimum octane rating or a maximum vapor pressure level. The United Oil Company model presented here is a simplified version of such a model. Other industries where similar blending models are useful include the garment and food industries, which blend several raw materials from various sources into finished products.

UNITED OIL COMPANY

United Oil.xls

Concepts: Variable Definitions for Blending Models
Calculation of Objective Coefficients
Ratio Constraints
Summation Variables
Alternate Optimal Solutions
Hidden Cells on Spreadsheet

United Oil blends two input streams of crude oil products—alkylate and catalytic cracked (c.c.)—to meet demand for weekly contracts for regular (12,000 barrels), mid-grade (7500 barrels), and premium (4500 barrels) gasolines. Each week United can purchase up to 15,000 barrels of alkylate and up to 15,000 barrels of catalytic cracked. Because of demand, it can sell all blended gasolines, including any production that exceeds its contracts.

To be classified as regular, mid-grade, or premium, gasolines must meet minimum octane and maximum vapor pressure requirements. The octane rating and vapor pressure of a blended gasoline is assumed to be the weighted average of the crude oil products in the blend. Relevant cost/pricing, octane, and vapor pressure data are given in Tables 9.4 and 9.5.

United must decide how to blend the crude oil products into commercial gasolines in order to maximize its weekly profit.

SOLUTION

The problem for United Oil is to:

■ determine how many barrels of alkylate to blend into regular, mid-grade, and premium and how many barrels of catalytic cracked to blend into regular, mid-grade, and premium each week

■ maximize total weekly profit

TABLE 9.4

Cost/pricing, Octane, and Vapor Pressure Data—United Oil

Product	Crude Oil Product Data		
	Octane Rating	Vapor Pressure (lb./sq.in.)	Cost per Barrel
Alkylate	98	5	$19
Catalytic cracked	86	9	$16

TABLE 9.5

Gasoline Octane Rating, Vapor Pressure, and Barrel Profit

Gasoline	Blended Gasoline Requirements		
	Minimum Octane Rating	Maximum Vapor Pressure	Selling Price per Barrel
Regular	87	9	$18
Mid-grade	89	7	$20
Premium	92	6	$23

- remain within raw gas availabilities
- meet contract requirements
- produce gasoline blends that meet the octane and vapor pressure requirements

Decision Variables (First Pass)

The pending decision is to determine how much of each crude oil (X, Y) to blend into each of the three grades (1, 2, 3) each week:

X_1 = number of barrels of alkylate blended into regular weekly
X_2 = number of barrels of alkylate blended into mid-grade weekly
X_3 = number of barrels of alkylate blended into premiumweekly
Y_1 = number of barrels of catalytic cracked blended into regular weekly
Y_2 = number of barrels of catalytic cracked blended into mid-grade weekly
Y_3 = number of barrels of catalytic cracked blended into premium weekly

Objective Function

The profit made on a barrel of crude product blended into a commercial gasoline is the difference between the selling price of the blended gasoline and the cost of the crude product. Table 9.6 gives the profit coefficients. The objective function is:

$$MAX - 1X_1 + 1X_2 + 4X_3 + 2Y_1 + 4Y_2 + 7Y_3$$

Constraints

United must consider the following constraints in its analysis:

Crude Availability: United cannot blend more than the product available from either input source. The total amount blended from a source is simply the sum of the amounts blended into regular, mid-grade, and premium gasoline:

$$X_1 + X_2 + X_3 \leq 15,000$$
$$Y_1 + Y_2 + Y_3 \leq 15,000$$

Contract Requirements: Although the contract requirements must be met, they may be exceeded; thus, although at least 12,000 barrels of regular must be produced, the actual amount produced will be the sum of the amounts of alkylate and catalytic cracked blended into regular: $X_1 + Y_1$. Similarly, the amount of mid-grade gas produced will

TABLE 9.6		
Profit Coefficients for Oil		

Variable	Crude Product Cost	Gasoline Selling Price	Barrel Profit
X_1	$19	$18	–$1
X_2	$19	$20	$1
X_3	$19	$23	$4
Y_1	$16	$18	$2
Y_2	$16	$20	$4
Y_3	$16	$23	$7

be $X_2 + Y_2$, and the amount of premium gas produced will be $X_3 + Y_3$. Since these quantities are of interest to United Oil (and will figure into the remaining constraints), to simplify the formulation, summation variables can be used.

Decision Variables (Second Pass)

Define the following summation variables

$$R = \text{barrels of regular gasoline produced weekly}$$
$$M = \text{barrels of mid-grade gasoline produced weekly}$$
$$P = \text{barrels of premium gasoline produced weekly}$$

Doing so requires adding the following summation constraints:

$$X_1 + Y_1 - R = 0$$
$$X_2 + Y_2 - M = 0$$
$$X_3 + Y_3 - P = 0$$

Now the contract constraints can then be written as

$$R \geq 12{,}000$$
$$M \geq 7500$$
$$P \geq 4500$$

Octane and Vapor Constraints: The octane rating for regular gasoline is the weighted average of the octane ratings for alkylate and catalytic cracked blended into regular. The appropriate weights are the ratios of the amount of alkylate to the amount of regular and the amount of catalytic cracked to the amount of regular, respectively:

$$98 \text{ (Amount of alkylate in regular/Total amount of regular)} +$$
$$86 \text{ (Amount of catalytic cracked in regular/Total amount of regular)} =$$
$$98(X_1/R) + 86(Y_1/R)$$

Since this must be at least 87, the constraint is:

$$98(X_1/R) + 86(Y_1/R) \geq 87$$

The terms (X_1/R) and (Y_1/R) make this a *nonlinear* constraint. Since R will be positive in the optimal solution, however, multiplying both sides by R gives the following linear constraint:

$$98X_1 + 86Y_1 \geq 87R$$

or

$$98X_1 + 86Y_1 - 87R \geq 0$$

The remaining octane and vapor pressure constraints are constructed similarly; thus, the complete set of octane and vapor pressure restrictions is:

$$98X_1 + 86Y_1 - 87R \geq 0$$
$$98X_2 + 86Y_2 - 89M \geq 0$$
$$98X_3 + 86Y_3 - 92P \geq 0$$
$$5X_1 + 9Y_1 - 9R \leq 0$$
$$5X_2 + 9Y_2 - 7M \leq 0$$
$$5X_3 + 9Y_3 - 6P \leq 0$$

The Mathematical Model

The complete model is as follows:

$$
\begin{array}{llll}
\text{MAXIMIZE} & -1X_1 + 1X_2 + 4X_3 + 2Y_1 + 4Y_2 + 7Y_3 \\
\text{ST} & X_1 + X_2 + X_3 & \le 15{,}000 \\
& \quad\quad Y_1 + Y_2 + Y_3 & \le 15{,}000 \\
& X_1 \quad\quad + Y_1 \quad\quad - R & = 0 \\
& \quad X_2 \quad\quad + Y_2 \quad\quad - M & = 0 \\
& \quad\quad X_3 \quad\quad + Y_3 \quad\quad - P & = 0 \\
& \quad\quad\quad R & \ge 12{,}000 \\
& \quad\quad\quad M & \ge 7500 \\
& \quad\quad\quad P & \ge 4500 \\
& 98X_1 \quad\quad - 86Y_1 \quad\quad - 87R & \ge 0 \\
& \quad 98X_2 \quad\quad + 86Y_2 \quad\quad - 89M & \ge 0 \\
& \quad\quad 98X_3 + 9Y_1 \quad\quad + 86Y_3 \quad - 92P & \ge 0 \\
& 5X_1 \quad\quad + 9Y_1 \quad\quad - 9R & \le 0 \\
& \quad 5X_2 \quad\quad + 9Y_2 \quad\quad - 7M & \le 0 \\
& \quad\quad 5X_3 \quad\quad + 9Y_3 \quad - 6P & \le 0 \\
\end{array}
$$

All variables ≥ 0

Excel Input/Output and Analysis

Figure 9.10a shows the completed worksheet for United Oil. On the left side in columns A:E are the parameter inputs. On the right side, columns H:K give output values generated when Solver solves the model. The values of the decision variables are given in cells H7:J8. Cell formulas used in the spreadsheet are described in Table 9.7.

FIGURE 9.10a

Optimal Spreadsheet for United Oil Company

United Oil.xls

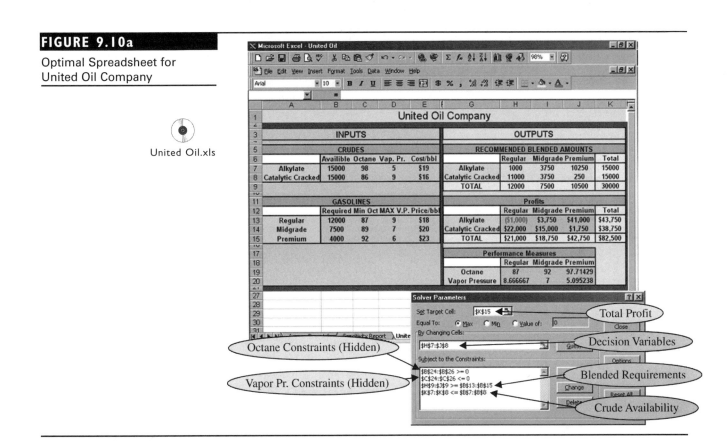

TABLE 9.7			Cell Formulas and Analysis of Spreadsheet in Figure 9.10a

		Spreadsheet Formulas/Analysis	
Cell	**Quantity**	**Formula**	**Observations**
K7	Alkylate Used	=SUM(H7:J7)	*All 15,000 barrels of each are used*
K8	Catalytic Cracked Used	=SUM(H8:J8)	
H9	Regular Produced	=SUM(H7:H8)	*Regular and mid-grade are produced at the minimum*
I9	Midgrade Produced	=SUM(I7:I8)	*required levels. The 10,500 barrels of premium exceed*
J9	Premium Produced	=SUM(J7:J8)	*the minimum requirement of 4000 barrels by 6,500 barrels.*
K9	Total Gasoline Produced	=SUM(H9:J9)	*30,000 barrels are produced.*
H13	Profit from Alk. in Reg.	=(E13-E7)*H7	*There is actually a loss for blending alkylate into regular.*
H14	Profit from Alk. in Mid.	=(E14-E7)*I7	
H15	Profit from Alk. in Prem.	=(E15-E7)*J7	
I13	Profit from C.C. in Reg.	=(E13-E8)*H8	
I14	Profit from C.C. in Mid.	=(E14-E8)*I8	
I15	Profit from C.C. in Prem.	=(E15-E8)*J8	
K13	Total Profit from Alk.	=SUM(H13:J13)	*Profit from alkylate = $43,750*
K14	Total Profit from C.C.	=SUM(H14:J14)	*Profit from c.c. = $38,750*
H15	Total Profit from Reg.	=SUM(H13:H14)	*Profit from Reg. = $21,000*
I15	Total Profit from Mid.	=SUM(I13:I14)	*Profit from Mid. = $18,750*
J15	Total Profit from Prem.	=SUM(J13:J14)	*Profit from Prem. = $42,750*
K15	Total Profit (Maximized)	=SUM(H15:J15)	*Max. Total Profit = $82,500*
H19	Octane Rating Regular	=C7*(H7/H9)+C8*(H8/H9)	*Octane ratings are found by weighting the octane ratings of*
I19	Octane Rating Midgrade	=C7*(I7/I9)+C8*(I8/I9)	*alkylate and cc by the proportion in each blended gasoline.*
J19	Octane Rating Premium	=C7*(J7/J9)+C8*(J8/J9)	*Regular and mid-grade meet minimum octane ratings; the*
			premium rating of 97.5 exceeds its minimum rating of 92.
H20	Vapor Pressure Regular	=D7*(H7/H9)+D8*(H8/H9)	*Vapor pressure of a blended gasoline is found by weighting the*
I20	Vapor Pressure Midgrade	=D7*(I7/I9)+D8*(I8/I9)	*vapor pressure of alkylate and cc by the proportion in each*
J20	Vapor Pressure Premium	=D7*(J7/J9)+D8*(J8/J9)	*blended gasoline. Mid-grade is produced at its highest possible*
			vapor pressure level. Regular and premium vapor pressures
			are less than their allowable limits.

Construction and Analysis of the Spreadsheet Hidden Cells

The octane ratings and vapor pressures of the blended gasolines in cells H19:J20 were found by taking the weighted averages of the octane ratings and vapor pressures of alkylate and catalytic cracked blended into each grade. For example, as seen in Table 9.7, the formula in cell H19 is: =C7*(H7/H9) + C8*(H8/H9). But the denominator, cell H9, is the sum of the six decision variables in H7:J8, making the expression in cell H19 nonlinear in terms of the decision variables. There are similar formulas in cells H20, I19, I20, J19, and J20. Thus, if this nonlinear term were included in the left side of a constraint, a linear programming approach could not be used. That is why we wrote the mathematical model the way we did—to obtain a linear programming formulation!

Accordingly, the formulas for the left side of the last six functional constraints of the model for the octane and vapor pressure constraints are entered into cells B24:B26 and C24:C26, respectively, as shown in Table 9.8. Although these values are required to be nonnegative for octane and nonpositive for vapor pressure, their precise values are meaningless and add nothing to the manager's analysis of the results. Thus, the corresponding rows were hidden in Figure 9.10a by holding down the left mouse key over the selected row numbers in the left margin and then clicking "Hide" with the right mouse key.

TABLE 9.8		Hidden Cells—Left-Hand Sides of the Last Six Functional Constraints	

Left-Hand Side Values of the Last Six Functional Constraints (Hidden in Rows 24-26)			
Cell	Left Side Quantity	Left-Hand Formula	Spreadsheet Formula
B24	Reg. Octane Rating	$98X_1+86Y_1-87R$	=SUMPRODUCT(C7:C8,H7:H8)-C13*H9
B25	Mid. Octane Rating	$98X_2+86Y_2-89M$	=SUMPRODUCT(C7:C8,I7:I8)-C14*I9
B26	Prem. Octane Rating	$98X_3+86Y_3-92P$	=SUMPRODUCT(C7:C8,J7:J8)-C15*J9
C24	Reg. Vapor Pressure	$5X_1+9Y_1-9R$	=SUMPRODUCT(D7:D8,H7:H8)-D13*H9
C25	Mid. Vapor Pressure	$5X_2+9Y_2-7M$	=SUMPRODUCT(D7:D8,I7:I8)-D14*I9
C26	Prem. Vapor Pressure	$5X_3+9Y_3-6P$	=SUMPRODUCT(D7:D8,J7:J8)-D15*J9

Analysis of the Sensitivity Report

Figure 9.10b shows the corresponding Sensitivity Report for this model. From this Sensitivity Report we observe the following.

Effects of Extra Crude All additional barrels of alkylate will add $4 each to the total profit. Additional barrels of catalytic cracked will add $7 each for each of the next 3166.67 barrels. That is, United should be willing to pay up to $19 + $4 = $23 for an additional barrel of alkylate and up to $16 + $7 = $23 for additional barrels of catalytic cracked.

Effects of Changing Grade Requirements Decreasing the requirement for regular from 12,000 barrels will increase profits by $5 per barrel up to a maximum decrease of 3562.5 barrels (to 8437.5 barrels); increasing this minimum requirement will decrease profits $5 per barrel, up to a maximum increase of 272.73 barrels (to 12,272.73 barrels). Changing the requirement for mid-grade will have a $3 effect for a maximum decrease of 7500 barrels (down to 0) or a maximum increase of 500 barrels (up to 8000). Changing the minimum requirement for premium would have no effect unless the increase puts the requirement above the proposed production level of 10,500 barrels.

FIGURE 9.10b	

Sensitivity Report for United Oil

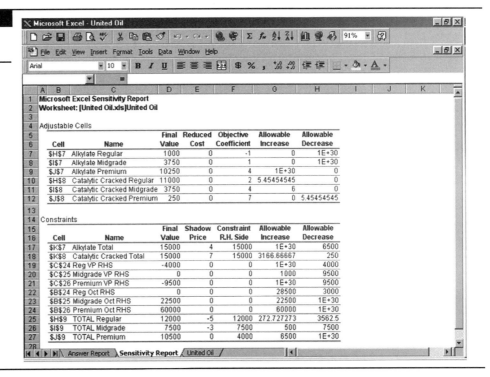

Alternative Optimal Solutions There are Allowable Increases and Allowable Decreases of 0 for the profit coefficients of the various blends, indicating the existence of alternate optimal solutions. Thus, the crudes can be blended in other ways to make a profit of $82,500 while meeting the octane and vapor pressure requirements.

Other Linear Models

Sections 9.4.1–9.4.5 described just a few possibilities which might be solved using linear programming models. Space considerations have precluded us from presenting even more examples of linear models in this text. However, two other slightly more complex, but very important applications are presented on the accompanying CD-ROM. These models illustrate a multiperiod cash flow scheduling model (Appendix 3.2) and a model for evaluating the efficiency operations using a process known as data envelopment analysis (Appendix 3.3). Since these models illustrate new ideas and spreadsheet approaches, you are encouraged to access them from the Appendix folder on the CD-ROM.

9.5 APPLICATIONS OF INTEGER LINEAR PROGRAMMING MODELS

In many real-life models, at least one of the decision variables is required to be integer-valued. If all the variables are required to be integer, the model is called an **all-integer linear programming model (AILP)** and if all are required to be binary (values of 0 or 1), the model is called a **binary integer linear programming model (BILP)**. If some of the variables are required to be either integer or binary whereas others have no such restriction, the model is called a **mixed integer linear programming model (MILP).** In this section we present several such models including a personnel scheduling (AILP), a project selection model (BILP), a supply chain model (MILP), and an advertising model (AILP) on the accompanying CD-ROM.

We observed in Chapter 8 that to convert a linear programming model to an integer programming model in an Excel spreadsheet only involves a mouse click in the Add Constraint dialogue box of Solver. We also stated, however, that when integer variables are present, the solution time can increase dramatically and no sensitivity output is generated. Thus, rounding a linear programming solution is sometimes a preferred option.

Using Binary Variables

Appropriate use of binary variables can aid the modeler in expressing comparative relationships. To illustrate, suppose Y_1, Y_2, and Y_3 are binary variables representing whether each of three plants should be built ($Y_i = 1$) or not built ($Y_i = 0$). The following relationships can then be expressed by these variables. (You can verify these relationships by substituting all combinations of 0's and 1's into the given constraints.)

- At least two plants must be built. $Y_1 + Y_2 + Y_3 \geq 2$
- If plant 1 is built, Plant 2 must not be built. $Y_1 + Y_2 \leq 1$
- If plant 1 is built, Plant 2 must be built. $Y_1 - Y_2 \leq 0$
- One but not both of Plants 1 and 2 must be built. $Y_1 + Y_2 = 1$
- Both or neither of Plants 1 and 2 must be built. $Y_1 - Y_2 = 0$
- Plant construction cannot exceed $17 million, and the costs to build Plants 1, 2, and 3 are $5 million, $8 million, and $10 million, respectively. $5Y_1 + 8Y_2 + 10Y_3 \leq 17$

Binary variables can also be used to indicate restrictions in certain conditional situations. For example, suppose X_1 denotes the amount of a product that will be produced at Plant 1. (Note that $X_1 \geq 0$.) If Plant 1 is built, there is no other restriction on the value of X_1, but if it is not built, X_1 must be 0. This relation can be expressed by:

$$X_1 \leq MY_1$$

In this expression, M denotes an extremely large number that does not restrict the value of X_1 if $Y_1 = 1$. For example we might use 10^{20} (or 1E + 20) for M. If Plant 1 is not built ($Y_1 = 0$), the constraint becomes $X_1 \leq 0$; however, since $X_1 \geq 0$, this implies $X_1 = 0$; that is, no product will be produced at Plant 1. If Plant 1 is built ($Y_1 = 1$), then $X_1 \leq M$, which, because of the extremely large value assigned to M, effectively does restrict the value of X_1.

Now suppose that we are considering building a new plant in Chicago to produce two products, bicycles and tricycles. Suppose each bicycle requires 3 pounds of steel and each tricycle 4 pounds of steel. If the plant is built, it should have 2000 pounds of steel available per week. Thus, there will be at most 2000 pounds of steel if the plant is built but 0 pounds of steel available if it is not built. Define:

X_1 = the number of bicycles produced each week at the Chicago plant
X_2 = the number of tricycles produced each week at the Chicago plant

Now let Y_1 represent whether or not the Chicago plant is built. This situation can then be modeled as: $3X_1 + 4X_2 \leq 2000Y_1$ or, $3X_1 + 4X_2 - 2000Y_1 \leq 0$. We see that if the plant is built ($Y_1 = 1$), then the constraint is $3X_1 + 4X_2 \leq 2000$. If it is not built ($Y_1 = 0$), the constraint reduces to $3X_1 + 4X_2 \leq 0$ (which will hold only if both X_1 and X_2 are 0). That is, if the plant is not built, there is no production.

These are just some of the ideas that are modeled in the examples in this section.

9.5.1 Personnel Scheduling Models

One problem that requires an integer solution is the assignment of personnel or machines to meet some minimum coverage requirements. Typically, these models have constraints that link the resources available during one period with those available for subsequent periods. The situation faced by the City of Sunset Beach is an example of one such problem.

SUNSET BEACH LIFEGUARD ASSIGNMENTS	*Concepts:*	Integer Variables Linking Constraints Hidden Cells

Sunset.xls

In the summer, the City of Sunset Beach staffs lifeguard stations seven days a week. Regulations require that city employees (including lifeguards) work five days a week and be given two consecutive days off. For most city employees, these days are Saturday and Sunday, but for lifeguards, these are the two busiest days of the week.

Insurance requirements mandate that Sunset Beach provide at least one lifeguard per 8000 average daily attendance on any given day. Table 9.9 gives the average daily attendance figures and the minimum number of lifeguards required during the summer months, at Sunset Beach.

Given the current budget situation, Sunset Beach would like to determine a schedule that will employ as few lifeguards as possible.

TABLE 9.9	Day	Average Attendance	Lifeguards Required
Average Daily Attendance and Lifeguard Requirements	Sunday	58,000	8
	Monday	42,000	6
	Tuesday	35,000	5
	Wednesday	25,000	4
	Thursday	44,000	6
	Friday	51,000	7
	Saturday	68,000	9

SOLUTION

Sunset Beach's problem is to:

- Schedule lifeguards over five consecutive days
- Minimize the total number of lifeguards required
- Meet the minimum daily lifeguard requirements

Decision Variables

Sunset Beach must decide how many lifeguards to schedule beginning Sunday and working for five consecutive days, the number to schedule beginning Monday and working for five consecutive days, and so on:

X_1 = number of lifeguards scheduled to begin on Sunday
X_2 = number of lifeguards scheduled to begin on Monday
X_3 = number of lifeguards scheduled to begin on Tuesday
X_4 = number of lifeguards scheduled to begin on Wednesday
X_5 = number of lifeguards scheduled to begin on Thursday
X_6 = number of lifeguards scheduled to begin on Friday
X_7 = number of lifeguards scheduled to begin on Saturday

Objective Function

The goal is to minimize the total number of lifeguards scheduled:

$$\text{MIN } X_1 + X_2 + X_3 + X_4 + X_5 + X_6 + X_7$$

Constraints

For each day, at least the minimum required number of lifeguards must be on duty. Those on duty on Sunday begin their shift either on Sunday, Wednesday, Thursday, Friday, or Saturday; those on duty on Monday begin their shift either on Monday, Thursday, Friday, Saturday, or Sunday; and so on. Thus,

$$(\text{The number of lifeguards on duty Sunday}) \geq 8$$

or

$$X_1 \qquad\quad + X_4 + X_5 + X_6 + X_7 \geq 8$$

For Monday the constraint would be:

$$X_1 + X_2 \qquad\quad + X_5 + X_6 + X_7 \geq 6$$

The Mathematical Model

The constraints for the other days are similarly derived, yielding the following model:

$$
\begin{array}{llllllllll}
\text{MIN} & X_1 & + X_2 & + X_3 & + X_4 & + X_5 & + X_6 & + X_7 & \\
\text{ST} & X_1 & & & + X_4 & + X_5 & + X_6 & + X_7 & \geq 8 \ \text{(Sunday)} \\
& X_1 & + X_2 & & & + X_5 & + X_6 & + X_7 & \geq 6 \ \text{(Monday)} \\
& X_1 & + X_2 & + X_3 & & & + X_6 & + X_7 & \geq 5 \ \text{(Tuesday)} \\
& X_1 & + X_2 & + X_3 & + X_4 & & & + X_7 & \geq 4 \ \text{(Wednesday)} \\
& X_1 & + X_2 & + X_3 & + X_4 & + X_5 & & & \geq 6 \ \text{(Thursday)} \\
& & X_2 & + X_3 & + X_4 & + X_5 & + X_6 & & \geq 7 \ \text{(Friday)} \\
& & & X_3 & + X_4 & + X_5 & + X_6 & + X_7 & \geq 9 \ \text{(Saturday)}
\end{array}
$$

$$\text{All variables} \geq 0 \text{ AND Integer}$$

Excel Input/Output and Analysis

Figure 9.11 shows a spreadsheet for this model. The formula in cell B5 (=ROUNDUP(B4/8000,0)) gives the number of required lifeguards on Sunday by dividing the projected attendance (B4) by the 8000 lifeguard to attendance ratio and rounding this number up. The 0 means include 0 decimal places. This formula is dragged to cells C5:H5 to obtain the daily requirements.

FIGURE 9.11   Optimal Spreadsheet for Sunset Beach Lifeguard Assignments

Sunset.xls

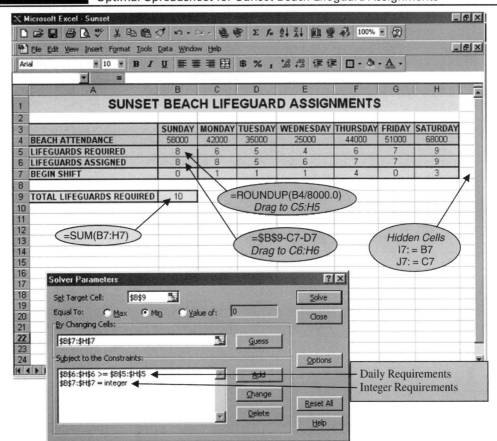

The formula in cell B6 (=$B$9-C7-D7) states that the number of lifeguards on duty on Sunday includes all lifeguards ($B$9) except those who begin their shift on Monday (C7) or Tuesday (D7). Those who begin their shift on Monday or Tuesday will finish their shifts on Friday and Saturday, respectively. So that we can drag this formula across to cells C6:H6, formulas have been assigned to (hidden) cells I7 and J7; they also give the number of lifeguards who begin their shift on Sunday and Monday.

We see that the city can get by with a total of 10 lifeguards, 1 of whom starts his shift on Monday, 1 on Tuesday, 1 on Wednesday, 4 on Thursday, and 3 on Saturday.[4] The minimum requirement for lifeguards is met on each day, with Monday and Wednesday having two extra lifeguards and Thursday one extra lifeguard assigned.

9.5.2 Project Selection Models

Project selection models involve a set of "go/no-go" decisions, represented by binary decision variables, for various projects under consideration. Such models typically involve budget, space, or other restrictions, as well as a set of priorities among certain projects. For example, one might specify that project 1 may be done (or will be done) only if project 2 is done, or only if project 3 is not done, or that at least two of projects 1, 2, 3, 4, and 5 be accomplished. The situation faced by the Salem City Council is a simplified version of one such model.

<table>
<tr><td>**SALEM CITY COUNCIL**</td><td>*Concepts*:</td><td>Binary Decision Variables</td></tr>
<tr><td></td><td></td><td>Priority Relationships</td></tr>
</table>

Salem.xls

At its final meeting of the fiscal year, the Salem City Council will be making plans to allocate funds remaining in this year's budget. Nine projects have been under consideration throughout the entire year.

To gauge community support for the various projects, questionnaires were randomly mailed to voters throughout the city asking them to rank the projects (9 = highest priority, 1 = lowest priority). The council tallied the scores from the 500 usable responses it received. Although the council has repeatedly maintained that it will not be bound by the results of the questionnaire, it plans to use this information while taking into account other concerns when making the budget allocations.

The estimated cost of each project, the estimated number of permanent new jobs each would create, and the questionnaire point tallies are summarized in Table 9.10.

The council's goal is to maximize the total perceived voter support (as evidenced through the questionnaires), given other constraints and concerns of the council, including the following:

- $900,000 remains in the budget.

- The council wants to create at least 10 new jobs.

- Although crime deterrence is a high priority with the public, the council feels that it must also be fair to other sectors of public service (fire and education). Accordingly, it wishes to fund at most three of the police-related projects.

- The council would like to increase the number of city emergency vehicles but feels that, in the face of other pressing issues, only one of the two emergency vehicle projects should be funded at this time. Thus, *either* the two police cars *or* the fire truck should be purchased.

---

[4] It turns out that there are several optimal solutions to this model, each of which requires a total of 10 lifeguards.

TABLE 9.10		Project	Cost ($1000)	New Jobs	Points
Project Costs, New Jobs, and Point Tallies	X_1	Hire seven new police officers	$400	7	4176
	X_2	Modernize police headquarters	$350	0	1774
	X_3	Buy two new police cars	$ 50	1	2513
	X_4	Give bonuses to foot patrol officers	$100	0	1928
	X_5	Buy new fire truck/support equipment	$500	2	3607
	X_6	Hire assistant fire chief	$ 90	1	962
	X_7	Restore cuts to sports programs	$220	8	2829
	X_8	Restore cuts to school music	$150	3	1708
	X_9	Buy new computers for high school	$140	2	3003

- The council believes that if it decides to restore funds cut from the sports programs at the schools, it should also restore funds cut from their music programs, and vice versa.

- By union contract, any additional school funding must go toward restoring previous cuts before any new school projects are undertaken. consequently, both sports funds and music funds must be restored before new computer equipment can be purchased. Restoring sports and music funds, however, does not imply that new computers *will* be purchased, only that they *can* be.

SOLUTION

The Salem City Council must choose which projects to fund. Its objective is to determine, within the constraints and concerns listed earlier, the set of projects that maximizes public support for its decisions as evidenced through the returned questionnaires.

Decision Variables

The variables, $X_1, X_2, \ldots, X_9$, are binary decision variables: $X_j = 1$ if project j is funded, and $X_j = 0$ if project j is not funded.

Objective Function

The council's objective is to maximize the overall point score of the funded projects:

$$\text{MAXIMIZE}\quad 4176X_1 + 1774X_2 + 2513X_3 + 1928X_4 + 3607X_5 + 962X_6 + 2829X_7 + 1708X_8 + 3003X_9$$

Constraints

Budget Constraint   The maximum amount of funds to be allocated cannot exceed $900,000. Using coefficients to represent the number of thousands of dollars, this constraint can be written as:

$$400X_1 + 350X_2 + 50X_3 + 100X_4 + 500X_5 + 90X_6 + 220X_7 + 150X_8 + 140X_9 \leq 900$$

Job Creation Constraint   The number of new jobs created must be at least 10:

$$7X_1 + X_3 + 2X_5 + X_6 + 8X_7 + 3X_8 + 2X_9 \geq 10$$

Maximum of Three Out of Four Police Projects Constraint The number of police-related activities to be funded is at most 3:

$$X_1 + X_2 + X_3 + X_4 \leq 3$$

Mutually Exclusive Projects Constraint (Two Police Cars or a Fire Truck) Either the two police cars should be purchased or the fire truck should be purchased. This is equivalent to saying that the number of police car purchase projects plus the number of fire truck purchase projects to be funded is exactly 1:

$$X_3 + X_5 = 1$$

Corequisite Projects Constraint—Sports Funding/Music Funding If sports funds are restored music funds will be restored, and if sports funds are not restored music funds will not be restored. This constraint implies that the number of restored music fund projects funded must equal the number of sports fund projects funded; that is $X_7 = X_8$, or:

$$X_7 - X_8 = 0$$

Prerequisite Projects Constraint—Equipment vs. Sports and Music Funding Sports funding and music funding must be restored before new computer equipment can be purchased. This relationship can be expressed as two prerequisite constraints: the number of sports projects funded must be at least as great as the number of computer equipment projects funded ($X_7 \geq X_9$) AND the number of music projects funded must be at least as great as the number of computer equipment projects funded ($X_8 \geq X_9$), or:

$$X_7 - X_9 \geq 0$$
$$X_8 - X_9 \geq 0$$

Note that, taken together, these constraints mean that if $X_9 = 1$, then both X_7 and X_8 must be 1, but if either or both X_7 and $X_8 = 1$, X_9 is not required to be 1.

Mathematical Model for the Salem City Council

The complete model for the Salem City Council, which includes the objective function, the functional and conditional constraints, and the binary restrictions, can now be stated as follows:

MAXIMIZE

$$4176X_1 + 1774X_2 + 2513X_3 + 1928X_4 + 3607X_5 + 962X_6 + 2829X_7 + 1708X_8 + 3003X_9 \leq 900$$

ST

$400X_1 +$	$350X_2 +$	$50X_3 +$	$100X_4 +$	$500X_5 +$	$90X_6 +$	$220X_7 +$	$150X_8 +$	$140X_9 \leq 900$
$7X_1 +$		$X_3 +$		$2X_5 +$	$X_6 +$	$8X_7 +$	$3X_8 +$	$2X_9 \geq 10$
$X_1 +$	$X_2 +$	$X_3 +$	X_4					≤ 3
		$X_3 +$		X_5				$= 1$
						$X_7 -$	X_8	$= 0$
						$X_7 -$		$X_9 \geq 0$
							$X_8 -$	$X_9 \geq 0$

All X's = 0 or 1

Excel Input/Output and Analysis

Figure 9.12 shows an optimal spreadsheet for the decisions faced by the Salem City Council. The binary decision variables are in cells B4:B12, and we present the formulas for the left side of the constraints shown in cells B17:B23.

Much to the council's surprise, the optimal solution does not fund the two items the people most wanted—hiring seven new police officers and purchasing a new fire truck and fire support equipment! Upon further observation, the council noted that these items were also the most costly, but they were still amazed that neither would be funded given the extremely high public support for them. The solution also does not recommend funding renovations to police headquarters; instead it recommends funding all six other projects. If this recommendation is followed, the council will create five more jobs than its goal of 10 and will have a budget surplus of $1,500,000 that it can apply to next year's projects or return to the people as a tax rebate (a very popular political idea!)

FIGURE 9.12   Optimal Spreadsheet for the Salem City Council

Salem.xls

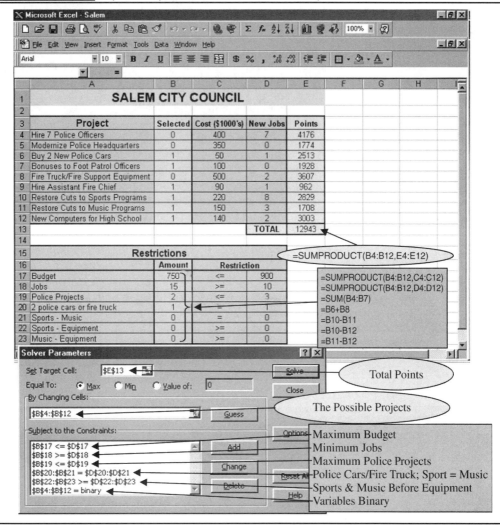

9.5.3 Supply Chain Management Models

One of the most significant managerial developments in recent years has been the emergence of supply chain management models that integrate the process of manufacturing goods and getting them to the consumer. A typical supply chain can be thought of as a decision support system that treats the acquisition of materials to produce products as well as the manufacturing, storing, and shipping of finished products as an integrated system of events rather than as stand-alone separate components of the process.

Numerous management science models discussed in this text, including manufacturing models, network models, scheduling models, forecasting models, inventory models, and queuing models, are now embraced under the ever growing set of supply chain management techniques. The overall objective of these models has been, and continues to be, to minimize total system costs while maintaining appropriate production levels and transporting needed quantities to the right locations in a timely and efficient manner. While just a few short years ago, employing efficient supply chain models gave many firms an edge in the market, today their use has nearly become essential to even compete in the marketplace.

One link in the supply chain can involve determining which plants should be made operational, which should produce specified items, and what shipping pattern should be used to distribute the finished products to retailers. Such is the situation faced by Globe Electronics, Inc.

GLOBE ELECTRONICS, INC.		
Concepts:	Supply Chain Management	
	Mixed Integer Modeling of Fixed Charges	
	Rounding Noninteger Solutions	

Globe.xls
Globe Plant Analysis.xls

Globe Electronics, Inc. manufactures two styles of remote control cable boxes (the G50 and the H90) that various cable companies supply to their customers when cable service is established. Different companies require different models. During the late 1980s and early 1990s, due to an explosion in the demand for cable services, Globe expanded rapidly to four production facilities located in Philadelphia (the original plant), St. Louis, New Orleans, and Denver. The manufactured items are shipped from the plants to regional distribution centers located in Cincinnati, Kansas City, and San Francisco; from these locations they are distributed nationwide.

Because of a decrease in demand for cable services and technological changes in the cable industry, demand for Globe's products is currently far less than the total of the capacities at its four plants. As a result, management is contemplating closing one or more of its facilities.

Each plant has a fixed operating cost, and, because of the unique conditions at each facility, the production costs, production time per unit, and total monthly production time available vary from plant to plant, as summarized in Table 9.11.

The cable boxes are sold nationwide at the same prices: $22 for the G50, and $28 for the H90.

Current monthly demand projections at each distribution center for both products are given in Table 9.12.

To remain viable in each market, Globe must meet at least 70% of the demand for each product at each distribution center. The transportation costs between each plant and each distribution center, which are the same for either product, are shown in Table 9.13.

Globe management wants to develop an optimal distribution policy utilizing all four of its operational plants. It also wants to determine whether closing any of the production facilities will result in higher company profits.

TABLE 9.11 Production Costs, Times, Availability		Fixed Cost/ Month ($1000)	Production Cost Per Unit		Production Time (Hr./Unit)		Available Hours per Month
	Plant		G50	H90	G50	H90	
	Philadelphia	40	10	14	.06	.06	640
	St. Louis	35	12	12	.07	.08	960
	New Orleans	20	8	10	.09	.07	480
	Denver	.30	13	15	.05	.09	640

TABLE 9.12 Monthly Demand Projections		Demand		
		Cincinnati	Kansas City	San Francisco
	G50	2000	3000	5000
	H90	5000	6000	7000

TABLE 9.13 Transportation Costs per 100 Units		To		
	From	Cincinnati	Kansas City	San Francisco
	Philadelphia	$200	$300	$500
	St. Louis	$100	$100	$300
	New Orleans	$200	$200	$300
	Denver	$300	$100	$100

SOLUTION

The situation facing Globe Electronics is the portion of the supply chain that involves the manufacture and delivery of finished products to various distribution centers. Prior to this, Globe would be involved with ordering raw materials and scheduling personnel in the production process. Subsequent links would involve the storage process at the distribution centers and the sale and dissemination of the completed goods to retail establishments. Specifically for this portion of the model, Globe is seeking to:

- Determine the number of G50 and H90 cable boxes to be produced at each plant
- Determine a shipping pattern from the plants to the distribution centers
- Maximize net total monthly profit
- Not exceed the production capacities at any plant
- Ensure that each distribution center receives between 70% and 100% of its monthly demand projections

The model Globe uses to solve for the optimal solution with all four plants operating is developed in the following section.

Decision Variables

Management must decide the total number of G50 and H90 cable boxes to produce monthly at each plant, the total number to be shipped to each distribution center, and the shipping pattern of product from the plants to the distribution centers. The entries in the following two matrices designate the decision variables for this model.

Shipment of G50 Cable Boxes:

	Cincinnati	Kansas City	San Francisco	Total Produced
Philadelphia	G_{11}	G_{12}	G_{13}	G_P
St. Louis	G_{21}	G_{22}	G_{23}	G_{SL}
New Orleans	G_{31}	G_{32}	G_{33}	G_{NO}
Denver	G_{41}	G_{42}	G_{43}	G_D
Total Received	G_C	G_{KC}	G_{SF}	G

Shipment of H90 Cable Boxes:

	Cincinnati	Kansas City	San Francisco	Total Produced
Philadelphia	H_{11}	H_{12}	H_{13}	H_P
St. Louis	H_{21}	H_{22}	H_{23}	H_{SL}
New Orleans	H_{31}	H_{32}	H_{33}	H_{NO}
Denver	H_{41}	H_{42}	H_{43}	H_D
Total Received	H_C	H_{KC}	H_{SF}	H

Objective Function

The *gross profit* (exclusive of fixed plant costs) is given by \$22 (Total G50's Produced) + \$28 (Total H90's Produced) − (Total Production Cost) − (Total Transportation Costs). Thus, the objective function is:

$$\text{MAX } 22G + 28H - 10G_P - 12G_{SL} - 8G_{NO} - 13G_D - 14H_P - 12H_{SL} - 10H_{NO} - 15H_D - 2G_{11}$$
$$- 3G_{12} - 5G_{13} - 1G_{21} - 1G_{22} - 4G_{23} - 2G_{31} - 2G_{32} - 3G_{33} - 3G_{41} - 1G_{42} - 1G_{43} - 2H_{11}$$
$$- 3H_{12} - 5H_{13} - 1H_{21} - 1H_{22} - 4H_{23} - 2H_{31} - 2H_{32} - 3H_{33} - 3H_{41} - 1H_{42} - 1H_{43}$$

From this quantity we would subtract the total monthly fixed costs for the four plants of \$125,000.

Constraints

This model contains summation constraints for the total amounts of G50 and H90 cable boxes produced at each plant and the total number shipped to each distribution center, production time limits at the plants, and shipping limits to the distribution plants.

1. *Summation Constraints for Total Production*

	Total G50's Produced	Total H90's Produced
Philadelphia:	$G_{11} + G_{12} + G_{13} = G_P$	$H_{11} + H_{12} + H_{13} = H_P$
St. Louis:	$G_{21} + G_{22} + G_{23} = G_{SL}$	$H_{21} + H_{22} + H_{23} = H_{SL}$
New Orleans:	$G_{31} + G_{32} + G_{33} = G_{NO}$	$H_{31} + H_{32} + H_{33} = H_{NO}$
Denver:	$G_{41} + G_{42} + G_{43} = G_D$	$H_{41} + H_{42} + H_{43} = H_D$
TOTAL:	$G_P + G_{SL} + G_{NO} + G_D = G$	$H_P + H_{SL} + H_{NO} + H_D = H$

2. *Summation Constraints for Total Shipments*

	Total G50's Shipped	Total H90's Shipped
Cincinnati:	$G_{11} + G_{21} + G_{31} + G_{41} = G_C$	$H_{11} + H_{21} + H_{31} + H_{41} = H_C$
Kansas City:	$G_1 + G_{22} + G_{32} + G_{42} = G_{KC}$	$H_{12} + H_{22} + H_{32} + H_{42} = H_{KC}$
San Francisco:	$G_{13} + G_{23} + G_{33} + G_{43} = G_{SF}$	$H_{13} + H_{23} + H_{33} + H_{43} = H_{SF}$

3. *Production Time Limits at Each Plant*

Philadelphia:	$.06G_P + .06H_P \leq 640$
St. Louis:	$.07G_{SL} + .08H_{SL} \leq 960$
New Orleans:	$.09G_{NO} + .07H_{NO} \leq 480$
Denver:	$.05G_D + .09H_D \leq 640$

4. *Minimum Amount Shipped to Each Distribution Center $\geq 70\%$ (Total Demand); Maximum Amount Shipped to Each Distribution Center $\leq$ (Total Demand)*

	Minimum Shipment	Maximum Shipment
Cincinnati:	$G_C \geq 1400$	$G_C \leq 2000$
	$H_C \geq 3500$	$H_C \leq 5000$
Kansas City:	$G_{KC} \geq 2100$	$G_{KC} \leq 3000$
	$H_{KC} \geq 4200$	$H_{KC} \leq 6000$
San Francisco:	$G_{SF} \geq 3500$	$G_{SF} \leq 5000$
	$H_{SF} \geq 4900$	$H_{SF} \leq 7000$

5. *Nonnegativity*

All G's and H's ≥ 0

Theoretically, we should also require that the variables be integers, but we will ignore this restriction and round if necessary. This will substantially reduce the solution time. The rounding could result in a slightly less than optimal result, or it might slightly violate one of the constraints. But in the context of this problem, such minor violations would probably be acceptable.

Excel Input/Output and Analysis

Figure 9.13 shows a spreadsheet and the resulting solution for this model. In this figure cells F5:F9 and F14:F18 contain the row sums giving the total G50 and H90 production at the plants. Cells C9:E9 and C18:E18 contain the column sums giving the total shipments to the distribution centers. Hidden cells C29:E29 and C30:E30 contain formulas giving 70% of the G50 and H90 demand at the distribution centers respectively. The objective function formula in cell K19 is the total revenue of G50's + the total revenue of H90's less the total production costs of G50's, the total production costs of H90's, the total shipping costs of G50's, the total shipping costs of H90's, and the fixed costs of operating each plant.

When the model is solved, we see that the optimal solution contains noninteger values in cells D5, D6, E16, and E17. But if these values are simply rounded down, the result is a feasible solution with a net monthly profit reduced to $231,550. Because this is so close to the optimal value for the linear programming model of $231,571.43 shown in cell K19, while it may not be the exact optimal integer solution, it is at least very close to it!

The preceding solution assumes that all plants are operational. However, because of the large fixed cost component at each plant, this may not be the best overall solution. As part of the supply chain model, Globe should consider which plants it wishes to keep operational.

FIGURE 9.13   Optimal Spreadsheet for Globe Electronics with All Plants Operational

Globe.xls

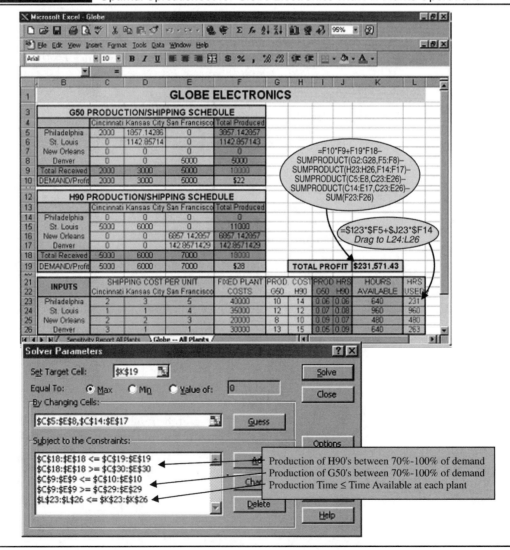

Using Binary Variables to Model Fixed Charge Components

Whether or not each plant remains operational can be expressed by using the following binary variables.

$$Y_P = \text{number of operational Philadelphia plants}$$
$$Y_{SL} = \text{number of operational St. Louis plants}$$
$$Y_{NO} = \text{number of operational New Orleans plants}$$
$$Y_D = \text{number of operational Denver plants}$$

The fixed operating costs can be accounted for in the objective function by subtracting from the previous objective function the expression: $40,000Y_P + 35,000Y_{SL} + 20,000Y_{NO} + 30,000Y_D$.

The production constraints are modified as follows:

$$\begin{aligned}
.06G_P &+ .06H_P &\leq 640Y_P \\
.07G_{SL} &+ .08H_{SL} &\leq 960Y_{SL} \\
.09G_{NO} &+ .07H_{NO} &\leq 480Y_{NO} \\
.05G_D &+ .09H_D &\leq 640Y_D
\end{aligned}$$

Thus if, for instance, the Philadelphia plant is closed ($Y_P = 0$), the first constraint will force total production at the Philadelphia plant to be 0. This in turn implies that all shipments from the Philadelphia plant would also be 0.

The revised spreadsheet model is shown in Figure 9.14. Note that the binary decision variables are in cells A5:A8. These values are copied to cells A14:A17 and to cells A23:A26. Hidden cell N23 contains the formula K23*A5, which is dragged to N24:N26. These cells give the actual production hour availability depending on whether or not the corresponding plant is operational. This allows for easy modification of the last entry in the Solver dialogue box.

Although we require binary variables, we will not require that the shipping variables be integers. If you try it, you will see that this would increase the solution time from a couple of seconds to many minutes, if not hours!

From Figure 9.17 we see that this supply chain model is optimized by closing the Philadelphia plant, running the other three plants at capacity, and scheduling monthly production according to quantities (rounded down) shown in the spreadsheet.[5] The rounded down solution gives a net monthly profit of $266,083 (again very close to the linear programming value of $266,114.91). This is $266,083 − $231,550 = $34,533 per month greater than the optimal monthly profit with all four plants operational, resulting in an annual increase in profit of 12($34,533) = $414,396!

A Management Report

The results from this supply chain model and the one used to solve the problem with no plant closures can form the basis for a management report. One item of interest to management may be a breakdown of the distribution of costs and production time under each plan so that Globe can determine where the major costs lie. In addition, management may wish to explore further options. These issues are addressed in the memorandum to Globe Electronics on the following page.

Other Integer Models

Numerous other situations lend themselves to integer programming formulations. One such application, dealing with the selection of advertising media, is discussed in Appendix 3.4 in the Appendix folder on the accompanying CD-ROM. Since several formulation and spreadsheet concepts are illustrated by this example, the reader is encouraged to read and study this model.

---

[5] Note that the entry in cell C5 is 9.6E-09 = .0000000096. This is a roundoff error; it should be 0.

FIGURE 9.14   Optimal Spreadsheet for Globe Electronics Allowing for Closure of Plants

Globe Plant
Analysis.xls

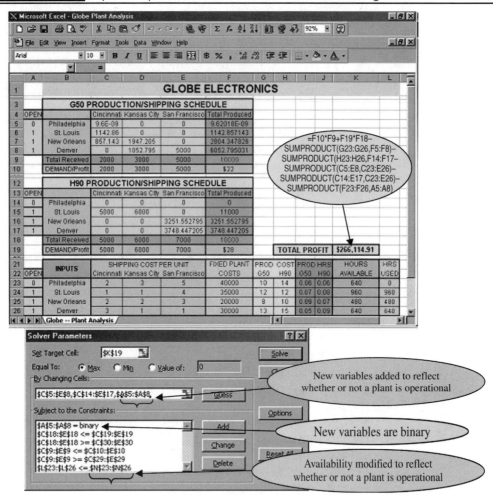

·SCG·
STUDENT CONSULTING GROUP

MEMORANDUM

To: Carol Copley, Vice President
Globe Electronics, Inc.

From: Student Consulting Group

Subj: Recommendation for Monthly Operations

We have been asked to evaluate plant production of the G50 and H90 cable boxes manufactured at the Philadelphia, St. Louis, New Orleans, and Denver plants. Recent product demand projections for the coming year from the Cincinnati, Kansas City, and San Francisco distribution centers have dropped to such a point that a substantial amount of unused production time is available at the plants. Given the large fixed plant operating costs, we have been asked to evaluate the feasibility and the potential cost savings of closing one or more of the plants.

In our analysis we assumed that the demand forecast for the upcoming year, as shown in Table I, is an accurate reflection of future sales.

Table I   Monthly Demand Forecasts for the Next Fiscal Year

	Cincinnati	Kansas City	San Francisco
G50	2000	3000	5000
H90	5000	6000	7000

Based on production time data and the information in table I, we developed profit maximization models for your situation. These models assume a $22 and $28 selling price for G50 and H90 models, respectively, and take into account the following:

1. The fixed operating cost at each plant
2. The variable production costs associated with each product at each plant
3. The unit transportation costs of shipping cable boxes from the plants to the distribution centers.
4. Production not exceeding demand

Management's imposed condition that at least 70% of the demand for each product be supplied to each distribution center did not turn out to be a limiting factor in the analysis.

Optimal Production Schedules

Given the current situation at the four plants in operation, Table II gives a production schedule that should maximize Globe's total net monthly profit.

Table II   Production/Transportation Schedule: All Plants Operational

Plant	Product	Amount	Cincinnati	Kansas City	San Francisco
Philadelphia	G50	3857	2000	1857	
	H90	0			
St. Louis	G50	1143		1143	
	H90	11000	5000	6000	
New Orleans	G50	0			
	H90	6857			6857
Denver	G50	5000			5000
	H90	143			143
Total	G50	10000	2000	3000	5000
	H90	18000	5000	6000	7000

Notice that, although this production plan meets the full demand at the distribution centers, no G50 models are produced in New Orleans, no H90 models are produced in Philadelphia, and only 143 H90 models are produced monthly at the Denver plant. As a result, there is considerable excess capacity at both the Philadelphia and Denver plants.

Under this plan, as shown in Table III, Globe will be utilizing only 1934 production hours, or 71% of available production capacity. Observe from Table IV that the Philadelphia plant will be *un*profitable, while the Denver plant will be only marginally profitable.

Table III   Distribution of Production Time (Hours) All Plants Operational

Plant	G50	H90	Total	Total Capacity	Excess Capacity
Philadelphia	231	0	231	640	409
St. Louis	80	880	960	960	0
New Orleans	0	480	480	480	0
Denver	250	13	263	640	377
Total	561	1373	1934	2720	786

Table IV   Distribution of Monthly Revenues and Costs (All Plants Operational)

Plant	Revenue Sales	Production	Costs Trans-portation	Operations	Total Cost	Net Profit
Philadelphia	$ 84,854	$ 38,570	$ 9,751	$ 40,000	$ 88,141	($ 3,287)
St. Louis	$333,146	$145,716	$12,143	$ 35,000	$192,859	$140,287
New Orleans	$191,996	$ 68,570	$20,571	$ 20,000	$109,141	$ 82,855
Denver	$114,004	$ 67,145	$ 5,143	$ 30,000	$102,288	$ 11,716
Total	$724,000	$320,001	$47,428	$125,000	$492,429	$231,571

Plant Closings

Tables V, VI, and VII give a production and distribution schedule that would result from closing the Philadelphia plant. We estimate that, by closing the Philadelphia plant, Globe can achieve an approximate 15% increase in profit, from $231,571 to $266,115 per month. This is an annual increase in profit of $414,528.

Table V   Production/Transportation Schedule (Philadelphia Plant Closed)

Plant	Product	Amount	Cincinnati	Kansas City	San Francisco
St. Louis	G50	1143		1143	
	H90	11000	5000	6000	
New Orleans	G50	2804	2000	804	
	H90	3252			3252
Denver	G50	6053		1053	5000
	H90	3748			3748
Total	G50	10000	2000	3000	5000
	H90	18000	5000	6000	7000

Table VI   Distribution of Production Time (Hours) (Philadelphia Plant Closed)

Plant	G50	H90	Total	Total Capacity	Excess Capacity
St. Louis	80	880	960	960	0
New Orleans	252	228	480	480	0
Denver	303	337	640	640	0
Total	635	1445	2080	2080	0

Table VII   Distribution of Monthly Revenues and Costs (All Plants Operational)

Plant	Revenue Sales	Production	Costs Trans-portation	Operations	Total Cost	Net Profit
St. Louis	$333,146	$145,716	$12,143	$35,000	$192,859	$140,287
New Orleans	$152,744	$ 54,952	$15,364	$20,000	$ 90,316	$ 62,428
Denver	$238,110	$134,909	$ 9,801	$30,000	$174,710	$ 63,400
Total	$724,000	$335,577	$37,308	$85,000	$457,885	$266,115

Based on this analysis, it would seem prudent to close the Philadelphia plant. The remaining three plants will the be fully utilized, and all projected demand will be met.

Because Globe Electronics has roots in the Philadelphia area, however, the company may wish to examine additional alternatives. We conducted another analysis to determine the most profitable production schedule while keeping the Philadelphia plant operational.

The best production plan in this case is to close the Denver plant and execute the manufacturing and distribution plan detailed in Table VIII. Net profit under this plan would be $256,667 per month, approximately 4% less than if the Philadelphia plant were closed. Although this amounts to an annual profit that is approximately $113,000 less than if the firm closes the Philadelphia plant, it is still approximately an 11% (or about a $300,000) annual increase over the best schedule with all plants operational.

Note that under this plan:

- The Philadelphia plant produces only G50 models.

- The St. Louis plant produces only H90 models

- The New Orleans plant ships only to San Francisco.

Table VIII   Production/Transportation Schedule (Denver Plant Closed)

Plant	Product	Amount	Cincinnati	Kansas City	San Francisco
Philadelphia	G50	9333	2000	3000	4333
	H90	0			
St. Louis	G50	0			
	H90	12000	5000	6000	1000
New Orleans	G50	667			667
	H90	6000			6000
Total	G50	10000	2000	3000	5000
	H90	18000	5000	6000	7000

Such a pattern may have additional benefits or detractions of which we are unaware and which were not considered in our analysis. Barring such additional costs or cost savings, Tables IX and X detail the production time and cost distribution for this schedule. Note that this schedule also has the benefit of the availability of some excess capacity (at the Philadelphia plant) to cover any unanticipated surges in demand.

Table IX   Distribution of Production Time (Hours) (Denver Plant Closed)

Plant	G50	H90	Total	Total Capacity	Excess Capacity
Philadelphia	560	0	560	640	80
St. Louis	0	960	960	960	0
New Orleans	60	420	480	480	0
Total	620	1380	2000	2080	80

Table X   Distribution of Monthly Revenues and Costs (Denver Plant Closed)

Plant	Sales	Revenue Production	Costs Transportation	Operations	Total Cost	Net Profit
Philadelphia	$205,326	$ 93,330	$34,665	$40,000	$167,995	$ 37,331
St. Louis	$336,000	$144,000	$15,000	$35,000	$194,000	$142,000
New Orleans	$182,674	$ 65,336	$20,000	$20,000	$105,336	$ 77,338
Total	$724,000	$302,666	$69,665	$95,000	$467,331	$256,669

SUMMARY AND RECOMMENDATION

The results of our analysis are as follows:

Options for Globe Electronics, Inc.

Option	Annual Profit
Close the Philadelphia Plant	$3,193,380
Close the Denver Plant	$3,080,028
All Plants Operational	$2,778,852

Although we have detailed the cost and transportation distribution of each plan, management must decide whether extenuating circumstances would make one of the less profitable plans more acceptable. Factors such as the impact on the community of plant closings, the costs (not included in this report) of actually closing a facility, and the benefits of a structured distribution pattern or available excess capacity to meet demand fluctuations should all be considered before a final decision is made.

Should management require further study on any of these points, we would be happy to assist in the analysis.

SUMMARY

Linear and integer programming models have been applied successfully in a wide variety of business and government applications, some of which are cited in the first section of this chapter. We have given an outline and numerous hints on how to build successful mathematical models and how to convert these models into good, easy to understand spreadsheet models. We have applied these concepts to simplified applications taken from a variety of business and government sectors. In the process, we offered a thorough analysis of output results and illustrated many of the pitfalls and anomalies that can occur in both the modeling and solution phases. These include how to detect and resolve situations involving unboundedness, infeasibility, and multiple optimal solutions; when and how to use summation variables and constraints; and how to use integer and binary variables to appropriately model particular situations. We have also introduced the concepts of data envelopment analysis (on the CD-ROM) and supply chain management, both of which are important topics in today's business climate.

Not all mathematical models can be modeled by a linear objective function and linear constraints. Chapter 13 on the accompanying CD-ROM discusses the topics of goal programming (which can involve repeated solving of linear programs), dynamic programming (which involves making a sequence of interrelated decisions), and the general nonlinear model.

ON THE CD-ROM

■ Excel spreadsheet for linear programming models	**Galaxy Expansion.xls**
	Jones Investment.xls
Infeasibility	**St. Joseph.xls**
Alternate Optimal Solutions	**St. Joseph (Revised).xls**
Unbounded Solution	**Euromerica Liquors.xls**
	Euromerica Liquors (Revised).xls
	United Oil.xls
	Powers.xls
	Sir Loin.xls
	Sir Loin Composite.xls
■ Excel spreadsheets for integer linear programming models	**Sunset.xls**
	Vertex Software.xls
	Salem.xls
	Globe.xls
	Globe Plant Expansion.xls
■ Duality	**Supplement CD2**
■ The Simplex Method	**Supplement CD3**
■ Algorithms for Solving Integer Models	**Supplement CD4**
■ Problem Motivations	**Problem Motivations**
■ Additional "Real Life" Applications	**Appendix 3.1**
■ A Multiperiod Cash Flow Scheduling Model	**Appendix 3.2**
■ Data Envelopment Analysis	**Appendix 3.3**
■ An Integer Programming Advertising Model	**Appendix 3.4**
■ Problems 41–50	**Additional Problems/Cases**
■ Cases 4–6	**Additional Problems/Cases**

PROBLEMS

Problems 1–27 can be formulated as linear programming models.

Problems 28–40 can be formulated as integer linear programming models.

1. PRODUCTION SCHEDULING. Coolbike Industries manufactures boys and girls bicycles in both 20-inch and 26-inch models. Each week it must produce at least 200 girl models and 200 boys models. The following table gives the unit profit and the number of minutes required for production and assembly for each model.

Bicycle	Unit Profit	Production Minutes	Assembly Minutes
20-inch girls	$27	12	6
20-inch boys	$32	12	9
26-inch girls	$38	9	12
26-inch boys	$51	9	18

The production and assembly areas run two (eight-hour) shifts per day, five days per week. This week there are 500 tires available for 20-inch models and 800 tires available for 26-inch models. Determine Coolbike's optimal schedule for the week. What profit will it realize for the week?

2. APPLIANCE PRODUCTION. Kemper Manufacturing can produce five major appliances—stoves, washers, electric dryers, gas dryers, and refrigerators. All products go through three processes—molding/pressing, assembly, and packaging. Each week there are 4800 minutes available for molding/pressing, 3000 available for packaging, 1200 for stove assembly, 1200 for refrigerator assembly, and 2400 that can be used for assembling washers and dryers. The following table gives the unit molding/pressing, assembly, and packing times (in minutes) as well as the unit profits.

	Molding/ Pressing	Assembly	Packaging	Unit Profit
Stove	5.5	4.5	4.0	$110
Washer	5.2	4.5	3.0	$ 90
Electric Dryer	5.0	4.0	2.5	$ 75
Gas Dryer	5.1	3.0	2.0	$ 80
Refrigerators	7.5	9.0	4.0	$130

a. What weekly production schedule do you recommend? What is the significance of the fractional values?

b. Suppose the following additional conditions applied:

■ The number of washers should equal the combined number of dryers.

■ The number of electric dryers should not exceed the number of gas dryers by more than 100 per week.

■ The number of gas dryers should not exceed the number of electric dryers by more than 100 per week.

Now what weekly production schedule do you recommend?

3. MANUFACTURING. Kelly Industries manufactures two different structural support products used in the construction of large boats and ships. The two products, the Z345 and the W250, are produced from specially treated zinc and iron and are produced in both standard and industrial grades. Kelly nets a profit of $400 on each standard Z345 and $500 on each standard W250. Industrial models net a 40% premium.

Each week, up to 2500 pounds of zinc and 2800 pounds of iron can be treated and made available for production. The following table gives the per unit requirements (in pounds) for each model.

	Z345		W250	
	Standard	Industrial	Standard	Industrial
Zinc	25	46	16	34
Iron	50	30	28	12

Kelly has a contract to supply a combined total of at least 20 standard or industrial Z345 supports to Calton Shipbuilders each week. Company policy mandates that at least 50% of the production must be industrial models and that neither Z345 models nor W250 models can account for more than 75% of weekly production. By adhering to this policy, Kelly feels, it can sell all the product it manufactures.

a. Determine a weekly production plan for Kelly Industries. What interpretation can you give to the fractional values that are part of the optimal production quantities?

b. What proportion of the production are W250 models? What does that tell you about how the profit will be affected if the 75% limit is loosened or eliminated?

c. State whether you should buy *additional* shipments of zinc, should they become available at the following premiums above zinc's normal cost.

    i.   100 pounds for $1500

    ii.   100 pounds for $2600

    iii. 800 pounds for $10,000

4. FINANCIAL INVESTMENT. The Investment Club at Bell Labs has solicited and obtained $50,000 from its members. Collectively, the members have selected the three stocks, two bond funds, and a tax-deferred annuity shown in the following table as possible investments.

Crop	Yield (bu./acre)	Labor (hr./acre)	Expenses ($/acre)	Water (acre-ft./ acre)	Price ($/bu.)
Wheat	210	4	$50	2	$3.20
Corn	300	5	$75	6	$2.55
Oats	180	3	$30	1	$1.45
Soybeans	240	10	$60	4	$3.10

Bill wishes to produce at least 30,000 bushels of wheat and 30,000 bushels of corn, but no more than 25,000 bushels of oats. He has $25,000 to invest in his crops, and he plans to work up to 12 hours per day during the 150-day season. He also does not wish to exceed the base water supply of 1200 acre-feet allocated to him by the Kansas Agriculture Authority.

a. Formulate the problem for BP Farms as a linear program and solve for the optimal number of acres of each crop Bill should plant in order to maximize his total expected return from the harvested crops.

b. If the selling price of oats remains $1.45 a bushel, to what level must the yield increase before oats should be planted? If the yield for oats remains 180 bushels per acre, to what level would the price of oats have to rise before oats should be planted?

c. If there were no constraint on the minimum production of corn, would corn be planted? How much would the profit decrease if corn were not grown?

d. La Mancha Realty owns an adjacent 40-acre parcel, which it is willing to lease to Bill for the season for $2000. Should Bill lease this property? Why or why not?

16. SUPPLY CHAIN MANAGEMENT. Lion Golf Supplies operates three production plants in Sarasota, Florida; Louisville, Kentucky; and Carson, California. The plant in Sarasota can produce the high-end "professional" line of golf clubs and the more moderate "deluxe" line. The plant in Louisville can produce the deluxe line and basic "weekender" line, while the one in Carson can produce all three models. The amount of steel, aluminum, and wood required to make a set of each line of clubs (including waste), the monthly availability of these resources at each of three plants, and the gross profit per set are given in the following table.

	Steel	Aluminum	Wood	Gross Profit
Professional	3.2 lbs.	5.0 lbs.	5.2 lbs.	$250
Deluxe	3.6 lbs.	4.0 lbs.	4.8 lbs.	$175
Weekender	2.8 lbs.	4.5 lbs.	4.4 lbs.	$200
Available Monthly— Sarasota	5000 lbs.	7000 lbs.	10000 lbs.	
Available Monthly— Louisville	9000 lbs.	13000 lbs.	18000 lbs.	
Available Monthly— Carson	14000 lbs.	18000 lbs.	20000 lbs.	

Lion has three major distribution centers in Anaheim, California, Dallas, Texas, and Toledo, Ohio. The projected monthly demand and the unit transportation costs for each line between the manufacturing centers and distribution centers are given in the following table. Lion must ship between 80% and 100% of the demand for each line to each distribution center.

Professional	Sarasota	Louisville	Carson	Total Demand
Anaheim	$45		$9	600
Dallas	$32		$40	400
Toledo	$30		$50	200

Deluxe	Sarasota	Louisville	Carson	Total Demand
Anaheim	$40	$34	$6	800
Dallas	$28	$18	$35	1000
Toledo	$25	$10	$40	1100

Weekender	Sarasota	Louisville	Carson	Total Demand
Anaheim		$30	$5	800
Dallas		$15	$30	1500
Toledo		$9	$36	1000

Determine an optimal production/shipping pattern for Lion Golf Supplies.

17. SUPPLY CHAIN MANAGEMENT. Consider the Lion Golf Supplies model of problem 16.

a. Suppose that the following table gives the fixed monthly operating cost of each of the production plants.

Plant	Cost
Sarasota	$250,000
Louisville	$350,000
Carson	$500,000

Assuming that between 80% and 100% of the demand for each line must be filled at each distribution center, what recommendation would you now make concerning which plants should be operational and the production and shipping distribution pattern at each operational plant?

b. Suppose that *in addition to the fixed plant operating* expenses, each distribution center has fixed monthly operating expenses as shown in the following table.

Distribution Center	Cost
Anaheim	$ 50,000
Dallas	$100,000
Toledo	$ 90,000

Assuming that between 80% and 100% of the demand for each line must be met at each distribution center that is operational, what recommendation would you now make concerning which plants should be operational and the production and shipping distribution pattern at each operational plant?

18. PORTFOLIO ANALYSIS. Sarah Williams has $100,000 to allocate to the investments listed in the following table. Bill Wallace, her investment counselor, has prepared the following estimates for the potential annual return on each investment.

Investment	Expected Return	Minimum Return	Maximum Return
Bonanza Gold (high-risk stock)	15%	−50%	100%
Cascade Telephone (low-risk stock)	9%	3%	12%
Money market account	7%	6%	9%
Two-year Treasury bonds	8%	8%	8%

Sarah wishes to invest her money in such a way as to maximize her expected annual return based on Bill Wallace's projections, with the following restrictions:

- At most $50,000 of her investment should be in stocks.

- At least $60,000 of her investment should have the potential of earning a 9% or greater annual return.

- At least $70,000 should be liquid during the year; this implies that at most $30,000 can be in two-year Treasury bonds.

- The minimum overall annual return should be at least 4%.

- All $100,000 is to be invested.

Assume that the investments will perform independently of one another so that the returns on the investment opportunities are uncorrelated. Formulate and solve a linear program for Sarah.

19. BLENDING—OIL REFINING. California Oil Company (Caloco) produces two grades of unleaded gasoline (regular and premium) from three raw crudes (Pacific, Gulf, and Middle East). The current octane rating, the availability (in barrels), and the cost per barrel for a given production period are given in the following table.

Crude	Octane	Availability	Cost
Pacific	85	3000 barrels	$14.28/barrel
Gulf	87	2000 barrels	$15.12/barrel
Middle East	95	8000 barrels	$19.74/barrel

For this period, Caloco has contracts calling for a minimum of 200,000 gallons of regular and 100,000 gallons of premium gasoline, and it has a refining capacity of 400,000 total gallons. (A barrel is 42 gallons.) Caloco sells regular gasoline to retailers for $0.52 and premium gasoline for $0.60 per gallon.

To be classified as "regular," the refined gas must have an octane rating of 87 or more; premium must have an octane rating of 91 or more. Assume that the octane rating of any mixture is the weighted octane rating of its components.

a. Solve for the optimal amount of each crude to blend into each gasoline during this production period.

b. Suppose Caloco could obtain an additional 50,000 gallons in refining capacity for the period by putting other projects on hold. Putting these projects on hold is estimated to cost Caloco $5000 in contract penalties. Should the company absorb these fees and secure this extra 50,000-gallon refining capacity?

c. Given your answer to part (a), calculate the amount Caloco would spend purchasing Middle East oil for the period. Suppose Middle East distributors currently have a glut of crude and are in need of some hard currency. They are willing to enter into a contract with Caloco to sell it all 8000 barrels at $16.80 a barrel. Would the Middle East distributors receive more cash from Caloco under this arrangement? Would it be profitable to Caloco to accept this offer? Discuss the ramifications of this action for domestic oil producers.

20. PERSONNEL EVALUATION. At Nevada State University, the process for determining whether or not a professor receives tenure is based on a combination of qualitative evaluations and a quantitative formula derived by using linear programming. The process works as follows.

In an Annual Personnel File (APF), the professor submits evidence of his or her (1) teaching effectiveness, (2) research performance, (3) other professional activities, and (4) on-campus professional service. A personnel committee of three evaluators (who are full professors) independently evaluate the professor's file and assign a numerical rating between 0 and 100 to each of the four categories. For each category, the scores from the three evaluators are averaged together to give a single score for that category.

To determine the maximum overall score for the professor, a linear program is used for selecting the best weights (percentages) to assign to each category, satisfying the following university criteria.

- Teaching must be weighted at least as heavily as any other category.

- Research must be weighted at least 25%.

- Teaching plus research must be weighted at least 75%.

- Teaching plus research must be weighted no more than 90%.

- Service is to be weighted at least as heavily as professional activities.

- Professional activities must be weighted at least 5%.

- The total of the weights must be 100%.

Professor Anna Sung is up for tenure. To receive tenure, she must receive a weighted total score of at least 85. The three personnel committee members evaluated Anna as follows:

26. HEALTH FOODS. Health Valley Foods produces three types of health food bars in two-ounce sizes: the Go Bar, the Power Bar, and the Energy Bar. The Energy Bar also comes in an 8-ounce size. The three main ingredients in each bar are a protein concentrate, a sugar substitute, and carob. The recipes for each bar in terms of percentage of ingredients (by weight) and the daily availabilities of each of the ingredients are as follows.

Bar	% Protein Concentrate	% Sugar Substitute	% Carob
Go	20	60	20
Power	50	30	20
Energy	30	40	30
Daily availability	600 lbs.	1000 lbs.	800 lbs.

The following costs are incurred in the production of the health food bars:

	Costs
Labor and packaging (2-oz. bars)	$0.03/bar
Labor and packaging (8-oz. bars)	$0.05/bar
Protein concentrate	$3.20/lb.
Sugar substitute	$1.40/lb.
Carob	$2.60/lb.

Health Valley's wholesale selling prices to health food stores are $0.68, $0.84, and $0.76, respectively, for 2-ounce sizes of the Go Bar, the Power Bar, and the Energy Bar, and $3.00 for the 8-ounce Energy Bar. The company has facilities for producing up to 25,000 2-ounce bars and 2000 8-ounce bars daily. It manufactures at least 2500 of each of the 2-ounce bars daily. No 2-ounce bar is to account for more than 50% of the total production of 2-ounce bars, and the total production (by weight) of Energy Bars is not to exceed more than 50% of the total production (by weight).

Determine an optimal daily production schedule of health food bars for Health Valley Foods.

27. ADVERTISING. JL Foods is planning to increase its advertising campaign from $1.4 million to $2 million based, in part, on the introduction of a new product, JL Taco Sauce, to accompany its traditional products, JL Ketchup and JL Spaghetti Sauce. In the past, JL Foods promoted its two products individually, splitting its advertising budget equally between ketchup and spaghetti sauce.

From past experience, the marketing department estimates that each dollar spent advertising only ketchup increases ketchup sales by four bottles and each dollar spent advertising *only* spaghetti sauce increases its sales by 3.2 bottles. Since JL makes $0.30 per bottle of ketchup and $0.35 per bottle of spaghetti sauce sold (excluding the sunk cost of the given advertising budget), this amounts to a return of $1.20 (=4 × $0.30) per advertising dollar on ketchup and $1.12 (=3.2 × $0.35) per advertising dollar on spaghetti sauce. Because taco sauce is a new product, its initial return is projected to be only $0.10 per bottle,

but each advertising dollar spent solely on taco sauce is estimated to increase sales by 11 bottles. The company also projects that sales of each product would increase by another 1.4 bottles for each dollar spent on joint advertising of the three products.

JL wishes to maximize its increase in profits this year from advertising while also "building for the future" by adhering to the following guidelines for this year's advertising spending:

- A maximum of $2 million total advertising
- At most $400,000 on joint advertising
- At least $100,000 on joint advertising
- At least $1 million promoting taco sauce, either individually or through joint advertising
- At least $250,000 promoting ketchup only
- At least $250,000 promoting spaghetti sauce only
- At least $750,000 promoting taco sauce only
- At least as much spent this year as last year promoting ketchup, either individually or by joint advertising
- At least as much spent this year as last year promoting spaghetti sauce, either individually or by joint advertising
- At least 7.5 million total bottles of product sold

a. Determine the optimal allocation of advertising dollars among the four advertising possibilities (advertising for each product individually and joint advertising). Give the total return per advertising dollar of this solution and express this as a percentage of the $2 million advertising budget.

b. What is the return on additional advertising dollars?

c. Suppose the constraint requiring that at least $750,000 be spent promoting only taco sauce were lowered to $700,000. How much would the profit increase?

28. RESTAURANT CREW ASSIGNMENT. Burger Boy Restaurant is open from 8:00 A.M. to 10:00 P.M. daily. In addition to the hours of business, a crew of workers must arrive one hour early to help set up the restaurant for the day's operations, and another crew of workers must stay one hour after 10:00 P.M. to clean up after closing.

Burger Boy operates with nine different shifts:

Shift	Type	Daily Salary
1. 7AM–9AM	Part-time	$15
2. 7AM–11AM	Part-time	$25
3. 7AM–3PM	Full-time	$52
4. 11AM–3PM	Part-time	$22

Shift	Type	Daily Salary
5. 11AM–7PM	Full-time	$54
6. 3PM–7PM	Part-time	$24
7. 3PM–11PM	Full-time	$55
8. 7PM–11PM	Part-time	$23
9. 9PM–11PM	Part-time	$16

A needs assessment study has been completed, which divided the workday at Burger Boy into eight 2-hour blocks. The number of employees needed for each block is as follows:

Time Block	Employees Needed
7AM–9AM	8
9AM–11AM	10
11AM–1PM	22
1PM–3PM	15
3PM–5PM	10
5PM–7PM	20
7PM–9PM	16
9PM–11PM	8

Burger Boy wants at least 40% of all employees at the peak time periods of 11:00 A.M. to 1:00 P.M. and 5:00 P.M. to 7:00 P.M. to be full-time employees. At least two full-time employees must be on duty when the restaurant opens at 7:00 A.M. and when it closes at 11:00 P.M.

- Formulate and solve a model Burger Boy can use to determine how many employe es it should hire for each of its nine shifts to minimize its overall daily employee costs.

29. LAW ENFORCEMENT. The police department of the city of Flint, Michigan, has divided the city into 15 patrol sectors, such that the response time of a patrol unit (squad car) will be less than three minutes between any two points within the sector.

Until recently, 15 units, one located in each sector, patrolled the streets of Flint from 7:00 P.M. to 3:00 A.M. However, severe budget cuts have forced the city to eliminate some patrols. The chief of police has mandated that each sector be covered by at least one unit located either within the sector or in an adjacent sector.

The accompanying figure depicts the 15 patrol sectors of Flint, Michigan. Formulate and solve a binary model that will determine the minimum number of units required to implement the chief's policy.

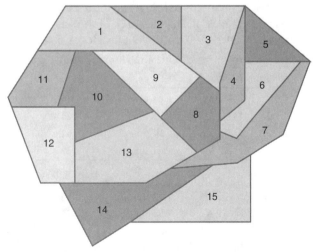

Police Patrol Sectors, Flint, Michigan

30. POLLUTION CONTROL. General Motors has received orders from the City of Los Angeles for 30 experimental cars, 20 experimental vans, and 10 experimental buses that meet clean air standards due to take effect in three years. The vehicles can be manufactured in any of four plants located in Michigan, Tennessee, Texas, and California. Due to differences in wage rates, availability of resources, and transportation costs, the unit cost of production of each of these vehicles varies from location to location. In addition, there is a fixed cost for producing any experimental vehicles at each location. These costs (in $1000's) are summarized in the following table.

	Cars	Vans	Buses	Fixed Cost
Michigan	15	20	40	150
Tennessee	15	28	29	170
Texas	10	24	50	125
California	14	15	25	500

Using an integer model with 12 integer variables (representing the number of each model produced at each plant) and four binary variables (indicating whether or not a particular plant is to be used for production of the experimental vehicles), determine how many experimental vehicles should be produced at each plant? What are the total production costs and fixed costs of this plan?

31. REAL ESTATE. Atlantic Standard Homes is developing 20 acres in a new community in the Florida Keys. There are four models it can build on each lot, and Atlantic Standard must satisfy three requirements: at least 40 are to be one story; at least 50 are to have three or more bedrooms; and there are to be at least 10 of each model. Atlantic Standard estimates the following gross profits:

Model	Lot Size (acre)	Stories	Bedrooms	Profit
Tropic	.20	1	2	$40,000
Sea Breeze	.27	1	3	$50,000
Orleans	.22	2	3	$60,000
Grand Key	.35	2	4	$80,000

a. Formulate the problem as an integer linear programming model and solve for Atlantic Standard's optimal production of homes in this community.

b. If the variables had not been restricted to be integers, the optimal linear programming solution gives $X_1 = 30$, $X_2 = 10$, $X_3 = 35.45$, $X_4 = 10$. Round this solution to an integer point. Is it feasible? How much lower is the optimal profit of the rounded solution than the optimal integer solution found in part (a)?

c. Assume that a minimum of 12 homes must be built for at least three of the four models. Using four additional binary variables and five additional constraints, modify the model to reflect this new condition and solve for the new optimal distribution of homes for the Atlantic Standard project.

32. VANPOOLING. Logitech, a rapidly growing high-tech company located in suburban Boston, Massachusetts, has been encouraging its employees to carpool. These efforts have met with only moderate success, and now the company is setting aside up to $250,000 to purchase small- and medium-size vans and minibuses to establish a van-pool program that will transport employees between various pickup points and company headquarters. Four models of vans and two models of minibuses are under consideration, as detailed in the following table.

	Maker	Cost	Passenger Capacity	Annual Maintenance
Vans				
Nissan	Japan	$26,000	7	$ 5000
Toyota	Japan	$30,000	8	$ 3500
Plymouth	U.S.	$24,000	9	$ 6000
Ford (Stretch)	U.S.	$32,000	11	$ 8000
Minibuses				
Mitsubishi	Japan	$50,000	20	$ 7000
General Motors	U.S.	$60,000	24	$11,000

a. Formulate and solve a vehicle purchase model for Logitech that will maximize the total passenger capacity of the fleet given that:

■ Up to $250,000 will be spent on vehicles.

■ Annual maintenance cost should not exceed $50,000.

■ Total number of vehicles purchased should not exceed eight.

■ At least one minibus should be purchased.

■ At least three vans should be purchased.

■ At least half the vehicles should be made in the United States.

b. Determine the optimal solution if the amount Logitech committed for vehicle purchase were: (i) $253,900; (ii) $254,000; (iii) $249,900; (iv) $259,900; (v) $260,000. Comment.

c. Characterize the problem if the amount Logitech committed to the program were $100,000.

33. MERCHANDISING. Office Warehouse has been downsizing its operations. It is in the process of moving to a much smaller location and reducing the number of different computer products it carries. Coming under scrutiny are 10 products Office Warehouse has carried for the past year. For each of these products, Office Warehouse has estimated the floor space required for effective display, the capital required to restock if the product line is retained, and the short-term loss that Office Warehouse will incur if the corresponding product is eliminated (through liquidation sales, etc.).

Product Line	Manufacturer	Cost of Liquidation	Capital to Restock	Floor Space (ft2)
Notebook computer	Toshiba	$10,000	$15,000	50
Notebook computer	Compaq	$ 8,000	$12,000	60
PC	Compaq	$20,000	$25,000	200
PC	Packard Bell	$12,000	$22,000	200
MacIntosh computer	Apple	$25,000	$20,000	145
Monitor	Packard Bell	$ 4,000	$12,000	85
Monitor	Sony	$15,000	$13,000	50
Printer	Apple	$ 5,000	$14,000	100
Printer	HP	$18,000	$25,000	150
Printer	Epson	$ 6,000	$10,000	125

Office Warehouse wishes to minimize the loss due to liquidation of product lines subject to the following conditions:

■ At least four of these product lines will be eliminated.

■ The remaining products will occupy no more than 600 square feet of floor space.

■ If one product line from a particular manufacturer is eliminated, all products from that manufacturer will be eliminated. (This affects Compaq, Packard Bell, and Apple.)

■ At least two computer models (notebook, PC, or MacIntosh), at least one monitor model, and at least one printer model will continue to be carried by Office Warehouse.

■ At most $75,000 is to be spent on restocking product lines.

■ If the Toshiba notebook computer is retained, the Epson line of printers will also be retained.

Solve for the optimal policy for Office Warehouse.

34. SOFTWARE DEVELOPMENT. The Korvex Corporation is a company concerned with developing CD-ROM software applications that it sells to major computer manufacturers to include as "packaged items" when consumers purchase systems with CD-ROM drives. The company is currently evaluating the feasibility of developing six new applications. Specific information concerning each of these applications is summarized in the following table.

Application	Projected Development Cost	Programmers Required	Projected Present Worth Net Profit
1	$ 400,000	6	$2,000,000
2	$1,100,000	18	$3,600,000
3	$ 940,000	20	$4,000,000
4	$ 760,000	16	$3,000,000
5	$1,260,000	28	$4,400,000
6	$1,800,000	34	$6,200,000

Korvex has a staff of 60 programmers and has allocated $3.5 million for development of new applications.

a. Formulate and solve a binary integer linear programming model for the situation faced by the Korvex Corporation.

b. Assume also that the following additional conditions hold:

- It is anticipated that those interested in application 4 will also be interested in application 5, and vice versa. Thus, if either application 4 or application 5 is developed, the other must also be developed.

- The underlying concepts of application 2 make sense only if application 1 is included in the package. Thus, application 2 will be developed only if application 1 is developed.

- Applications 3 and 6 have similar themes; thus, if application 3 is developed, application 6 will not be developed, and vice versa.

- To ensure quality products, Korvex does not wish to expand its product line too rapidly. Accordingly, it wishes to develop at most three of the potential application products at this time.

Incorporate these constraints into the model developed for part (a), and determine the optimal choice of applications Korvex should develop.

35. ACCOUNTING/PERSONNEL HIRING. Jones. Jimenez, and Sihota (JJS) is expanding its tax service business into the San Antonio area. The company wishes to be able to service at least 100 personal and 25 corporate accounts per week.

JJS plans to hire three levels of employees: CPAs, experienced accountants without a CPA, and junior accountants. The following table gives the weekly salary level as well as the projection of the expected number of accounts that can be serviced weekly by each level of employee.

Employee	Total Number of Accounts	Maximum Number of Corporate Accounts	Weekly Salary
CPAs	6	3	$1200
Experienced accountant	6	1	$ 900
Junior accountant	4	0	$ 600

JJS wishes to staff its San Antonio office so that at least two-thirds of all its employees will be either CPAs or experienced accountants. Determine the number of employees from each experience level the firm should hire for its San Antonio office to minimize its total weekly payroll.

36. ADVERTISING. Century Productions is in the process of promotion planning for its new comedy motion pic-

ture. *Three Is a Crowd*, through television, radio, and newspaper advertisements. The following table details the marketing department's estimate of the cost and the total audience reached per exposure in each medium.

	TV	Radio	Newspaper
Cost per exposure	$4,000	$500	$1,000
Audience reached per exposure	500,000	50,000	200,000

The marketing department does not wish to place more than 250 ads in any one medium.

a. What media mix should Century use if it wishes to reach the maximum total audience with an advertising budget of $500,000?

b. What media mix should Century use if it wishes to reach an audience of 30 million at minimum total cost?

c. The cost of producing the television advertisement is $500,000; the radio spot costs $50,000 to write and produce; and the newspaper ad costs $100,000 for design, graphics, and copy. If the total promotional budget is not to exceed $1 million (including the cost of producing the television or radio spot or the newspaper advertisement), use a mixed integer model to determine the production and media mix Century Productions should use.

37. MANUFACTURING. Floyd's Fabrication has just received an order from Gimbal Plumbing Fixtures for 100,000 specially designed three-inch-diameter casings to be delivered in one week. The contract price was negotiated up front; hence, Floyd's maximum profit will be obtained when its costs are minimized.

Floyd's has three production facilities capable of producing the casings. Production costs do not vary between locations, but the changeover (setup) costs do vary, as does the cost of transporting the finished items to Gimbal. The following table details these costs.

Location	Changeover Cost	Transportation Cost (per 1000)	Maximum Weekly Production
Springfield	$1200	$224	65,000
Oak Ridge	$1100	$280	50,000
Westchester	$1000	$245	55,000

Formulate and solve this problem as a mixed integer linear programming model.

38. PERSONAL FINANCE. After many years of earning extremely low bank interest rates, Shelley Mednick has decided to give the stock market a try. This is her first time investing, and she wants to be extra cautious. She has heard that a new stock offering from TCS, a telecommunication company, is being sold at $55 per share (including commissions) and is projected to sell at $68 per share in a year. She is also considering a

Plan	Selling Price	Size (sq. ft.)	Bedrooms	Bathrooms	Stories	Garage Size
Grand Estates						
The Trump*	$700,000	4000	5 + den	4	2	3 car
The Vanderbilt*	$680,000	3600	4 + den	3	2	3 car
The Hughes*	$650,000	3000	4	3	1	3 car
The Jackson*	$590,000	2600	3	3	1	3 car
Glen Wood Collection						
Grand Cypress*	$420,000	2800	4 + den	3	2	3 car
Lazy Oak	$380,000	2400	4	3	2	2 car
Wind Row	$320,000	2200	3	3	2	2 car
Orangewood	$280,000	1800	3	2 1/2	1	2 car
Lakeview Patio Homes						
Bayview*	$300,000	2000	4	2 1/2	2	2 car
Shoreline	$270,000	1800	3 + den	2 1/2	2	2 car
Docks Edge	$240,000	1500	3	2 1/2	1	2 car
Golden Pier	$200,000	1200	2	2	1	2 car
Country Condominiums						
Country Stream	$220,000	1600	3	2	2	—
Weeping Willow	$160,000	1200	2	2	1	—
Picket Fence	$140,000	1000	2	1 1/2	1	—

*Some of these models may occupy larger premium or lakeside lots with higher selling prices.

Objectives

1. LSDC needs to determine the number of units of each plan of each product to build in order to maximize its profit.

2. If LSDC builds a 10-acre sports/recreation complex on the property, this would:

   ■ Decrease the usable area to build houses by 10 acres—all other constraints still apply.

   ■ Cost LSDC $8,000,000 to build.

   ■ Enhance the value of all houses so that LSDC would raise the selling prices of the homes by the following amounts:

      —Grand Estates (not on lake)—add 5% (e.g., add $35,000 to profit for Trumps, etc.)

      —Grand Estates (on lake)—add another $40,000 (e.g., profits increase by $40,000)

      —Glen Wood and Lakeview Patio Homes (nonpremium except Golden Pier)

         —Add 3% (e.g., add $12,600 to profit of Grand Cypress)

      —Premium Models—add a flat $16,000

      —Golden Pier—$0 (no change, so that it can still qualify as affordable housing)

      —Country Condominiums—add a flat $10,000

All of the selling price increases would be added to the original gross profits to determine the new gross profit (prior to subtracting the $8,000,000 for the complex).

The Report

Prepare a detailed report analyzing this project and make suggestions for the number of each type of each unit to be built. Give and support your recommendations on whether or not to build the sports/recreation complex. Do appropriate "what-if" analyses and give a summary of your final recommendations. (*Hint:* You may wish to solve as a linear program and round.)

CASE 3: PENTAGONAL PICTURES, INC.

Pentagonal Pictures produces motion pictures in Hollywood and distributes them nationwide. Currently, it is considering 10 possible films; these include dramas, comedies, and action adventures. The success of each film depends somewhat on both the strength of the subject matter and the appeal of the cast. Estimating the cost of a film and its potential box office draw is inexact at best; still, the studio must rely on its experts' opinions to help it evaluate which projects to undertake.

The following table lists the films currently under consideration by Pentagonal Pictures, including the projected cost and box office gross receipts.

Film	Rating	Type	No-Name Cast		Big Star Cast	
			Cost	Box Office Gross	Cost	Box Office Gross
Two-Edged Sword	PG-13	Action	$ 5M	$ 8M	$10M	$15M
Lady in Waiting	R	Drama	$12M	$20M	$25M	$35M
Yesterday	PG	Drama	$ 8M	$10M	$12M	$26M
Golly Gee	PG	Comedy	$ 7M	$12M	$15M	$26M
Why I Cry	PG-13	Drama	$15M	$30M	$30M	$45M
Captain Kid	PG	Comedy	$10M	$20M	$17M	$28M
Oh Yes!	R	Comedy	$ 4M	$ 7M	$ 8M	$12M
Nitty Gritty	PG	Comedy	$11M	$15M	$14M	$20M
The Crash	R	Action	$20M	$28M	$40M	$65M
Bombs Away	R	Action	$25M	$37M	$50M	$80M

In addition to these production costs, each movie will have a $1 million advertising budget, which will increase to $3 million if the movie is to have a "big star" cast. Assume that the studio receives 80% of a film's gross receipts. The company would like to maximize its net profit (gross profit – production costs – advertising costs) for the year.

Pentagonal has a production budget of $100 million and an advertising budget of $15 million. In addition, it would like to adhere to the following restrictions:

1. At least half the films produced should have a rating of PG or PG-13.
2. At least two comedies are to be produced.
3. If *The Crash* is produced, *Bombs Away* will not be.
4. At least one drama is to be produced.
5. At least two films should have big-name casts.
6. At least two PG films should be produced.
7. At least one action movie with a big-name cast should be produced.

Prepare a report for Pentagonal Pictures that recommends which films should be produced and with which casts. Detail how the budgets will be spent. Include in your report a sensitivity analysis that considers how varying budgets for both production costs and advertising (while spending at most a total of $115 million) would affect your recommendation. Finally, discuss the effects of Pentagonal's seven restrictions and report the effect of requiring only six of the seven, five of the seven, and four of the seven to hold.

CASES 4–6 ARE ON THE CD.

CHAPTER 10

Decision Models

Lindal Cedar Homes, Inc.

Lindal Cedar Homes, Inc. (http://www.lindal.com/) is engaged primarily in the manufacture and distribution of customer cedar homes, windows, and sunrooms. The Company also remanufactures standard dimensional cedar lumber. Founded in 1945, the company is the world's oldest and largest manufacturer of top-of-the-line, year-round cedar homes.

Lindal Cedar Homes' management makes numerous decisions throughout the year. Among these, the company must decide which new product lines to introduce, what promotional materials to develop, what forms of financing to obtain, what advertising media to select, which material hedging strategies to adopt, and what prices to charge for its products.

A recent decision that has had a major impact on the company's operations was the introduction of the Select product line of housing. This product line, which utilizes conventional design and construction techniques, costs approximately 30% less than the company's cedar frame specification and is aimed at the middle of the custom housing market. In determining whether to introduce this line, the company had to estimate the potential product market, analyze its manufacturing capabilities and forecast the product's impact on the sales of existing product lines.

Another recent company decision was to close and subsequently sell a Canadian sawmill. In this decision, the company had to forecast future lumber needs, the cost of relocating and/or laying off employees, and the immediate costs versus long-term savings of taking this action. Complicating this decision was the fact that closing the sawmill could jeopardize a timber award made by the Province of British Columbia to the company.

To address these issues, Lindal management uses decision analysis techniques.

10.1 INTRODUCTION TO DECISION ANALYSIS

Throughout our day we are faced with numerous decisions, many of which require careful thought and analysis. In such cases, large sums of money might be lost or other severe consequences can result from the wrong choice. For example, you probably would do a careful analysis of the car you are going to purchase, the house you are going to buy, or the college you will attend.

Businesses continuously make many crucial decisions, such as whether or not to introduce a new product or where to locate a new plant. The outcome of these decisions can severely affect the firm's future profitability. The field of **decision analysis** provides the necessary framework for making these types of important decisions.

Decision analysis allows an individual or organization to select a decision from a set of possible *decision alternatives when uncertainties regarding the future* exist. The goal is to optimize the resulting return or *payoff* in terms of some decision criterion.

Consider an investor interested in purchasing an apartment building. Possible decisions include the type of financing to use and the building's rehabilitation plan. Unknown to the investor are the future occupancy rate of the building, the amount of rent that can be charged for each unit, and possible modifications in the tax laws associated with real estate ownership. Depending on the investor's decisions and their consequences, the investor will receive some payoff.

Although the criterion used in making a decision could be noneconomic, most business decisions are based on economic considerations. When probabilities can be assessed for likelihoods of the uncertain future events, one common economic criterion is maximizing expected profit. If probabilities for the likelihoods of the uncertain future events cannot be assessed, the economic criterion is typically based on the decision maker's attitude toward life.

Often, elements of risk need to be factored into the decision-making process. This is especially true if there is a possibility of incurring extremely large losses or achieving exceptional gains. **Utility theory** can provide a mechanism for analyzing decisions in light of these risks, as well as evaluating situations in which the criterion is noneconomic.

While decision analysis typically focuses on situations in which the uncertain future events are due to chance, there are business situations in which competition shapes these events. **Game theory** is a useful tool for analyzing decision making in light of competitive action.

10.2 PAYOFF TABLE ANALYSIS

We begin our discussion of decision analysis by focusing on the basic elements of decision making: (1) decision alternatives, (2) states of nature, and (3) payoffs.

Payoff Tables

When a decision maker faces a finite set of discrete *decision alternatives* whose outcome is a function of a single future event, a **payoff table** analysis is the simplest way of formulating the decision problem. In a payoff table, the rows correspond to the possible decision alternatives and the columns correspond to the possible future events (known as **states of nature**). The states of nature of a payoff table are defined so that they are mutually exclusive (at most one possible state of nature will occur) and collectively exhaustive (at least one state of nature will occur). This way we know that exactly one state of nature must occur. The body of the table contains the *payoffs* resulting from a particular decision alternative when the corresponding state of nature occurs. Although the decision maker can determine which decision alternative to select, he or she has no control over which state of nature will occur.

Figure 10.1 shows the general form of a payoff table. In this figure a payoff table with three states of nature and four possible decision alternatives is shown. To illustrate payoff table analysis, consider the following example.

PUBLISHERS CLEARING HOUSE

Publishers Clearing House is a nationwide firm that markets magazine subscriptions. The primary vehicle it uses to contact customers is a series of mailings known collectively as the Publishers Clearing House Sweepstakes. Individuals who receive these mailings can enter the sweepstakes even if they do not order any magazine subscriptions. Various prizes are available, the top prize being $10 million. Suppose you are one of the many individuals who are not interested in ordering magazines. You must decide whether or not to enter the contest.

SOLUTION

To help evaluate this problem, you can construct a payoff table. In this model, you have two possible *decision alternatives*.

D1: Spend the time filling out the contest application and pay the postage.
D2: Toss the letter in the recycling bin.

Obviously, if you knew the outcome in advance, your decision would be quite simple: Enter the contest if you are going to win something valuable; do not enter the contest if you are not. Unfortunately, winners are not known in advance, and you cannot win unless you enter. The act of winning or losing is something over which you have no control.

A number of different prizes are available. In a recent contest, these ranged from a flag to $10 million. The possible outcomes, or *states of nature*, for this model are:

S1: The entry would be a losing one.
S2: The entry would win a flag.
S3: The entry would win $100.
S4: The entry would win $500.
S5: The entry would win $10,000.
S6: The entry would win $1 million.
S7: The entry would win $10 million.

Note that these states of nature are mutually exclusive and collectively exhaustive.

For each decision alternative and state of nature combination there is a resulting payoff. For example, if you enter the contest and do not win, the loss is equivalent to the opportunity cost of the time spent completing the contest application plus the cost of the postage. Let's assume that these costs total $1.

FIGURE 10.1

A Payoff Table with Four Decisions and Three States of Nature

		Possible States of Nature		
		S1	S2	S3
Possible Decisions	D1	P_{11}	P_{12}	P_{13}
	D2	P_{21}	P_{22}	P_{23}
	D3	P_{31}	P_{32}	P_{33}
	D4	P_{41}	P_{42}	P_{43}

"Payoff" if decision D1 and state of nature S2 occur

If, on the other hand, you enter the contest and win $100, this results in a net payoff of $99 ($100 minus the $1 cost). Similarly, if the flag is worth $5, winning a flag will result in a net payoff of $4 ($5 – $1).

The $1 million and $10 million prizes are paid out over several years. To get the present value of these prizes you must calculate their discounted future cash flows. If you assume that the discounted present value of these prizes amounts to approximately 35% of their face amount, then the net payoff values for the $1 million and $10 million winners would be $349,999 and $3,499,999, respectively.

The resulting payoff table is shown in Table 10.1. Once this payoff table is constructed, you can utilize it to determine which decision alternative you should pursue.

Choosing the States of Nature

Although determining the states of nature for the Publishers Clearing House example was rather straightforward, often the decision maker has a great deal of flexibility in defining them. Selecting the appropriate definition for the states of nature can require careful thought about the situation being modeled. To illustrate, consider the situation faced by Tom Brown.

TOM BROWN INVESTMENT DECISION

Tom Brown Maximin.xls
Tom Brown Minimax Regret.xls
Tom Brown Minimax Regret Revised.xls
Tom Brown Maximax.xls
Tom Brown Insufficient Reason.xls
Tom Brown Expected Value.xls
Tom Brown.xls

Tom Brown has inherited $1000 from a distant relative. Since he still has another year of studies before graduation from Iowa State University, Tom has decided to invest the $1000 for a year. Literally tens of thousands of different investment possibilities are available to him, including growth stocks, income stocks, corporate bonds, municipal bonds, government bonds, futures, limited partnerships, annuities, and bank accounts.

Given the limited amount of money he has to invest, Tom has decided that it is not worthwhile to spend the countless hours required to fully understand these various investments. Therefore, he has turned to a broker for investment guidance.

The broker has selected five potential investments she believes would be appropriate for Tom: gold, a junk bond, a growth stock, a certificate of deposit, and a stock option hedge. Tom would like to set up a payoff table to help him choose the appropriate investment.

SOLUTION

The first step in constructing a payoff table is to determine the set of possible decision alternatives. For Tom, this is simply the set of five investment opportunities recommended by the broker.

The second step is to define the states of nature. One choice might be the percentage change in the gross national product (GNP) over the next year (rounded to the nearest percent). A principal drawback of this approach, however, is the difficulty

---

TABLE 10.1

Payoff Table for Publishers Clearing House

Decision Alternatives	States of Nature						
	Do Not Win	Win Flag	Win $100	Win $500	Win $10,000	Win $1 Million	Win $10 Million
Enter Contest	–$1	$4	$99	$499	$9,999	$349,999	$3,499,999
Do Not Enter Contest	$0	$0	$0	$0	$0	$0	$0

most people would have in determining the payoff for a given investment from the percentage change in the GNP. Even if Tom had a doctorate in economics, he might find it extremely difficult to assess how a 2% rise in GNP would affect the value of a particular investment.

Another possibility is to define the states of nature in terms of general stock market performance as measured by the Standard & Poor's 500 or Dow Jones Industrial Average. But even if he were to spend the time doing this, it is doubtful whether Tom or anyone else could correctly differentiate the return on an investment if, say, the Dow Jones Industrial Average went up 800 points as opposed to 810 points. Even if Tom used 100-*point* intervals, modeling a possible 3000-point increase or decrease in the Dow Jones Industrial Average would still require 61 states of nature for each of the five investments.

Instead Tom decided to define the states of nature qualitatively as follows:

S1: A large rise in the stock market over the next year
S2: A small rise in the stock market over the next year
S3: No change in the stock market over the next year
S4: A small fall in the stock market over the next year
S5: A large fall in the stock market over the next year

Since these states must be mutually exclusive and collectively exhaustive, there should be a clear understanding as to exactly what each of these terms means. In terms of the Dow Jones Industrial Average, for example, Tom might use the following correspondence:

State of Nature	Change in Dow Jones Industrial Average
S1: large rise	an increase of over 1500 points
S2: small rise	an increase of between 500 and 1500 points
S3: no change	a decrease or increase of less than 500 points
S4: small fall	a decrease of between 500 and 1200 points
S5: large fall	a decrease of more than 1200 points

Although the intervals corresponding to these states of nature are not of the same size, the states of nature are mutually exclusive and collectively exhaustive.

Based on these definitions for the states of nature, the final step in constructing the payoff table is to determine the payoffs resulting from each decision alternative (investment) and state of nature. In doing so, Tom's broker reasoned that stocks and bonds generally move in the same direction as the general market, whereas gold is an investment hedge that tends to move in the opposite direction from the market. The C/D account always pays 6% ($60 profit). The specific payoffs for the five different investments, based on the broker's analysis, are given in Table 10.2.

TABLE 10.2

Payoff Table for Tom Brown

Decision Alternatives	States of Nature				
	Large Rise	Small Rise	No Change	Small Fall	Large Fall
Gold	−$100	$100	$200	$300	$ 0
Bond	$250	$200	$150	−$100	−$150
Stock	$500	$250	$100	−$200	−$600
C/D Account	$ 60	$ 60	$ 60	$ 60	$ 60
Stock Option Hedge	$200	$150	$150	−$200	−$150

Dominated Decisions

It is worth comparing the payoffs associated with the stock option hedge investment to those associated with the bond investment. For each state of nature, Tom would do at least as well with the bond investment as with the stock option hedge, and for several of the states of nature, the bond actually offers a higher return. In this case, the decision alternative to invest in the bond is said to *dominate* the stock option hedge decision alternative. A decision alternative that is dominated by another can never be optimal and thus, it can be dropped from further consideration. Eliminating the dominated decision alternative of "stock option hedge" gives a payoff table with the remaining four decision alternatives.

Now that a payoff table has been created, an optimization criterion can be applied to determine the best decision for Tom.

10.3 DECISION-MAKING CRITERIA

In this section, we consider approaches for selecting an "optimal" decision based on some decision-making criterion. One way of categorizing such criteria involves the decision maker's knowledge of which state of nature will occur. The decision maker who knows "for sure" which state of nature will occur is said to be **decision making under certainty**.

Knowing which state of nature will occur makes choosing the appropriate decision alternative quite easy. For example, in the Publishers Clearing House Model, if you knew for certain that you were going to win the $10 million grand prize, you would definitely enter the contest. Because few things in life are certain, however, you might wonder whether decision making under certainty is really ever done. The answer is an emphatic "yes!" Many management science models assume that the future is known with certainty.

For example, the linear programming model for Galaxy Industries discussed in Chapter 8 assumed that the unit profit and production time required per dozen Space Rays and Zappers, as well as the amount of plastic and available production time, were all known with certainty. Although we investigated relaxing these assumptions through sensitivity analysis, solving the problem as a linear program was, in effect, making a decision under certainty.

If the decision maker does not know with certainty which state of nature will occur, the model is classified as either decision making under uncertainty or decision making under risk. **Decision making under risk** assumes that the decision maker has at least some knowledge of the probabilities for the states of nature occurring; no such knowledge is assumed in **decision making under uncertainty**.

One method for making decisions under risk is to select the decision with the best expected payoff, which is calculated using the probability estimates for the states of nature. However, since decision making under uncertainty assumes no knowledge of the probabilities for the states of nature, expected values cannot be calculated, and decisions must be made based on other criteria. Because probability information regarding the states of nature is not always available, many decision problems are analyzed using decision making under uncertainty.

To contrast decision making under uncertainty and risk, let us return to the Publishers Clearing House situation. In this model, the values of the prizes in the contest are known to participants. Because the chance of winning a prize depends on the number of entries received, the exact probabilities of winning a given prize are unknown; thus, decision making under uncertainty should be used to analyze this problem.

On the other hand, if you called Publishers Clearing House and learned that it receives an average of 1.75 million entries a day for its contest, you would be able to estimate the probability of winning each of the prizes offered. In this case, decision making under risk would be possible.

Decision Making Under Uncertainty

When using decision making under uncertainty to analyze a situation, the decision criteria are based on the decision maker's attitudes toward life. These include an individual being pessimistic or optimistic, conservative or aggressive.

Pessimistic or Conservative Approach—Maximin Criterion

A *pessimistic* decision maker believes that, no matter what decision is made, the worst possible result will occur. A *conservative* decision maker wishes to ensure a guaranteed minimum possible payoff, regardless of which state of nature occurs.

For either individual, the **maximin criterion** may be used to make decisions. Since this criterion is based on a worst-case scenario, the decision maker first finds the minimum payoff for each decision alternative. The optimal decision alternative is the one that *max*imizes the *min*imum payoff.

To illustrate, let us return to the Tom Brown investment model. (Recall that the dominated stock option hedge decision was eliminated.) From Table 10.2 we see that if Tom chooses to buy gold, the worst possible outcome occurs if there is a large rise in the stock market, resulting in a $100 loss. If he buys the bond or stock, the worst possible outcome occurs if the stock market has a large fall; in this case, his loss would be $150 for the bond and $600 for the stock. If Tom chooses the C/D account, he will earn $60 no matter which state of nature occurs. Hence, if Tom is a conservative decision maker, he will try to maximize his returns under this worst-case scenario. Accordingly, he will select the decision that results in the best of these minimum payoffs—in this case, the C/D account.

Figure 10.2 shows an Excel spreadsheet for the Tom Brown investment problem. Column H is added to identify the minimum payoff for each decision. The optimal decision for the maximum criterion is identified in cell B11 using the VLOOKUP command shown, and the maximin payoff is given in cell B10.

Minimization Models

In the Tom Brown investment model, the numbers in the payoff table represented returns or profits. If the numbers in the payoff table represented costs rather than profits, however, the worst outcome for each decision alternative would be the one

---

FIGURE 10.2   Excel Spreadsheet Showing Maximin Decision

Tom Brown
Maximin.xls

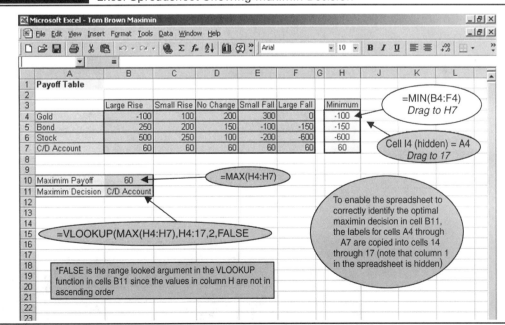

with the maximum cost. A pessimistic or conservative decision maker would then select the decision alternative with the *min*imum of these *max*imum costs; that is, use a **minimax criterion**.

Maximin Approach for Profit Payoffs

1. Determine the minimum payoff for each decision alternative.
2. Select the decision alternative with the maximum minimum payoff.

Minimax Approach for Cost Payoffs

1. Determine the maximum cost for each decision alternative.
2. Select the decision alternative with the minimum maximum cost.

Minimax Regret Criterion

Another criterion that pessimistic or conservative decision makers frequently use is the **minimax regret criterion**. This approach is identical to the minimax approach for cost data except that the optimal decision is based on "lost opportunity," or "regret" rather than costs. It involves calculating the regret or lost opportunity corresponding to each payoff and then using the minimax criterion on the calculated regret values.

In decision analysis, the decision maker incurs regret by failing to choose the "best" decision (the one with the highest profit or lowest cost). Of course, this best decision depends on the state of nature. For this model, if there is a small rise in the stock market, the best decision is to buy the stock (yielding a return of $250). Tom will have no regret if this is his decision. If, instead, Tom purchases gold, his return will be only $100, resulting in a regret of $150 (=$250 – $100). Similarly, the regret associated with buying the bond for this state of nature is $50 (=$250 – $200), and from investing in the C/D it is $190 (=$250 – $60).

Calculation of Regret Values for a State of Nature

1. Determine the best value (maximum payoff or minimum cost) for the state of nature.
2. Calculate the regret for each decision alternative as the difference between its payoff value and this best value.

When this process is repeated for each state of nature, the result is the regret table shown in Table 10.3

TABLE 10.3

Regret Table for Tom Brown

Decision Alternatives	States of Nature				
	Large Rise	Small Rise	No Change	Small Fall	Large Fall
Gold	$600	$150	$ 0	$ 0	$ 60
Bond	$250	$ 50	$ 50	$400	$210
Stock	$ 0	$ 0	$100	$500	$660
C/D Account	$440	$190	$140	$240	$ 0

The decision maker using the minimax regret criterion also assumes that the worst state of nature (the one with the maximum regret) will occur no matter what decision is made. He therefore chooses the decision that has the minimum of the maximum regrets.

Minimax Regret Approach

1. Determine the best value (maximum payoff or minimum cost) for each state of nature.

2. For each state of nature, calculate the regret corresponding to a decision alternative as the difference between its payoff value and this best value.

3. Find the maximum regret for each decision alternative.

4. Select the decision alternative that has the minimum maximum regret.

Figure 10.3 is an Excel spreadsheet showing the original payoff table as well as the regret table for the Tom Brown investment problem. The optimal decision using the minimax regret criterion is identified in this spreadsheet in cell B19, and the corresponding payoff is given in cell B18. We see from the Excel spreadsheet that if Tom uses the minimax regret criterion, he should decide to buy the bond.

The difference between the maximin and minimax regret criteria is as follows. When using the maximin criterion, the decision maker wishes to select the decision with the best possible assured payoff. Under the minimax regret criterion, the decision maker wishes to select the decision that minimizes the maximum deviation from the best return possible for each state of nature. In this case, it is not the return itself that is important, but rather how well a *given* return compares to the *best possible* return for that state of nature.

FIGURE 10.3   Excel Spreadsheet Showing Regret Table

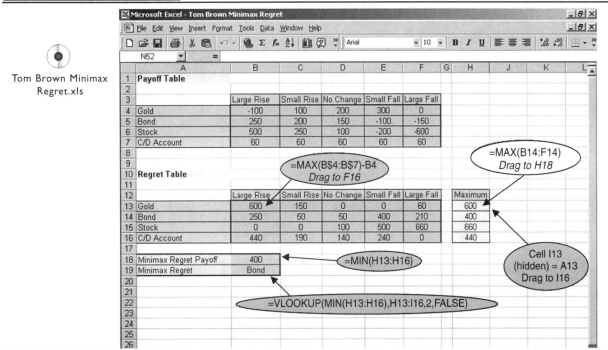

Tom Brown Minimax
Regret.xls

Effects of Nonoptimal Alternatives

When using the minimax regret criterion, the optimal decision can be influenced by introducing a nonoptimal decision alternative. For example, suppose the broker had suggested that Tom consider the purchase of a put option instead of the stock option hedge, resulting in the payoff and regret table shown in Figure 10.4.

We see that now Tom's optimal decision using the minimax regret criterion would be to invest his $1000 in the C/D account instead of his earlier decision to invest in the bond. This is because the addition of the put option investment increases the maximum regret for the bond from $400 to $450 which is now higher than that for the C/D.

Some may argue that it should be no surprise Tom's optimal decision could change since the introduction of the put option as a decision alternative changes his attitude toward the different investments. Others, however, feel that because a decision model frequently does not consider every possible alternative, changing the decision selection due to the introduction of additional nonoptimal decision alternatives is a major shortcoming of the minimax regret approach.

Optimistic or Aggressive Approach—Maximax Criterion

In contrast to a pessimistic decision maker, an optimistic decision maker feels that luck is always shining and whatever decision is made, the best possible outcome (state of nature) corresponding to that decision will occur.

Given a payoff table representing profits, an optimistic decision maker would use a **maximax criterion** that determines the maximum payoff for each decision alternative and selects the one that has the *max*imum "*max*imum payoff." The maximax criterion also applies to an aggressive decision maker looking for the decision with the best payoff.

FIGURE 10.4   Excel Spreadsheet Showing Minimax Regret Decision with Put Option Included

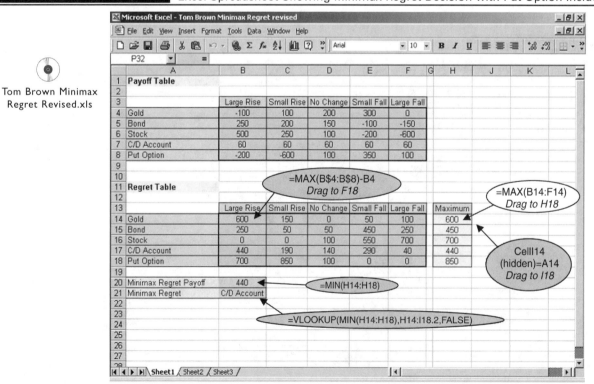

Tom Brown Minimax
Regret Revised.xls

Based on the data in Table 10.2 (with the stock option hedge eliminated), the maximum payoffs for each decision alternative in the Tom Brown investment problem are as shown in Table 10.4. If Tom were an optimistic or aggressive decision maker, he would choose the stock investment since it is the alternative with the maximum of the maximum payoffs. The file Tom Brown Maximax.xls on the accompanying CD-ROM illustrates how one can construct an Excel spreadsheet to do this analysis.

Note that the alternative chosen using the maximax decision criterion is the one associated with the highest value in the payoff table. Hence to use this criterion we need only locate the highest payoff in the table and select the corresponding decision.

If a payoff table represents costs rather than profits, an optimistic or aggressive decision maker would use the **minimin criterion** and select the alternative with the lowest possible, or *min*imum *min*imum, cost. In this case, the optimal decision would be the one corresponding to the lowest entry in the payoff table.

Maximax Approach for Profit Payoffs

1. Determine the maximum payoff for each decision alternative.
2. Select the decision alternative that has the maximum maximum payoff.

Minimin Approach for Cost Payoffs

1. Determine the minimum cost for each decision alternative.
2. Select the decision alternative that has the minimum minimum cost.

Principle of Insufficient Reason

Another decision criterion that can be used is the **principle of insufficient reason**. In this approach each state of nature is assumed to be equally likely. The optimal decision alternative can be found by adding up the payoffs for each decision alternative and selecting the alternative with the highest sum. (If the payoff table represents costs, we select the decision alternative with the lowest sum of costs.)

The principle of insufficient reason might appeal to a decision maker who is neither pessimistic nor optimistic. Table 10.5 gives the sum of the payoffs for each decision alternative for the Tom Brown investment problem. Thus, if Tom uses the principle of insufficient reason, he should invest in gold. The file Tom Brown Insufficient Reason.xls on the

---

TABLE 10.4	**Decision Alternatives**	**Maximum Payoff**	
Tom Brown Investment Decision—Maximum Payoff	Gold	$300	
	Bond	$250	
	Stock	$500	← maximum
	C/D Account	$ 60	

TABLE 10.5		
Tom Brown Investment Decision—Sum of Payoffs	**Decision Alternatives**	**Sum of Payoffs**	

Decision Alternatives	Sum of Payoffs	
Gold	$500	← maximum
Bond	$350	
Stock	$ 50	
C/D Account	$300	

accompanying CD-ROM illustrates how one can construct an Excel spreadsheet to do this analysis.

While it is not difficult to determine the optimal decision for the different criteria used in decision making under uncertainty either by hand or using Excel, we have developed a spreadsheet template, Decision Payoff Table.xls (contained on the accompanying CD-ROM), to solve payoff table problems with up to eight decisions and eight states of nature. Complete details on using this spreadsheet are given in Appendix 10.1 at the conclusion of the chapter. The worksheet labeled Payoff Table can be used for analyzing a payoff table when doing decision making under uncertainty.

Figure 10.5 gives the results of using this template for the Tom Brown investment problem. The default names for the decision alternatives (d1, d2, etc.) and states of nature (s1, s2, etc.) were changed to the actual decisions and states of nature for this problem. Note that we have hidden the rows and columns in this spreadsheet that are not needed for analysis of this problem.

The optimal decisions and payoffs for the different criteria are given in cells B17 through B20 and cells C17 through C20 respectively. We observe that each decision is optimal for some decision criterion.

FIGURE 10.5

Excel Spreadsheet Showing Payoff Table Template for Tom Brown Investment Problem

Tom Brown.xls

	A	B	C	D	E	F
1	Payoff Table					
2						
3		Large Rise	Small Rise	No Change	Small Fall	Large Fall
4	Gold	-100	100	200	300	0
5	Bond	250	200	150	-100	-150
6	Stock	500	250	100	-200	-600
7	C/D Account	60	60	60	60	60
15	RESULTS					
16	Criteria	Decision	Payoff			
17	Maximin	C/D Account	60			
18	Minimax Regret	Bond	400			
19	Maximax	Stock	500			
20	Insufficient Reason	Gold	100			

Since the criterion depends on the decision maker's attitude toward life (optimistic, pessimistic, or somewhere in between), utilizing decision making under uncertainty can present a problem if these attitudes change rapidly. One way to avoid the difficulty of using subjective criteria is to obtain probability estimates for the states of nature and implement decision making under risk.

Decision Making Under Risk

Expected Value Criterion

If a probability estimate for the occurrence of each state of nature is available, it is possible to calculate an expected value associated with each decision alternative. This is done by multiplying the probability for each state of nature by the associated return and then summing these products. Using the **expected value criterion**, the decision maker would then select the decision alternative with the best expected value.

For the Tom Brown investment problem, suppose Tom's broker offered the following projections based on past stock market performance:

$$P(\text{large rise in market}) = .2$$
$$P(\text{small rise in market}) = .3$$
$$P(\text{no change in market}) = .3$$
$$P(\text{small fall in market}) = .1$$
$$P(\text{large fall in market}) = .1$$

Using these probabilities, we can calculate the expected value (EV) of each decision alternative as follows:

$$
\begin{aligned}
EV(\text{gold}) &= .2(-100) + .3(100) + .3(200) + .1(300) + .1(0) &= \$100 \\
EV(\text{bond}) &= .2(250) + .3(200) + .3(150) + .1(-100) + .1(-150) &= \$130 \\
EV(\text{stock}) &= .2(500) + .3(250) + .3(100) + .1(-200) + .1(-600) &= \$125 \\
EV(\text{C/D}) &= .2(60) + .3(60) + .3(60) + .1(60) + .1(60) &= \$\ 60
\end{aligned}
$$

Since the bond investment has the highest expected value, it is the optimal decision.

Figure 10.6 gives an Excel spreadsheet containing the calculation of the optimal decision using the expected value (EV) criterion.

FIGURE 10.6

Excel Spreadsheet Showing Expected Value Criterion

Tom Brown Expected Value.xls

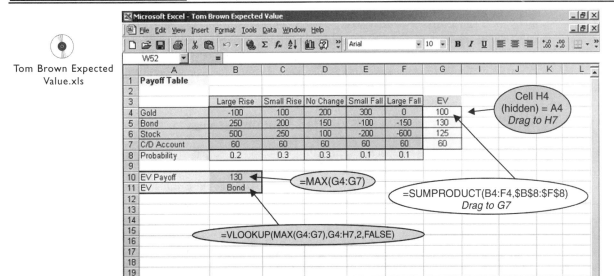

The Payoff Table Worksheet on the Decision Payoff Table.xls template determines the optimal decision using the expected value approach in row 21.

Expected Value Approach

1. Determine the expected payoff for each decision alternative.
2. Select the decision alternative that has the best expected payoff.

Expected Regret Criterion

The approach used in the expected value criterion can also be applied to a regret table. Because the decision maker wishes to minimize regret, under the **expected regret criterion**, he or she calculates the expected regret (ER) for each decision and chooses the decision with the smallest expected regret.

By applying this approach to the regret table for the Tom Brown investment problem, the expected regrets for the decision alternatives are calculated as

$$
\begin{aligned}
\text{ER(gold)} &= .2(600) + .3(150) + .3(0) + .1(0) + .1(60) = \$171 \\
\text{ER(bond)} &= .2(250) + .3(50) + .3(50) + .1(400) + .1(210) = \$141 \\
\text{ER(stock)} &= .2(0) + .3(0) + .3(100) + .1(500) + .1(660) = \$146 \\
\text{ER(C/D)} &= .2(440) + .3(190) + .3(140) + .1(240) + .1(0) = \$211
\end{aligned}
$$

Using this approach, Tom would again select the bond investment since it is the decision alternative with the smallest expected regret.

Expected Regret Approach

1. Determine the best value (maximum payoff or minimum cost) for each state of nature.
2. For each state of nature, the regret corresponding to a decision alternative is the difference between its payoff value and this best value.
3. Find the expected regret for each decision alternative.
4. Select the decision alternative that has the minimum expected regret.

Note that the same optimal decision was found using the expected regret criterion and the expected value criterion. This is true for any decision problem because, for pairs of decision alternatives, the differences in expected regret values are the same as the differences in expected return values. Because the two approaches yield the same results, the expected value approach is generally used since it does not require the calculation of a regret table.

When to Use the Expected Value Approach

Because the expected value and expected regret criteria base the optimal decision on the relative likelihoods that the states of nature will occur, they have a certain advantage over the criteria used in decision making under uncertainty. It is worth noting, however, that basing a criterion on expected value assures us only that that the decision will be optimal in the long run when the same problem is faced over and over again. In many situations, however, such as the Tom Brown investment problem, the decision maker faces the problem a single time; in this case, basing an optimal decision solely on expected value may not be optimal.

Another drawback to the expected value criterion is that it does not take into account the decision maker's attitude toward possible losses. Suppose, for example, you had a chance to play a game in which you could win $1000 with probability .51 but could also lose $1000 with probability .49. While the expected value of this game is .51($1000) + .49(−$1000) = $20, many people (perhaps even yourself) would decline the opportunity to play due to the possibility of losing $1000. As we will see in Section 10.7, utility theory offers an alternative to the expected value approach.

10.4 EXPECTED VALUE OF PERFECT INFORMATION

Suppose it were possible to know with certainty the state of nature that was going to occur prior to choosing the decision alternative. The **expected value of perfect information (EVPI)** represents the *gain* in expected return resulting from this knowledge.

To illustrate this concept, recall that using the expected value criterion, Tom Brown's optimal decision was to purchase the bond. However, Tom can't be sure if this will be one of the 20% of the times that the market will experience a large rise, or one of the 10% of the times that the market will experience a large fall, or if some other state of nature will occur. If Tom repeatedly invested $1000 in the bond, under similar economic conditions (and assuming the same probabilities for the states of nature), we showed that in the long run he should earn an average of $130 per investment. The $130 is known as the **expected return using the expected value criterion (EREV).**

But suppose Tom could find out in advance which state of nature were going to occur. Each time Tom made an investment decision, he would be practicing decision making under certainty (see Section 10.3).

For example, if Tom knew the stock market were going to show a large rise, naturally he would choose the stock investment because it gives the highest payoff ($500) for this state of nature. Similarly, if he knew a small rise would occur, he would again choose the stock investment because it gives the highest payoff ($250) for this state of nature, and so on. These results are summarized as follows.

If Tom Knew in Advance the Stock Market Would Undergo	His Optimal Decision Would Be	With a Payoff of
a large rise	stock	$500
a small rise	stock	$250
no change	gold	$200
a small fall	gold	$300
a large fall	C/D	$ 60

(Interestingly, Tom would never choose the bond investment, the expected value decision, if he knew in advance which state of nature would occur.)

Under these conditions, since 20% of the time the stock market would experience a large rise, 20% of the time Tom would earn a profit of $500. Similarly, 30% of the time the market would experience a small rise and Tom would earn $250, 30% of the time the market would experience no change and he would earn $200; and so on.

The expected return from knowing for sure which state of nature will occur prior to making the investment decision is called the **expected return with perfect information (ERPI).** For Tom Brown

$$ERPI = .2(500) + .3(250) + .3(200) + .1(300) + .1(60) = 271.$$

This is a gain of $271 − $130 = $141 over the EREV. The difference ($141) is the *expected value of perfect information* (EVPI).

Another way to determine EVPI for the investment problem is to reason as follows: If Tom knows the stock market will show a large rise, he should definitely buy the stock, giving him $500, or a *gain of $250 over what he would earn from the bond investment* (the optimal decision without the additional information as to which state of nature would occur). Similarly, if he knows the stock market will show a small rise, he should again buy the stock, earning him $250, or a *gain of $50 over the return from buying the bond*, and so on. These results are summarized as follows.

If Tom Knew in Advance the Stock Market Would Undergo	His Optimal Decision Would Be	With a Gain in Payoff of
a large rise	stock	$250
a small rise	stock	$ 50
no change	gold	$ 50
a small fall	gold	$400
a large fall	C/D	$210

Hence, to find the expected gain over always investing in the bond (i.e., the EVPI), we simply take the possible gains from knowing which state of nature will occur and weight them by the likelihood of that state of nature actually occurring:

$$EVPI = .2(250) + .3(50) + .3(50) + .1(400) + .1(210) = 141$$

This calculation of EVPI might look somewhat familiar since it is the same one we performed in order to calculate the expected regret for the bond investment.

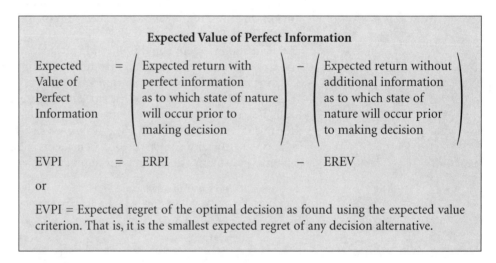

Expected Value of Perfect Information

Expected Value of Perfect Information $=$ (Expected return with perfect information as to which state of nature will occur prior to making decision) $-$ (Expected return without additional information as to which state of nature will occur prior to making decision)

EVPI $=$ ERPI $-$ EREV

or

EVPI = Expected regret of the optimal decision as found using the expected value criterion. That is, it is the smallest expected regret of any decision alternative.

The Payoff Table worksheet on the Decision Payoff Table.xls template determines the expected value of perfect information (EVPI) in row 22 (see Figure A10.1 of Appendix 10.1).

Having perfect information regarding the future for any situation is virtually impossible. However, often it is possible to procure imperfect, or *sample*, information regarding the states of nature. We calculate EVPI because it gives an upper limit on the expected value of any such sample information.

10.5 BAYESIAN ANALYSES—DECISION MAKING WITH IMPERFECT INFORMATION

In Section 10.3 we contrasted decision making under uncertainty with decision making under risk. Some statisticians argue that it is unnecessary to practice decision making under uncertainty because one always has at least some probabilistic information that can be used to assess the likelihoods of the states of nature. Such individuals adhere to what is called **Bayesian statistics**.[1]

---

[1] Named for Thomas Bayes, an eighteenth-century British clergyman and mathematician.

Using Sample Information to Aid in Decision Making

Bayesian statistics play a vital role in assessing the value of additional *sample information* obtained from such sources as marketing surveys or experiments, which can assist in the decision-making process. The decision maker can use this input to revise or fine tune the original probability estimates and possibly improve decision making.

Making Decisions Using Sample Information

To illustrate decision making using sample information, again consider the Tom Brown investment problem.

TOM BROWN INVESTMENT DECISION (CONT.)

Toma.xls
Tomb.xls

Tom has learned that, for only $50, he can receive the results of noted economist Milton Samuelman's multimillion dollar econometric forecast, which predicts either "positive" or "negative" economic growth for the upcoming year. Samuelman has offered the following verifiable statistics regarding the results of his model:

1. When the stock market showed a large rise, the forecast predicted "positive" 80% of the time and "negative" 20% of the time.

2. When the stock market showed a small rise, the forecast predicted "positive" 70% of the time and "negative" 30% of the time.

3. When the stock market showed no change, the forecast was equally likely to predict "positive" or "negative."

4. When the stock market showed a small fall, the forecast predicted "positive" 40% of the time and "negative" 60% of the time.

5. When the stock market showed a large fall, the forecast always predicted "negative."

Tom would like to know whether it is worthwhile to pay $50 for the results of the Samuelman forecast.

SOLUTION

Tom must first determine what his optimal decision should be if the forecast predicts positive economic growth and what it should be if it predicts negative economic growth. If Tom's investment decision changes based on the results of the forecast, he must determine whether knowing the results of Samuelman's forecast would increase his expected profit by more than the $50 cost of obtaining the information.

Using the relative frequency method, we have the following conditional probabilities based on the forecast's historical performance:

P(forecast predicts "positive"|large rise in market)	=	.80
P(forecast predicts "negative"|large rise in market)	=	.20
P(forecast predicts "positive"|small rise in market)	=	.70
P(forecast predicts "negative"|small rise in market)	=	.30
P(forecast predicts "positive"|no change in market)	=	.50
P(forecast predicts "negative"|no change in market)	=	.50
P(forecast predicts "positive"|small fall in market)	=	.40
P(forecast predicts "negative"|small fall in market)	=	.60

P(forecast predicts "positive"|large fall in market) = 0
P(forecast predicts "negative"|large fall in market) = 1.00

What Tom really needs to know, however, is how the results of Samuelman's economic forecast affect the probability estimates of the stock market's performance. That is, he needs probabilities such as P(large rise in market|forecast predicts "positive"). Unfortunately, in general, P(A|B) ≠ P(B|A), so it is incorrect to assume P(large rise in market|forecast predicts "positive") = .80.

One way to obtain probabilities of this form from the above probabilities is to use a Bayesian approach, which enables the decision maker to revise initial probability estimates in light of additional information. The original probability estimates are known as the set of *prior* or *a priori* probabilities. A set of revised or *posterior probabilities* is obtained based on knowing the results of *sample* or *indicator* information.

Bayesian Analysis

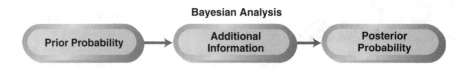

Bayes' Theorem

The Bayesian approach utilizes *Bayes' Theorem* to revise the prior probabilities.[2] This theorem states:

Given events B and $A_1, A_2, A_3, \ldots, A_n$, where $A_1, A_2, A_3, \ldots, A_n$ are mutually exclusive and collectively exhaustive, posterior probabilities, $P(A_i|B)$ can be found by:

$$P(A_i|B) = \frac{P(B|A_i)\,P(A_i)}{P(B|A_1)\,P(A_1) + P(B|A_2)\,P(A_2) + \ldots + P(B|A_n)\,P(A_n)}$$

Although the notation of Bayes' Theorem may appear intimidating, a convenient way of calculating the posterior probabilities is to use a tabular approach. This approach utilizes five columns:

Column 1—States of Nature A listing of the states of nature for the problem (the A_i's).

Column 2—Prior Probabilities The prior probability estimates (before obtaining sample information) for the states of nature, $P(A_i)$.

Column 3—Conditional Probabilities The known conditional probabilities of obtaining sample information given a particular state of nature, $P(B|A_i)$.

Column 4—Joint Probabilities The joint probabilities of a particular state of nature and sample information occurring simultaneously, $P(B \cap A_i) = P(A_i)*P(B|A_i)$. These numbers are calculated for each row by multiplying the number in the second column by the number in the third column. The sum of this column is the marginal probability, $P(B)$.

---

[2] Bayes' Theorem is a restatement of the conditional law of probability $[P(A|B) = P(A \cap B)/P(B)]$. In the parlance of decision theory, the A's correspond to the states of nature, and B is the sample or indicator information. We give a discussion of Bayes' Theorem in Supplement CD1 on the accompanying CD-ROM.

TABLE 10.6

Indicator Information—
"Positive" Economic Forecast
for Tom Brown

States of Nature S_i	Prior Possibilities $P(S_i)$	Conditional Probabilities $P(positive|S_i)$	Joint Probabilities $P(positive \cap S_i)$	Posterior Probabilities $P(S_i|positive)$
Large rise	.20	.80	.16	.16/.56 = .286
Small rise	.30	.70	.21	.21/.56 = .375
No change	.30	.50	.15	.15/.56 = .268
Small fall	.10	.40	.04	.04/.56 = .071
Large fall	.10	0	0	0/.56 = 0
			P(positive) = .56	

Column 5—Posterior Probabilities The posterior probabilities found by Bayes'
Theorem, $P(A_i|B)$. Since $P(A_i|B) = P(B \cap A_i)/P(B)$, these numbers are calcu-
lated for each row by dividing the number in the fourth column by the sum
of the numbers in the fourth column.

Table 10.6 gives the tabular approach for calculating posterior probabilities assuming
that Tom responds to Milton Samuelman's offer and learns that Samuelman's economic forecast for next year is "positive."

As you can see, although the initial probability estimate of the stock market's
showing a large rise was .20, after Samuelman's "positive" economic forecast Tom has
revised this probability upward to .286. Similarly, based on this forecast Tom has
revised his probability estimates for a small rise, no change, small fall, or large fall in
the market from .30, .30, .10, and .10 to .375, .268, .071, and 0, respectively. We also see
that the probability that Samuelman's forecast will be "positive" is .56 (the sum of the
values in Column 4). A similar procedure is used to obtain the posterior probabilities
corresponding to a "negative" economic forecast, as shown in Table 10.7.

As you can see, for a "negative" economic forecast the respective probability estimates
for the states of nature have been revised to .091, .205, .341, .136, and .227. Also note
that the probability that Samuelman's forecast will give a "negative" forecast is .44 (the
sum of the values in Column 4).

The Bayesian Analysis worksheet on the Decision Payoff Table.xls template calculates posterior probabilities and is linked to the Payoff Table worksheet in the template. Figure 10.7 shows the worksheet for the Tom Brown investment problem. To use
this worksheet, conditional probabilities are entered for the four indicators in the
appropriate cells in columns C and I. (Note that the rows associated with the unused
states of nature are hidden.) The worksheet then calaculates the posterior probabilities in columns E and K.

TABLE 10.7

Indicator Information—
"Negative" Economic Forecast
for Tom Brown

States of Nature S_i	Prior Possibilities $P(S_i)$	Conditional Probabilities $P(negative|S_i)$	Joint Probabilities $P(negative \cap S_i)$	Posterior Probabilities $P(S_i|negative)$
Large rise	.20	.20	.04	.04/.44 = .091
Small rise	.30	.30	.09	.09/.44 = .205
No change	.30	.50	.15	.15/.44 = .341
Small fall	.10	.60	.06	.06/.44 = .136
Large fall	.10	1.00	.10	.10/.44 = .227
			P(negative) = ..44	

Bayesian Analysis Worksheet for the Tom Brown Investment Problem

Tom Brown.xls

	A	B	C	D	E	G	H	I	J	K
1	**Bayesian Analysis**									
2										
3	Indicator 1					Indicator 2				
4										
5	States	Prior	Conditional	Joint	Posterior	States	Prior	Conditional	Joint	Posterior
6	of Nature	Probabilities	Probabilities	Probabilities	Probabilites	of Nature	Probabilities	Probabilities	Probabilities	Probabilites
7	Large Rise	0.2	0.8	0.16	0.286	Large Rise	0.2	0.2	0.04	0.091
8	Small Rise	0.3	0.7	0.21	0.375	Small Rise	0.3	0.3	0.09	0.205
9	No Change	0.3	0.5	0.15	0.268	No Change	0.3	0.5	0.15	0.341
10	Small Fall	0.1	0.4	0.04	0.071	Small Fall	0.1	0.6	0.06	0.136
11	Large Fall	0.1	0	0	0.000	Large Fall	0.1	1	0.1	0.227
15			P(Indicator 1)	0.56				P(Indicator 2)	0.44	
16										
17	Indicator 3					Indicator 4				
18										
19	States	Prior	Conditional	Joint	Posterior	States	Prior	Conditional	Joint	Posterior
20	of Nature	Probabilities	Probabilities	Probabilities	Probabilites	of Nature	Probabilities	Probabilities	Probabilities	Probabilites
21	Large Rise	0.2		0		Large Rise	0.2		0	
22	Small Rise	0.3		0		Small Rise	0.3		0	
23	No Change	0.3		0		No Change	0.3		0	
24	Small Fall	0.1		0		Small Fall	0.1		0	
25	Large Fall	0.1		0		Large Fall	0.1		0	
29			P(Indicator 3)	0				P(Indicator 4)	0	

Payoff Table ╲ **Bayesian Analysis** ╱ Posterior Analysis ╱ Utility ╱

Expected Value of Sample Information

The Samuelman forecast generates two sets of probabilities for the states of nature, one based on a positive economic forecast and the other on a negative economic forecast. We can now determine the optimal investment for each forecast using the expected value criterion.

If Samuelman forecasts positive economic growth, the revised expected values for the decision alternatives (rounded to the nearest dollar) are:

$$
\begin{aligned}
EV(\text{gold}|\text{"positive"}) &= .286(-100) + .375(100) + .268(200) + .071(300) + 0(0) &= \$84 \\
EV(\text{bond}|\text{"positive"}) &= .286(250) + .375(200) + .268(150) + .071(-100) + 0(-150) &= \$180 \\
EV(\text{stock}|\text{"positive"}) &= .286(500) + .375(150) + .268(100) + .071(-200) + 0(-600) &= \$249 \\
EV(\text{C/D}|\text{"positive"}) &= .286(60) + .375(60) + .268(60) + .071(60) + 0(60) &= \$60
\end{aligned}
$$

If Samuelman's forecast is negative, the expected returns are:

$$
\begin{aligned}
EV(\text{gold}|\text{"negative"}) &= .091(-100) + .205(100) + .341(200) + .136(300) + .227(0) &= \$120 \\
EV(\text{bond}|\text{"negative"}) &= .091(250) + .205(200) + .341(150) + .136(-100) + .227(-150) &= \$67 \\
EV(\text{stock}|\text{"negative"}) &= .091(500) + .205(150) + .341(100) + .136(-200) + .227(-600) &= -\$33 \\
EV(\text{C/D}|\text{"negative"}) &= .091(60) + .205(60) + .341(60) + .136(60) + .227(60) &= \$60
\end{aligned}
$$

Thus, if Samuelman's forecast is positive, buying the stock would be optimal since it yields Tom the highest expected value ($249); if the forecast is negative, buying gold would be optimal since it yields the highest expected value ($120).

We see that information regarding Samuelman's forecast dramatically changes the probability estimates for the states of nature and, therefore, the optimal decision. But is knowing the results of the Samuelman forecast worth $50? To answer this question, Tom must calculate his expected gain from making decisions based on the forecast results. This expected gain is known as the **expected value of sample information (EVSI).**

To determine the EVSI, we compare the expected return available *with* the sample information (ERSI) to the expected return available *without* the additional sample information (EREV). The difference is the EVSI.

Expected Value of Sample Information

$$
\begin{array}{ccc}
\begin{array}{l}\text{Expected Value}\\ \text{of Sample}\\ \text{Information}\end{array} & = & \left(\begin{array}{l}\text{Expected Return with}\\ \text{Sample Information}\end{array}\right) - \left(\begin{array}{l}\text{Expected Return Without}\\ \text{Additional Information}\end{array}\right)\\
\\
\text{EVSI} & = & \text{ERSI} \qquad\qquad - \qquad\qquad \text{EREV}
\end{array}
$$

The investment with the largest expected return for a positive forecast is the stock (expected return = \$249.11); for a negative forecast, it is the gold (expected return = \$120.45). The probability Samuelman's forecast will be positive is .56; the probability his forecast will be negative is .44. Hence,

$$\text{ERSI} = .56(249.11) + .44(120.45) = \$192.50$$

Since the expected return without Samuelman's forecast, EREV, is the \$130 obtained from buying the bond, the expected value of sample information is:

$$\text{EVSI} = \$192.50 - \$130 = \$62.50$$

Because the expected gain from the Samuelman forecast is greater than its \$50 cost, Tom should acquire it.

Figure 10.8 shows the worksheet Posterior Analysis contained in the Decision Table.xls template for the Tom Brown investment problem. The prior probabilities and payoff values are linked to those inputted in the Payoff Table worksheet, while the posterior probabilities used in the analysis are linked to the ones calculated in the Bayesian Analysis worksheet.

FIGURE 10.8

Posterior Analysis Worksheet for the Tom Brown Investment Problem

Tom Brown.xls

	A	B	C	D	E	F	J	K	L	P	Q
1	Payoff Table										
2											
3		Large Rise	Small Rise	No Change	Small Fall	Large Fall	EV(prior)	EV(ind. 1)	EV(ind. 2)		
4	Gold	-100	100	200	300	0	100	83.93	120.45		
5	Bond	250	200	150	-100	-150	130	179.46	67.05		
6	Stock	500	250	100	-200	-600	125	249.11	-32.95		
7	C/D Account	60	60	60	60	60	60	60.00	60.00		
12	Prior Prob.	0.2	0.3	0.3	0.1	0.1					
13	Ind. 1 Prob.	0.286	0.375	0.268	0.071	0.000		0.56			
14	Ind 2. Prob.	0.091	0.205	0.341	0.136	0.227			0.44		
17											
18											
19	RESULTS										
20		Prior	Ind. 1	Ind. 2	Ind. 3	Ind. 4					
21	optimal payoff	130.00	249.11	120.45	0.00	0.00					
22	optimal decision	Bond	Stock	Gold							
23											
24	EVSI =	62.5									
25	EVPI =	141									
26	Efficiency=	0.44									

Payoff Table / Bayesian Analysis / Posterior Analysis / Utility /

The optimal decisions for the different indicators are given in row 22, and the expected values corresponding to these indicators are given in row 21. The EVSI is given in cell B24, while the EVPI is given in cell B25.

It is important to note that the Samuelman forecast gives additional, but not perfect, information. If the forecast could perfectly predict the future, the gain from the information would be the expected value of perfect information (EVPI) discussed earlier. If the same decision would be made regardless of the results of the indicator information, the value of the information would be 0. Thus,

$$0 \le \text{EVSI} \le \text{EVPI}$$

Efficiency

A measure of the relative value of sample information is its **efficiency,** defined as the ratio of its EVSI to its EVPI.

Efficiency

$$\text{Efficiency} = \frac{\text{EVSI}}{\text{EVPI}}$$

Since $0 \le \text{EVSI} \le \text{EVPI}$, efficiency is a number between 0 and 1. For Tom Brown's problem, the efficiency of the Samuelman information is:

$$\text{Efficiency} = \text{EVSI}/\text{EVPI} = 62.50/141 = .44$$

Efficiency provides a convenient method for comparing different forms of sample information. Given that two different types of sample information could be obtained at the same cost, the one with the higher efficiency is preferred. Note that the efficiency for the sample information is calculated on the Posterior Analysis worksheet in cell B26.

10.6 DECISION TREES

Although the payoff table approach is quite handy for some problems, its applicability is limited to situations in which the decision maker needs to make a single decision. Many real-world decision problems consist of a sequence of dependent decisions. For these, a **decision tree** can prove useful.

A decision tree is a chronological representation of the decision process. The root of the tree is a node that corresponds to the present time. The tree is constructed outward from this node into the future using a network of **nodes**, representing points in time where decisions must be made or states of nature occur, and **arcs (branches)**, representing the possible decisions or states of nature, respectively. The following table summarizes the elements of decision trees.

Decision Tree Construction

Node Type	Branches	Data on Branches
Decision (Square Nodes)	Possible decisions that can be made at this time	Cost or benefit associated with the decision
States of Nature (Circle Nodes)	Possible states of nature that can occur at this time	Probability the state of nature will occur given all previous decisions and states of nature

To illustrate how a decision tree can be a useful tool, let us consider the following situation faced by the Bill Galen Development Company.

The Bill Galen Development Company (BGD) needs a variance from the city of Kingston, New York, in order to do commercial development on a property whose asking price is a firm $300,000. BGD estimates that it can construct a shopping center for an additional $500,000 and sell the completed center for approximately $950,000.

A variance application costs $30,000 in fees and expenses, and there is only a 40% chance that the variance will be approved. Regardless of the outcome, the variance process takes two months. If BGD purchases the property and the variance is denied, the company will sell the property and receive net proceeds of $260,000. BGD can also purchase a three-month option on the property for $20,000, which would allow it to apply for a variance. Finally, for $5000 an urban planning consultant can be hired to study the situation and render an opinion as to whether the variance will be approved or denied. BGD estimates the following conditional probabilities for the consultant's opinion:

P(consultant predicts approval | approval granted) = .70
P(consultant predicts denial | approval denied) = .80

BGD wishes to determine the optimal strategy regarding this parcel of property.

SOLUTION

Initially, the company faces two decision alternatives: (1) hire the consultant and (2) do not hire the consultant. Figure 10.9 shows the initial tree construction corresponding to this decision. Note that the root of the tree is a decision node, two branches lead out from that node. The value on the "do not hire consultant" branch is 0 (there is no cost to this decision), while the –$5000 value on the "hire consultant" branch is the cash flow associated with hiring the consultant.

Consider the decision branch corresponding to "do not hire consultant." If the consultant is not hired, BGD faces three possible decisions: (1) do nothing; (2) buy the land; or (3) purchase the option. Thus we find a decision node at the end of this branch and three branches (corresponding to the three decision alternatives) leaving the node. As shown in Figure 10.10, the values on the three decision branches— 0, –$300,000, and –$20,000—correspond to the cash flows associated with each action.

If BGD does not hire the consultant and decides to do nothing, the total return to the company is 0. If, on the other hand, it decides to buy the land, it must then decide whether or not to apply for a variance. Clearly, if BGD were not going to apply for a

FIGURE 10.9

Bill Galen Development Company

FIGURE 10.10

Bill Galen Development Company

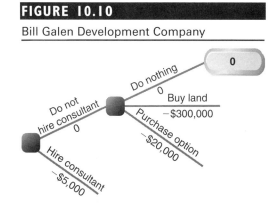

variance, it would not have bought the land in the first place. Therefore, there is only one logical decision following "buy land," and that is to "apply for variance."

Extrapolating this path further into the future, BGD will next learn whether the variance will be approved or denied. This is a chance or state of nature event, signified by a round node at the end of the "apply for variance" branch. This node leads to two branches—"variance approved" or "variance denied"—on which the values, .4 and .6, respectively, are the corresponding state of nature probabilities.

At the end of each path through the tree is the total profit or loss connected with that particular set of decisions and outcomes. These values are calculated by adding the cash flows on the decision branches making up the path. This is shown in Figure 10.11.

For example, if BGD does not hire the consultant, buys the land, gets the variance approved, builds the shopping center, and sells it, the profit will be 0 − $300,000 − $30,000 − $500,000 + $950,000 = $120,000. If, after buying the land, the variance is denied, BGD will sell the property for $260,000, and the total profit will be 0 − $300,000 − $30,000 + $260,000 = −$70,000, i.e., a net loss of $70,000.

Now if BGD decides to purchase the option, it would apply for the variance, which would then be either approved or denied. If the variance is approved, BGD will exercise the option and buy the property for $300,000, construct the shopping center for $500,000, and sell it for $950,000. If the variance is denied, BGD will simply let the option expire. Figure 10.12 shows the complete decision tree emanating from the decision not to hire the consultant.

FIGURE 10.11   Bill Galen Development Company

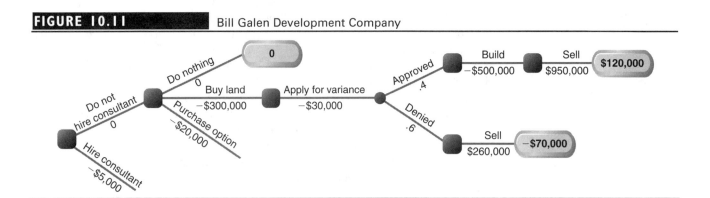

FIGURE 10.12   Bill Galen Development Company

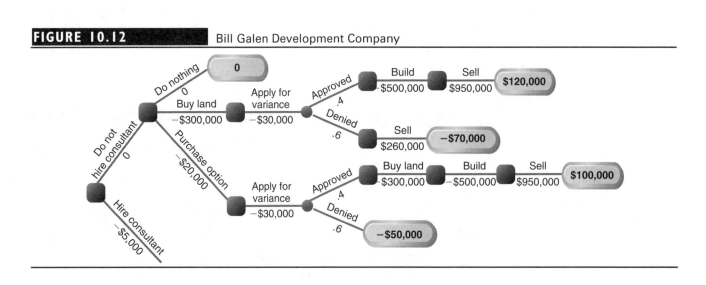

Now consider the decision process if BGD does hire the consultant. The consultant will predict that the variance will either be approved or denied. This chance event is represented by a round state of nature node. The probability that the consultant will predict approval or denial is not readily apparent but can be calculated using Bayes' Theorem.

Let us first determine the posterior probabilities for approval and denial assuming that the consultant predicts that the variance will be *approved*.

Since:

$$P(\text{consultant predicts approval} \mid \text{approval granted}) = .70$$

then

$$P(\text{consultant predicts denial} \mid \text{approval granted}) = 1 - .70 = .30$$

Similarly, since

$$P(\text{consultant predicts denial} \mid \text{approval denied}) = .80$$

then

$$P(\text{consultant predicts approval} \mid \text{approval denied}) = 1 - .80 = .20$$

Tables 10.8 and 10.9 detail the Bayesian approach. Table 10.8 corresponds to the consultant's prediction of approval, and Table 10.9 corresponds to the consultant's prediction of denial.

Once the consultant's prediction is known, BGD faces the same decision choices it did when the consultant was not hired: (1) do nothing; (2) buy the land; or (3) purchase the option. The differences here are the probabilities for the states of nature and the fact that the firm has spent $5000 for the consultant. Using this information, we can complete the decision tree as shown in Figure 10.13.

To determine the optimal strategy, we work backward from the ends of each branch until we come to either a state of nature node or a decision node.

TABLE 10.8 Indicator Information— Consultant Predicts Approval of Variance	States of Nature	Prior Probabilities	Conditional Probabilities	Joint Probabilities	Posterior Probabilities
	Variance approved	.40	.70	.28	.28/.40 = .70
	Variance denied	.60	.20	.12	.12/.40 = .30
			P(consultant predicts approval)	.40	

TABLE 10.9 Indicator Information— Consultant Predicts Denial of Variance	States of Nature	Prior Probabilities	Conditional Probabilities	Joint Probabilities	Posterior Probabilities
	Variance approved	.40	.30	.12	.12/.60 = .20
	Variance denied	.60	.80	.48	.48/.60 = .80
			P(consultant predicts denial)	.60	

FIGURE 10.13   Bill Galen Development Company

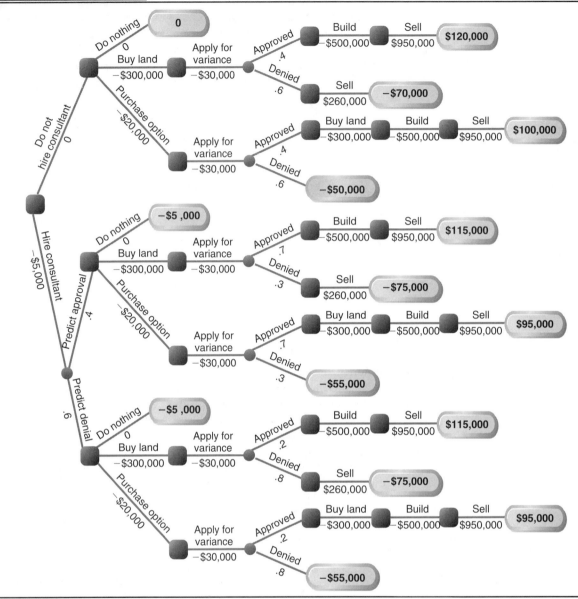

At a state of nature node, we calculate the expected value of the node using the ending node values for each branch leading out of the node and the probability associated with that branch. The expected value is the sum of the products of the branch probabilities and corresponding ending node values. This sum becomes the value for the state of nature node.

At a decision node, the branch that has the highest ending node value is the optimal decision. This highest ending node value, in turn, becomes the value for the decision node. Nonoptimal decisions are indicated by a pair of lines across their branches.

To illustrate, consider in Figure 10.13 the possible paths reached if BGD does not hire the consultant. If BGD decides to buy the property and applies for the variance, two outcomes (branches) are possible: (1) the variance is approved and BGD earns $120,000; or (2) the variance is denied and BGD loses $70,000. The expected return at this state of nature node is found by (Probability Variance Is Approved)*(Expected Return If Variance Is Approved) + (Probability Variance Is Denied)*(Expected Return If Variance Is Denied) = .4($120,000) + .6(−$70,000) = $6000. This is the expected value associated with buying the land. The expected value associated with buying the option is .40($100,000) + .60(–$50,000) = $10,000.

Thus, if BGD decides not to hire the consultant, the corresponding expected values that result if it does nothing, buys the land, or purchases the option are $0, $6000, and $10,000, respectively; thus purchasing the option is the optimal decision. The expected return corresponding to the purchase option decision ($10,000) then becomes the expected return corresponding to the decision node not to hire the consultant.

The remaining portion of the tree, in which BGD *does* hire the consultant, is calculated by working backwards in a similar fashion. The completed decision tree is given in Figure 10.14. As you can see, the optimal decision is to hire the consultant. Then if the consultant predicts approval, BGD should buy the property, but if the consultant predicts denial, BGD should do nothing.

FIGURE 10.14 Bill Galen Development Company

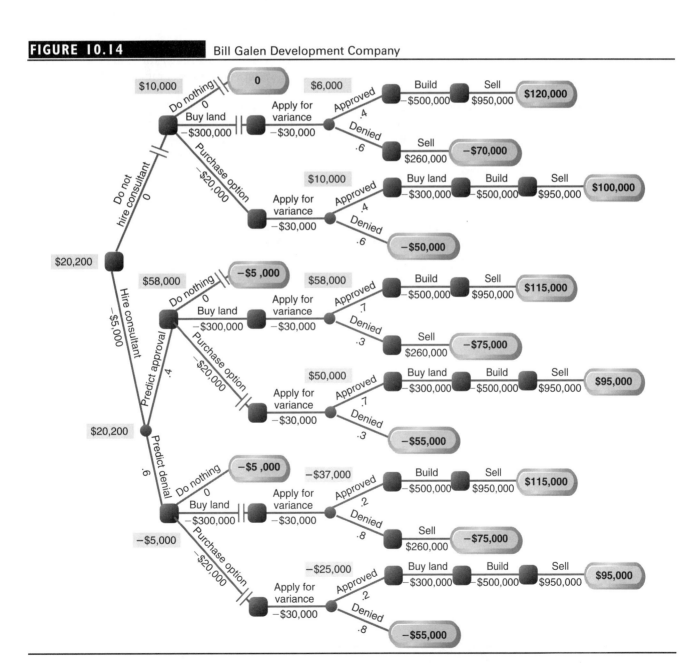

This problem illustrates that the calculations required to analyze a problem using a decision tree can be lengthy and cumbersome. Fortunately, specialized computer programs and Excel add-ins exist to help the analyst set up and analyze decision trees. One such Excel add-in is TreePlan which is available on the CD-ROM accompanying this textbook.

Let us use TreePlan to construct the decision tree for the Bill Galen Development problem. To simplify the tree, we will combine actions where appropriate. For example, since BGD will always apply for a variance if it buys the land or purchases the option, we will combine these activities into one branch. Similarly, if the variance is approved, BGD will always Build and then Sell and we will combine these activities into one branch.

After installing the TreePlan software open up the add-in by selecting Decision Tree under Tools on the menu bar. You will see the opening tree as shown in Figure 10.15.

The default decision tree has two decision arcs leading from the root node. One can rename the arc names by putting the cursor in the appropriate cell and retyping the desired name. For the BGD problem, we would rename Decision 1 in Cell D2 to "Do not hire consultant" and Decision 2 in Cell D7 to "Hire Consultant." Below each arc are two 0 values. The value on the left is where you enter the cash flow associated with the particular decision. The value on the right is the cumulative cash flow along the branches of the tree and is determined by the program.

For example, the cash flow associated with not hiring the consultant is 0, but the cash flow of hiring the consultant is –$5,000. Expressing the values in the tree in $1000's, –5 is entered under the "Hire Consultant" branch. Note that the cash flow at the end of the path also changes to –5 and the decision tree looks as shown in Figure 10.16.

FIGURE 10.15

Opening Spreadsheet When Using TreePlan

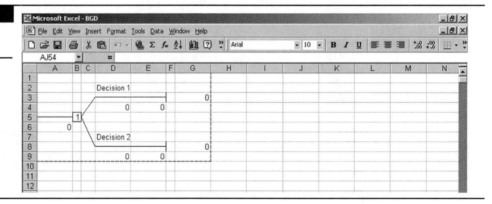

FIGURE 10.16

Initial TreePlan Tree as Modified for Bill Galen Development

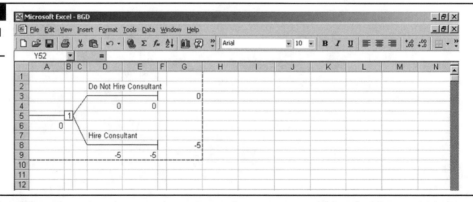

We also note the number 1 in the node box. This indicates that for the problem, as currently formulated, the optimal decision is decision 1. This is because it is better to gain nothing than to lose $5000.

The principal way of modifying the tree is to put the cursor in the appropriate cell and hold down the Control and t keys (control + t). For example, for the BGD model to add a decision node at the end of the "Do not hire" consultant branch, put the cursor in cell F3 (the end of the branch) and press the Control and t keys. Since cell F3 is currently a terminal node, this brings up the dialogue box shown in Figure 10.17.

Because this node is to be a decision node with three decisions emanating from it, we would leave the "Change to decision node" button highlighted but change the number of branches from "Two" to "Three."

The names for Decisions 3, 4, and 5 would then be changed to "Do nothing," "Buy land/Apply for variance," and "Purchase option/Apply for variance" by entering these names in cells H2, H7, and H12, respectively. Since the "Buy land/Apply for variance" decision results in a $330,000 cash outflow and the "Purchase option/Apply for variance" decision results in a $50,000 outflow, we enter a −330 in cell H9 and −50 in cell H14. This gives the tree shown in Figure 10.18.

FIGURE 10.17

Dialogue Box for Terminal Node

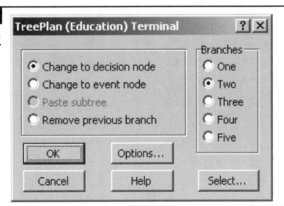

FIGURE 10.18

Modified TreePlan Tree Showing Decisions if Consultant Is Not Hired

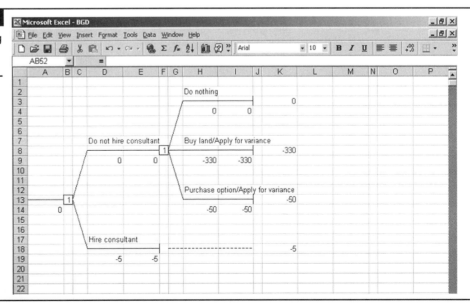

To complete the section of the tree corresponding to "Buy land/Apply for variance," we now add a state of nature node at the end of the "Buy land/Apply for variance" branch to allow the possibility of the variance either being approved or denied. This is done by positioning the cursor in cell J10, typing Control + t, highlighting the button corresponding to "Change to event node," and indicating that the number of branches should be "Two." This gives the tree as shown in Figure 10.19.

Notice that cell J10 is a round node as it corresponds to a chance event. Since there are two possible events the default probabilities inserted by TreePlan are .5 and .5. Modify the default names "Event 7" and "Event 8" in cells L7 and L12 to "Variance approved/Build/Sell" and "Variance denied/Sell," respectively. Also change the probability of .5 in cell L6 and L11 to .4 and .6, respectively, since these are the probabilities of the variance being approved or denied. Since the cash flow associated with the Variance approved/Build/Sell is −$500,000 + $950,000 = $450,000, put +450 in cell L9. Similarly, since the cash flow associated with Variance denied/Sell is +$260,000, put +260 in cell L14. The completed section of this tree looks as shown in Figure 10.20.

Note that TreePlan automatically calculates the ending values for each node as well as the expected value at the chance node (the value of 6 in cell I11).

To finish the tree for the "Purchase option/Apply for variance" branch, use the same procedure as for adding the branches following the "Buy land/Apply for Variance" branch. Specifically, the cursor is positioned at cell J18 to add two branches. The branches are then renamed, and the relevant probability and cash flow information is added to the appropriate cells. Note that the cash flow for the branch "Variance approved/Buy land/Build/Sell" is 300 less than the branch "Variance approved/Build/Sell" since the cost of the land is $300,000. This results in the decision tree shown in Figure 10.21.

FIGURE 10.19

Modified TreePlan Tree Showing States of Nature Following Buy Land/Apply for Variance

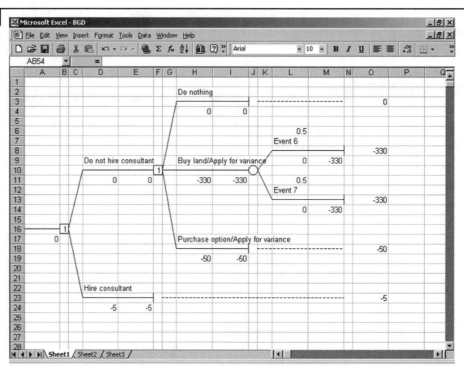

FIGURE 10.20

TreePlan Tree Showing Ending Branches Following Buy Land/Apply for Variance

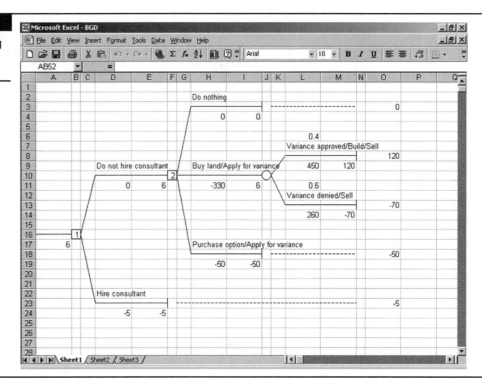

FIGURE 10.21

Decision Tree if Consultant Is Not Hired

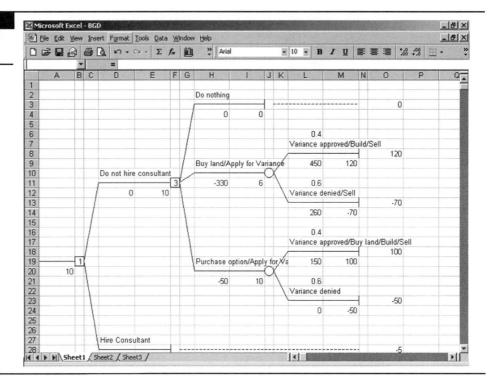

We see from this tree that the best decision if the consultant is not hired is to Purchase the option and Apply for the variance since there is a 3 (third decision) in cell F11. The expected value corresponding to this action is 10 (the value given in cell E12).

Now consider the subtree dealing with hiring the consultant. The consultant will predict either approval or denial. These branches are added by clicking on cell

F28 (the end of the "Hire consultant" branch), typing Control + t, highlighting the "Change to event node" button, and indicating that there are two branches. Inserting the appropriate event names and probabilities gives rise to the tree shown in Figure 10.22.

The easiest way to complete the decision tree following the consultant "Predicts approval" is to copy the portion of the tree following the branch "Do not hire consultant." This is done by positioning the cursor at cell F11, the end of the branch, and typing Control + t. This results in the dialogue box shown in Figure 10.23.

FIGURE 10.22

Portion of Decision Tree Corresponding to Hiring Consultant

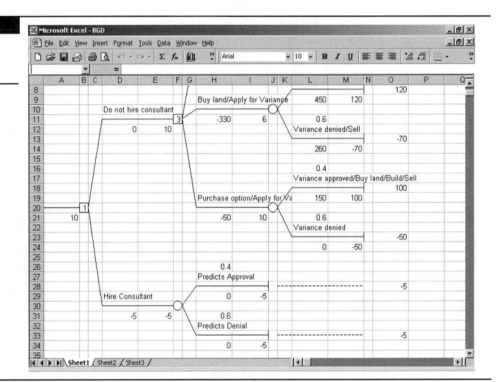

FIGURE 10.23

Dialogue Box for Existing Node

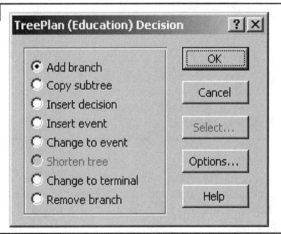

Since we wish to copy the subtree following cell F11, highlight the radio button next to "Copy subtree" and click on OK. The cursor is then positioned at cell J28, the end of the "Predicts approval" branch. Pressing Control + t again gives rise to the same dialogue box shown in Figure 10.17, but now with "Paste subtree" as an active option. Pasting the subtree and changing the probabilities for the variance being approved and denied to the correct posterior values gives the tree shown in Figure 10.24.

Note that in Figure 10.24 there is a value of 2 in cell J36. Hence we see that, if the consultant predicts approval, the best course of action is to buy the land and apply for the variance. The expected value of this decision is 58 (the value in cell I37).

To complete the tree, again paste the subtree into the node following the consultant "Predicts denial" branch. Changing the probabilities to reflect the correct posterior probabilities results in the completed decision tree. This is contained in the Excel file *BGD.xls* on the accompanying CD-ROM.

TreePlan has several options that one may use in analyzing the decision tree. One of these options enables the analyst to use the expected utility criterion (discussed in the next section) instead of the expected value criterion. If this option is selected, TreePlan assumes that the utility function is exponential. To consider different criteria when using TreePlan, one selects Options in the appropriate TreePlan dialogue box.

A Business Report

Using the information obtained from the decision tree analysis, we can prepare the following business report to assist BGD in determining an optimal decision strategy. This memorandum cogently identifies the critical factors BGD should consider and highlights the possible risks the company may encounter.

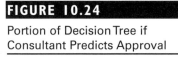

FIGURE 10.24

Portion of Decision Tree if Consultant Predicts Approval

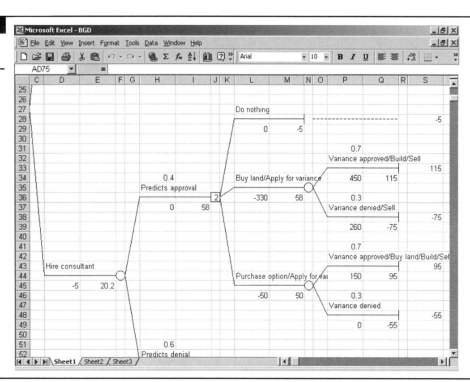

·SCG·
STUDENT CONSULTING GROUP

MEMORANDUM

To: Bill Galen, President, Bill Galen Development Company

From: Student Consulting Group

Subj: 5th and Main Street Property

We have analyzed the situation regarding the parcel of property located at 5th and Main Streets in Kingston, New York, which your firm is interested in developing for a strip shopping center. The property is currently zoned residential and would require a variance in order to complete construction. Our analysis was completed assuming that BGD wishes to maximize the expected profit this project could potentially generate.

Based on the cost and revenue estimates supplied by management, the following table gives the returns available from different strategies the firm might persue.

Table I   Expected Return Available from Different Possible Strategies

Strategy	Expected Return
Consultant not hired	
Do nothing	$0
Buy land	$6000
Buy option	$10,000
Consultant hired and predicts variance will be approved	
Do nothing	−$5000
Buy land	$58,000
Buy option	$50,000
Consultant hired and predicts variance will be denied	
Do nothing	−$5000
Buy land	−$37,000
Buy option	−$25,000

We analyzed this information using standard decision-making techniques and recommend the following strategy:

> Hire the consultant for $5,000. If the consultant predicts that the variance will be approved, BGD should purchase the property for $300,000. If the consultant predicts that the variance will be denied, BGD should not proceed with this project. *Your expected return from this strategy is $20,200.*

Table II summarizes the potential maximum loss from each strategy and the probability that the firm will incur such a loss.

If the consultant predicts that the variance will be approved and it is, in fact, *not* approved, BGD potentially will suffer a loss of $75,000. The likelihood of the consultant predicting an approval is estimated to be 40%, and the possibility that thevariance will be denied in this case is estimated to be 30%. Hence, there is approximately a 12% chance that BGD will incur a loss of $75,000, if this recommendation is followed.

Table II	Maximum Potential Loss and Likelihood of Such Loss from Different Possible Strategies		
Strategy		**Maximum Loss**	**Probability**
Consultant not hired			
Do nothing		$0	100%
Buy land		$70,000	40%
Buy option		$50,000	40%
Consultant hired and predicts variance will be approved			
Do nothing		$5000	40%
Buy land		$75,000	12%
Buy option		$55,000	12%
Consultant hired and predicts variance will be denied			
Do nothing		$5000	60%
Buy land		$75,000	48%
Buy option		$55,000	48%

If BGD feels that the potential loss from the recommended strategy is greater than the company can afford, instead of purchasing the property if the consultant predicts the variance will be approved, the company can buy the option. This lowers the expected return to $17,000 but will only expose BGD to a maximum potential loss of $55,000. Should this potential loss still be too large, we would be happy to meet with management to discuss alternative strategies.

10.7 DECISION MAKING AND UTILITY

The underlying basis for using the expected value criterion is that the decision maker wishes to choose the decision alternative that maximizes the expected return (or minimizes the expected cost). This criterion may not be appropriate, however, if the decision is a one-time opportunity with substantial risks.

For example, as pointed out in the BGD management memo, following the recommended strategy carries a potential loss of $75,000 for the company. If the maximum the company could currently afford to lose is $55,000, it may prefer to buy the option and not hire the consultant, even though this strategy has a lower expected return. The concept of utility has been developed to explain such behavior in a rational format.

Social scientists have long observed that individuals do not always choose decisions based on the expected value criterion, even when the payoffs and probabilities for the states of nature are known. For example, suppose you could play a coin toss game in which you will win $1 if the coin is heads and lose $1 if the coin is tails. If the coin is bent so that the probability of the coin landing heads is 55% and tails is 45%, your expected return from playing the game would be .55($1) + .45(−$1) = $.10. Given this expected return, you probably would wish to play this game.

Consider what happens, however, when the stakes increase so that you win $100,000 if the coin comes up heads and lose $100,000 if the coin comes up tails. Even though this game has an expected return of $10,000 = .55($100,000) + .45(−$100,000), you might be reluctant to play due to the potential of losing $100,000.

Playing state lottery games is an example of a case in which people do not base a decision on expected value. In most state lottery games, the expected return to the purchaser of a $1.00 lottery ticket is only about $0.50. Thus, if people decided whether or not to buy a lottery ticket based on expected value alone, lottery sales would be nonexistent.

Purchasing insurance is another such example. Insurance industry profits are predicated on the fact that, on the average, people will pay more for a policy than the expected present value of the loss for which they are insured. Again, if people's decisions were based solely on the expected value criterion, no one would buy insurance.

Utility Approach

In the utility approach to decision making, **utility values**, U(V)s, reflective of the decision maker's perspective are determined for each possible payoff. The utility of the least preferred outcome is given the lowest utility value (usually 0), whereas the most preferred outcome is given the highest utility value (usually 1). Utility values for the other possible payoffs are set between these values, with higher payoffs receiving higher utility values, although not necessarily proportionally higher. The optimal decision is then chosen by an **expected utility criterion**, which uses these values rather than the payoff values in the calculations.

Determining Utility values, U(V)

Although the following technique for finding utility values corresponding to payoffs may seem contrived, it does provide an insightful look into the amount of risk the decision maker is willing to take. The concept is based on the decision maker's preference to taking a sure thing (a particular payoff) versus risking receiving only the highest or lowest payoff.

Indifference Approach For Assigning Utility Values

1. List every possible payoff in ascending order.

2. Assign a utility of 0 to the lowest payoff and a utility of 1 to the highest payoff.

3. For all other possible payoff values ask the decision maker, "Suppose you could receive this payoff for sure, or, alternatively, you could receive either the highest payoff with probability p and the lowest payoff with probability (1 − p). What value of p would make you *indifferent* between the two situations?" These *indifference probabilities* for the payoffs are the utility values.

To illustrate the utility approach, let us consider once again the Tom Brown investment problem.

TOM BROWN INVESTMENT PROBLEM (CONT.)

Tom Brown.xls

We observed that the highest possible return for Tom in the payoff table calculated based on the broker's analysis was $500. Tom would achieve this payoff if he invested in the stock and there were a large rise in the market. The lowest possible payoff was a loss of $600, which Tom would incur if he invested in the stock and there were a large fall in the market.

The second highest possible return was $300. Tom would receive this sum if he invested in gold and there were a small fall in the market. We asked Tom, "If you could receive $300 for sure or you could receive $500 with probability p and lose $600 with probability (12p), what value of p would make you indifferent between these two choices?"

Tom thought for a moment and replied, "I'd have to be pretty certain of receiving the $500 payoff to pass up a certain payoff of $300; say about 90%." We repeated this question for all possible outcomes from the payoff table, and Tom's responses were as follows:

Certain Payoff	Probability
−600	0
−200	.25
−150	.30
−100	.36
0	.50
60	.60
100	.65
150	.70
200	.75
250	.85
300	.90
500	1.00

In light of these preferences, Tom wishes to determine his optimal investment decision.

SOLUTION

The indifference preferences Tom gave in response to our questions are his utility values for the payoffs. To determine the optimal decision under the expected utility criterion, we substitute the corresponding utility values for the nondominated payoffs given in Table 10.2 and calculate the expected utility for each decision.

Figure 10.25 shows the Utility worksheet contained in the Decision Payoff Table.xls template for the Tom Brown investment problem with unused columns hidden.

In this spreadsheet, the certain payoffs and corresponding utility values are entered in columns M and N. The optimal decision and corresponding expected utility are given in cells B17 and C17. Since the decision with the highest expected utility is the stock investment, it would be selected using the expected utility criterion. Comparing the expected utility of the stock investment to the bond investment, however, we note there is little difference in the two values. In fact, had the utility values been slightly different, the bond investment could have had the *higher* expected utility.

It is therefore important not to dismiss the bond investment from consideration. (Remember that in management science we are modeling in order to obtain insights into the optimal decision.) Tom may, in fact, wish to do some further investigation before making a final choice between the stock and the bond.

FIGURE 10.25

Utility Analysis Spreadsheet for the Tom Brown Investment Problem

Tom Brown.xls

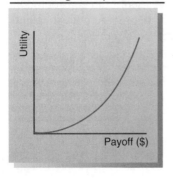

Microsoft Excel - Tom Brown

File   Edit   View   Insert   Format   Tools   Data   Window   Help

Q52

	A	B	C	D	E	F	J	L	M	N	O
1	Utility Analysis								Certain Payoff	Utility	
2									-600	0	
3		Large Rise	Small Rise	No Change	Small Fall	Large Fall	EU		-200	0.25	
4	Gold	0.36	0.65	0.75	0.9	0.5	0.632		-150	0.3	
5	Bond	0.85	0.75	0.7	0.36	0.3	0.671		-100	0.36	
6	Stock	1	0.85	0.65	0.25	0	0.675		0	0.5	
7	C/D Account	0.6	0.6	0.6	0.6	0.6	0.6		60	0.6	
8	d5						0		100	0.65	
9	d6						0		150	0.7	
10	d7						0		200	0.75	
11	d8						0		250	0.85	
12	Probability	0.2	0.3	0.3	0.1	0.1			300	0.9	
13									500	1	
14											
15	RESULTS										
16	Criteria	Decision	Value								
17	Exp. Utility	Stock	0.675								
18											

Payoff Table / Bayesian Analysis / Posterior Analysis \ Utility /

FIGURE 10.26

Risk-Averse Utility Curve

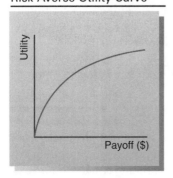

Risk-Averse, Risk-Neutral, and Risk-Taking Decision Makers

Within the context of utility theory, behavior can be classified as risk averse, risk taking, or risk neutral. A *risk-averse* decision maker prefers a certain outcome to a chance outcome having the same expected value. For example, suppose you have the choice of receiving $10,000 with probability .20 and $0 with probability .80. The expected value of this outcome is $2000 (=.20*$10,000 + .80*0). If you preferred receiving $2000 with certainty to the random outcome, you would be exhibiting risk-averse behavior. An example of risk-averse behavior is the purchase of an insurance policy. The concave utility curve depicted in Figure 10.26 is that of a risk-averse decision maker.

A *risk-taking* decision maker prefers a chance outcome to a certain outcome having the same expected value. Returning to the above example, if you were a risk-taking decision maker, you would prefer the chance outcome to receiving $2000. An example of risk-taking behavior is the purchase of a lottery ticket. The convex utility curve depicted in Figure 10.27 is that of a risk-taking decision maker.

A *risk-neutral* decision maker is indifferent between a chance outcome and a certain outcome having the same expected value. Using the above example once again, if you were a risk-neutral decision maker, you would be indifferent between the two outcomes. Typically, large corporations are assumed to be risk neutral because they do not have a preference for or an aversion to risk with regard to the amounts of money involved in normal business situations. The linear utility curve depicted in Figure 10.28 is that of a risk-neutral decision maker.

The optimal decision for a risk-neutral decision maker can be determined using the expected value criterion on the payoff values. Therefore, the expected value criterion is generally used in decision making at large corporations.

FIGURE 10.27

Risk-Taking Utility Curve

FIGURE 10.28

FIGURE 10.28

Risk-Neutral Utility Curve

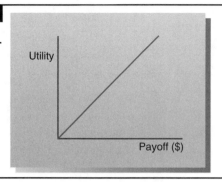

Most individuals are not entirely risk averse, risk taking, or risk neutral. Social scientists have shown that, in general, people tend to be risk taking when dealing with small amounts of money while they tend to be risk averse when it comes to large amounts. Between large and small amounts of money, people are generally risk neutral. This explains why the same individual might purchase a lottery ticket as well as fire insurance. Figure 10.29 depicts Tom Brown's utility values. As you can see, Tom appears to exhibit such typical behavior.

10.8 GAME THEORY

Playing games is a popular form of amusement. People typically play games such as poker, bridge, and chess, for the challenge and enjoyment they afford (and, if betting is allowed, for financial gain).

Similarly, the business environment provides numerous decision-making situations in which one firm or individual is "playing" against another. For example, an oil company bidding for exploration rights to a tract of land is, in a sense, playing a game against other oil companies bidding for the tract. When an airline lowers its fare on a particular route in order to capture a greater market share, it is playing a game against the other carriers serving that route.

Game theory can be used to determine the optimal decision in the face of other decision-making players. In game theory, the payoff is based on the action taken by competing individuals who are also seeking to maximize their return. In decision theory, however, an individual (player) makes a decision and receives a payoff based on the outcome of a noncompetitive random event (the state of nature). You can therefore view decision theory as a special case of game theory in which the decision maker is playing against a single disinterested party (nature).

As shown in Table 10.10, games can be classified in a number of ways—by the number of players, the total return to all players, or the sequence of moves, to name a few.

FIGURE 10.29

Tom Brown's Utility Curve

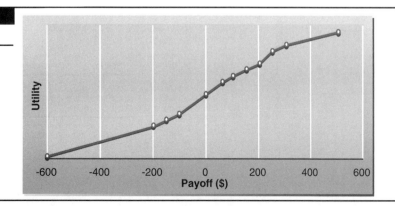

TABLE 10.10			
Classification of Games	**Classification**	**Description**	**Example**
	Number of players		
	Two player	Two competitors	Chess
	Multiplayer	More than two competitors	Poker
	Total Return		
	Zero sum	The amount won by all players equals the amount lost by all players.	Poker among friends
	Nonzero sum	The amount won by all players does not equal the amount lost by all players.	Poker in a casino; the "house takes a percentage of each pot
	Sequence of moves		
	Sequential	Each player gets a turn in a given sequence.	*Monopoly*
	Simultaneous	All players must make their decisions simultaneously.	Paper, rock, scissors

While game theory is an extensive topic, here we focus solely on two-person, zero-sum games in which all decisions are made simultaneously. The situation faced by IGA Supermarket can be modeled by such a game.

IGA SUPERMARKET

IGA.xls

The town of Gold Beach, Oregon, is served by two supermarkets—IGA and Sentry. In a given week, the market share of the two supermarkets can be influenced by their advertising policies. In particular, the manager of each supermarket must decide weekly which area of operations to discount heavily and emphasize in the store's newspaper flyer. Both supermarkets have three areas of operation in common: meat, produce, and groceries. Sentry, however, has a fourth—an in-store bakery.

The weekly percentage gain to IGA in market share as a function of the advertising emphasis of each store is indicated by the following payoff table (Table 10.11). Here it is assumed that a gain in market share to IGA will result in the equivalent loss in market share to Sentry, and vice versa.

Since the IGA manager does not know which operation Sentry will emphasize each week, she wishes to determine an optimal advertising strategy that will maximize IGA's expected change in market share *regardless* of Sentry's action.

TABLE 10.11						
Percentage change in IGA's Market Share as a Function of Advertising Emphasis				*Sentry's Emphasis*		
			Meat	**Produce**	**Groceries**	**Bakery**
IGA's Emphasis		Meat	2	2	–8	6
		Produce	–2	0	6	–4
		Groceries	2	–7	1	–3

SOLUTION

The IGA manager should vary the weekly advertising emphasis; otherwise the Sentry manager will always be able to select an advertising emphasis that ensures a loss of market share for IGA. Hence, the optimal strategy for the IGA manager is to change her advertising emphasis randomly. But what proportion of the time should the emphasis be on meat or produce or groceries?

Let us define:

$$X_1 = \text{the probability IGA's advertising focus is on meat}$$
$$X_2 = \text{the probability IGA's advertising focus is on produce}$$
$$X_3 = \text{the probability IGA's advertising focus is on groceries}$$

The manager at IGA wants to maximize the store's expected change in market share, regardless of Sentry's advertising focus. This expected change, which we denote by V, is known as the value of the game.

Let us see what restrictions are placed on V. If Sentry's advertising focus is on meat, then the expected change in IGA's market share is expressed as $2X_1 - 2X_2 + 2X_3$. This expected change must be at least V, since V represents IGA's change in market share regardless of Sentry's action. Thus, $2X_1 - 2X_2 + 2X_3 \geq V$.

By using similar reasoning for Sentry's advertising emphasis on produce, groceries, and bakery, we arrive at the following conditional relationships:

Sentry's Advertising Emphasis	Relationship
Meat	$2X_1 - 2X_2 + 2X_3 \geq V$
Produce	$2X_1 \qquad\quad - 7X_3 \geq V$
Groceries	$-8X_1 + 6X_2 + X_3 \geq V$
Bakery	$6X_1 - 4X_2 - 3X_3 \geq V$

Because the sum of the probabilities of IGA's advertising focus must equal 1, we also know that $X_1 + X_2 + X_3 = 1$. These conditions result in the following linear programming model, which IGA can use to determine its optimal advertising strategy:

MAX   V
ST

$$2X_1 - 2X_2 + 2X_3 - V \geq 0$$
$$2X_1 \qquad\quad - 7X_3 - V \geq 0$$
$$-8X_1 + 6X_2 + X_3 - V \geq 0$$
$$6X_1 - 4X_2 - 3X_3 - V \geq 0$$
$$X_1 + X_2 + X_3 \qquad\quad = 1$$
$$X_1, X_2, X_3 \geq 0, \text{V unrestricted}$$

Solver can be used to determine the oprtimal solution.[3] Figure 10.30 shows the resulting Sensitivity Report for this model. Thus IGA should focus its advertising on meat about 39% of the time, on produce 50% of the time, and on groceries about 11% of the time.

The average change in IGA's market share using this strategy is 0%, implying that, in the long run, the market shares of the two supermarkets will not change. When the value of a game is 0, it is known as a *fair game*.

---

[3] Since V is an unrestricted variable the "Assume Non-Negative" box would not be checked. Rather the constraints $X_1 \geq 0$, $X_2 \geq 0$, and $X_3 \geq 0$ are entered in the constraints section of the solver dialogue box.

FIGURE 10.30

Partial Output for IGA Problem

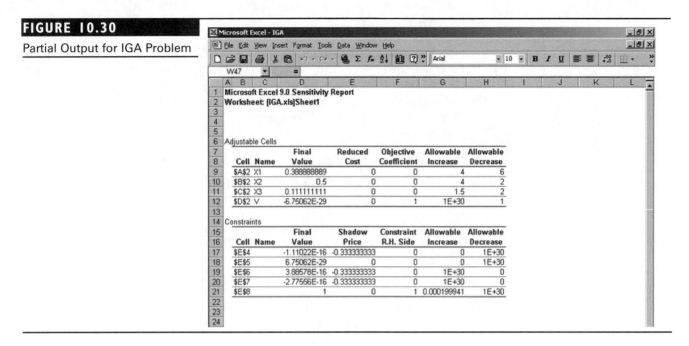

Had the value of the game not been zero, then, on the average, each week the market share would change by that value. If this trend continued, at some point, the estimated percentage changes given in Table 10.11 would cease to be valid.

The Optimal Strategy for Sentry Market

From Sentry's perspective, the model can be formulated by letting

$$Y_1 = \text{the probability Sentry's advertising focus is on meat}$$
$$Y_2 = \text{the probability Sentry's advertising focus is on produce}$$
$$Y_3 = \text{the probability Sentry's advertising focus is on groceries}$$
$$Y_4 = \text{the probability Sentry's advertising focus is on bakery}$$

Sentry also wishes to maximize its expected change in market share regardless of IGA's advertising focus. Since IGA's "gain" is Sentry's loss, this is equivalent to maximizing $-V$. Because the numbers in Table 10.11 are expressed as "gains" in market share to IGA, negatives of these numbers are the "gains" in market share for Sentry. Thus, $-2Y_1 - 2Y_2 + 8Y_3 - 6Y_4$ represents the expected gain in market share to Sentry if IGA focuses its advertising on meat.

Using the reasoning developed for the IGA model, we see that the following conditional relationships hold for the Sentry model:

IGA's Advertising Emphasis	*Relationship*
Meat	$-2Y_1 - 2Y_2 + 8Y_3 - 6Y_4 \geq -V$
Produce	$2Y_1 \quad\quad - 6Y_3 + 4Y_4 \geq -V$
Groceries	$-2Y_1 + 7Y_2 - Y_3 + 3Y_4 \geq -V$

Note that maximizing $-V$ is equivalent to minimizing V. Multiplying the above expressions by -1 (allowing us to use the original numbers in Table 10.11), we can use the following linear programming model[4] to solve for Sentry's optimal advertising strategy:

$$\text{MIN} \qquad\qquad\qquad\qquad\qquad\qquad\qquad V$$
$$\text{ST}$$
$$-Y_1 + 2Y_2 - 8Y_3 + 6Y_4 - V \le 0$$
$$-2Y_1 \qquad\;\; + 6Y_3 - 4Y_4 - V \le 0$$
$$2Y_1 - 7Y_2 + \;\; Y_3 - 3Y_4 - V \le 0$$
$$Y_1 + \;\; Y_2 - \;\; Y_3 + \;\; Y_4 \qquad = 1$$
$$Y1, Y2, Y3, Y4 \ge 0, V \text{ unrestricted}$$

Solving this model using Excel will indicate that Sentry's advertising focus should be on meat 1/3 of the time, groceries 1/3 of the time, and the bakery 1/3 of the time.[5] However, these values are the negative of the corresponding shadow prices in the Sensitivity Report shown in Figure 10.30.

We would be remiss if we did not point out that using changes to market share as the decision criterion may not be appropriate. A business typically wishes to maximize its long-term weekly profit rather than its market share. If the cost structures for the two supermarkets are similar, however, it is probably not unreasonable to assume that a change in a store's market share is directly proportional to a change in its profitability.

SUMMARY

Decision analysis is useful for making decisions that have major profit or cost implications. Payoff tables, in which rows correspond to the decision alternatives and columns correspond to states of nature, are useful for analyzing problems that concern a single decision.

When probability information regarding the states of nature is not available, maximax, maximin, minimax regret, and principle of insufficient reason criteria can be used. The choice of criterion is a function of the decision maker's attitude. When probability information for the states of nature are available, the decision can be determined using an expected payoff or expected regret approach.

Bayes' Theorem can be used to revise the probabilities for the states of nature based on additional experimentation.

Using this information, the decision maker can determine the expected value of sample or indicator information. The expected value of perfect information provides an upper limit on the expected value of sample information.

For problems that are too complex to fit into the form of a payoff table, a decision tree approach can be utilized. Utility theory provides a rational basis for human behavior and to make optimal decisions incorporating risk attitudes. Game theory is an approach used for decision situations involving competitive play. The optimal strategy for a two-person zero-sum game can be determined using a linear programming approach.

---

[4] This problem is known as the dual of the problem faced by IGA. Duality in linear programming is discussed in Supplement CD2 on the accompanying CD-ROM

[5] This problem actually has alternative optimal solutions. Another possible solution is to have Sentry focus on meat 60% of the time, produce 20% of the time and groceries 20% of the time.

ON THE CD-ROM

■ Excel spreadsheet for determining maximin decision for Tom Brown investment problem	**Tom Brown Maximin.xls**
■ Excel spreadsheet for determining minimax regret decision for Tom Brown investment problem	**Tom Brown Minimax Regret.xls**
■ Excel spreadsheet for determining minimax regret decision for Tom Brown investment problem	**Tom Brown Minimax Regret Revised.xls**
■ Excel Spreadsheet for determining maximax decision for Tom Brown investment problem	**Tom Brown Maximax.xls**
■ Excel spreadsheet for determining insufficient reason decision for Tom Brown investment problem	**Tom Brown Insufficient Reason.xls**
■ Excel Spreadsheet for determining expected value payoff decision for Tom Brown investment problem	**Tom Brown Expected.xls**
■ Excel template for solving decision payoff table problems	**Decision Payoff Table.xls**
■ Excel template for Tom Brown investment problem	**Tom Brown.xls**
■ Decision tree for BGD model	**BGD.xls**
■ Linear programming output for IGA model	**IGA.xls**
■ Problem motivations	**Problem Motivations**
■ Problems 41–50	**Additional Problems/Cases**
■ Case 4	**Additional Problems/Cases**

APPENDIX 10.1   USING THE DECISION PAYOFF TABLE.XLS TEMPLATE

The Excel Spreadsheet Decision Payoff Table.xls allows one to solve payoff table problems with up to eight decision alternatives and eight states of nature. The template contains four worksheets: Payoff Table, Bayesian Analysis, Posterior Analysis, and Utility. These worksheets are linked so that the information you input into the Payoff Table worksheet appears in the Bayesian Analysis, Posterior Analysis, and Utility worksheets and the results of the Bayesian Analysis worksheet appear in the Posterior Analysis worksheet.

The Payoff Table Worksheet

Figure A10.1 shows the Payoff Table worksheet on the template. The worksheet can handle up to eight decision alternatives and eight states of nature. The names of the decision alternatives are entered in cells A4 through A11. The names of the states of nature are entered in cells B3 through I3. The payoff values corresponding to a partic-

FIGURE A10.1

Payoff Table Worksheet in
Decision Payoff Table.xls
Template

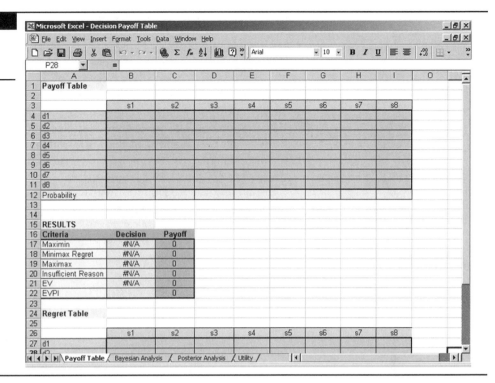

ular decision alternative and state of nature are entered into the appropriate cell in the range from cells B4 through I11. If probability information is known for the states of nature, these values are entered into cells B12 through I12. Note that columns J through N are used for determining the outputs and are hidden.

For the four criteria for decision making under uncertainty, the optimal decisions and corresponding payoffs are given in rows 17 through 20. The regret table values are given in rows 27 through 34. If probability information is provided, the spreadsheet will calculate the optimal decision and expected payoff under the expected value (EV) criterion in row 21 and the EVPI value in cell C22.

Figure A10.2 gives the payoff table for the Tom Brown investment problem.

FIGURE A10.2

Payoff Table for the Tom Brown
Investment Problem

Microsoft Excel - Tom Brown

	A	B	C	D	E	F	G	H	I	O
1	Payoff Table									
2										
3		Large Rise	Small Rise	No Change	Small Fall	Large Fall	s6	s7	s8	
4	Gold	-100	100	200	300	0				
5	Bond	250	200	150	-100	-150				
6	Stock	500	250	100	-200	-600				
7	C/D Account	60	60	60	60	60				
8	d5									
9	d6									
10	d7									
11	d8									
12	Probability	0.2	0.3	0.3	0.1	0.1				
13										
14										
15	RESULTS									
16	**Criteria**	**Decision**	Payoff							
17	Maximin	C/D Account	60							
18	Minimax Regret	Bond	400							
19	Maximax	Stock	500							
20	Insufficient Reason	Gold	100							
21	EV	Bond	130							
22	EVPI		141							
23										
24	Regret Table									
25										
26		Large Rise	Small Rise	No Change	Small Fall	Large Fall	s6	s7	s8	
27	Gold	600	150	0	0	60				
28	Bond	250	50	50	400	210				

Payoff Table / Bayesian Analysis / Posterior Analysis / Utility /

The Bayesian Analysis Worksheet

The Bayesian Analysis worksheet can solve models having up to eight states of nature and four indicators. Figure A10.3 shows the Bayesian Analysis worksheet on the template.

If probabilities are entered in the Payoff Table worksheet, these are carried forward in the Bayesian Analysis worksheets in the cells in columns B and H. If these values are not entered on the Payoff Table worksheet, the appropriate values can be entered in columns B and H of the worksheet. Similarly, if the names of the state of nature are entered in the Payoff Table worksheet, they are carried forward in columns A and G of the Bayesian Analysis worksheet.

The conditional probabilities are entered in columns C and I corresponding to the appropriate indicator. The joint and posterior probabilities are then calculated, and the posterior probabilities are carried forward to the Posterior Analysis worksheet.

Figure 10.7 in Section 10.5 gives the Bayesian Analysis worksheet for the Tom Brown investment problem.

Posterior Analysis Worksheet

The Posterior Analysis worksheet will solve models with up to eight decision alternatives, eight states of nature, and four indicators. Figure A10.4 gives the Posterior Analysis worksheet on the template.

If information has been entered in the Payoff Table and Bayesian Analysis worksheets, no additional information need be entered in this worksheet. The optimal payoff and decision based on the prior probabilities as well as for each indicator is given in rows 20 and 21. The EVSI, EVPI, and Efficiency are determined in cells B23 through B25. If data has not been entered in either the Payoff Table or Bayesian Analysis worksheets, it may be entered directly on the Posterior Analysis worksheet. Figure 10.8 in Section 10.5 shows the Posterior Analysis worksheet for the Tom Brown investment problem.

FIGURE A10.3

Bayesian Analysis Worksheet

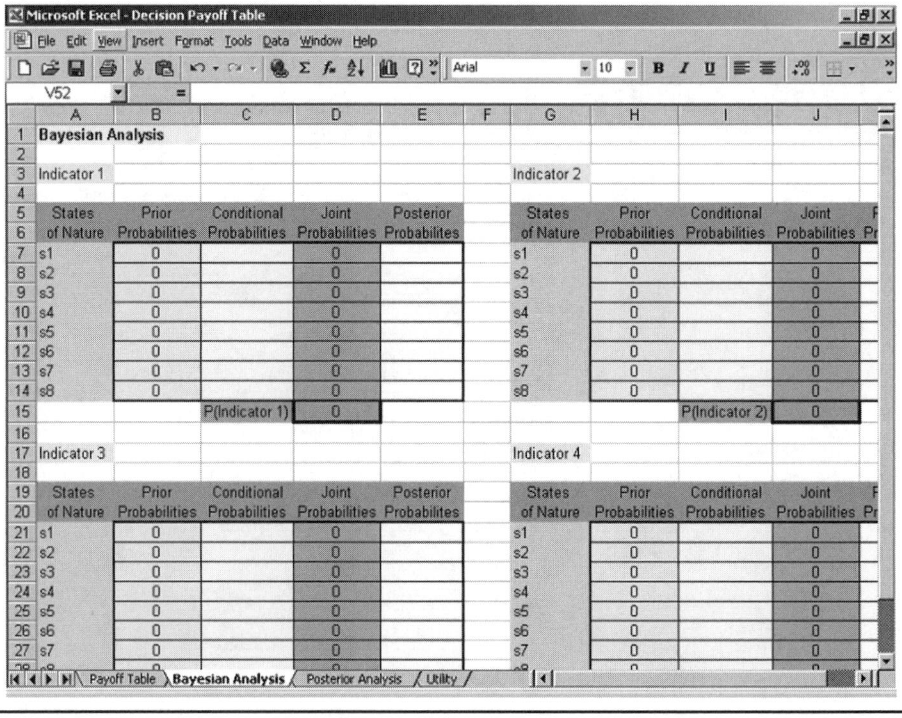

FIGURE A10.4

Posterior Analysis Worksheet

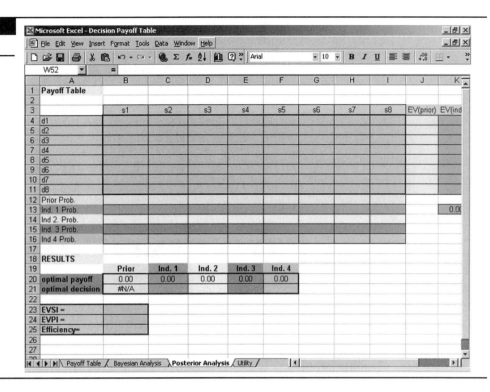

Utility Worksheet

The utility worksheet will solve models having up to eight decision alternatives, eight states of nature, and twenty different certainty equivalent (utility) values. Figure A10.5 gives the utility worksheet on the template.

FIGURE A10.5

Utility Worksheet

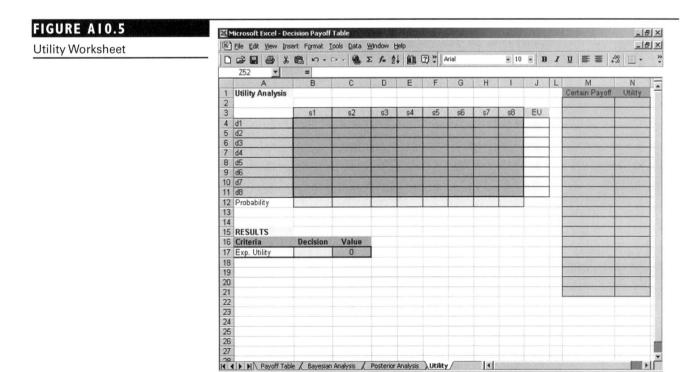

If payoff table information has been entered on the Payoff Table worksheet, this information is carried over to the Utility Worksheet. If this information has not been entered on the Payoff Table worksheet, the payoff table data should be entered in cells B4 through I11 and the relevant probability information should be entered in cells B12 through I12. The certain payoffs and corresponding utilities are entered in columns M and N in ascending order. They should be entered in ascending order. The spreadsheet will calculate expected utility values for each decision in column J and identify the optimal decision under the expected utility criterion in cell B17 and the corresponding expected utility in cell C17.

Figure 10.25 in Section 10.7 shows the Utility Worksheet for the Tom Brown investment problem.

PROBLEMS

1. The Campus Bookstore at East Tennessee State University must decide how many economics textbooks to order for the next semester's class. The bookstore believes that either seven eight, nine, or ten sections of the course will be offered next semester; each section contains 40 students. The publisher is offering bookstores a discount if they place their orders early. If the bookstore orders too few texts and runs out, the publisher will air express additional books at the bookstore's expense. If it orders too many texts, the store can return unsold texts to the publisher for a partial credit. The bookstore is considering ordering either 280, 320, 360, or 400 texts in order to get the discount. Taking into account the discounts, air express expenses, and credits for returned texts, the bookstore manager estimates the following resulting profits.

Number of Textbooks to Order	Number of Introductory Economics Classes Offered			
	7	8	9	10
280	$2800	$2720	$2640	$2480
320	$2600	$3200	$3040	$2880
360	$2400	$3000	$3600	$3440
400	$2200	$2800	$3400	$4000

a. What is the optimal decision if the bookstore manager uses the maximax criterion?

b. What is the optimal decision if the bookstore manager uses the maximin criterion?

c. What is the optimal decision if the bookstore manager uses the minimax regret criterion?

2. Consider the data given in problem 1 for the Campus Bookstore at East Tennessee State University. Based on conversations held with the chair of the economics department, suppose the bookstore manager believes that the following probabilities hold:

P(7 classes offered) = .10
P(8 classes offered) = .30
P(9 classes offered) = .40
P(10 classes offered) = .20

a. Using the expected value criterion, determine how many economics books the bookstore manager should purchase in order to maximize the store's expected profit. Do you think the expected value criterion is appropriate for this problem?

b. Based on the probabilities given in part a, determine the expected value of perfect information. Interpret its meaning.

3. National Foods has developed a new sports beverage it would like to advertise on Super Bowl Sunday. National's advertising agency can purchase either one, two, or three 30-second commercials advertising the drink. It estimates that the return will be based on Super Bowl viewership, which in turn, is based on fans' perception of whether the game is "dull," "average," "above average," or "exciting."

National Foods' ad agency has constructed the following payoff table giving its estimate of the expected profit (in $100,000's) resulting from purchasing one, two, or three advertising spots. (Another possible decision is for national Foods not to advertise at all during the Super Bowl.) The states of nature correspond to the game being "dull," "average," "above average," or "exciting."

Number of 30-Second Commercials Purchased	Perceived Game Excitement			
	Dull	Average	Above Average	Exciting
One	-2	3	7	13
Two	-5	6	12	18
Three	-9	5	13	22

a. What is the optimal decision if the National Foods advertising manager is optimistic?

b. What is the optimal decision if the National Foods advertising manager is pessimistic?

c. What is the optimal decision if the National Foods advertising manager wishes to minimize the firm's maximum regret?

4. Consider the data given in problem 3 for National Foods. Based on past Super Bowl games, suppose the decision maker believes that the following probabilities hold for the states of nature:

P(Dull Game) = .20
P(Average Game) = .40
P(Above-Average Game) = .30
P(Exciting Game) = .10

a. Using the expected value criterion, determine how many commercials National Foods should purchase.

b. Based on the probabilities given here, determine the expected value of perfect information.

5. Consider the data given in problems 3 and 4 for National Foods. The firm can hire the noted sport's pundit Jim Worden to give his opinion as to whether or not the Super Bowl game will be interesting. Suppose the following probabilities hold for Jim's predictions:

P(Jim predicts game will be interesting|game is dull) = .15

P(Jim predicts game will be interesting|game is average) = .25

P(Jim predicts game will be interesting|game is above average) = .50

P(Jim predicts game will be interesting|game is exciting) = .80

P(Jim predicts game will not be interesting|game is dull) = .85

P(Jim predicts game will not be interesting|game is average) = .75

P(Jim predicts game will not be interesting|game is above average) = .50

P(Jim predicts game will not be interesting|game is exciting) = .20

a. If Jim predicts the game will be interesting, what is the probability the game will be dull?

b. What is national's optimal strategy if Jim predicts the game will be (i) interesting or (ii) not interesting?

c. What is the expected value of Jim's information?

6. Wednesday Afternoon is a chain of stores that specialize in selling close-out merchandise. The firm has the opportunity to acquire either three, six, nine, or twelve store leases from the bankrupt In Focus chain. Each lease runs five years, and the profitability of these leases depends on the economy over this time period. The economists at Wednesday Afternoon believe that the average growth rate in GNP will be either 2, 3, 4, 5, or 6% per annum during the five-year period, with probabilities .1, .2, .2, .4, and .1, respectively. The following tables give the expected return to Wednesday Afternoon over the next five years (in $100,000s) as well as the utility values for these amounts.

Number of	Average Annual Growth in GNP				
Leases Acquired	2%	3%	4%	5%	6%
3	7	6	6	5	3
6	2	6	8	7	4
9	1	5	7	8	6
12	1	4	7	8	9

	Payoff (in $100,000s)								
	1	2	3	4	5	6	7	8	9
Utility	0	.05	.15	.30	.50	.65	.75	.90	1.0

Determine the number of leases the company should acquire if its objective is to:

a. Maximize expected profit over the next five years.

b. Maximize expected utility over the next five years.

7. EIEIO.com is a new website devoted to providing news to farmers. The company plans to make money by selling banner ads and providing links to companies that wish to sell items to this market. To run its website, the server the company is considering purchasing is from one of four manufacturers, IBM, H-P, Compaq, or Dell. Since the company has limited funding, this server will have to meet its needs for the next six months.

The company estimates that its profits over the six-month period will be a function of the server purchased and the average number of "hits" per hour that the website generates. The following payoff table (showing total estimated profits over the six-month period in $10,000s) has been developed to assist management in determining which model of server to purchase.

Server Model 300	Average Number of "Hits" Per Hour			
	10	25	50	100
IBM	−20	−10	5	15	10
H-P	−30	−15	8	22	45
Compaq	−45	−25	2	30	75
Dell	−40	−20	6	18	50

Management wishes to use a utility function of the form

$$U(x) = 1 - [(x - 75)/120]^2$$

(where x is the estimated profit in $10,000s)

a. Would you characterize management as risk averse, risk loving, or risk neutral?

b. Suppose management believes the following probabilities hold for the states of nature: P(10) = .05, P(25) = .15, P(50) = .40, P(100) = .30, and P(300) = .10. Which server should the firm purchase if it uses the expected utility criterion for decision making?

8. Steve Johnson believes that this winter is going to be extremely rainy, and he is trying to decide whether he should repair or replace his roof. Steve can install a new roof for $7000 or have it repaired for $1000. While the repair work will probably mean that the house will not have any leaks during the upcoming year, Steve believes that he will definitely need a new roof next year and would have to pay $7000 at that time if he does not get the roof replaced this year.

There is a 60% chance that Steve will be transferred during the upcoming year and will have to put his house on the market. Steve feels that a new roof will enable him to get $4000 more if he sells his house. If he does not repair or replace the roof Steve believes there is a 70% chance that there will be rain damage to his home. He estimates the likelihood that the damage will be $500 is .10, $1000 is .20, $1500 is .30 and $2000 is .40. Using a decision tree analysis, determine Steve's optimal strategy for dealing with his roof.

9. Brenton Software Publishing Company (BSP) offers its sales representatives a choice of three compensation plans based on how many universities adopt Brenton's new statistical software package. The three plans are as follows:

Plan 1: A fixed salary of $2000 per month.

Plan 2: A fixed salary of $1000 per month plus a commission of $300 for each university that adopts the statistical package.

Plan 3: A commission of $700 for each university that adopts the statistical package.

Ted Benson is a new sales representative for BSP and must decide which compensation plan to accept. Experienced sales representatives have told him that he can expect that up to six universities per month will adopt the software. Ted is free to change his compensation plan at the beginning of any month.

a. Construct a payoff table showing Ted's monthly compensation as a function of the compensation plan he chooses and the monthly adoptions.

b. Which plan should Ted choose if he uses the minimax regret criterion?

c. Suppose Ted believes that the following probabilities hold regarding monthly adoptions for his first month with the firm:

$$P(0 \text{ adoptions}) = .10$$
$$P(1 \text{ adoptions}) = .15$$
$$P(2 \text{ adoptions}) = .25$$
$$P(3 \text{ adoptions}) = .20$$
$$P(4 \text{ adoptions}) = .15$$
$$P(5 \text{ adoptions}) = .10$$
$$P(6 \text{ adoptions}) = .05$$

On the basis of these data, which compensation plan should Ted select for the upcoming month?

10. The town of Boswell, British Columbia, has two bed and breakfast resorts: Kootenay Rose and Kootenay Lake Lodge. Currently, the Kootenay Rose gets 35% of the town's bookings, and the Kootenay Lake Lodge gets 65% of the town's bookings. Each season the two resorts prepare a brochure stressing different aspects of the resort. These include room price, recreational facilities, breakfast quality, and room décor. The following table gives the change in the expected market share of the Kootenay Rose based on its and the Kootenay Lake Lodge's brochure's principal focus.

| | | **Kootenay Lake Lodge** | | | |
		Room Price	Recreational Facilities	Breakfast Quality	Room Decor
Kootenay Rose	Room Price	−2	−4	+6	+1
	Recreational Facilities	+2	−2	+3	−1
	Breakfast Quality	−4	+1	+2	−3
	Room Decor	+1	−3	−6	+3

a. Determine the optimal strategy for the Kootenay Rose to use in preparing the principal focus of their advertising brochure.

b. What will be the expected change in the market share for the Kootenay Rose?

11. Southern Homes is a home builder located in a suburb of Atlanta. The company must decide whether to leave its model homes unfurnished, furnish them with minimal accessories, or completely furnish them using a custom decorator. The new-home market is generally quite profitable, but Southern is suffering cash flow problems. The following table gives the expected profit per lot for Southern Homes based on how Southern furnishes its model homes and the overall demand for housing in the Atlanta market:

| Model Furnishing | **Housing Market in Atlanta** | | | |
	Weak	Moderate	Strong	Very Strong
Unfurnished	−$1,500	$1,000	$2,000	$3,000
Minimal Accessories	−$4,000	$ 500	$3,500	$6,000
Custom Decorated	−$7,000	$1,500	$2,500	$9,500

a. If Southern management is conservative, how should it decorate the model homes?

b. If Southern believes that each state of nature is equally likely, how should it decorate the model homes? What approach did you use?

12. Consider the data given in problem 11 for Southern Homes. Although Southern management believes that each state of nature is equally likely, it is also considering hiring an economic forecaster to improve the probability estimates for the states of nature. The forecaster will predict whether there will be an above-average, average, or below-average rise in the GNP for the upcoming year. Based on past experience, the following

conditional probabilities are believed to hold for the forecaster's predictions:

P(above average rise|Weak Housing Market) = .1
P(above average rise|Moderate Housing Market) = .3
P(above average rise|Strong Housing Market) = .6
P(above average rise|Very Strong Housing Market) = .9
P(average rise|Weak Housing Market) = .3
P(average rise|Moderate Housing Market) = .4
P(average rise|Strong Housing Market) = .2
P(average rise|Very Strong Housing Market) = .1
P(below average rise|Weak Housing Market) = .6
P(below average rise|Moderate Housing Market) = .3
P(below average rise|Strong Housing Market) = .2
P(below average rise|Very Strong Housing Market) = 0

a. How should Southern decorate the homes if the forecaster predicts: (i) an above-average rise in GNP? (ii) an average rise in GNP? (iii) a below-average rise in GNP?

b. What is the expected value of the forecaster's information?

c. What is the efficiency of the forecaster's information?

d. The data for this problem were constructed to illustrate the concept of the Bayesian decision process. Realistically, do you feel that GNP is a good indicator for housing sales in Atlanta? List some other indicators that might yield a higher efficiency.

13. Ken Golden has just purchased a franchise from Paper Warehouse to open a party goods store in a newly developed suburb of Orlando, Florida. Paper Warehouse offers three sizes of stores that franchisees can develop: Standard Store—4000 square feet, Super Store—6500 square feet, or MegaStore—8500 square feet. Ken estimates the present worth profitability of this store will be based on the size of the store he selects to build as well as the number of competing party goods stores that will open in the suburb. He feels that between one and four stores will open to compete with his. Ken has developed the following payoff table (showing estimated present worth profits in $10,000s) to help him in his decision making.

Number of Competing Stores That Will Open

Type of Store	1	2	3	4
Standard	30	25	10	5
Super	60	40	30	20
Mega	100	65	15	−100

a. If Ken is an optimistic decision maker, what size store should he open?

b. If Ken wishes to minimize his maximum regret, what size store should he open?

c. Ken believes that there is a 50% chance that two competing stores will open and that the likelihood

that four competing stores will open is half the likelihood that three competing stores will open and three times the likelihood that one competing store will open. If Ken uses the expected value criterion, which size store should he open?

14. BMW is planning to launch a new sport utility vehicle (SUV). Initially it will have limited production for this model, with a total of only 20,000 units being produced for the year. King's BMW has been offered up to four of the SUV's for sale. King's estimates that the profit it earns from purchasing these SUV's will be based on the review it receives from *Road and Track* magazine. The review will give the SUV one of five ratings: poor, good, very good, excellent, or outstanding. The following table gives the profitability Jan King estimates the dealership will earn from ordering the SUV's based on the rating the vehicle receives.

Review in *Road and Track*

SUV's Ordered	Poor	Good	Very Good	Excellent	Out-standing
0	$2,000	$5,000	$3,000	−$1,000	−$4,000
1	−$1,000	$3,000	$6,000	$4,000	$1,000
2	−$5,000	−$1,000	$4,000	$8,000	$9,000
3	−$9,000	−$4,000	$3,000	$12,000	$15,000
4	−$14,000	−$7,000	$2,000	$12,000	$20,000

How many SUV's should the firm order if

a. It uses the maximin criterion.

b. It uses the minimax regret criterion.

c. It uses the principle of insufficient reason criterion.

15. Consider the data given in problem 14. Based on some preliminary information provided by BMW, Jan King estimates that the following probabilities hold for the states of nature: P(Poor review) = .10, P(Good review) = .15, P(Very Good review) = .25, and P(Excellent review) = .35.

a. Calculate the probability of an Outstanding review and use the expected value criterion to determine how many SUV's King's should order.

b. What is the most amount of money King's should pay for advance information regarding the review the SUV will get from Road and Track.

16. The dean of the School of Business at Northern Connecticut State University has been approached by a government agency in Hunan Province, China, to provide MBA training to a group of 30 midlevel officials. The dean is considering submitting a bid of $225,000, $250,000, or $300,000 for providing this program. If the bid is $225,000, the dean estimates there is a 90% chance that the school will get the contract. This probability decreases to .60 if the bid is $250,000 and .20 if the bid is $300,000.

Materials are expected to cost an average of $1000 per participant. The dean estimates that she will have to pay total faculty salaries of either $180,000 or $220,000. There is a 40% chance that the faculty union will accept $180,000 and a 60% chance that the union will hold out for $220,000.

Using a decision tree approach, determine the dean's optimal strategy.

17. The Jeffrey William Company is considering introducing a new line of Christmas tree ornaments that glow in the dark and play melodies. If it introduces the product, it will back it up with a $100,000 advertising campaign using the slogan "let your tree sing out in joy." The company estimates that sales will be a function of the economy and demand will be for 10,000, 50,000, or 100,000 cases. Each case nets the company $24 and costs $18 to produce (not including the expense of the advertising campaign). Because the ornaments will be produced in a factory in Asia, the firm must order in multiples of 40,000 cases. Any unsold cases can be sold to a liquidator for $15 per case. If the company introduces the product and demand for the ornaments exceeds availability, management estimates it will suffer a goodwill loss of $1 for each case the company is short.

a. Determine the payoff table for this problem.

b. If the company president wishes to minimize the firm's maximum regret, what decision will she make regarding the ornaments?

c. Suppose demand for 100,000 ornaments is twice as likely as demand for 10,000 ornaments, and demand for 50,000 ornaments is three times as likely as demand for 100,000 ornaments. What decision should the company make using the expected value criterion?

d. Suppose the company can conduct a marketing survey to get a better idea of the demand for the ornaments. What is the most the company should pay for any such survey?

18. Consider the data given in problem 17 for the Jeffrey William Company. Suppose the firm uses a utility function of the form $U(x) = [(x + 37)/81]^2$ (where x is the firm's expected profit in $10,000s).

a. Would you characterize the firm as risk averse, risk loving, or risk neutral?

b. Using the expected utility criterion, determine the firm's optimal strategy.

19. Mildred Smith has a friend who claims she can tell whether cream is added to coffee before or after the coffee is poured. Mildred's prior belief of her friend's claim is 20%. That is, she believes that the probability her friend's claim is true is .20. Mildred decides to test her friend's claim by making 10 cups of coffee and not showing her friend how the coffee was prepared. To pre-

pare the coffee, she flips a coin. If the coin comes up heads she adds cream to the coffee, and if the coin comes up tails she adds coffee to the cream. Mildred's friend correctly identifies how the coffee was made in each of the 10 cases. What should Mildred's posterior belief be regarding her friend's claim?

20. Marriott Hotels is planning to build a new hotel property in a suburb of Portland, Oregon. The company is considering one of four sizes of hotels to construct: 120 rooms, 200 rooms, 260 rooms, or 320 rooms. Construction will take one year to complete. Profitability of the property will, to a great extent, depend on whether an industrial park or a university is developed in the area. The following table gives the long-term present worth profit (in $100,000s) based on the size of hotel constructed and the development that could take place in the area.

	Type of Development to Occur			
Room Size	None	Industrial Park Only	University Only	Industrial Park and University
120	12	22	18	30
200	8	28	25	40
260	3	34	28	48
320	−10	30	22	65

Marriott management estimates that there is a 60% chance that an industrial park will be developed and a 30% chance that the university will be developed. The two developments are believed to be independent of each other. Determine the optimal size hotel Marriott should construct based on the expected value criterion.

21. Bill Peterson has been offered the opportunity to invest $15,000 in a start-up company that intends to supply personal digital assistants (PDAs) to physicians in order to enable them to determine the approved medication for each HMO patient they treat. The business plan for this start-up calls for raising a total of between $10 million and $40 million in financing and then taking the company public.

To be successful in raising these funds, the firm must first be able to hire a respected professional in the medical industry to be the firm's CEO. Bill believes that there is a 60% chance of the firm accomplishing this requirement. Following the hiring of the CEO, the firm will also need to get backing from at least two of the leading four HMOs. Bill believes that there is a 30% chance that each of the leading four HMOs will want to be involved in this project. If two HMOs sign on to the project, Bill believes the firm can raise $10 million. Bill believes that the firm can raise an additional $5 million for each additional HMO that signs on to the project.

Once the HMOs have signed on, the firm must then recruit physicians to adopt the system. If fewer than

5000 physicians agree to sign on to test the system, the project will fail. Bill believes that there is only a 35% chance that the firm will be able to recruit 5000 or more physicians. Finally, if the firm is successful in getting HMO and physician support, it will try to get two major drug chains to each invest $10 million. The likelihood of one drug chain investing is 30%, and the likelihood of two drug chains investing is 10%.

If the project fails to hire a CEO, recruit at least 5000 physicians, or to raise at least $10 million, Bill feels he will lose his entire investment. Bill estimates the following profits on his investment if the firm is successful in raising the required funds.

Amount Firm Raises (in $millions)	Bill's Profit
10	$60,000
15	$100,000
20	$130,000
25	$180,000
30	$250,000
35	$350,000
40	$500,000

On the basis of this data, determine whether Bill should invest the $15,000.

22. TV Town must decide how many, if any, new Panasony 50-inch television sets to order for next month. The sets cost TV Town $1850 each and sell for $2450 each. Because Panasony is coming out with a new line of big-screen television sets in a month, any sets not sold during the month will have to be marked down to 50% of the normal retail price to be sold at the TV Town Clearance Center. TV Town estimates that if it does not have enough television sets on hand to satisfy demand, it will suffer a goodwill loss of $150 for each customer who cannot get a set. TV Town management feels that the maximum customer demand over the next month will be for three big-screen sets. Defining the states of nature to correspond to the number of sets demanded by customers and the decision alternatives to the number of sets ordered, determine the payoff table for TV Town.

23. Consider the data given in problem 22 for TV Town. Suppose the manager of TV Town estimates customer demand for next month as follows:

$$P(\text{demand} = 0 \text{ sets}) = .20$$
$$P(\text{demand} = 1 \text{ sets}) = .30$$
$$P(\text{demand} = 2 \text{ sets}) = .30$$
$$P(\text{demand} = 3 \text{ sets}) = .20$$

a. How many Panasony big-screen television sets should TV Town order?

b. The manager of TV Town is considering conducting a telephone survey of 30 randomly selected customers. The survey will determine whether at least one of the 30 is likely to buy a big-screen set within

the next month. What is the maximum amount TV Town should pay for the telephone survey?

24. Consider the data given in problems 22 and 23 for TV Town. Suppose the manager of TV Town believes that the following conditional probabilities hold for the telephone survey being conducted on 30 randomly selected customers:

P(At Least One Survey Customer Likely to Buy|Demand = 0) = .1

P(At Least One Survey Customer Likely to Buy|Demand = 1) = .2

P(At Least One Survey Customer Likely to Buy|Demand = 2) = .4

P(At Least One Survey Customer Likely to Buy|Demand = 3) = .7

a. If TV Town conducts the survey, what is the optimal strategy for ordering the Panasony big-screen television sets?

b. What is the most amount of money TV Town should pay for this telephone survey?

c. What is the efficiency of the telephone survey?

d. Discuss in general terms how the results of the survey could be modified to result in improved efficiency.

25. The AMC 24-plex cinema is trying to decide how many screens it should have showing the new action comedy movie *Lost Wages in Las Vegas*. The theater must sign a contract with the movie's distributor indicating how many screens it will play the movie on before reviews of the movie are public. The manager has decided, based on the actors involved in the movie, to devote between one and five screens to this movie during its two-week summer run. The profit the manager expects to earn on the movie is based on the consensus review of the movie (one to four stars). The payoff table showing these estimated profits is as follows.

# of Screens	Consensus Rating			
	*	**	***	****
One	−200	600	400	−100
Two	−800	100	1200	600
Three	−1800	−500	1100	1200
Four	−2500	−1500	700	1900
Five	−4000	−2000	300	3500

a. If the theater manager wishes to minimize his maximum regret, how many screens should the movie be booked in?

b. If the theater manager is risk averse and wishes to use the maximin criterion, how many screens should the movie be booked in?

c. Suppose the theater manager believes, based on the director's previous releases, that the probability the movie will be rated one star is .10, two stars .20, three stars .40, and four stars .30. If the manager wishes to use the expected value criterion, how many screens should the movie be booked in?

26. Consider the situation faced by the theater manager in problem 25. Suppose the probabilities given in part c hold.

   a. What is the most amount of money the theater manager should pay for advance information regarding the review the movie will receive?

   b. The theater manager can subscribe to "Advance Screening," a rating service that purports to predict the review a movie will receive. The rating service either gives the movie a "thumbs up" or a "thumbs down." Based on previous predictions made by this service, the manager believes the following conditional probabilities hold.

   $$P(\text{Thumbs Up}|\text{One Star}) = .20$$
   $$P(\text{Thumbs Up}|\text{Two Stars}) = .40$$
   $$P(\text{Thumbs Up}|\text{Three Stars}) = .60$$
   $$P(\text{Thumbs Up}|\text{Four Stars}) = .90$$

   If "Advance Screenings" wants a fee of $50 for giving its prediction, should the theater manager purchase the information?

   c. What is the efficiency of "Advance Screenings" information?

27. Bees Candy Company must decide whether or not to introduce a new lower-calorie candy assortment for Christmas. Management feels that if it introduces the candy, it will earn a profit of $150,000 if sales are 70,000 pounds and a profit of $50,000 if sales are 40,000 pounds. It will lose $100,000 if sales are only 10,000 pounds. If Bees does not introduce the lower-calorie candy assortment, it believes it will lose $20,000 due to lost sales.

   a. Construct a payoff table for this problem.

   b. Should Bees introduce the candy if management is conservative?

   c. Construct a regret table for this problem.

   d. If Bees management uses the minimax regret criterion, should the new candy be introduced?

28. Consider the information given in problem 27 for Bees Candy. Suppose Bees management believes that the following probabilities hold:

   $$P(\text{Sales} = 70,000 \text{ pounds}) = .2$$
   $$P(\text{Sales} = 40,000 \text{ pounds}) = .5$$
   $$P(\text{Sales} = 10,000 \text{ pounds}) = .3$$

   a. Using the expected value criterion, determine whether the company should introduce the lower-calorie candy assortment.

   Bees is considering hiring a market consulting firm to analyze people's attitudes toward lower-calo-

rie candy. The market research firm will report back to Bees management whether attitudes are favorable or unfavorable. Management believes that the following conditional probabilities hold:

   $$P(\text{favorable attitude}|\text{Sales} = 70,000 \text{ pounds}) = .90$$
   $$P(\text{favorable attitude}|\text{Sales} = 40,000 \text{ pounds}) = .60$$
   $$P(\text{favorable attitude}|\text{Sales} = 10,000 \text{ pounds}) = .20$$

   b. If the survey is performed and results in a favorable attitude toward lower-calorie candy, would you recommend that the candy be produced?

   c. Determine the expected value and efficiency of this sample information.

29. Craig Computer Company (CCC) manufactures supercomputers based on parallel processing technology. Next month the firm has scheduled demonstrations for its new Model 4365 with four potential customers. This model sells for $725,000 and CCC believes that the probability of each customer purchasing a computer is 30%. The company cannot completely shut down its assembly line over the next month and plans to manufacture at least one computer; it could manufacture as many as four. Production costs for the month are as follows:

Number of Computers Built	Total Production Costs
1	$ 800,000
2	$1,400,000
3	$1,800,000
4	$2,400,000

   Any computers Craig manufactures during a given month but does not sell are exported overseas. Craig receives $500,000 for these computers and can sell as many as it is willing to export. If Craig sells more computers than it manufactures in a month, the customer must wait for delivery. In this case, Craig estimates it loses a total of $30,000 on the sale.

   a. Determine the payoff table for this problem.

   b. What decision alternatives are undominated?

   c. Determine the optimal strategy using the expected value criterion. (*Hint: The binomial distribution can be used to determine the probabilities for the states of nature.*)

30. Stefan Chirac has a cabana rental business in the exclusive resort of St. Tropez. Stefan can handle up to four cabanas daily. These must be assembled in the morning and taken down in the evening. Stefan pays the company he gets the cabanas from a rental fee of $50 per cabana per day, and he rents the cabanas to tourists for either $80 or $100 per day.

   The weather in St. Tropez is either rainy, cloudy, or sunny. Each day there is a 10% chance of rainy weather, a 20% chance of cloudy weather, and a 70% chance of sunny weather. While Stefan must decide how many cabanas to rent before knowing what the weather will be, he can set the rental price after determining the day's weather.

If the weather is rainy, there will be no rental demand. If the weather is cloudy, demand will follow a Poisson distribution with a mean of 2 if Stefan charges $80 for the rental and a mean of 1.5 if Stefan charges $100. If the weather is sunny, demand will follow a Poisson distribution with a mean of 4 if Stefan charges $80 and a mean of 3 if Stefan charges $100. Using a decision tree analysis, determine how many cabanas Stefan should rent and what price he should charge if the weather is cloudy or sunny.

31. Zeus Athletic Wear is in the process of lining up potential Olympic athletes to endorse its planned line of sports apparel in company advertisements. Zeus is quite interested in signing Dan Miller, an athlete who will be vying for a medal in the decathlon. The firm has been negotiating with Dan's agent for a two-year contract (six months before the upcoming games and a year and a half afterward). The parties have discussed one of three arrangements.

I. Dan will work exclusively for Zeus and be paid $1 million.

II. Dan will work for Zeus on a semi-exclusive basis (he can also work for at most one other noncompeting firm) and be paid $400,000.

III. Dan will be a Zeus-sponsored athlete. This means that Zeus will supply Dan's garments but Dan will not appear in advertisements for Zeus. Dan will be paid $100,000 for this arrangement.

Zeus's management estimates that the gain in profitability it will achieve from its association with Dan will be a function of the type of medal, if any, Dan wins at the Olympics. Based on the results of previous advertising campaigns involving Olympic medal winners, management has prepared the following payoff table. (The figures are profits or losses in $100,000s.)

Compensation Arrangement	Medal Won by Dan at the Olympics			
	Gold	Silver	Bronze	None
Plan I	100	20	10	−20
Plan II	60	40	20	−5
Plan III	15	10	5	0

According to sports pundits, Dan has a 20% chance of wining a gold medal, a 30% chance of winning a silver medal, and a 10% chance of wining a bronze medal. Which endorsement plan should Zeus management select?

32. In the game of rock, scissors, paper, each of two players simultaneously puts out either a fist (for rock), two fingers (for scissors), or an open hand (for paper). If player 1 puts out rock and player 2 puts out scissors, then player 1 wins (rock breaks scissors). Alternatively, if player 1 puts out rock and player 2 puts out paper, then player 2 wins (paper covers rock). If player 1 puts out scissors and player 2 puts out paper, then player 1 wins (scissors cuts paper). If both players put out the same symbol, the game is a draw. The following is the payoff table from player 1's point of view:

		PLAYER 2		
		Rock	Scissors	Paper
PLAYER 1	Rock	0	1	−1
	Scissors	−1	0	1
	Paper	1	−1	0

Determine the optimal strategies for players 1 and 2 for this game.

33. Roney Construction Company is considering purchasing a home in the historic district of Lexington, Massachusetts, for restoration. The cost of the home is $150,000, and Roney believes that, after restoration, the home can be sold for $290,000. Roney will pay $2000 per month in finance charges until the project is completed.

The company's architect has developed two sets of plans for the restoration. Plan A does not require changes to the front facade. Under this plan, the renovation will cost $120,000 and take three months to complete. Plan B does involve changes in the front facade of the building. Under this plan, Roney believes that it can do the restoration work in four months, at a cost of $80,000.

Because Plan B changes the exterior of the house, it must be approved by the town's Historic Commission. The approval process takes two months and will cost $10,000. If Roney decides on Plan B, it can play it safe and wait to begin construction until after the plan has been approved by the Historic Commission. Alternatively, it can take a chance and begin construction immediately in the hopes that the commission will approve the plan.

If the Historic Commission denies Plan B, Roney will have to resort to Plan A for the renovation work. If Roney begins construction under Plan B and the Historic Commission denies the plan, the company estimates that doing the construction work under Plan A will cost $140,000 and the project will take five additional months to complete.

Roney estimates that there is a 40% chance that the Historic Commission will approve Plan B. However, if the firm were to contribute $6000 to the mayor's reelection campaign, Roney believes the chances for approval would increase to 50%. Determine an optimal strategy for the Roney Construction Company.

34. Steve Greene is considering purchasing fire insurance for his home. According to statistics for Steve's county, Steve estimates the damage from fire to his home in a given year is as follows:

Amount of Damage	Probability
0	.975
$10,000	.010
$20,000	.008
$30,000	.004
$50,000	.002
$100,000	.001

a. If Steve is risk neutral, how much should he be willing to pay for the fire insurance?

b. Suppose Steve's utility values are as follows:

Amount of Loss ($1000s)						
100	50	30	20	10	1	0
Utility 0	.65	.75	.8	.95	.995	1

What is the expected utility corresponding to fire damage?

c. Determine approximately how much Steve would be willing to pay for the fire insurance.

35. Rolley's Rentals of Lahaina, Hawaii, rents bicycles and roller skates. Mr. Rolley is considering expanding his line of bicycle rentals to include tandem bicycles. He estimates that he will need a maximum of three tandem bicycles to handle estimated demand for the upcoming year.

Profitability from the tandem bicycles in the upcoming year will be a function of the number of tandem bicycles purchased and the number of sunny days during the year in Lahaina. To help him determine how many tandem bicycles to purchase, Mr. Rolley has developed the following payoff table representing expected profits.

Number of Tandem Bicycles to Purchase	Number of Sunny Days in Lahaina During Upcoming Year			
	250	275	300	325
0	0	0	0	0
1	−140	80	130	220
2	−130	120	180	280
3	−160	−10	250	400

a. What decision alternatives, if any, are dominated?

b. If Rolley's wishes to minimize its maximum regret, how many tandem bicycles should it purchase?

c. Suppose that Rolley's believes that the likelihood of 250 sunny days in Lahaina over the upcoming year is equal to the probability of 325 sunny days. In addition, the probability of 300 sunny days is twice as great as the probability of 325 sunny days and three times as great as the probability of 275 sunny days. Using the expected monetary criterion, determine how many tandem bicycles Rolley's should purchase.

36. The Post Office uses two freight carriers, Federal Parcel and Emery Express, to carry mail between New York and Boston. Federal Parcel has 30% of this business, and Emery Express has 70%. The Post Office is interested in signing an exclusive contract with one of the carriers to handle the mail between the cities. Federal Parcel is considering bidding either $0.02, $0.04, or $0.06 per ounce as the fee charged the Post Office. Emery Express is considering bidding either $0.02, $0.05, or $0.06 per ounce as the fee charged the Post Office. The carrier who submits the lower bid will get the contract; if both bids are the same, the Post Office will use the carriers to carry an equal amount of mail.

The following table describes the change in market share that Federal Parcel will experience as a function of the amount that the two carriers bid.

		Emery Express's Bid		
		$.02	$.05	$.06
Federal Parcel's Bid	$.02	+20%	+70%	+70%
	$.04	−30%	+70%	+70%
	$.06	−30%	−30%	+20%

a. What is Federal Parcel's optimal strategy if it wishes to maximize its expected change in market share?

b. Suppose that Federal Parcel estimates that the total weight the Post Office will be sending between the two cities this year will be 1.5 million pounds. Federal Parcel estimates that serving this route will cost it a fixed amount of $20,000 plus $0.01 per ounce. If Emery Express is believed to be equally likely to bid $0.02, $0.05, or $0.06 per pound, what should Federal Parcel's bid be in order to maximize its expected profit?

37. Consider the following two-player game played in a particular office lunch room. Player 1 picks an integer between 1 and 4, and player 2 picks an integer between 3 and 6. If the sum of the two numbers equals 7, player 2 wins $8 from player 1. If the sum of the two numbers equals 6, player 1 wins $6 from player 2. If the sum of the two numbers equals 9, player 1 wins $9 from player 2. If the sum of the numbers is anything other than 6, 7, or 9, the game is a tie and neither player wins or loses.

Determine the expected strategy for player 1 and the expected value of this game to player 1.

38. Two oil brokerage firms, Murphy Company and Sardon Brothers, supply heating oil to 10 oil delivery companies in northern New Jersey. Each day the two brokerage firms fax their offering prices to these delivery companies, and the delivery companies purchase their daily needs from the firm that has the cheapest offering price. (If both brokerage firms have the same offering price, Murphy Company tends to get 40% of the business, while Sardon Brothers gets 60%.)

The two oil brokers' offering price is pegged at $0.01, $0.02, or $0.03 above the New York spot price of Number 2 fuel oil. The management science analyst working for Sardon Brothers believes that the following payoff table holds regarding the expected daily profit earned by Sardon Brothers based on its and Murphy Company's offering price.

The management scientist also believes that Murphy Company will use an offering price of Spot + $.0.01 with probability 30% and an offering price of Spot + $0.02 with probability 50%.

a. If the company's objective is to maximize its expected daily profit, what should Sardon Brothers use as an offering price?

b. What is the most that Sardon Brothers should pay for information that would improve its probability estimates for Murphy Company's pricing strategy?

c. Suppose Sardon Brothers uses the following utility function: $U(x) = 2^{(x+600)/1600} - 1$. (For example, the utility of a $200 profit to the company equals $2^{(200+600)/1600} - 1 = 2^{(1/2)} - 1 = 1.41 - 1 = .41$.) Would you characterize Sardon Brothers as risk averse, risk neutral, or risk loving?

d. Using the utility function given in part (c), what offering price should Sardon Brothers use for the oil if its objective is to maximize its expected utility?

39. United Aerospace has been invited to bid on doing the development work for a new U.S. Air Force bomber. United estimates that the cost of doing the development work will depend on potential technical difficulties but will be either $150 million or $200 million. United estimates that it is three times more likely that the cost will be $150 million than $200 million.

United is planning to bid $125 million, $175 million, $200 million, or $225 million for this project. If it bids $125 million, it feels that there is a 85% chance it will win the contract, whereas if it bids $175 million it feels that there is a 70% chance it will get the contract. If the firm bids $200 million it feels that the chance of winning the contract decreases to 40%, and if the firm bids $225 million it feels that there is only a 15% chance that it will win the contract.

Following the development work, the Air Force will want to hire a firm to build 100 of these bombers. If United Aerospace wins the development contract, it feels that it will have the inside track for winning the contract to build the 100 bombers. Specifically, United Aerospace believes that there is a 70% chance that it will win this contract, whereas if it does not do the development work, the chance of the firm getting the contract to build the

bombers is only 15%. On the building project, United Aerospace estimates that there is a 30% chance it would earn $300 million, a 40% chance that it would earn $100 million, a 20% chance that it would earn $50 million, and a 10% chance that it would lose $75 million.

Determine United Aerospace's optimal strategy for bidding on the development project.

40. Little Trykes is considering offering a toy scooter that it will sell for $20 each. The company has two production options:

(i) Manufacture the scooters in their existing facilities.

(ii) Import the scooters from overseas

Little Trykes believes that the demand for the scooters will be between 100 and 300 units per day and has decided to model the situation as a decision analysis problem with three states of nature: demand = 100 units per day; demand = 200 units per day; and demand = 300 units per day. This was done because the company will either manufacture or import the units in lot sizes that are multiples of 100. The following table gives the per unit costs for the two production options.

Option	Amount Supplied Per Day		
	100	200	300
Use Existing Facilities	$18	$14	$10
Import	$15	$13	$ 9

If the company decides to import the scooters, there is a 30% chance that a tariff of $2 per unit will be imposed on the scooters. The company will learn whether there is a tariff only after it has made its decision on the source of its scooter production. The amount produced or imported will correspond to daily demand. The probability distribution for daily demand with no advertising versus spending $1000 a day on advertising is as follows:

Daily Demand	Probability with No Advertising	Probability with Spending $1000 a Day for Advertising
100	.3	.1
200	.5	.2
300	.2	.7

Determine Little Trykes's optimal course of action regarding manufacturing, importing, and advertising the scooters.

Table for Problem 38

		Murphy Company Offering Price		
		Spot + $0.01	Spot + $0.02	Spot + $0.03
Sardon Brothers Offering Price	Spot + $0.01	$160	$420	$420
	Spot + $0.02	−$600	$300	$1000
	Spot = $0.03	−$600	−$600	$500

CASE 1: SWAN VALLEY FARMS

Swan Valley Farms produces dried apricots, which it sells to two cereal producers—Kellogg's and General Foods. Swan Valley forecasts that for the upcoming year Kellogg's will want to purchase either 10, 20, or 30 tons of dried apricots, and General Foods will want to purchase either 10, 20, 30, or 40 tons. Kellogg's and General Foods order independently of each other. The following probability distributions are believed to hold:

Kellogg's Demand	Probability	General Food's Demand	Probability
10 tons	.20	10 tons	.20
20 tons	.50	20 tons	.30
30 tons	.30	30 tons	.30
		40 tons	.20

Swan Valley is currently contracting with local farmers for delivery of apricots for drying. It takes approximately four pounds of apricots to produce one pound of dried apricots. Swan Valley can purchase apricots at $0.15 per pound; it costs an additional $0.02 to produce one pound of dried apricots.

Swan Valley's contract with Kellogg's and General Foods calls for purchase in units of 10 tons at a price of $1500 per ton plus delivery costs.

The process of drying apricots takes several weeks; therefore, Swan Valley must sign its contract with growers before it knows the exact amount that Kellogg's and General Foods will be ordering. If Swan Valley dries more apricots than its two customers demand, it will sell the surplus dried apricots to a food wholesaler at a price of $1100 per ton, plus delivery. If Swan Valley produces fewer dried apricots than the two cereal manufacturers demand, it can purchase additional dried apricots from a competitor at a price of $1400 per ton.

Swan Valley is considering offering one of two new pricing plans. Under the first plan, Swan Valley will lower its selling price to $1400 a ton if the cereal company agrees to order four months in advance of delivery. This will enable Swan Valley to know how many apricots will be demanded by a customer prior to its having to contract with growers. The company believes that there is a 30% chance that Kellogg's will accept this offer and a 40% chance that General Foods will accept this offer.

Under the second plan, Swan Valley will lower the selling price to $1375 a ton if the cereal company agrees to order four months in advance of delivery. Swan Valley believes there is a 60% chance that Kellogg's will accept this plan and an 80% chance that General Foods will accept.

Prepare a business report to Henry Swan, owner of Swan Valley Farms, giving your recommendation as to which of the two pricing plans, if any, the firm should adopt. Include in your report a recommendation for the number of pounds of apricots Swan Valley should purchase from farmers and the expected profit the company will earn.

CASE 2: PHARMGEN CORPORATION

Pharmgen Corporation has developed a new medication for the treatment of high blood pressure. Tests on laboratory animals have been promising, and the firm is ready to embark on human trials in order to gain approval from the Food and Drug Administration (FDA). The firm estimates that it will cost an additional $4 million to do the required testing. Although the firm has this amount of money available, if the product turns out to be unsuccessful, the company will be virtually wiped out.

If the tests prove successful, the firm believes that the amount it will earn on the drug will be a function of the number of competing drugs of this type that also gain approval. If no other drugs gain approval, the firm estimates it will earn $50 million in present worth profits on the drug. For every other drug that gains approval, Pharmgen believes the expected present worth profit will drop by $10 million. Based on industry publications, four other firms are working on similar drugs. Pharmgen's management estimates that the probability that its drug will gain FDA approval is 40% but that each of its four competitors' drugs only has a 20% chance of FDA approval.

Wyler Laboratories, a larger drug firm, has approached Pharmgen about acquiring the rights to the drug. Wyler is willing to pay Pharmgen $5 million for a half interest in the drug (and split any costs or profits from the drug with Pharmgen) or $8 million for the full rights to the drug. Pharmgen's management has used the indifference approach to determine the utility values shown below.

Prepare a business report to Dr. Joseph Wolf, president of Pharmgen, detailing your recommendation regarding the development of this drug.

Expected Present Worth Profit or Loss (in Millions)	24	3	8	10	15	20	25	30	40	50
Utility	0	.30	.40	.45	.50	.55	.65	.75	.85	1.0

CASE 3: PICKENS EXPLORATION COMPANY

Pickens Exploration Company has been offered a lease to drill for oil on a particular piece of property. While oil has been found on nearby land, there are no assurances that Pickens will be successful in finding oil. The company feels that it will strike either a major find, an average find, or a dry hole. A major find can be sold to an oil company for $6 million, while an average find will only bring in $2 million. A dry hole will cost the company $80,000 to cap.

The cost of the lease is $400,000 plus 20% of the revenue if the oil well is sold to an oil company. Pickens estimates that it can drill a well at a cost of $160,000. Without further testing, Pickens' geologist estimates that there is a 5% chance that the well will be a major find, a 35% chance that it will be an average find, and a 60% chance that it will be a dry hole.

In order to get a better estimate of the probability of finding oil in the well, the geologist is contemplating performing either a geologic or a seismic test. A geologic test will cost $20,000. If the test predicts oil, the geologist believes that the following probabilities hold:

P(test predicts oil|major find) = .70
P(test predicts oil|average find) = .50
P(test predicts oil|dry hole) = .30

Instead of the geologic test, the firm can perform the more detailed seismic test, which costs $50,000. If this test predicts oil, the geologist believes that the following probabilities hold:

P(test predicts oil|major find) = .90
P(test predicts oil|average find) = .70
P(test predicts oil|dry hole) = .10

Pickens can do the testing prior to deciding whether or not to procure the lease. If Pickens gets a prediction of oil from either the geologic or seismic tests, it can sell a half-interest in the well to a Dallas investor for $800,000. In this case Pickens will be responsible for any and all losses on the well should it lose money, but will split profits on the well equally with the investor.

Prepare a business report that recommends Pickens' optimal strategy. Include in your report an analysis of the change in probability estimates due to the outcomes of the geologic and seismic tests.

CASE 4 IS ON THE CD

CHAPTER 11

Simulation Models

Hunt Wesson

Hunt Wesson (http://www.hunt-wesson. com) is one of the world's largest food processing companies. One of its principal product lines is Wesson Oil, which is made from a variety of vegetable oils and packaged in various-sized bottles. Management is particularly concerned about the operation of the production line used to bottle the oil.

The bottling process begins by using a decaser to remove empty plastic bottles from their shipping cases and place them on the bottling line. The bottles are then air cleaned and moved onto a conveyer belt for transport to the filling station. After filling, they are sealed and capped and proceed to a labeler. A caser places the filled bottles in cases. Finally, the cases are sealed using a case sealer and loaded on pallets by a palletizer.

Management conducted a simulation study to develop procedures for ensuring that the bottling line operates at a sufficient capacity to meet sales projections. They gathered data on the frequency, length, and repair cost of breakdowns for each workstation on the bottling line and determined the cost and effects of modifications to the existing equipment. They also investigated different line speeds as well as the placement of buffer areas (accumulation tables) between workstations.

As a result of the simulation analysis, management was able to redesign the bottling process to meet the firm's production requirements and to develop procedures for dealing with future breakdowns which will minimize the variation in production rates.

11.1 OVERVIEW OF SIMULATION

In the preceding chapters, we have studied many analytical models. Often, however, the underlying assumptions necessary for these models to provide good results are not met. For example, in a single-server queuing system if service time does not follow an exponential distribution or if customers do not arrive according to a Poisson process we cannot expect the M/M/1 queuing formulas to accurately describe steady-state results. Inventory systems for which demand varies greatly from period to period cannot be adequately analyzed using the EOQ formula. In cases such as these, we may use a simulation approach to perform the desired analysis.

A **simulation** develops a model to evaluate a system numerically over some time period of interest. Its purpose is to estimate characteristics for the system, which can then be used to select the best policy from a set of alternatives under consideration. Unlike many analytical techniques, a simulation does not rely on an algorithm to solve for the optimal solution; instead, a computer program known as a **simulator** is used to evaluate each option.

It is important for the simulator to be as accurate as possible in capturing the important aspects of the operation of the system. A challenging aspect of developing a simulation, therefore, is to identify the relevant factors affecting system performance. For example, if we are interested in determining a customer's average waiting time in a queuing system, the arrival process, the service time, the number of servers, and the priority rule for selecting the next customer are all important attributes. By contrast, the hair color of an arriving customer does not affect waiting time and is ignored.

Other attributes, such as the gender of a customer, may or may not be a factor. If we are modeling a queuing system for a bank, for example, a customer's gender is probably not a factor. But if we are modeling the waiting line at a campground rest room, a customer's gender probably is an important factor, since the time men and women spend in a rest room generally differs.

Simulation is used for many purposes in business and industry. Airlines use flight simulators to train prospective pilots; the weather service uses simulation analysis to predict future weather patterns; and process engineers use simulation to determine the operating characteristics of projects, such as a proposed oil refinery. These are all examples of **continuous simulation systems**, in which the state of the system changes continuously over time. For example, a plane rises continuously as a pilot moves the throttle; weather changes from instant to instant; and oil flows continuously through the refining process. Since in many cases, continuous simulation systems require the use of differential equations to model changes in system parameters, these systems are beyond the scope of this text.

Other simulation models, such as those involving queuing or inventory systems, monitor changes that occur at discrete points in time. These are known as **discrete simulation systems**. Still other simulation models are hybrids of continuous and discrete simulation systems. For example, in simulating jet fuel inventory at an airport, customers (airplanes) arrive on a discrete basis, while the fuel going into each airplane is a continuous flow. In this chapter a number of discrete simulation systems, typical of those found in business and industry are considered.

Although simple simulation models may be solved by hand, simulation of most practical problems requires the use of a computer program. Computer simulations can be written in any computer language or performed by using a spreadsheet program such as Excel.

One advantage of using Excel to develop a simulation model is that specific Excel add-ins have been developed to allow the analyst to easily run multiple simulations so that confidence intervals and probabilities can be calculated for the various policies considered. Two of the most popular of these add-ins are @Risk and Crystal Ball. A student version of Crystal Ball is included on the accompanying CD-ROM.

While many simulations have been written in general-purpose programming languages, such as FORTRAN, PL/1, Pascal, and BASIC, specialized computer simulation languages have been developed to assist in writing the computer code. Among the more popular simulation languages are GPSS, SIMSCRIPT, SIMAN, and SLAM. The principal advantage of using a specialized language is that compared to a general-purpose language, fewer lines of computer code are required, allowing the program to be written and debugged more quickly and easily. In addition, many specialized languages include an animation ability, enabling the user to view the effects of the simulation as the program is running. This can be especially valuable in identifying potential bottlenecks in the system or critical areas requiring further modeling. Even though these specialized languages share many similarities, they also have certain differences that make one language more appropriate than another for a particular application.

An alternative to using Excel or a programming or simulation language is to develop the simulation using a **simulator program**. These programs typically contain objects that can be dragged and dropped to allow easy creation of the simulation model. The resulting models usually include the ability to observe an animation of the process and contain the ability to provide the simulation results in a tabular or graphical format. Some of the more popular simulators currently used in business and industry are Alpha/Sim, SIMPROCESS, ProModel, and Extend. A student version of Extend is included on the accompanying CD-ROM. Appendix 10.1, also on the accompanying CD-ROM, covers the basic concepts of developing simulations using Extend by illustrating the simulation of a discrete system.

Deciding whether to learn a particular simulation language or simulator program depends on how frequently it will be necessary to develop simulation models. For the infrequent modeler, using Excel to develop simulation models may be the easiest and most accessible solution.

Approaches to Solving a Simulation Problem

- Excel—Including the Use of Add-In Programs such as Crystal Ball
- Using a General-Purpose Computer Language such as BASIC
- Using a Simulation Language such as SIMSCRIPT
- Using a Simulator Program such as Extend

The Simulation Process

The approach to simulation analysis is quite similar to that of a general management science process. The key steps in the analysis are:

- Defining the Problem
- Developing the Simulation Model
- Running the Simulation Model and Obtaining Results
- Communicating the Results

It is worthwhile commenting on the second step of the simulation process—developing the simulation model. Often in simulation studies, the first step in developing a model is to create a flow chart representation of the system being simulated. The modeler must then select an appropriate methodology for constructing the simulation model (i.e., a general-purpose computer language, a specialized simulation language, a simulator program, and Excel). The methodology selected depends on the type of problem being simulated.

Besides determining the approach to be used to develop the simulation, the analyst must also collect the data needed to construct the model. This involves estimating probability distributions for parts of the process being simulated. Once the methodology for model development has been determined and the data collected, the model can be constructed (programmed) and run.

As with any management science procedure, enhancements to the model can be made after the initial run. In this approach one starts with a relatively simple model that is easy to construct (program) and then, after analyzing the results of the model, adds desired enhancements. This iterative procedure is continued until the analyst is satisfied that the model is giving valuable insights into the problem being studied.

While the concept of simulation is quite intuitive, great care must be taken not only in modeling the system, but also in conducting the simulation. As discussed in this chapter, simulation requires both good modeling and good programming skills. Knowledge of statistics is also important for determining the overall design of the simulation and other critical factors, such as the required length of individual simulation runs and the number of runs that should make up the simulation study.

11.2 MONTE CARLO SIMULATION

If the system being simulated includes data inputs that are random variables, the simulation model should reflect them as accurately as possible. One way of doing so is to use a technique known as **Monte Carlo simulation**, in which the simulator is designed so that the **simulated events** both occur randomly and reflect the theoretical frequencies being modeled.

Monte Carlo simulation uses *random numbers*, which can either be generated by a computer program (Excel has several ways to generate random numbers) or taken from a random number table (see Appendix A.1), to generate simulated events. The process for matching random numbers to simulated events is called **random number mapping**. To illustrate how random number mappings are developed and how random numbers are used in a Monte Carlo simulation consider the situation faced by Bill Jewel, owner of the Jewel Vending Company.

JEWEL VENDING COMPANY

Jewel Vending.xls
JVCb.xls

Bill Jewel is the owner of the Jewel Vending Company (JVC), which installs and stocks gum and novelty vending machines in supermarkets, discount stores, and restaurants. Bill is considering installing a Super Sucker jaw breaker dispenser at the new Saveway Supermarket on Lincoln Avenue. The vending machine holds 80 jaw breakers. Ideally, Bill would like to fill the machine whenever it becomes half empty. (Bill does not want the machine to appear too empty, because he fears that potential customers will believe the jaw breakers are not fresh and so will elect not to make a purchase.)

Based on performance of similar vending machine placements, Bill has estimated the following distribution for daily jaw breaker demand:

P(daily demand = 0 jaw breakers)	= .10
P(daily demand = 1 jaw breaker)	= .15
P(daily demand = 2 jaw breakers)	= .20
P(daily demand = 3 jaw breakers)	= .30
P(daily demand = 4 jaw breakers)	= .20
P(daily demand = 5 jaw breakers)	= .05

Bill would like to estimate the expected number of days it takes for a filled machine to become half empty (i.e., the average number of days it takes to sell 40 jaw breakers). This information will help him to determine how often to refill the machine.

SOLUTION

Bill might consider estimating the expected time between refills by calculating the average (expected) daily demand based on the assumed probability distribution and dividing this value into 40.

$$\text{Expected time between refills} = \frac{40}{.10(0) + .15(1) + .20(2) + .30(3) = .20(4) + .05(5)}$$

$$= \frac{40}{2.5} = 16 \text{ days}$$

Bill is not certain that this method yields the true average number of days required to sell 40 or more jaw breakers, but he feels it probably yields a good approximation. To test it, Bill has decided to employ a simulation approach.

Simulation of the Daily Demand for Jaw Breakers

To properly simulate the JVC system, let us define the random variable:

X = daily demand for jaw beakers at the Saveway store

Based on Bill's estimates, the probability distribution function for X is as shown in Table 11.1.

The theory behind generating a random event, such as daily demand, is that the event outcomes should not occur in any particular pattern, but, in the long run, they should occur with relative frequencies equal to the probability distribution being modeled. In particular, the probability distribution for each day's demand should follow the same distribution as that given above for X, regardless of the results of the simulated demand generated for any other day.

For example, if 1000 days of demand at JVC were simulated, one would expect demand to be zero on approximately 100 days (since $P(X = 0) = .10$), one on approximately 150 days (since $P(X = 1) = .15$) and so on. However, there should be no pattern, such as demand is zero on days 1, 11, 21, etc.

Random Number Mappings

One way to simulate random events that follow the desired probability distribution would be to generate numbers between 00 and 99 so that each number has an equal

TABLE 11.1	x	$P(X = x)$
Probability Distribution for Daily Jaw Breaker Demand	0	.10
	1	.15
	2	.20
	3	.30
	4	.20
	5	.05

likelihood of being selected (e.g., follows a discrete uniform distribution). We could then assign 10 of these numbers to correspond to the event "daily demand = 0," 15 of the numbers to correspond to the event "daily demand = 1," and so on. Since each number between 00 and 99 has an equal likelihood of being selected, the probability of any one number being selected is 1/100. Hence, if 10 of the numbers are assigned to the event "daily demand = 0," this event will occur with a probability of .10.

The easiest way to do this assignment is to let the first 10 numbers correspond to the event "daily demand = 0," the next 15 numbers correspond to the event "daily demand = 1," and so on. This process is called a *random number mapping* because it "maps" a random number (the number corresponding to the ball selected) to the outcome of a simulated event (the daily demand for jaw breakers). Table 11.2 shows the random number mapping for JVC.[1]

The Cumulative Distribution Approach for a Random Number Mapping

Although this approach works well for discrete random variables, a more comprehensive approach is required for continuous distributions. One approach that can be used for both discrete and continuous distributions involves the use of the cumulative distribution function for the random variable, X. A cumulative distribution, $F(x)$, gives the probability that X is less than or equal to some value, x; that is, $F(x) = P(X \leq x)$. Table 11.3 provides the cumulative distribution function for customer arrivals in the JVC problem. This is illustrated graphically in Figure 11.1.

TABLE 11.2

Random Number Mapping for JVC

Daily Demand	Corresponding Random Numbers
0	00–09
1	10–24
2	25–44
3	45–74
4	75–94
5	95–99

TABLE 11.3

Cumulative Distribution for Customer Arrivals

x	$F(x) = P(X \leq x)$
0	.10
1	.25
2	.45
3	.75
4	.95
5	1.00

[1] Two-digit numbers are used because the probability distribution for X is accurate to two decimal places. If the probabilities were accurate to three decimal places, three-digit numbers would be used, that is, 000–999. Similarly, if the probabilities were accurate to only one decimal place, one-digit numbers, 0–9, would be used.

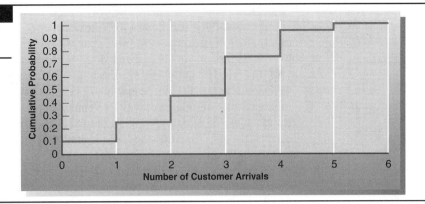

FIGURE 11.1

Cumulative Distribution for
Customer Arrivals

Now if a random number Y (between 0 and 1) is chosen, we can determine the value for the event by finding the smallest value for x such that $F(x) \geq Y$. For example, suppose the number 34 is chosen. Since we are using only two-digit probabilities, the number 34 is converted to the two-digit decimal .34. Referring to the cumulative distribution function in Figure 11.1, you will note the smallest value of x such that $F(x) \geq .34$ is 2. This is the same value for demand we obtained using the random number mapping in Table 11.2. As we shall illustrate in this chapter, the VLOOKUP function in Excel can be used to easily determine the random variable value corresponding to a selected random number.

Generating Random Numbers

One way to generate numbers between 00 and 99 would be to mark each of one hundred balls, each with a different two-digit number and put them in a box. A random number could then be generated by selecting one ball at random from the box, looking at the number and then replacing the ball.

Of course, in practice, balls are not selected out of a box. Instead, this process is mimicked as closely as possible on a computer by using a **random number generator**. A random number generator actually generates what are called *pseudo-random numbers* ("pseudo" means false) because the numbers are not truly random but are obtained using a mathematical formula.

A random number generator begins with a starting value, known as a seed (which the user can supply), and produces a sequence of numbers that meets the following statistical properties for randomness:

1. Each number has an equally likely chance of occurring.
2. There is no apparent correlation between the numbers generated by the mathematical formula.

Appendix 10.2 on the accompanying CD-ROM describes a commonly used technique for generating pseudo-random numbers, known as the *linear congruential method*.

In Excel, pseudo-random numbers can be generated by using the RAND() function or the Random Number Generation option found in Data Analysis under Tools on the menu bar. The RAND() function returns a uniformly distributed random number greater than or equal to 0 and less than 1. A new random number is returned every time the worksheet is calculated. The values in Appendix A.1 in the back of the book were generated by using the RAND() function in Excel.

If one wishes to generate uniformly distributed integer valued random numbers between two specified values, the RANDBETWEEN function can be used. For example, to generate a random valued integer between 7 and 10, one would type the formula =RANDBETWEEN(7,10).

Using Random Number Generation in Data Analysis allows one to generate numbers from a variety of different distributions. For example, in addition to the continuous uniform distribution, numbers can be generated that follow normal, Bernoulli, binomial, Poisson, or generalized discrete distributions. Information for using the Random Number Generation option in Excel can be found in Excel's Help commands.

One advantage that the Random Number Generation option has over the RAND() function is that one can specify a seed value when using Random Number Generation. The advantage of using a specific seed value is that the same set of random numbers will be generated each time the same seed is used. Using the same set of random numbers to evaluate different policies results in certain statistical efficiencies. As a result, typically fewer simulation runs are necessary to get the same level of statistical precision than when different random numbers are used to evaluate different policies.

Simulation of the JVC Problem

We shall use the set of pseudo-random numbers in Appendix A.1 to illustrate how to conduct a fixed time simulation for the JVC problem. The approach is as follows:

Beginning with day 1, a random number is selected to determine the demand for jaw breakers on that day. The demand value will be used to update the total demand to date. The simulation is repeated for a second day, then a third day, etc.; it stops once total demand to date reaches 40 or more. The number of "simulated" days required for the total demand to reach 40 or more is then recorded.

Since only two-digit random numbers are needed to generate jaw breaker demands, the simulation begins by using the first two digits in the top row of column 1 in Appendix A.1. For each subsequent day, a new demand is determined using the two-digit number in the next row down in column 1.

As you can see, the first number in column 1 is 6506. The first two digits of this number are 65. According to the random number mapping in Table 11.2, the random number 65 corresponds to a demand of three jaw breakers. For day 2, we use the first two digits of the random number in the second row of column 1 (77). This corresponds to a demand of 4 for day 2. Continuing down column 1 in this fashion generates the results shown in Table 11.4.

TABLE 11.4 A Typical Simulation for JVC	Day	Random Number	Demand	Total Demand to Date
	1	65	3	3
	2	77	4	7
	3	61	3	10
	4	88	4	14
	5	42	2	16
	6	74	3	19
	7	11	1	20
	8	40	2	22
	9	03	0	22
	10	62	3	25
	11	54	3	28
	12	10	1	29
	13	16	1	30
	14	69	3	33
	15	16	1	34
	16	02	0	34
	17	31	2	36
	18	79	4	40

Day	Random Number	Demand	Total Demand to Date
1	42	2	2
2	74	3	5
3	93	4	9
4	84	4	13
5	89	4	17
6	89	4	23
7	12	1	24
8	64	3	25
9	64	3	28
10	38	2	30
11	61	3	33
12	53	3	36
13	12	1	37
14	76	4	41

TABLE 11.5

A Second Simulation for JVC

In this simulation, we see that it took 18 days to sell 40 jaw breakers, two days more than the 16 days Bill had originally estimated. It is difficult, however, to draw any firm conclusions based on only one simulation run. To get a better estimate, additional simulation runs should be conducted and the results averaged.

Let us now perform a second simulation run by using the random numbers in column 15 in Appendix A.1. Table 11.5 shows these results. This time it took 14 days to sell 40 or more jaw breakers. Note, also, that by day 14 the total demand was 41 jaw breakers rather than 40.

Programmers often use flow charts to guide the development of a computer program for problem solving. Figure 11.2 shows a possible flow chart that could be used to perform the above JVC jaw breaker simulation.

Using Simulation Results to Conduct Hypothesis Tests

The purpose of performing the simulation runs is to determine whether the average number of days required to sell 40 jaw breakers is, in fact, 16. Neither run gave a value of 16; however, the average of the times of the two runs, 18 and 14, is 16. As additional simulation runs are done, the laws of probability suggest that the calculated average should become closer and closer to the true average. Thus, for the JVC problem, to test whether or not $\mu = 16$, the following two-tailed hypothesis test is performed:

$$H_O: \mu = 16$$
$$H_A: \mu \neq 16$$

If it is assumed that the distribution of the number of days to sell 40 jaw breakers, x, is approximately normal, then since the population variance is unknown, a t-test would be performed. If n is the number of simulation runs the test would have n − 1 degrees of freedom (df). To conduct this test, a level of significance, α, which is the probability of concluding that the alternate hypothesis, H_A, is true when it in fact is *not* must be selected. Then for a two-tailed test, the interval $-t_{\alpha/2,d.f.}$ to $+t_{\alpha/2,d.f.}$ is constructed. If the test statistic t lies outside this interval, the conclusion is that the alternate hypothesis is true (and the null hypothesis is false). If the test statistic lies within this interval, there is *not* enough evidence to conclude that the alternate hypothesis is true.

FIGURE 11.2

Flow Chart for Jewel Vending
Company

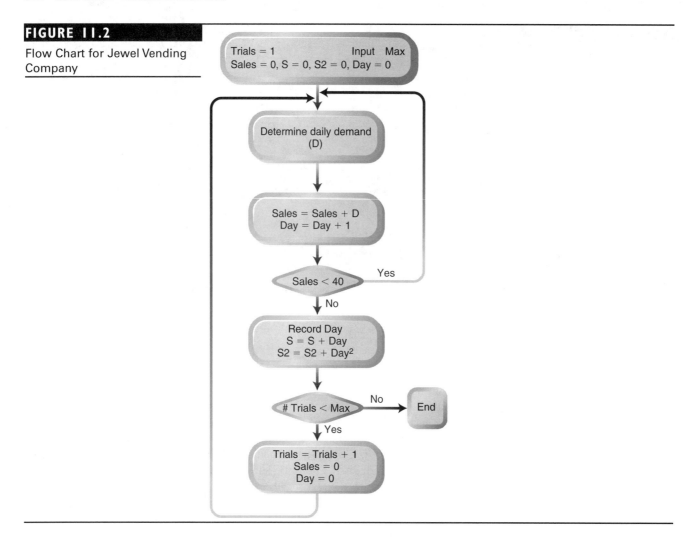

Using Excel to Perform a Simulation

Figure 11.3 shows the worksheet and formulas used to simulate the JVC problem using Excel. This simulation was set up as follows:

- Using IF statements, the day is printed in column A if 40 or fewer jaw breakers have been sold by that day.

- Daily demand is generated in column B using random variables and the VLOOKUP command shown on Figure 11.3. The lookup table, given in columns K and L, is based on the cumulative demand probabilities.

- The cumulative demand is generated in column C by summing the daily demand and the previous day's cumulative demand.

- Assuming it will never take more than 100 days to sell 40 jaw breakers, the formulas in cells A6:C6 are dragged 100 rows to cells A105:C105.

- The maximum number in column A is the number of simulated days it will take to sell 40 or more jaw breakers. This value is given in cell F1.

- Replication of this simulation can be made in Excel by pressing the F9 **function key** on the keyboard.

To test the hypothesis that the average number of days to sell 40 or more jaw breakers differs from 16, 10 such replications were performed. The results of these 10 replications are given in columns A and B of Figure 11.4.

FIGURE 11.3   Excell Output — Simulation Run for JVC

Jewel Vending.xls

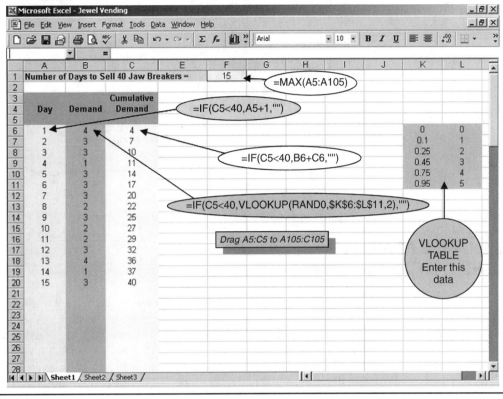

FIGURE 11.4   Determining the p-value for the Hypothesis Test of μ = 16

JVCb.xls

To perform the two-tailed test, the t statistic must first be calculated. An easy way to do this is to generate the mean and standard error of the data in column B using Tools/Data Analysis/Descriptive Statistics. (Make sure Summary Statistics is checked in the dialogue box.) These values are given in column E of Figure 11.4. Then t = (Mean − 16)/(Standard Error). Once the t value is found, the p-value for the test is generated by the formula =TDIST(ABS (t-value), degrees of freedom, 2), in this case =TDIST(ABS(H5),9,2).

As can be seen from Figure 11.4, the p-value is quite high (.2967) compared to any reasonable significance level such as α = .05. Thus, *based on this data*, we cannot conclude that the mean number of days differs from 16. Collecting additional sample evidence could lead to a different conclusion.

This analysis was performed using only basic Excel spreadsheet commands. In Section 11.7 a more thorough analysis of this model using the Crystal Ball Excel add-in program is presented.

11.3 SIMULATION OF AN INVENTORY SYSTEM USING A FIXED TIME APPROACH

We'll now discuss inventory models for which analytical solutions exist. Each is based on a particular set of assumptions. When these assumptions are not met, the models may not provide reasonable solutions. In such cases, simulation can predict the outcome of inventory policies.

By supplying the simulation with the values of parameters, such as the order and holding cost as well as the lead time and demand distributions, an average total inventory cost for a particular inventory policy can be estimated. While simulation cannot be used to determine an optimal policy, it can be used to identify which policy appears to yield the best results from the set of policies being considered.

Frequently, a *fixed time* approach is used for modeling an inventory system. In this approach, the system is monitored and updated at fixed time intervals (daily, weekly, monthly). During each time period, activities associated with demands, orders, and shipments are determined, and the system is updated accordingly.

To illustrate the fixed time simulation approach, we consider the inventory situation faced by the Allen Appliance Company.

ALLEN APPLIANCE COMPANY

AAC inventory.xls
allen (r,q).xls

Allen Appliance Company (AAC) is a small appliance wholesaler that stocks the KitchenChef electric mixer. Each unit costs Allen $200. Allen, in turn, sells them for $260 each. Allen uses an annual holding cost rate for the mixers of 26%. Orders are placed at the end of the week, and order costs seem to average about $45. Lead time for the receipt of orders from Kitchen Chef has been fairly consistent, averaging two weeks.

Management believes that if the company runs out of the mixers, all customers will backorder. Allen estimates that it will suffer a weekly goodwill cost due to future lost sales of $5 per backordered unit. The company also incurs a fixed administrative cost of $2 for each unit backordered, regardless of the length of time it is backordered.

Allen believes that the number of customers who arrive weekly can be approximated by the following distribution:

Number of Arrivals Per Week	Probability
0	.10
1	.30
2	.25
3	.20
4	.15

The number of machines each customer wishes to purchase can be approximated by the following distribution.

Demand Per Customer	Probability
1	.10
2	.15
3	.40
4	.35

Mixers arrive at the beginning of a week. That is, an order placed at the end of week 2 will arrive at the beginning of week 5. Allen wishes to determine an optimal inventory policy for the KitchenChef mixer.

SOLUTION

One approach is to apply the planned shortage model. While values for the order cost, $C_o = \$45$, the weekly per unit backorder cost, $C_s = \$5$, the administrative backorder cost, $C_b = \$2$, and the lead time, $L = 2$ are given, estimates are needed for the average weekly demand, D, and the per unit weekly holding cost, C_h.

To estimate the average weekly demand, note that the average number of retailers who arrive each week is:

$$.10(0) + .30(1) + .25(2) + .20(3) + .15(4) = 2$$

The average demand for each retailer who purchases mixers is:

$$.10(1) + .15(2) + .40(3) + .35(4) = 3 \text{ units}$$

The average demand is found by multiplying the average number of retailers who arrive (2) by the average retailer demand (3). This gives an average weekly demand, D = 2*3 = 6 units.

The unit weekly holding cost, C_h, is:

$$C_h = \frac{(\text{annual holding cost rate})^*(\text{wholesale cost per unit})}{52 \text{ weeks per years}}$$

$$= (.26^*\$200/52) = \$1 \text{ per unit per week}$$

If this problem is solved using the planned shortage worksheet on the inventory.xls template by assuming demand is a constant 6 units per week, the results are those shown in Figure 11.5.

FIGURE 11.5

Excel Spreadsheet for Solving Allen Appliance Problem as a Planned Shortage Model

AAC inventory.xls

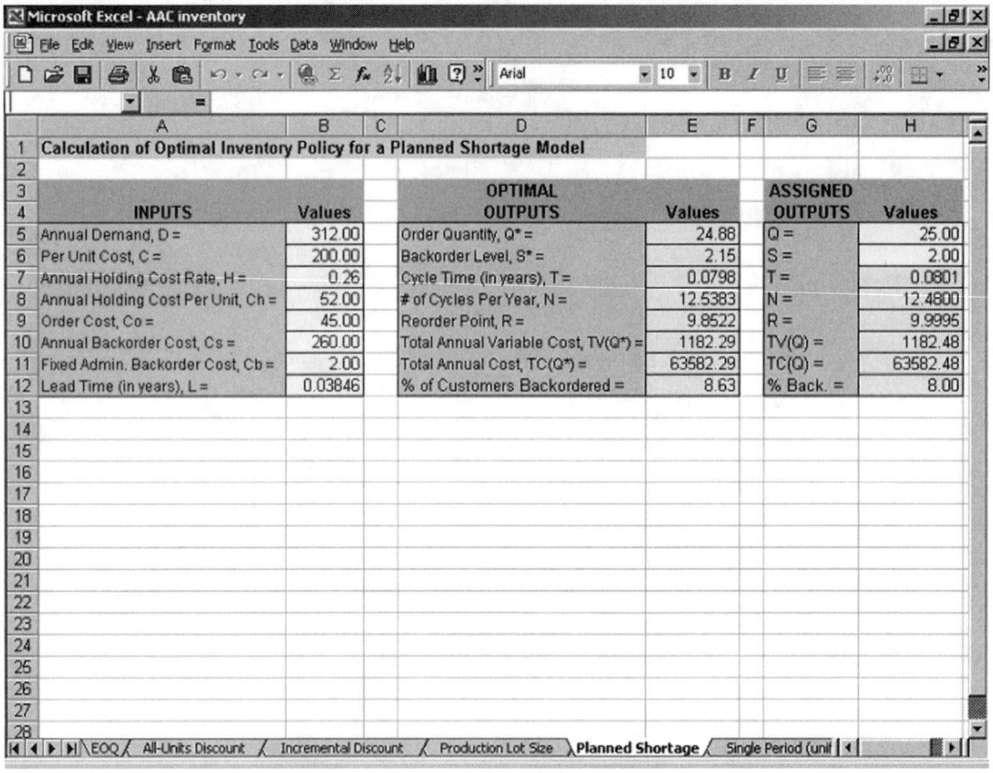

	A	B	C	D	E	F	G	H
1	Calculation of Optimal Inventory Policy for a Planned Shortage Model							
2								
3				OPTIMAL			ASSIGNED	
4	INPUTS	Values		OUTPUTS	Values		OUTPUTS	Values
5	Annual Demand, D =	312.00		Order Quantity, Q* =	24.88		Q =	25.00
6	Per Unit Cost, C =	200.00		Backorder Level, S* =	2.15		S =	2.00
7	Annual Holding Cost Rate, H =	0.26		Cycle Time (in years), T =	0.0798		T =	0.0801
8	Annual Holding Cost Per Unit, Ch =	52.00		# of Cycles Per Year, N =	12.5383		N =	12.4800
9	Order Cost, Co =	45.00		Reorder Point, R =	9.8522		R =	9.9995
10	Annual Backorder Cost, Cs =	260.00		Total Annual Variable Cost, TV(Q*) =	1182.29		TV(Q) =	1182.48
11	Fixed Admin. Backorder Cost, Cb =	2.00		Total Annual Cost, TC(Q*) =	63582.29		TC(Q) =	63582.48
12	Lead Time (in years), L =	0.03846		% of Customers Backordered =	8.63		% Back. =	8.00
13								

Sheet tabs: EOQ / All-Units Discount / Incremental Discount / Production Lot Size \ **Planned Shortage** / Single Period (unit

This output indicates an optimal inventory policy is to order 24.88 units, which should arrive when the backorder level reaches 2.15. Rounding these values gives an inventory policy of ordering 25 mixers when the inventory on hand reaches 10 units. Because the weekly demand is a random quantity, however, Allen has some concern that the solution generated by the planned shortage model may not be the optimal policy.

Selecting the Inventory System

Allen is considering implementing a continuous review system to monitor its inventory position. Two types of continuous review systems are (1) the order point, order up to level (R,M) inventory system, and (2) the order point, order quantity (R,Q) inventory system.

Under both systems, orders are placed when the inventory level reaches R units or less. In an (R,M) system, the firm orders enough inventory to bring the inventory level back up to a projected level of M when the order arrives. In an (R,Q) system, the firm simply orders Q units each time an order is placed.

Based on the planned shortage results, Allen is considering using an (R,Q) system of ordering 25 mixers when inventory on hand reaches 10 units or less for controlling this inventory. To analyze the cost of using the policy, Allen has decided to develop a simulation model.

Using the specified probability distributions for the number of customer arrivals and customer demands, the random number mappings are shown in Tables 11.6 and 11.7.

The bank uses a first-come, first-served priority rule for serving customers. Management would like to use simulation to determine the anticipated average customer waiting time on Saturday morning.

SOLUTION

Before developing the simulation model, let us determine if the requirement for steady-state will be satisfied. Here,

$$E(\text{Interarrival Time}) = \frac{1}{\lambda} = .5(.65) + 1(.15) + 1.5(.15) + 2(.05) = .80 \text{ minute}$$

This is equivalent to $\lambda = 1/.80 = 1.25$ customers per minute or $60*1.25 = 75$ customers per hour.

$$E(\text{Service Time} - \text{Ann}) = .5(.05) + 1(.10) + 1.5(.20) + 2(.30) + 2.5(.2) + 3(.10) + 3.5(.05) = 2 \text{ minutes}$$

$$E(\text{Service Time} - \text{Bill or Carla}) = 1(.05) + 1.5(.15) + 2(.20) + 2.5(.3) + 3(.10) + 3.5(.10) + 4(.05) + 4.5(.05) = 2.5 \text{ min.}$$

Hence Ann can serve $60/2 = 30$ customers per hour, and Bill and Carla can each serve $60/2.5 = 24$ customers per hour. Thus the average number of customers who can be served per hour is $30 + 2*24 = 78$. Since this is greater than the arrival rate of 75, steady-state will be reached.

The first step in developing the simulation is to determine the random number mappings. Based on the given probabilities, the random number mappings shown in Tables 11.9a, b and c were developed.

Table 11.10 shows the results of a 20-customer simulation using random numbers from column 4 of Appendix A.1 to determine the customer interarrival times and numbers from column 5 to determine the customer service times.

TABLE 11.9a
Customer Inerarrival Times

Time	Random #'s
.5 minute	00-64
1 minute	65-79
1.5 minutes	80-94
2 minutes	95-99

TABLE 11.9b
Ann's Service Time

Time	Random #'s
.5 minute	00-04
1 minute	05-14
1.5 minutes	15-34
2 minutes	35-64
2.5 minutes	65-84
3 minutes	85-94
3.5 minutes	95-99

TABLE 11.9c
Bill and Carla's Service Time

Time	Random #'s
1 minute	00-04
1.5 minutes	05-19
2 minutes	20-39
2.5 minutes	40-69
3 minutes	70-79
3.5 minutes	80-89
4 minutes	90-94
4.5 minutes	95-99

TABLE 11.10   Capital Bank Simulation for 20 Customer Arrivals

Customer	Random Number	Arrival Time	Random Number	Ann Start	Ann Finish	Bill Start	Bill Finish	Carla Start	Carla Finish	Waiting Time
1	89	1.5	63	1.5	3.5					0
2	88	3	46			3	5.5			0
3	90	4.5	86	4.5	7.5					0
4	26	5	00					5	6	0
5	79	6	56			6	8.5			0
6	55	6.5	67					6.5	9	0
7	26	7	59	7.5	9.5					0.5
8	16	7.5	28			8.5	10.5			1
9	40	8	79					9	12	1
10	65	9	64	9.5	11.5					0.5
11	61	9.5	33			10.5	12.5			1
12	68	10.5	81	11.5	14					1
13	75	11.5	17					12	13.5	0.5
14	65	12.5	63			12.5	15			0
15	08	13	66					13.5	16	0.5
16	31	13.5	27	14	15.5					0.5
17	20	14	04			15	16			1
18	40	14.5	34	15.5	17					1
19	99	16.5	07			16.5	18			0
20	09	17	69	17	19.5					0

The simulation proceeds as follows:

- A customer will go to Ann if she is free.
- If Ann is not free, the customer will go to Bill if he is free.
- If both Bill and Ann are busy, the customer will go to Carla if she is free.
- If all tellers are busy, the customer waits in line and then goes to the first teller who becomes available.
- The waiting time for a customer represents the time a customer spends in line prior to beginning service. This is calculated by taking the difference between the time the customer begins service and the time the customer arrives.

Let us examine a few of the customer arrivals to understand how the simulation is carried out. For customer 1 the random number used to determine the interarrival time is 89 (the first number in column 4 of Appendix A.1). Using the random number mapping in Table 11.9a this corresponds to an interarrival time of 1.5 minutes. Hence the arrival time of customer 1 is time 1.5. Since all three servers are free, customer 1 is served by Ann. The random number for customer 1's service time is 63 (the first number in column 5 of Appendix A.1). Using Table 11.9b for the random number mapping for Ann, this corresponds to a service time of 2 minutes. Hence for customer 1 service begins at time 1.5 (the time the customer arrives) and is completed at time 3.5 (arrival time 1.5 plus service time of 2). Thus Ann is busy serving customer 1 until time 3.5.

The interarrival time for customer 2 is determined by the random number 88 (the second number in column 4). From Table 11.9a this also corresponds to an interarrival time of 1.5 minutes. Since customer 1 arrived at time 1.5, this means that customer 2 arrives at time 3. Since Ann is busy at time 3, customer 2 is served by Bill. The random number for customer 2's service time is 46 (the second number in column 5). Using Table 11.9c the random number mapping for the associate tellers, the random number of 46 corresponds to a service time of 2.5 minutes. Hence customer 2 will complete service at time 5.5 (the arrival time of 3 plus the service time of 2.5) and Bill will be busy serving customer 2 during this time.

This process is repeated for all customers. Since both the first and second customers were served immediately, their waiting times are 0. To illustrate a customer for whom the waiting time is not 0, consider customer 7 who arrives at time 7. At this time all three servers are busy. The first server who becomes free is Ann at time 7.5. Hence service for customer 7 begins at time 7.5, and the waiting time for customer 7 is .5, the difference between the time service begins (7.5) and the time the customer arrives (7).

To estimate the average customer waiting time, you might think that we should simply add the values in the Waiting Time column and divide by the number of customers in the simulation (20). This would give an average waiting time of 8.5/20 = .425 minute. But as with most queuing simulations that start empty, there is a certain start up bias associated with the first several customers before the system reaches steady state. Hence a number of the initial waiting time values should be excluded from the calculation of the average waiting time.

If the first 10 customers are excluded then the average waiting time of the last 10 customers can be used to give the estimated average waiting time of 5.5/10 = .55 minute. This is probably a more valid estimate of the average customer waiting time. Of course, the true average customer waiting time may in fact be very different from .425 or .55 minute. A different set of simulation numbers would most likely generate a different value for the average waiting time. Doing a 20-customer simulation does not give enough waiting time values to yield a very accurate estimate.

However, one would not want to have to do a simulation of 10,000, 1000, or even 100 customers by hand. Fortunately, Excel spreadsheets can be constructed to do this simulation. Figure 11.7 shows such a portion of the spreadsheet Capital Bank.xls, given on the accompanying CD-ROM, that simulates 1000 customer arrivals. Note that both the time a customer spends in line and the time a customer spends in the

FIGURE 11.7 Excel Spreadsheet for Performing Capital Bank Simulation

Capital Bank.xls

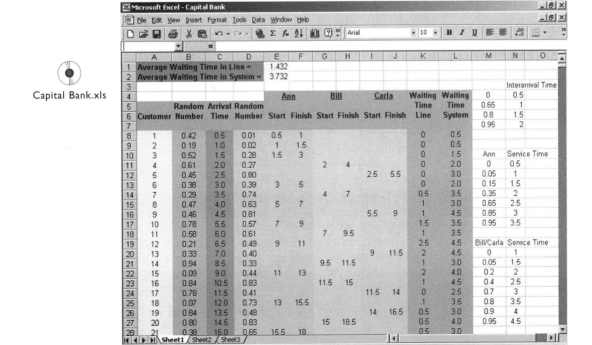

system are calculated on this spreadsheet. With this many customers in the system, the start-up bias should have little effect and has been ignored.

The formulas for the spreadsheet shown in Figure 11.7 are discussed in Appendix 10.4 on the accompanying CD-ROM. It can be seen, however, that the simulation calculates the average waiting time in line in cell E1 and the average waiting time in the system in cell E2. Little's formulas can be used to determine the average number of customers in line and in the system. Specifically, the average number of customers in line and in the system are found by multiplying the average arrival rate by the simulated results for the average waiting time in line and in the system respectively.

Since for this problem, the expected interarrival time is .80 minute, the arrival rate, l, is 1/.80 = 1.25 customers per minute. Hence we have the following values from this simulation.

Average Customer Waiting Time in Line (W_q) = 1.432 minutes
Average Customer Waiting Time in the System (W) = 3.732 minutes
Average Number of Customers Waiting in Line (L_q) = 1.25*1.432 = 1.790
Average Number of Customers in the System (L) = 1.25*3.732 = 4.665

Using a Fixed Time versus a Next-Event Approach

Although it is generally easier to understand a fixed time simulation process, the majority of discrete simulations are carried out using the next-event approach. The reason for this is that simulations generally deal with events that do not occur in regular time intervals, and therefore the fixed time approach would not be very efficient.

For example, we could have conceivably developed the simulation model for the Capital Bank problem using a fixed time approach. However, we would have had to standardize the time unit at .5 minute (the largest time unit that divides into all possible interarrival and service times). Hence, if the fixed time approach were used there would be a great many periods in which there were no arrivals or completions of service. For example, in Table 11.10 it can be seen that after 20 customers the simulated time has reached 17 minutes. If a fixed time simulation with a time interval of .5 had been used, 20 time periods would have only simulated a time of 10 minutes.

11.5 RANDOM NUMBER MAPPINGS FOR CONTINUOUS RANDOM VARIABLES

In Section 11.2 two methods for generating random variables corresponding to discrete probability distributions were illustrated. One used the probability distribution itself, and the other used the cumulative distribution function, F(x). In this section, techniques for simulating continuous random variables are discussed.

The Explicit Inverse Distribution Method

In the **explicit inverse distribution method** the cumulative distribution function, F(x), is used to determine a value for the random variable. In particular, an equation, known as the *inverse distribution function*, which expresses x in terms of F(x) is developed. A pseudo-random number, Y, which corresponds to a uniformly distributed random variable between 0 and 1 is then generated, and the inverse distribution function is used to find the value of x that corresponds to $Y = F(x)$. For example, if the random number $Y = .37268$, is generated, the simulated event has a value x, such that $F(x) = .37268$.

To illustrate this technique, consider the M/M/k queuing system. In this model, an exponential distribution describes customer interarrival times. A different exponential distribution describes customer service times.

The probability density function for the exponential distribution of the service time is:

$$f(x) = \mu e^{-ux} \quad \text{for } x \geq 0 \tag{11.1}$$

and its cumulative distribution is:

$$F(x) = 1 - e^{-\mu x} \tag{11.2}$$

In these expressions, μ is the server's mean service rate, and $1/\mu$ is the server's mean service time.

If Y is a random number generated from a uniform distribution over the interval from 0 to 1, a simulated service time, x, is generated by finding the value of x such that

$$Y = 1 - e^{-\mu x} \tag{11.3}$$

Rearranging these terms gives:

$$e^{-\mu x} = 1 - Y \tag{11.4}$$

Taking logarithms of both sides of Equation 11.4 to solve for x gives:

$$-\mu x = \ln(1 - Y) \tag{11.5}$$

or

$$x = \frac{-\ln(1 - Y)}{\mu} \tag{11.6}$$

In Equation 11.6, the time units for x are the same as those for μ. Thus, if μ is expressed in terms of customers per minute, x is in terms of minutes.

To illustrate the use of Equation 11.6, consider a queuing process that has an exponential service time distribution with an average service time of $1/\mu = .5$ minute. The service rate, therefore, is $\mu = 1/.5 = 2$ per minute. Using the *second* column of Appendix A.1 to simulate service times we see that the first value is .3338. Hence, using Equation 11.6 gives the following service time, x:

$$x = \frac{-\ln(1 - .3338)}{2} = .203 \text{ minute}$$

Excel can be used to generate exponential service times using its RAND() and LN functions as shown in Figure 11.8.

Notice that in this simulation, although the mean value for the service time is .5 minute, the 10 values we generated using Excel range from a low of .0088 minute to a high of 2.0442 minutes.

FIGURE 11.8 Excel Simulation of Service Times Using the Explicit Inverse Distribution Method

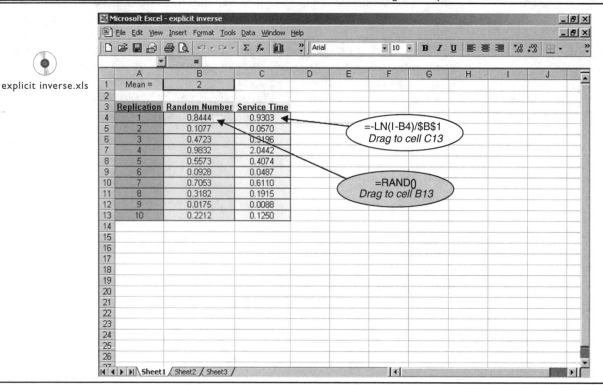

explicit inverse.xls

The interpolation Method

Although it is easy to map pseudo-random numbers in the case of the exponential distribution, such mapping is not always so simple because it may not be possible to obtain a closed-form solution for x in terms of F(x). In such cases, the *interpolation method* can be used instead of the explicit inverse method. This method is described in Appendix 10.5 on the accompanying CD-ROM.

Random Numbers and Excel

When using Excel, a number of continuously distributed random variables can be generated. For example, if one wishes to generate a normally distributed random variable with mean μ and standard deviation σ, one could use the function =NORMINV (Rand(),μ,σ). To illustrate, suppose that a traffic engineer believes that the speed at which cars travel down a certain road is normally distributed with a mean of 35 mph and a standard deviation of 3 mph and she wishes to develop a simulation to investigate the impact of a stoplight on this street. Using the NORMINV[2] function to generate the speeds of 20 cars gives the spreadsheet shown in Figure 11.9.

For this set of numbers, the mean value is 34.72 and the standard deviation is 3.80. These values are very close to the true mean and standard deviation of the distribution.

In addition to generating normally distributed random variables, Excel can generate random variables from a Beta distribution (use the function BETAINV), a Chi Square distribution (use the function CHIINV), an F distribution (use the function

---

[2] The function NORMSINV generates normally distributed random variables from a standard normal distribution (mean of 0 and standard deviation of 1).

FIGURE 11.9 Twenty Normally Distributed Values Generated by Excel

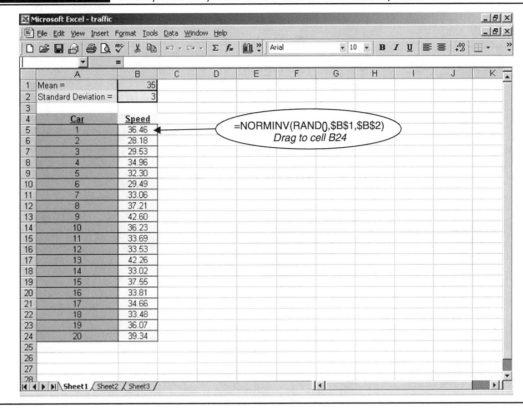

traffic.xls

FINV), a Gamma distribution (use the function GAMMAINV), and a lognormal distribution (use the function LOGINV).

As mentioned earlier in the chapter, Excel can also generate random numbers following some specific distributions using Random Number Generation found under Data Analysis. One drawback of this technique, however, is that a series of numbers following the desired distribution is placed into cells rather than the formulas that generate the random numbers. This can present certain shortcomings when one wishes to use Excel add-ins to do multiple simulation runs.

11.6 SIMULATION OF AN M/M/1 QUEUE

In Section 11.4 it was illustrated how one could simulate a queuing system with three servers in which the arrival process did not meet the conditions for a Poisson process and did not have identical service distributions for each server. In this section, a simulation for an M/M/1 system is presented. Although an M/M/1 system would never actually be simulated (because the closed-form steady-state results for this model are known), the simulation is done to illustrate the accuracy of the next-event queuing simulation process.

As in Section 11.4, a process-interaction approach is followed. That is, the arrival time of each customer is determined by adding a random interarrival time to the time of the previous customer's arrival. If an arriving customer finds no other customers in the system, service begins immediately; otherwise it begins when the previous customer has completed service. The time at which a customer completes service equals the time service begins plus a random service time. The average waiting time in the queue or system is estimated by keeping track of the time each simulated customer spends in the system.

To illustrate, consider the following situation faced by the Lanford Sub Shop.

Lanford Sub Shop.xls

The Lanford Sub Shop is a small sandwich shop serving downtown Dayton, Ohio. The sole employee is the owner, Frank Lanford, who makes a customer's sandwich in an average time of one minute.

During the lunch hour period (11:30 a.m. to 1:30 p.m.), an average of 30 customers an hour arrive at the Sub Shop. Frank believes that the customer arrival process is Poisson and that his service time follows an exponential distribution. He is interested in using simulation to determine the average time a customer must wait for service.

SOLUTION

The Lanford Sub Shop can be modeled as an M/M/1 queue with an arrival rate $\lambda = 30$ customers per hour (.5 per minute) and a service rate $\mu = 60$ customers per hour (1 per minute). A hand simulation for this operation can be performed by generating and recording the following data:

1. The number of the arriving customer (C#).
2. The random number used to determine the interarrival time (R#1).
3. The interarrival time (IAT).
4. The arrival time for the customer (AT).
5. The time at which service begins for the customer (TSB).
6. The waiting time a customer spends in line (WT).
7. The random number used to determine the service time (R#2).
8. The service time (ST).
9. The time at which service ends for the customer (TSE).

The simulation "clock" begins at time t = 0, which corresponds to 11:30 a.m. The explicit inverse method will be used to generate the interarrival times (IAT) and service times (ST). The AT, TSB, and TSE columns are times measured from time t = 0 on the simulation clock.

While separate columns could be used to select random numbers for arrival times and service times, in Table 11.11 random numbers from column 1 are used to gener-

TABLE 11.11

Lanford Sub Shop Simulation for First 10 Customers

C#	R#1	IAT	AT	TSB	WT	R#2	ST	TSE
1	.6506	2.10	2.10	2.10	0	.7761	1.50	3.60
2	.6170	1.92	4.02	4.02	0	.8800	2.12	6.14
3	.4211	1.09	5.11	6.14	1.03	.7452	1.37	7.51
4	.1182	.25	5.36	7.51	2.15	.4012	.51	8.02
5	.0335	.07	5.43	8.02	2059	.6299	.99	9.01
6	.5482	1.59	7.02	9.01	1.99	.1085	.11	9.12
7	.1698	.37	7.39	9.12	1.73	.6969	1.19	10.31
8	.1696	.37	7.76	10.31	2.55	.0267	.03	10.34
9	.3175	.76	8.52	10.34	1.82	.7959	1.59	11.93
10	.4958	1.37	9.89	11.93	2.04	.4281	.56	12.49

ate both R#1 for the interarrival times and R#2 for Frank's service times for the first 10 customers. (Times given are in minutes.)

To illustrate how the entries for this table were obtained, consider customer 3. At this point four random numbers (two for the interarrival times and two for the service times of customers 1 and 2) would have already been used. Thus the fifth random number from column 1, (.4211) is selected to determine the interarrival time for customer 3. Using the explicit inverse method generates an interarrival time of x = –ln(1 – .4211)/30 = .0182 hour = 1.09 minutes. Hence customer 3 arrives 1.09 minutes after customer 2. Since the arrival time for customer 2 occurred at a simulated clock time of 4.02 minutes, the arrival time for customer 3 would be 4.02 + 1.09 = 5.11 minutes.

Customer 2 did not complete service until 6.14 minutes. Since customer 3 cannot begin service until customer 2 leaves, the customer must wait in line 6.14 – 5.11 = 1.03 minutes.

The sixth random number from column 1 (.7452) is then selected to determine the service time for customer 3. Using the explicit inverse method .7452 generates a service time of x = –ln(1 – .7452)/60 = .0228 hour = 1.37 minutes. Hence, since customer 3's service begins at clock time 6.14 and lasts 1.37 minutes, his service ends at time 6.14 + 1.37 = 7.51 minutes.

From this limited simulation run, without correcting for start-up bias, the average waiting time for a customer in the queue can be estimated by averaging the 10 customers' waiting times:

(Average waiting time for this 10 customer simulation) =
[0 + 0 + 1.03 + 2.15 + 2.59 + 1.99 + 1.73 + 2.55 + 1.82 + 2.04]/10 = 1.59 minutes

The true steady-state value for the average customer waiting time at the Lanford Sub Shop derived from the formula for W_q is:

$$W_q = \frac{\lambda}{\mu(\mu-1)} = \frac{30}{60(60-30)} = \frac{1}{60} \text{ hours} = 1 \text{ minute}$$

It should be no surprise that the value calculated for W_q based on a single simulation run of only 10 customers is quite different from the steady-state value. However, as the number of customers used to calculate the average waiting time increases, we would expect the calculated value for W_q to become closer to the steady-state value.

Figure 11.10 shows the simulation of the same M/M/1 queue based on 1000 customer arrivals, using Excel.

The formulas used in this spreadsheet are as follows:

Cell	Value	Formula
E4	W_q	=AVERAGE(E8:E1007)
Row 8		
A8	Customer Number	=A7+1
B8	Customer Interarrival Time	=-LN(1-RAND())/($D$1/60)
C8	Arrival Time	=B8+C7
D8	Time Service Begins	=MAX(C8,G7)
E8	Waiting Time	=D8-C8
F8	Service Time	=-LN(1-RAND())/($D$2/60)
G8	Time Service Ends	=D8+F8

The formulas in row 8 are then dragged into rows 9 through 1007.

Note that for the simulation shown in Figure 11.10, the simulated average waiting time, 1.134243, differs approximately 13% from the steady-state value for W_q. This should not be unexpected since the simulation results are based on the set of random numbers selected. As additional simulations are run, the average waiting time taken over all simulation runs should become even closer to the steady-state value for W_q.

FIGURE 11.10 Simulation of an M/M/1 Queue Using Excel

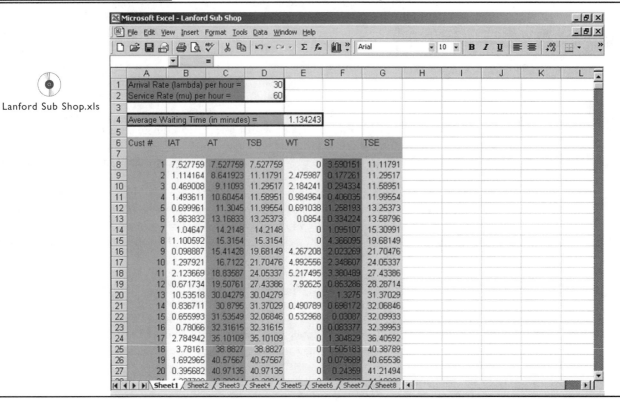

Lanford Sub Shop.xls

11.7 CONDUCTING SIMULATIONS USING CRYSTAL BALL

Overview of Crystal Ball

As seen in the previous sections, running a simulation only once can lead to a value that may be far from the true mean value. To get a result that is close to the true mean value, the simulation should be run multiple times and the results of these multiple runs averaged. A number of Excel add-on modules have been developed to perform such multiple simulations. These programs also generate relevant statistics dealing with the simulation outcomes. One of the most popular software packages for doing such analyses is Crystal Ball, developed by Decisioneering, Inc. On the accompanying CD-ROM you will find a student version of Crystal Ball that can be used in performing Excel simulations. Although this version has a limited set of options as compared to the professional version, it is powerful enough to do many of the analyses one would wish to perform as part of a simulation study.

The Crystal Ball Toolbar

After loading Crystal Ball, three new menu items and a new toolbar become part of the Excel screen. The new menu items are *Cell*, *Run*, and *CBTools*, which are to the immediate left of the Help command on the toolbar. The options contained under the Cell, Run, and CBTools menus are shown in Figures 11.11a, 11.11b, and 11.11c.

Figure 11.12 shows the toolbar added by Crystal Ball.

FIGURE 11.11a
Cell Menu in Crystal Ball

Define Assumption...
Define Decision...
Define Forecast...

Select All Assumptions
Select All Decisions
Select All Forecasts
Select Some...

Freeze Assumptions...

Copy Data
Paste Data
Clear Data

Cell Preferences...

FIGURE 11.11b
Run Menu in Crystal Ball

Run
Reset
Single Step

Run Preferences...

Forecast Windows...
Open Overlay Chart
Open Trend Chart
Open Sensitivity Chart

Create Report...
Extract Data...

Save Run...
Restore Run...

Close Crystal Ball
About Crystal Ball...

FIGURE 11.11c
Figure Title Goes Here

OptQuest
CB Predictor

Setup Tools:
  Batch Fit
  Correlation Matrix
  Tornado Chart

Analysis Tools:
  Bootstrap
  Decision Table
  Scenario Analysis
  2D Simulation

FIGURE 11.12   Crystal Ball Toolbar

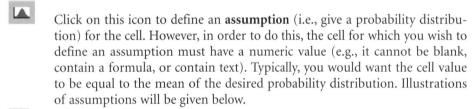

Of particular importance are the following selections:

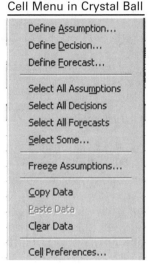

Click on this icon to define an **assumption** (i.e., give a probability distribution) for the cell. However, in order to do this, the cell for which you wish to define an assumption must have a numeric value (e.g., it cannot be blank, contain a formula, or contain text). Typically, you would want the cell value to be equal to the mean of the desired probability distribution. Illustrations of assumptions will be given below.

Click on this icon to define a cell as a **decision variable**. Making a cell a decision variable gives the analyst the opportunity to vary the cell value during a simulation run.

Click on this icon to select the cells you wish to have the **simulation** forecast. Specifically, the forecast cells are the ones for which Crystal Ball collects relevant statistics as well as graphs of values.

Click on this icon to set up the simulation **preferences**. Of particular importance is the specification of the number of simulation runs you wish to perform and the random number seed value you wish to specify.

Click on this icon to **run** the simulation.

Click on this icon to **stop** the simulation while it is running.

Click on this icon to **reset** the simulation and clear the forecast values.

 Click on this icon to **open** up the forecast.

 Click on this icon to **open up an overlay chart**. Such a chart is useful in comparing different forecasts.

Hypothesis Testing Using Crystal Ball

To illustrate how one uses Crystal Ball, consider the Jewel Vending Company problem discussed in Section 11.2. Recall that Bill Jewel wishes to determine the average number of days it will take for the vending machine to sell 40 or more jaw breakers. Specifically, Bill wishes to determine whether the average number of days is 16.

File JVC.xls on the accompanying CD-ROM contains a simulation for one filling of the vending machine. Opening this file in Crystal Ball gives the screen shown in Figure 11.13. Note that columns G and H are hidden in this spreadsheet. These columns contain the lookup table used for the VLOOKUP function.

The following sequence of three steps is used to perform the simulation with Crystal Ball.

1. The item we wish to forecast (the number of days to sell 40 jaw breakers) is in cell F1. Highlight this cell and click on the forecast icon—. This brings the dialogue box up shown in Figure 11.14. Change the Forecast Name from F1 to Time to Sell 40 Jaw Breakers and make the Units equal to Days. Then click on OK.

2. Click the set-up preferences icon—to indicate the desired number of simulation runs (trials). This gives the dialogue box shown in Figure 11.15. Note that initially the maximum number of trials has been set to 500. Click on OK to run the simulation.

FIGURE 11.13   Crystal Ball Screen for the Jewel Vending Company Model

JVC.xls

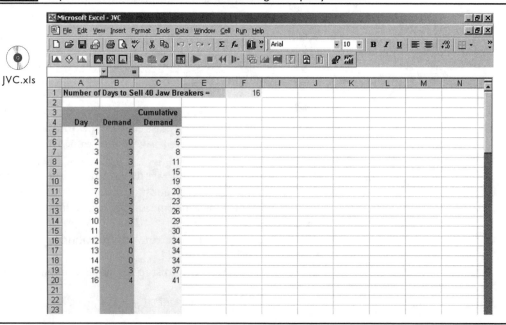

FIGURE 11.14

Crystal Ball Dialogue Box for
Naming a Forecast Cell

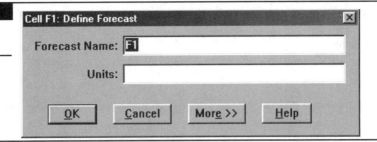

FIGURE 11.15

Crystal Ball Dialogue Box for
Setting Run Preferences

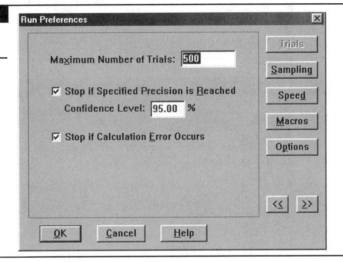

3. The result is the frequency chart shown in Figure 11.16. (Your results will be somewhat different due to a different selection of random numbers by your computer.)

Note: If you do not see this chart after running the simulation, you can view the chart by either clicking on the open forecast icon— *or by selecting Forecast Window in the Run menu. This gives the dialogue box shown in Figure 11.17. Clicking on the Open All Forecasts box should give the Forecast.*

FIGURE 11.16

Crystal Ball Frequency Chart

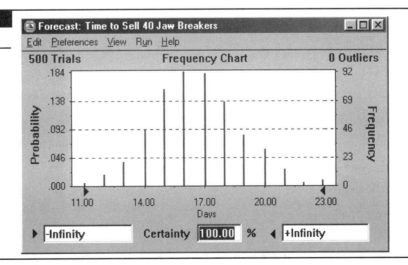

FIGURE 11.17

Crystal Ball Dialogue Box for
Opening or Closing Forecasts

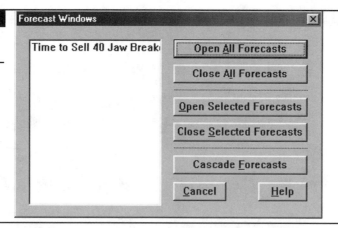

FIGURE 11.18

Crystal Ball Statistical Output

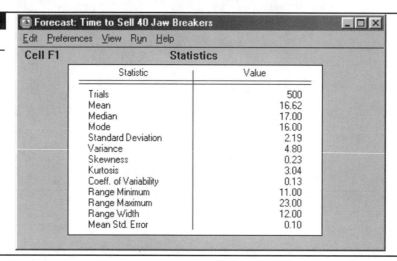

Click on the View/Statistics in the menu bar to see the statistics associated with
this chart. The output for the simulation is given in Figure 11.18.

Analysis of Output

Hypothesis Testing

Recall from Section 11.2 that Bill Jewel wished to do the following hypothesis test:

$$\text{Null:} \qquad H_O: \mu = 16$$
$$\text{Alternative:} \qquad H_A: \mu \neq 16$$

From the frequency chart in Figure 11.16 the time to sell 40 jaw breakers appears to
follow a normal distribution. (Crystal Ball actually has an option that allows one to do
a goodness of fit test to check this assumption.) Assuming a normal distribution, the
t distribution can be used to determine the outcome of this hypothesis test.
Specifically, the t statistic is calculated by subtracting $\mu_0 = 16$ from the sample mean
and dividing this amount by the mean standard error (the value in the last row of the
output). From Figure 11.18 therefore the t statistic is:

$$t = \frac{\text{mean} - 16}{\text{standard error}} = \frac{16.62 - 16}{.10} = 6.2$$

A t statistic of 6.2 is clearly significant. Thus it can be concluded that the average number of days to sell 40 or more jaw breakers is not equal to 16.

FIGURE 11.19

Crystal Ball Statistical Output

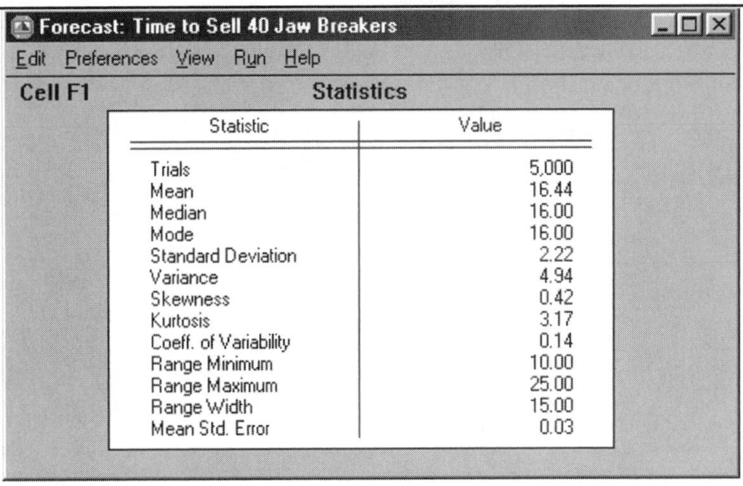

```
Forecast: Time to Sell 40 Jaw Breakers                    _ □ X
Edit  Preferences  View  Run  Help

Cell F1                        Statistics

        Statistic                    Value

   Trials                            5,000
   Mean                              16.44
   Median                            16.00
   Mode                              16.00
   Standard Deviation                 2.22
   Variance                           4.94
   Skewness                           0.42
   Kurtosis                           3.17
   Coeff. of Variability              0.14
   Range Minimum                     10.00
   Range Maximum                     25.00
   Range Width                       15.00
   Mean Std. Error                    0.03
```

Confidence Intervals

This same information can be used to generate a 95% confidence interval for the average number of days to sell 40 or more jaw breakers. However, for illustrative purposes let us rerun Crystal Ball, but this time with 5000 runs. To do this first reset the simulation (click on the ◀◀ icon) and then change the run preferences (click on the 📋 icon) to make the Maximum Number of Trials equal to 5000. As you run the simulation with the view set to statistics, you will observe that the mean standard error keeps decreasing. For our simulation run, the output shown in Figure 11.19 was obtained.

From this output a 95% confidence interval for the mean time to sell 40 or more jaw breakers will be:

$$\bar{x} - t_{.025}\frac{s}{\sqrt{n}}, \bar{x} + t_{.025}\frac{s}{\sqrt{n}} = (16.44 - 1.96^*.03, 16.44 + 1.96^*.03)$$

$$= (16.38, 16.50)$$

Note that since n = 5000, $z_{.025}$ was used to approximate $t_{.025}$. Hence, Bill is 95% confident that the true average time to sell 40 or more jaw breakers is somewhere between 16.38 and 16.50 days. Increasing the number of runs done by Crystal Ball for this problem beyond 5000 would give an even smaller confidence interval.

Using Crystal Ball to Determine an Inventory Policy

One of the important features of Crystal Ball is that it allows a comparison of policies. In Section 11.3 a simulation for the Allen Appliance Company based on an order point–order quantity or (R,Q) system we presented. One might be interested in whether an order point–order up to level or (R,M) system would be less expensive. To analyze this, the Excel simulation developed for the (R,Q) system (file allen(r,q).xls on the accompanying CD-ROM) was modified to represent a simulation of an (R,M) system. The corresponding simulation is contained in spreadsheet allen(r,m).xls on the accompanying CD-ROM.

On the average, an (R,M) policy is generally less expensive than an (R,Q) policy. To determine whether this is true for the situation faced by Allen Appliance, 500 simulation runs of each of the two policies using Crystal Ball were made.

The results of the simulation run for the (R,Q) policy are given in Figures 11.20 and 11.21, while those for the (R,M) policy are shown in Figures 11.22 and 11.23.

FIGURE 11.20

Crystal Ball Frequency Chart
Output for (R,Q) Policy

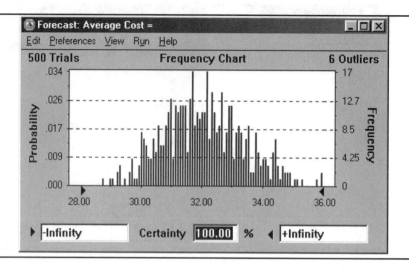

FIGURE 11.21

Crystal Ball Statistical Output
for (R,Q) Policy

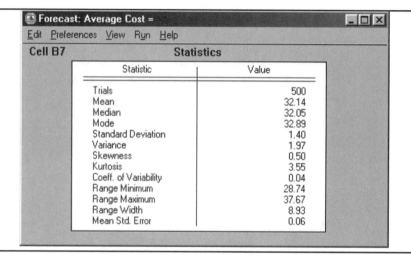

FIGURE 11.22

Crystal Ball Frequency Chart
Output for (R,M) Policy

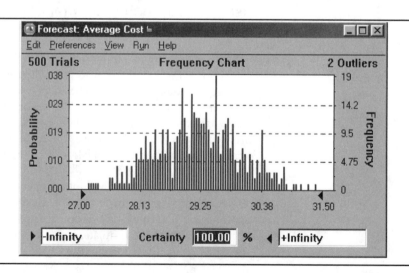

FIGURE 11.23

Crystal Ball Statistical Output for (R,M) Policy

Forecast: Average Cost =

Edit Preferences View Run Help

Cell B7 Statistics

Statistic	Value
Trials	500
Mean	29.22
Median	29.21
Mode	28.41
Standard Deviation	0.79
Variance	0.63
Skewness	0.12
Kurtosis	2.93
Coeff. of Variability	0.03
Range Minimum	27.17
Range Maximum	32.01
Range Width	4.84
Mean Std. Error	0.04

To determine whether the (R,M) policy is less expensive on average than the (R,Q) policy, the following one-tailed hypothesis test is performed.

$$\text{Null: } H_O: \mu_1 - \mu_2 = 0$$
$$\text{Alternative: } H_A: \mu_1 - \mu_2 > 0$$

Here population 1 refers to the (R,Q) policy and population 2 refers to the (R,M) policy. Since Figures 11.20 and 11.22 show that the average weekly cost for the two inventory policies approximately follows a normal distribution and large sample sizes have been taken from both populations, a z statistic can be used to approximate t to carry out this test. As the hypothesized mean difference is 0, the relevant z statistic is given by the formula:

$$z = \frac{(\bar{x}_1 - \bar{x}_2) - 0}{\sqrt{\dfrac{s_1^2}{n_1} + \dfrac{s_2^2}{n_2}}} = \frac{32.14 - 29.22}{\sqrt{\dfrac{1.40}{500} + \dfrac{.63}{500}}} = \frac{2.92}{.0637} = 45.83$$

Because this is an upper tail test, z = 45.83 is a clear indication that in this case the (R,M) policy is cheaper, on the average, than the (R,Q) policy.

Finding the Best (R,M) Policy

In light of the above result, one may be interested in finding the best (R,M) policy to use for Allen Appliance. Crystal Ball is ideal for analyzing different policies through the use of a **decision table.** For example, consider evaluating order quantities between 23 and 32 and reorder points between 8 and 17.

To have Crystal Ball perform the appropriate decision table analysis, the following steps are used:

1. Reset the simulation by pressing the icon.
2. Define the average cost (cell B7) as the forecast value by highlighting cell B7 and clicking on the icon.
3. Define the order quantity Q (cell B2) as a decision variable by highlighting cell B2 and clicking on the icon. This opens up the dialogue box shown in Figure 11.24. For this analysis, since Q will be evaluated for values between 23 and 32 the Lower bound is changed from 22.5 to 23 and the Upper bound from 27.5 to 32. We also wish the decision variable to be discrete and the step to be 1. Since decision names cannot contain an "=" sign, change the name of the decision variable from "Q =" to simply "Q."

Crystal Ball Dialogue Box for
Defining the Bounds for a
Decision Variable

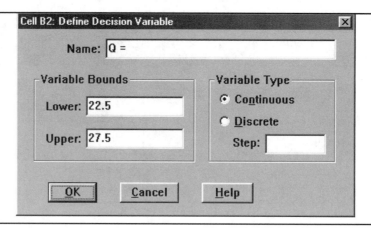

4. Define the reorder point R (cell B3) also as a decision variable by highlighting cell B3 and again clicking on the ◈ icon. For the reorder point the lower bound will be 8 and the upper bound 17. Again make the variable type discrete and the step equal to 1. Also change the name of the decision variable from "R =" to "R."

5. To set up the decision table, select Decision Table under CBTools in the menu bar. This brings up the dialogue box shown in Figure 11.25. Since Average Cost 5 is already highlighted, click on the Next button. This gives the dialogue box shown in Figure 11.26.

Initial Crystal Ball Dialogue Box
for Setting up a Decision Table

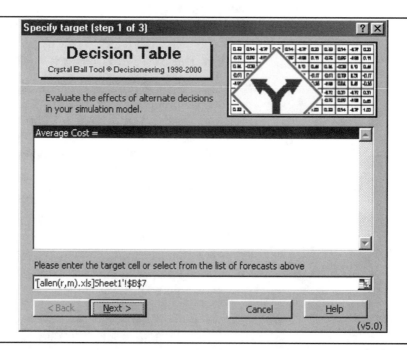

FIGURE 11.26

Second Crystal Ball Dialogue Box for Setting Up a Decision Table

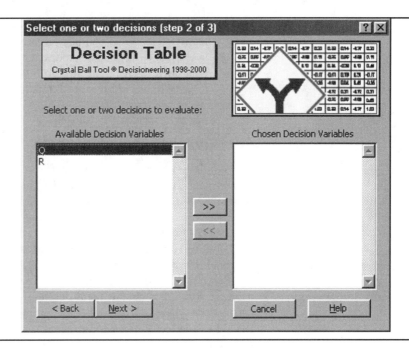

6. As the values of both Q and R vary, we highlight both quantities are highlighted in the left hand (Available Decision Variables) box. Then click the >> box to move each to the Chosen Decision Variables column on the right side of the dialogue box. Then click on Next. This gives the dialogue box shown in Figure 11.27.

FIGURE 11.27

Third Crystal Ball Dialogue Box for Setting Up a Decision Table

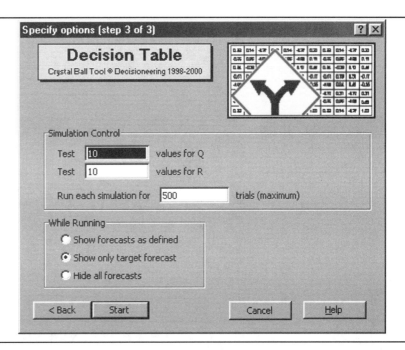

7. As can be seen from this dialogue box, 10 different values for Q and 10 different values for R will be evaluated. Since this results in 100 different simulations, one may wish to reduce the number of simulation trials to less than 500, say 100. (After all, you do not want to tie up your computer for too long.) Change "Run each simulation for" to 100 and click on Start.

Analyzing the Simulation Results

The simulation results are shown in Figure 11.28.

As can be seen from this figure, for this set of simulation runs the lowest average cost is 26.57487, which occurs when Q = 25 and R = 15. Of course, since many of the other values are close to this amount, additional simulation runs of greater duration may be done to further refine the analysis. In particular, if the analysis is redone based on 500 simulation runs but restricting attention to values of Q between 23 and 27 and values of R between 13 and 17 the output shown in Figure 11.29 is obtained.

Based on this simulation, it appears that the least expensive policy occurs when Q = 26 and R = 15. Of course, the difference in the average weekly cost between this policy and one where Q = 25 and R = 15 is approximately $.01, and that difference may be due to chance. While additional simulation runs could be undertaken to choose between the two policies, it does not appear that the difference in the average weekly costs would be significant enough to warrant further analysis. An order quantity, order up to policy based on Q equaling 26 and R equaling 15 is the recommended policy.

Based on this analysis, the following memorandum was prepared dealing with the situation faced by Allen Appliance Company. In this memorandum the effect of the weekly goodwill cost estimate on the optimal solution is considered by analyzing the effect of increasing this cost to $10 and decreasing it to $1.

FIGURE 11.28

Decision Table Output for Allen Appliance Model

Trend / Overlay	Q (23)	Q (24)	Q (25)	Q (26)	Q (27)	Q (28)	Q (29)	Q (30)	Q (31)	Q (32)	
R (8)	32.49628	32.0207	31.50864	31.2252	30.78742	30.57182	30.12943	30.11337	29.97291	29.80672	1
R (9)	31.18105	30.61218	30.34156	29.893	29.6994	29.46378	29.14451	29.2245	29.01147	28.99288	2
R (10)	29.98043	29.51874	29.19553	28.90977	28.74925	28.58188	28.48685	28.4306	28.23725	28.31075	3
R (11)	28.99812	28.58733	28.34429	28.14743	27.92502	27.89588	27.87937	27.6989	27.77291	27.7307	4
R (12)	28.25184	27.88557	27.62985	27.41844	27.42022	27.33165	27.32303	27.28231	27.43939	27.37879	5
R (13)	27.4851	27.30369	27.17235	26.94866	27.05684	27.02325	27.08892	27.0442	27.09872	27.26346	6
R (14)	27.05469	26.89896	26.76435	26.78153	26.75517	26.75468	26.85777	26.97326	26.9967	27.16476	7
R (15)	26.82684	26.67352	26.57487	26.66804	26.69624	26.70844	26.76642	26.97769	27.04016	27.18736	8
R (16)	27.2675	26.69879	26.60806	26.60756	26.74371	26.83556	26.97054	27.0455	27.21496	27.44263	9
R (17)	26.72559	26.68186	26.69509	26.83311	26.93133	27.04635	27.26293	27.33327	27.53253	27.73008	10
	1	2	3	4	5	6	7	8	9	10	

FIGURE 11.29

Decision Table Output for Allen Appliance Model

Trend Chart / Overlay Chart / Forecast Charts	Q (24)	Q (25)	Q (26)	Q (27)	
R (13)	27.357762	27.145664	27.074616	26.966922	1
R (14)	26.886306	26.79954	26.742982	26.76362	2
R (15)	26.668446	26.610806	26.598364	26.693134	3
R (16)	26.657282	26.641588	26.653122	26.72946	4
R (17)	26.737086	26.736996	26.813514	26.879124	5
	2	3	4	5	

·SCG·
STUDENT CONSULTING GROUP

MEMORANDUM

To: James P. Allen, President—Allen Appliance Company

From: Student Consulting Group, Inc.

Subj: Inventory Policy for Kitchen Chef Mixers

At you request, we conducted an analysis of the inventory policy for Kitchen Chef electric mixers at Allen Appliance Company. Based on historical data, we observed that both customer arrival and demand patterns possess a high degree of variability. We concluded that the problem could best be analyzed using a simulation approach.

We have held meetings with personnel in the accounting and marketing departments to gain information about relevant costs and demands for the product. On the basis of these meetings, we utilized the following data and assumptions in developing the simulation model.

1. Kitchen Chef mixers cost allen $200 per unit.

2. A 26% annual holding cost rate is used for this product.

3. The cost of placing an order with Kitchen Chef is $45.

4. If Allen runs short of mixers due to a higher-than-expected lead time demand, all potential customers place back orders for the item, incurring an administrative cost of $2 per unit.

5. The company suffers a goodwill cost of $5 per unit per week for each week that a unit is on back order.

6. Orders are placed at the end of a week, while delivery occurs at the beginning of a week.

Based on the data we collected, we developed probability distributions for:

1. Customer arrivals

2. Customer demands

Using only average values for these quantities, a simplified model indicates that Allen should implement an inventory policy of ordering 25 mixers when the supply reaches 10 or less. Using this policy as a starting point, we tested different inventory policies using simulation. Based on repeated runs simulating thousands of weeks (equivalent to approximately 200 years of operation), we recommend the following policy:

1. Reorder when the supply of Kitchen Chef mixers at the end of a week reaches 15 units or less.

2. Order an amount equal to 41 less the stock on hand at the end of the week in which the order is placed.

Under this policy, Allen can expect to incur an average total weekly inventory cost of approximately $26.60 for the Kitchen Chef mixers. This total includes all holding, back order, and ordering costs but does not include the cost of the machines themselves. The analysis also reveals that small changes from the recommended inventory policy do not greatly affect the average weekly inventory cost. For example, inventory policies for which the reorder point is increased by one point or the order up to level quantity varies by one unit increases the average total weekly inventory cost by less than 1%. Figure I shows the range in these weekly costs.

Since management is somewhat unsure of the assumed $5 goodwill cost per unit per week, we performed a sensitivity analysis to examine the effect that changing this cost to $1 and to $10 will have on the optimal inventory policy.

For a goodwill cost of $1 per week we recommend a policy of ordering 35 units minus the stock on hand when supply reaches seven units or less. We estimate the average weekly cost of this policy at $21.93. In contrast, using the recommended policy of ordering 41 units less the stock on hand when supply reaches 15 or less results, in this case, in an average weekly cost of $23.84.

If the goodwill cost is $10 per week, we recommend ordering 43 units less the stock on hand when supply reaches 19 units or less. We estimate the average weekly cost of this policy at $28.90. In contrast, using the recommended policy of ordering 41 units less the stock on hand when supply reaches 15 units or less results, in this case, in an average weekly cost of $30.13.

Hence, if the goodwill cost is actually $1/unit/week, the original recommended policy yields average weekly costs that are more than 8.7% greater than the optimal policy. If, however, the goodwill cost is actually $10/unit/week, the recommended policy yields an average weekly cost within 4.3% of the optimal policy. Because a significantly different policy results if the goodwill cost per unit per week is substantially less than the estimated $5 amount, we recommend that management undertake a focus group analysis to obtain firm estimates for the goodwill cost. We would be happy to assist you in this endeavor.

Figure I   Range in Average Weekly Inventory Costs

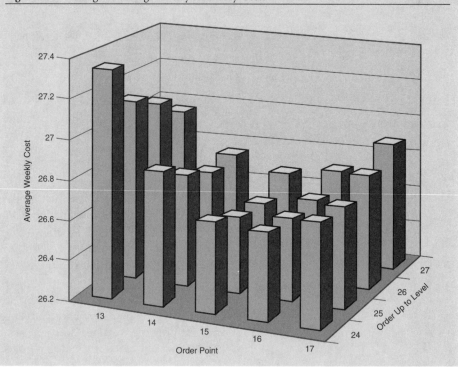

Other Applications of Crystal Ball

Crystal Ball can be used to analyze many different simulation models. Appendix 10.6 on the accompanying CD-ROM gives illustrations of the use of Crystal Ball in simulating queuing models, profit analysis models, and project management models.

11.8 ADVANTAGES AND DISADVANTAGES OF SIMULATION

Simulation as an analysis tool has several important advantages and disadvantages. The following are some of the principal advantages:

Advantages of Simulation Analysis

1. Simulation analysis provides insight into the problem solution when other management science methods fail.

2. Simulation enables the performance of an existing system under a proposed set of modifications to be analyzed without disrupting current system performance. Such performance may be analyzed over any time horizon.

3. Simulation models assist in the design of proposed systems by providing a convenient experimental laboratory for conducting "what-if" analyses.

These advantages do not come without a price, however. Some of the principal disadvantages of simulation are summarized as follows.

Disadvantages of Simulation

1. Simulation models are generally time consuming and expensive to develop.

2. Simulation models provide only an estimate of a model's true parameter values.

3. There is no guarantee that the policy shown to be optimal by the simulation is in fact, optimal.

The last disadvantage listed is an important one. It has been illustrated that simulation works by evaluating the results from different policies. Performance measures are calculated for each policy, and the "best" policy from this set is selected on the basis of such measures. If the true optimal policy is not one of the policies evaluated, however, or if a nonrepresentative set of random numbers occurs in the simulation, the optimal policy will not be found by the simulation.

For example, when simulation was used to study the Allen inventory problem in Sections 11.3 and 11.7, attention was restricted to a limited set of possible alternatives in order to make the analysis manageable. The EOQ model was initially used to get a rough idea of what the order quantity and reorder point should be, and then policy alternatives close to these values were considered. A policy such as ordering 40 units when the inventory level reaches 20 units was not considered. If this policy were indeed optimal, the simulation analysis would not have been able to detect it.

SUMMARY

Simulation can be used to model many complex business models, including problems in queuing and inventory. In Monte Carlo simulation, a random number mapping is developed to ensure that random variable inputs to the simulation correspond to the desired probability distribution.

Fixed time simulations are used when the simulation is set up so that each iteration corresponds to a set time period. When events do not correspond to exact time periods, a next event approach is used in developing the simulation model.

Simulations may be developed by hand, using general-purpose programming languages, specialized simulation programming languages, simulator programs such as Extend (see Appendix 10.1 on CD), or Excel and add-ins such as Crystal Ball. Use of Crystal Ball greatly enhances Excel's ability to perform simulations and provides valuable information to the analyst. Because not all of the features of Crystal Ball were discussed within the limited space of this book, the reader interested in learning more details about this program should consult the Crystal Ball user manual. It is available from Decisioneering, Inc.

One purpose of developing a simulation is to identify a recommended policy. When standard analytical models cannot be used to determine an optimal policy, a simulation model can identify a best course of action from the set considered. The simulation model also frequently provides a convenient laboratory for performing "what-if" analyses.

Although the concepts behind simulation analysis are relatively straightforward, the execution can be fairly complex. Not only must one develop appropriate models for the system being simulated, but one must also write and debug computer code to carry out the analysis. Because the costs involved in developing simulation models are typically high, they are generally used only in cases in which the payoff from the analysis is considerable.

PROBLEMS

Note: The Excel file corresponding to Appendix C is included on the accompanying CD-ROM. If you are using Excel to solve these problems, you may wish to import these values into your spreadsheet.

1. Price changes of shares of the Saveway Stores, Inc. have been recorded over the past 50 days. The frequency distribution is as follows:

Price Change	Frequency
−1/2	3 days
−3/8	4 days
−1/4	5 days
−1/8	6 days
0	10 days
+1/8	12 days
+1/4	4 days
+3/8	3 days
+1/2	3 days

   a. Develop a relative frequency distribution for the price change of Saveway stock.

   b. Using the relative frequency distribution developed in part (a), determine the mean daily change in the price of shares of Saveway Stores, Inc. If the current stock price is 32, what would be the expected stock price 30 days from now?

   c. If the current price of Saveway stock is 32, use the first two numbers in column 1 of Appendix C to simulate the price of the stock over the next 30 trading days.

   d. Compare the answer in part (c) with the expected stock price after 30 days calculated in part (b). Comment on the difference between the two values.

2. It has been estimated that customers arrive at the Quick Stop Convenience store during the evening according to a Poisson process at a mean rate of 40 per hour. Each customer buys between zero and five lottery tickets according to the following probability distribution:

Number of Lottery

Tickets Purchased	Probability
0	.45
1	.30
2	.15

Number of Lottery Tickets Purchased	Probability
3	.03
4	.02
5	.05

   If Quick Stop has 30 lottery tickets available at 6 p.m., use simulation to determine the time at which the store will sell out of the lottery tickets. Use column 1 of Appendix C to determine the interarrival times of customers and column 2 to determine the number of lottery tickets each customer will purchase.

3. Consider the following PERT project describing the planning of regional sales meetings by Craig Computer Corporation:

ON THE CD-ROM

■	Fixed tim simulation for Jewel Vending	**Jewel Vending.xls**
		JVCb.xls
		JVC.xls
■	Fixed time simulation for Allen Appliance	**AAC inventory.xls**
		allen(r,q).xls
		allen(r,m).xls
■	Next-event simulation for Capital Bank	**Capital Bank.xls**
■	Simulation of exponentially distributed service times	**explicit inverse.xls**
■	Simulation of normally distributed random variables	**traffic.xls**
■	Simulation of the M/M/1 queue	**Lanford Sub Shop.xls**
■	Simulation of a real estate investment using Crystal Ball	**Don Clark.xls**
■	Simulation of a project schedule using Crystal Ball	**Gordon.xls**
■	Simulation of Capital Bank using extend	**capitalbank.mox**
■	Appendix 10.1–Conducting a Next-Event Simulation using Extend	
■	Appendix 10.2–Generating Pseudo-Random Numbers Using the Linear Congruential Method	
■	Appendix 10.3–Statistical Tests for Comparing Simulation Results	
■	Appendix 10.4–Simulation of Capital Bank Model Using Excel	
■	Appendix 10.5–Interpolation Method for Generating Random Variable Inputs	
■	Appendix 10.6–Using Crystal Ball for Simulating Queuing, Profit Analysis, and Project Management Models	
■	Appendix 10.7–Variance Reduction Techniques	
■	Problem Motivations	**Problem Motivations**
■	Problems 41–50	**Additional Problems/Cases**
■	Case 4	**Additional Problems/Cases**

The immediate predecessor jobs and expected completion time for each job are as follows:

Job	Immediate Predecessor Jobs	Expected Completion Time in Weeks
A	—	6
B	A	4
C	—	9
D	—	7
E	D	8
F	B	3
G	C	5

a. Determine the critical path(s) and the expected completion time for the project.

b. Suppose each job has a 25% chance of being completed two weeks early, a 25% chance of being completed on time, and a 50% chance of being completed two weeks late. Using the first two digits in column 4 of Appendix C to determine the job times, calculate the project completion time for five different sets of job times. On the basis of these five simulations, determine the probability that each job is on the critical path.

c. Calculate a 95% confidence interval for the expected project completion time.

4. Taks Home Furnishing is currently having its year-end appliance clearance sale. The store has twelve 18-cubic-foot Whirlpool refrigerators on sale; 5 are white, 4 are almond, and 3 are harvest gold. Each day, the company expects between 0 and 4 customers interested in buying a refrigerator to arrive at the store according to the following probability distribution:

$$P(0 \text{ arrivals}) = .15$$
$$P(1 \text{ arrival}) = .25$$
$$P(2 \text{ arrivals}) = .30$$
$$P(3 \text{ arrivals}) = .20$$
$$P(4 \text{ arrivals}) = .10$$

For each of these customers, there is a 60% chance that the person will want to purchase one of the sale-priced Whirlpools.

Taks knows that 40% of customers desire a white refrigerator, 25% desire an almond refrigerator, and 35% desire a harvest gold refrigerator. If the store is sold out of a particular color choice, the customer will leave without making a purchase.

Use random numbers from column 1 of Appendix C to determine the number of customer arrivals, column 2 to determine whether an arriving customer will wish to purchase an 18-cubic-foot Whirlpool refrigerator, and column 3 to determine the choice of color. How many days will it take for Taks to sell all 12 refrigerators?

5. Dizzy Izzy is a discount appliance store specializing in home entertainment equipment. The firm carries two brands of satellite antenna systems: Panasony and ChannelMaster. Due to the high cost of ordering these systems and the rapid changes in the technology, Dizzy Izzy's policy is to not reorder additional systems until the store is completely sold out of both brands.

Presently, the store has six Panasony and four ChannelMaster systems in stock. The number of customers who arrive each day intending to buy a satellite system follows a Poisson distribution with a mean of 2. Forty percent of customers want to purchase a Panasony system, 50% want to purchase a ChannelMaster system, and 10% want to purchase a brand that Dizzy Izzy does not carry and therefore leave without making a purchase.

If a customer wants to purchase a Panasony system but Izzy is sold out, there is a 25% chance that the customer will buy the ChannelMaster system instead, a 35% chance of placing a backorder for the Panasony system, and a 40% chance that the sale will be lost.

If a customer wants to purchase a ChannelMaster system but Izzy is sold out, there is a 45% chance that the customer will buy a Panasony system instead, a 40% chance of placing a backorder, and a 15% chance that the sale will be lost.

Using simulation, determine how many days it will take for Dizzy Izzy to completely sell out of the existing inventory of satellite antennae systems. Determine the number of backordered systems and lost sales as of that date. Use column 3 of Appendix C to determine the number of customers who arrive each day to purchase satellite systems, column 4 to determine the choice of system, and column 5 to determine what will happen if the customer's selection is sold out.

6. At Steve's Super Scooper, two employees serve customers during the lunch hour. One employee gets the customer's ice cream selection, while the other receives payment. Customers arrive at Steve's according to a Poisson process, having a mean interarrival time of 1.5 minutes. The time it takes to get an ice cream selection follows an exponential distribution with a mean of one minute. The service time for payment follows a uniform distribution of between 30 and 80 seconds.

Using simulation, determine the average time a customer spends waiting in line to get and pay for ice cream. Base your results on a simulation of 20 customer arrivals using column 1 of Appendix C to determine the customer interarrival time, column 2 to determine the time a customer spends with the employee getting ice cream, and column 3 to determine the time a customer spends with the cashier.

7. Albright's Hardware sells Security brand dead-bolt locks in single packages and two-packs (one key fits

both locks). Single packages sell for $12 each, while two-packs sell for $30. Albright's cost is one-half the retail selling price.

Albright's is open seven days a week and receives a delivery from Security once a week. If Albright runs out of single packages but still has two-packs available, the store will break open a two-pack and sell each of the two at the single-package price. If the store is out of stock of the type of dead-bolt set the customer wants to purchase, Albright management believes that it will suffer a goodwill loss of $10.

Each day, between zero and three customers arrive to purchase dead-bolt locks with the following distribution:

$$P(0 \text{ arrivals}) = .30$$
$$P(1 \text{ arrival}) = .35$$
$$P(2 \text{ arrivals}) = .20$$
$$P(3 \text{ arrivals}) = .15$$

Sixty percent of purchasers want a single set, while 40% want a two-pack. The store's policy is to order a sufficient number of dead bolts to bring the beginning-of-the-week inventory up to five single sets and five two-packs.

Neglecting holding and ordering costs, determine a 95% confidence interval for Albright's mean weekly profit based on a four week simulation. Use column 1 of Appendix C to determine the daily number of arriving customers and column 2 to determine whether a customer wants to purchase a single set or a two-pack.

8. Consider the data given in problem 7 for Albright's Hardware. The company is considering changing its inventory policy so that it begins each week with six single sets and only four two-packs. Conduct a four-week simulation using the same random numbers as in problem 7 to determine whether there is any difference in the mean weekly profit. Test at a 5% significance level.

9. Attendees at the annual Orange County Small Business Administration Conference register by standing in line to pay their registration fee and then proceeding to a designated line based on their business interest to collect their materials. The conference addresses four types of small businesses: manufacturing, retailing, import/export, and financial services.

The registration period lasts from 8:30 a.m. to 9:30 a.m. During this period, the conference organizers estimate that the interarrival time of attendees approximately follows an exponential distribution with a mean time of one minute. The time to register an attendee is anticipated to be 30 seconds if the attendee pays by cash or check, or 90 seconds if the attendee pays by a credit card. The organizers estimate that 60% of attendees will use a credit card.

Based on similar conferences, the organizers estimate that 40% of attendees will be interested in manufacturing, 30% in retailing, 10% in import/export, and 20% in financial services. The time required to obtain materials for the manufacturing and retailing lines is estimated to be exactly two minutes, while the time to obtain materials for the import/export and financial services lines is estimated to be exactly three minutes.

Simulate the arrival of the first 20 customers at the conference using appropriate random number selections from Appendix C. For this simulation, determine:

a. The time it takes for the twentieth customer to complete registration.

b. The average waiting time in each of the five lines (registration, manufacturing, retailing, import/export, and financial services).

10. The Treasure Trove Casino in Las Vegas has a free telephone booth that allows customers to make a one-minute telephone call anywhere in the United States at no charge. Customers arrive to make their free calls according to a Poisson process at a mean rate of $\lambda = 40$ per hour. The time each customer is allowed to be in the phone booth is a constant 72 seconds. Management is interested in using simulation to determine the average waiting time for a customer at the free telephone booth.

Conduct the simulation for 20 customer arrivals assuming that there is no one initially present at the phone booth. Use column 5 of Appendix C to determine the customer interarrival times. Based on these 20 arrivals, calculate the average time a customer spends waiting in line to use the phone. Compare this result to that obtained for W_q using the formula for the M/G/1 queue.

11. The distribution for weekly demand of Cobra auto alarm systems at Big Al's Stereo is as follows:

Demand	Probability
0	.15
1	.10
2	.25
3	.20
4	.15
5	.10
6	.05

The alarm systems cost Big Al's $100 and sell for $200. The annual holding cost rate for these systems is 26%, and there is a $65 cost to place an order. Lead time can vary between one and three weeks according to the following probability distribution.

Lead Time	Probability
1 week	.10
2 weeks	.75
3 weeks	.15

Assume that orders are placed at the end of the week. For example, if the lead time is one week an order placed in week 2 will arrive at the start of week 4. If the firm runs out of stock of the alarm systems, a customer will leave without making any purchase.

Simulate the inventory for the Cobra alarm system at Big Al's over a 15-week period and determine its profit during this period if Big Al's uses an inventory policy in which it orders 26 alarms whenever the stock on hand reaches 6 units. Assume the holding cost is calculated based on the end of the week inventory level. Use column 1 to determine the number of customer arrivals and column 2 to determine the lead time when an order is placed.

12. Ricon, Inc. uses an assembly line to produce its office copiers. The final step in the assembly process is quality control inspection. Copiers arrive at the quality inspection area exactly every 90 seconds. The time it takes to perform a quality control inspection follows an exponential distribution, with a mean of 72 seconds. Ricon management is interested in using simulation to determine the average time it takes a copier to complete its quality control inspection.

Conduct a simulation for 20 copier arrivals assuming that the system starts empty. Use column 6 of Appendix C to determine the inspection times. Calculate the average time a copier spends in the system based on these 20 arrivals.

13. Shari Winslow has gone to Atlantic City to play roulette. Her strategy is to place $10 bets on red. She has $30 and will quit either when she loses all her money or wins $20.

If the roulette wheel is operating properly, the chance of landing on red is 18/38, the chance of landing on black is 18/38, and the chance of landing on green is 2/38. Hence Shari's chance of winning her bet is 18/38 (approximately .4737) and of losing her bet, 20/38 (approximately .5263).

Use simulation to determine the number of spins it will take before Shari will stop playing roulette. Conduct four simulation runs and determine a 95% confidence interval for the average number of plays based on these four simulations.

14. Terry Moore has three alternative routes to travel from his home in Tustin to his office in Anaheim. He can take the Santa Ana Freeway to the Orange Freeway; the Costa Mesa Freeway to the Riverside Freeway; or the Garden Grove Freeway to the Orange Freeway.

The travel time (in minutes) on each of the five freeways follows the accompanying probability distributions. For each of the three routes, conduct 10 simulation runs and calculate the average commuting time. Which route appears to take the least travel time?

15. During the dinner hour, the distribution of the interarrival time of customers at Burger Barn is estimated to be as follows:

Interarrival Time	Probability
30 seconds	.45
60 seconds	.25
90 seconds	.15
120 seconds	.10
150 seconds	.05

Sixty percent of customers pay with cash, while 40% pay with credit cards. The service times of the cash and credit card customers are estimated to be as follows:

Cash		Credit Card	
Service Time	Probability	Service Time	Probability
20 seconds	.35	30 seconds	.20
40 seconds	.30	60 seconds	.45
60 seconds	.25	90 seconds	.25
80 seconds	.10	120 seconds	.10

Simulate this system for 20 customer arrivals and determine the average time a cash and credit card customer must wait in line before paying the cashier. Use column 5 of Appendix C to determine the customer interarrival time, column 6 to determine whether the customer pays with cash or credit, and column 7 to determine the service time.

16. Consider the situation faced by Burger Barn discussed in problem 15. The restaurant has hired a second cashier. One cashier will handle cash purchases only while the other cashier will only handle credit card customers.

Using Excel, develop a simulation that determines the average time a customer spends in the system. Base the simulation on 1000 customer arrivals and calculate the average customer waiting time assuming the first 100 customer arrivals are ignored.

Data for problem 14

Santa Ana		Orange		Costa Mesa		Riverside		Garden Grove	
Time	Probability	Time	Probability	Time	Probability	Time	Probability	Time	Probability
8	.30	6	.25	7	.35	5	.20	3	.20
9	.25	7	.35	8	.20	6	.30	4	.10
10	.30	8	.20	9	.10	7	.25	5	.20
11	.10	9	.20	10	.25	8	.10	6	.50
12	.05			11	.10	9	.15		

17. Consider the situation faced by Burger Barn described in problems 15 and 16. Use Crystal Ball to develop a simulation for the model where each cashier handles both cash and credit card purchases. Run the simulation 500 times, each for 10 hours (36,000 seconds) and determine 95% confidence interval for the average time a customer must wait for service.

18. Harvest Supermarket has one loading dock for receiving deliveries. During any half-hour interval, either 0, 1, 2, or 3 delivery trucks arrive with the following probabilities:

    $$P(0 \text{ arrivals}) = .60$$
    $$P(1 \text{ arrival}) = .25$$
    $$P(2 \text{ arrivals}) = .10$$
    $$P(3 \text{ arrivals}) = .05$$

    Eighty percent of the delivery trucks can be unloaded in a half hour, while 20% of the trucks take a full hour to unload. Using fixed-time simulation, determine the average number of trucks waiting to unload during a 10-hour period. Assume that the simulation starts with the loading dock empty. Use column 6 of Appendix C to determine the number of trucks that arrive in a half-hour period and column 7 to determine how long it will take to unload a truck.

19. Customers arrive at the Blinkies Donut shop between 6:30 a.m. and 8:30 a.m. according to a Poisson process with a mean rate of one every minute. Seventy percent of the arriving customers purchase one or two donuts, while 30% purchase the Blinkies Dozen pack. For customers purchasing one or two donuts, the service time is uniformly distributed between 30 and 50 seconds. For customers purchasing the Blinkies Dozen pack, the service time is exponentially distributed with a mean of 90 seconds.

    Blinkies employs a single clerk to help customers. Simulate the arrival of the first 20 customers into the store during the 6:30 a.m. to 8:30 a.m. time period. Determine the maximum number of customers who will wait in line to begin service during this period. Use appropriate random number selections from Appendix C.

20. The Quick Stop Convenience Store has two gas pump islands, one for full service and one for self service. Cars arrive at the gas pumps according to a Poisson process at a mean rate of 20 per hour. Sixty percent of the cars want self serve, while 40% want full serve. The service time for the self-serve pump follows an exponential distribution with a mean of four minutes. The service time for the full-serve pump follows an exponential distribution with a mean of five minutes.

    If more than two cars are in line waiting for self serve, but no one is using the full-serve pump, an arriving car wanting self serve will join the self-serve queue with probability .3, balk (immediately leave without service) with probability .5, or go to the full-serve pump with probability .2. If more than two cars are in line waiting for self serve and the full-serve pump is occu-

pied, an arriving car wanting self serve will join the self-serve pump queue with probability .4 and balk with probability .6.

Simulate this system for 20 car arrivals. Use column 1 of Appendix C to determine the interarrival time of cars, column 2 to determine whether the car will want self serve or full serve, column 3 to determine the service time for obtaining the gasoline, and column 4 to determine whether an arriving car wanting self serve will join the queue, balk, or switch to full serve. What observations can you make based on this simulation?

21. Ontario, California, is a suburb of Los Angeles. Its airport serves primarily domestic air traffic; however, occasionally an international flight is diverted to Ontario if Los Angeles International Airport is fogged in. If an international flight arrives at Ontario, two customs inspectors set up operations to process the passengers.

    Passengers must line up to have their passports and visas checked by the first customs inspector. Inspection times follow a uniform distribution ranging between 20 and 70 seconds. Passengers then claim their baggage. The time it takes to retrieve baggage follows an exponential distribution with a mean of three minutes. Finally, the passengers join a line to have their baggage inspected by the second customs inspector. Forty percent of the passengers are waived through without inspection, 50% experience a cursory inspection of one minute duration, and 10% experience a full inspection of three minutes duration.

    Use simulation to determine how long it takes a plane load of 20 passengers to get through customs. Use column 1 of Appendix C to determine the time required to check a passenger's passport and visa, column 2 to determine the time required to obtain baggage, and column 3 to determine the type of baggage inspection a passenger experiences (none, cursory, or full).

22. Family Appliance specializes in selling major appliances for use in kitchen remodeling. One of its more popular items is the SubZero refrigerator. Over the past 40 weeks, the store has collected data regarding the weekly demand for this refrigerator. On the basis of these data, the following demand distribution has been estimated:

Weekly Demand	Probability
0	.25
1	.15
2	.15
3	.25
4	.10
5	.10

The store's policy is to reorder up to 15 refrigerators whenever the inventory on hand reaches five or fewer at the end of a week. The holding cost for each refrigerator is $2 per week, and the cost of reordering is $50. If a customer wants a SubZero refrigerator and Family is out of stock the customer will go elsewhere and the sale is lost. The company estimates that it suffers a goodwill cost of $40 for each lost sale. Currently, Family Appliance has an inventory of seven refrigerators.

Lead time for delivery can be described by the following distribution:

Lead Time	Probability
1 week	.30
2 weeks	.50
3 weeks	.20

a. Conduct a 10-week simulation of Family's inventory situation regarding the SubZero refrigerator to determine the total cost for this period. Use column 3 of Appendix C to determine the weekly demand and column 4 to determine the lead time.

b. SubZero is offering Family a new policy of automatically delivering five refrigerators every two weeks. The administrative cost of this policy is $5 per week, and the first delivery will be in two weeks. Conduct a 10-week simulation of Family's inventory situation under this plan and determine the total cost for the 10-week period.

c. On the basis of your answers to parts (a) and (b), what would you recommend to Family management regarding the supplier's offer?

23. Marv Portney is a salesman for Craftco Comfort Beds. Marv gets his leads when customers call the Craftco 800 number to arrange an in-house demonstration. (Customers receive a free clock-radio for agreeing to this demonstration.) Of the customers with whom Marv makes appointments, 10% turn out to be not at home. Of the others, 10% are single women, 30% are single men, and 60% are married couples.

Craftco offers four sizes of beds: king, queen, double, and twin. The list price of the king is $4000, the queen $3000, the double $2500, and the twin $2000. Marv can discount each bed up to 50% in order to make a sale, however. Therefore, he estimates that his commission is uniformly distributed within the following ranges:

Bed Size	Commission Uniformly Distributed Between
King	$400 and $1000
Queen	$300 and $800
Double	$200 and $600
Twin	$250 and $500

Marv has found that, among the single women he calls upon, he makes a sale 70% of the time. Of those, 40% want to buy a twin bed, 50% want a double, 5% want a queen, and 5% want a king. Marv makes a sale to 65% of the single men he calls on. Of these, 30% want a twin bed, 40% want a double, 25% want a queen, and 5% want a king. Among the married couples, Marv makes a

sale 55% of the time. Ten percent of these couples want to buy a single twin bed, 20% want two twin beds, 15% want a double, 40% want a queen, and 15% want a king.

Marv makes one, two, or three sales calls per day with the following probabilities:

Number of Sales Calls per Day	Probability
1	.50
2	.40
3	.10

a. Simulate Marv's activity over a 10-day period using an appropriate random number selection from Appendix C.

b. Calculate Marv's earnings over this 10-day period.

24. The speed at which cars travel down Main Street in Irvine, California, follows a normal distribution with a mean of 42 miles an hour and a standard deviation of 5 miles per hour. The Irvine Police Department is contemplating setting up a speed trap at the corner of Main and Alton streets to try to enforce the 45 mile per hour speed limit on Main Street. The speed trap is set up for a half hour each day. The interarrival time of cars passing the corner of Main and Alton follows an exponential distribution with a mean time of 45 seconds. If a police car does detect someone driving over the speed limit, the police officer will ticket the driver. The distribution of the time to write up a ticket is as follows:

Time to Write Up a Ticket	Probability
3 minutes	.15
3.5 minutes	.20
4 minutes	.25
4.5 minutes	.30
5 minutes	.10

While a police officer is writing up a ticket, he is unavailable to catch other speeders. Simulate a half hour of operations for this model to determine how many cars the police officer will catch speeding. Use column 3 to determine the interarrival time of a car, column 4 to determine the car's speed, and column 5 to determine the length of time the police officer spends writing up a ticket.

25. Among the products sold by Dominion Hardware is the Simoniz brand pressure washer. These are delivered to the store by a rack jobber who works under contract for Simoniz. The rack jobber comes to the store on Monday of each week, but in any week there is a 30% chance that he gets delayed and does not make it to the store. The store estimates that the holding cost per unit is $6 per week (based on the number of units that are in inventory at the end of the week). If the store runs short of pressure washers, it estimates that it suffers a goodwill cost of $7 for each unsatisfied customer and the sale is lost.

Dominion estimates the weekly washer demand has the following probability distribution.

Demand	Probability
0	.15
1	.20
2	.30
3	.15
4	.10
5	.05
6	.05

Not including inventory costs, the company calculates it earns $15 on each unit sold.

a. Do a 10-week simulation of operations and estimate the average weekly profit if the firm decides to have the rack jobber bring the inventory level up to 5 units when he arrives.

b. Develop an Excel simulation for this problem covering 100 weeks of operation. Then use Crystal Ball to determine the optimal stocking level for the firm. Base your results on doing 500 simulation runs of each policy considered.

26. During its first hour of operation customers arrive at the Wednesday Afternoon Store according to a Poisson process with a mean rate of 40 per hour. It takes the cashier an average of 90 seconds to check out a customer.

a. Simulate the arrival of 15 customers and determine the average time these customers spend waiting in line. Use column 3 of Appendix C to generate the interarrival times and column 4 to generate the service times.

b. Develop an Excel or Extend simulation for this problem and run it 10 times, each over a 60-minute interval. On the basis of these 10 simulation runs, determine a 95% confidence interval for the average time a customer must wait in line to begin service.

27. Daily demand for Webcor barbeques at Sharper Idea has the following probability distribution:

Demand	Probability
0	.08
1	.37
2	.33
3	.17
4	.05

Orders are placed at the end of the day, and lead time (in days) has the following probability distribution.

Lead Time	Probability
1	.05
2	.55
3	.30
4	.10

For example, an order placed on day 4 with a lead time of 2 days will be delivered at the beginning of day 7. Sharper Idea currently has an inventory of 10 Webcor barbeques. Order costs are approximately $50 per order, and inventory holding costs are estimated to be $2 per barbeque per day. The company suffers a goodwill cost of $30 for each barbeque demanded when it is out of stock and the sale is lost.

Sharper Idea's current policy is to reorder 10 barbeques when supply reaches 6 or less at the end of a day. Bob Hanson, one of the company's vice presidents, has recommended a new policy of reordering 12 barbeques when supply reaches 3 or less.

a. Develop a simulation in Excel for this model.

b. Using Crystal Ball, do 500 simulations of 1000 days each and determine whether Sharper Idea should switch to Bob Hanson's recommended policy.

28. MVC Computers is considering using e-commerce to sell its computers directly over the Internet. It is planning to staff the website 24 hours a day with a supervisor and a trainee. An incoming order that arrives when both the supervisor and trainee are busy is put in a "pending file" (a queue) for processing when one of the two servers becomes available. Operations data is estimated to be as follows.

Time Between Orders (minutes)	Proba-bility	Supervisor's Service Time (minutes)	Proba-bility	Trainee's Service Time (minutes)	Proba-bility
2	.35	4	.30	6	.10
3	.30	5	.25	7	.10
4	.20	6	.25	8	.60
5	.15	7	.20	9	.20

Management is interested in the average amount of time incoming orders will spend in the "pending file."

a. Develop a simulation in Excel to model this problem. Run the simulation for 1000 orders and eliminate the first 100 orders when calculating the average time spent in the pending file.

b. Using Crystal Ball, run the simulation 500 times and determine a 95% confidence interval for the average time an order spends in the pending file.

29. Kokanee Springs Golf Resort in British Columbia has a season that typically begins on April 15 and lasts until October 10. Unusually cold weather, however, can delay the start of the season or hasten the season closing date. Hence management believes that the length of the golfing season can be modeled as a uniform distribution with a minimum time of 169 days and a maximum time of 178 days.

The golf course offers season passes for $800 and charges day golfers (those without a season pass) between $29 and $68 to play a day of golf. Management estimates that the number of season passes that it will sell can be modeled by a triangular distribution with a minimum of 250, a maximum of 360, and a likeliest value of 320. The distribution of revenue for the day golfers is as follows:

Revenue	Probability
$29	.10
$48	.85
$68	.05

On sunny days, management believes the number of day golfers will follow a normal distribution with a mean of 290 and a standard deviation of 17; on non-sunny days management believes the number of day golfers will follow a normal distribution with a mean of 81 and a standard deviation of 9. Approximately 75% of the days are sunny.

Fixed operating costs for the golf course are estimated to follow a normal distribution with a mean of $1,500,000 and a standard deviation of $100,000. The golf course has a $600,000 loan that is due at the end of this year. Using Crystal Ball, determine the probability that the golf course will earn more than $600,000 during the golf season. Base your result on doing 2000 simulation runs.

30. Customers arrive at Ted's TV Repair Shop according to a Poisson process at an average of once every 2.5 hours. By using existing equipment, the service time to repair a television set is 2.25 hours with a standard deviation of 45 minutes. Suppose Ted decides to hire a second repair person and this person also takes an average of 2.25 hours to fix a television with a standard deviation of 45 minutes.

   a. Assuming that the service time of both Ted and his assistant follows a normal distribution, develop an Excel simulation for this system.

   b. Run the simulation for 1000 customers and determine the average time a television set spends at the shop by excluding the first 100 customers.

31. Consider the Ted's TV Repair Shop simulation developed in problem 30. Using Crystal Ball, run 1000 simulations. Based on the results of your simulation, determine:

   a. a 95% confidence interval for the average time a set spends in the system

   b. the probability the average time a set waits before being served is less than 30 minutes

32. Among the items sold at Hal's Bakery are loaves of sourdough bread. The daily number of customers who arrive at Hal's approximately follows a normal distribution with a mean of 240 and a standard deviation of 15.49. There is a .25 probability that a customer wishes to buy one loaf of sourdough bread, a .05 probability that a customer wishes to buy two loaves, and a .70 probability that a customer does not purchase the bread.

   The bread is baked once a day at 6 a.m. and sold beginning at 9 a.m. Each loaf of bread costs $.60 to produce and sells for $2.40. Unsold loaves of bread are donated to a soup kitchen and net the store a tax credit of $.20. If the store runs out of loaves of sourdough bread, it estimates that it suffers a goodwill loss of $3.00 for each loaf demanded when it is out of stock. Using Crystal Ball, determine how many loaves of sourdough bread the bakery should produce. Base your results on 500 simulations for each production quantity considered.

33. Bank Drug Store has two servers. One can serve a customer according to an exponential distribution with a mean speed of 1.5 minutes, and the other can serve a customer according to an exponential distribution with a mean speed of 2 minutes. Customers arrive according to a Poisson process at a mean rate of 60 per hour. Develop an Excel simulation and determine the average time a customer spends waiting in line. Assume the simulation begins recording the waiting time of the 101st customer and runs for 1000 customers.

34. Consider the situation faced by Bank Drug Store in problem 33. Using Extend, develop a simulation for this model and run the simulation over 10,000 minutes to determine the average time a customer spends in line before being served.

35. Steve Wilson, a budding college impresario, is considering booking the rock band Soggy Crackers to play a college concert. There are two possible locations that Steve can book for the concert: the college's amphitheater and its sports arena. The amphitheater will cost Steve $1000 plus 5% of ticket revenues. The sports arens will cost Steve $800 plus 7% of ticket revenues. The amphitheater can seat 1300 people. The sports arena is currently undergoing remodeling, and Steve believes that when the remodeling is completed the number of people it will be able to seat will follow a discrete uniform distribution of between 1501 and 1550 people.

   Steve will sell tickets through student clubs. He estimates that the ticket demand will follow a normal distribution, with a mean of 1200 tickets and a standard deviation of 250 tickets. Steve estimates that the revenue he will earn per ticket is $11.

Besides the location rental fee, Steve believes that the other fixed costs (e.g., advertising, paying the band, security, etc.) will follow a uniform distribution of between $10,000 and $11,500.

Using Crystal Ball, determine which location Steve should book and give a 95% confidence interval for his expected profit from booking the band. Base your analysis on 1,000 simulation runs.

36. Joe Marino is contemplating signing on to work as a fisherman on a four-person Alaska fishing boat this season. As a crew member, Joe will receive 10% of the revenue that the ship generates.

   The fishing season lasts anywhere from 125 to 144 days, depending on when the waters start to freeze up. Joe believes that the length of the fishing season can be modeled as a discrete uniform distribution. On any day during the fishing season, there is a 15% chance of stormy weather that would prevent the ship from fishing. The daily catch on the days that the boat does fish can be modeled as a normal distribution with a mean of 2400 pounds and a standard deviation of 500 pounds. The revenue the ship receives per pound each day is uniformly distributed between $.85 and $1.05 per pound.

   Using Crystal Ball, develop a simulation for Joe Marino to estimate the likelihood he will earn more than $26,000 during the fishing season. Base your results on 1000 simulation runs.

37. Campus Bookstore is trying to decide on how many management science textbooks to purchase to serve students taking a summer course. The class anticipates having 25 students enrolled. For each student in the class, the following probability distribution is believed to hold.

Student	Probability
Wants to purchase new textbook	.55
Wants to purchase used textbook	.35
Does not want to purchase textbook	.10

   The bookstore earns $20 on each new textbook it sells and $15 on each used textbook it sells. If it orders too few new books but has used books available, there is a 70% chance a student will purchase a used book. If it orders too few used books but has new books available,

there is a 55% chance the student will purchase a new book. For every unsold new textbook the bookstore has it loses $5, whereas for every unsold used textbook the bookstore has it loses $10.

   Do a simulation by hand to estimate the expected profit the bookstore will earn if it orders 13 new textbooks and 10 used textbooks.

38. Consider the situation faced by the campus bookstore in problem 37. Develop an Excel spreadsheet that will determine the bookstore's profit for various order quantities of new and used textbooks. Using Crystal Ball, determine the optimal order quantity for new and used textbooks, basing each ordering policy on 100 simulation runs.

39. Chris Block is a student who works on Saturdays selling ice cream in Central Park. The ice cream cart Chris uses holds 200 ice cream bars. Chris earns $.20 on each bar she sells. The distribution of the interarrival time of customers is estimated to be as follows.

Interarrival Time	Probability
1 minute	.50
2 minutes	.30
3 minutes	.15
4 minutes	.05

Each customer purchases between one and five ice cream bars according to the following distribution.

Number of Bars Purchased	Probability
1	.60
2	.20
3	.10
4	.05
5	.05

Chris will work in the park for up to three hours. Develop an Excel spreadsheet that can be used to determine the expected amount of money Chris will earn during that time. Do 10 simulation runs and on the basis of these 10 runs determine a 95% confidence interval for the average profit Chris will earn per day.

40. Consider the situation faced by Chris Block in problem 39. Using Crystal Ball, conduct 1000 simulation runs and determine the probability Chris earns at least $30.

CASE 1: OFFICE CENTRAL

Office Central is a nationwide mail-order firm specializing in selling office supplies. One of the items the company carries is the Ricon 436 copier. The copiers cost the firm $1825 each, and Office Central sells them for $2499 each. The firm uses a 20% annual holding cost rate so that the daily holding cost per unit is approximately $1. The cost of placing an order with Ricon is $150, and orders have a lead time between three and six working days (the store is open six days a week). The following distribution holds for the lead time:

$$P(\text{lead time} = 3 \text{ days}) = .2$$
$$P(\text{lead time} = 4 \text{ days}) = .4$$
$$P(\text{lead time} = 5 \text{ days}) = .3$$
$$P(\text{lead time} = 6 \text{ days}) = .1$$

If Office Central is out of Ricon copiers, it offers customers a $150 discount off the price and agrees to airfreight the copier to the customer as soon as it arrives. Airfreight costs Office Central an additional $95. Eighty percent of cus-

tomers agree to place a backorder, while 20% go elsewhere to buy their copier. The company has been considering eliminating the out-of-stock discount and estimates that the percentage of customers who will place a backorder will decline from 80% to 50%.

Daily demand for the copiers follows a Poisson distribution with a mean of three units. Office Central has decided to use an order point, order up to level policy for the copiers and wishes to determine an optimal policy.

Conduct a simulation analysis of this problem. From the output of this model, prepare a business report to Joe Dixon, Operations Manager of Office Central, with your recommendation regarding the inventory policy for the Ricon 436 copier under the current discount policy. Include in your report a recommendation regarding eliminating the discount as well as a discussion regarding the effect a 10% decrease in the holding cost would have on your inventory policy recommendations. Each simulation run should cover at least 5000 days of operations.

CASE 2: FOUR WHEEL TIRE SHOP

Four Wheel Tire Shop is a single bay tire store located in Ames, Iowa. The interarrival time of cars in need of tires follows a uniform distribution with times between 10 and 50 minutes. Twenty percent of arriving customers want a single tire replaced, 40% want two tires replaced, 5% want three tires replaced, and 35% want all four tires replaced. Customer service time approximately follows a uniform distribution that varies with the number of tires that need to be replaced. The following statistics hold:

Number of Tires Needing Replacement	Service Time Is Uniformly Distributed Between
1	10 minutes and 20 minutes
2	15 minutes and 35 minutes
3	20 minutes and 40 minutes
4	25 minutes and 50 minutes

The owner of the store, Ben Stern, is considering leasing a new computerized tire balancing machine, which will reduce the average service time, resulting in the following uniform service distributions:

Number of Tires Needing Replacement	Service Time Is Uniformly Distributed Between
1	8 minutes and 18 minutes
2	12 minutes and 32 minutes
3	15 minutes and 35 minutes
4	20 minutes and 40 minutes

The machine lease cost averages $1.50 per hour. Mr. Stern estimates that the goodwill cost of a customer's being in the tire shop (either being served or waiting to be served) is $4.00.

Use Excel to perform the simulation analysis and prepare a business report for Mr. Stern recommending whether or not he should lease the machine. Include in your report relevant service statistics, such as the average time a customer spends waiting to begin service as well as time in the system using both the existing tire balancing machine and the proposed computerized balancing machine. Each simulation run should cover at least 1000 cars.

CASE 3: SCANDIA HOUSE

Scandia House sells Scandinavian-style furnishings. One of its more popular items is a five-shelf teak veneer bookcase that costs $58.40 and sells for $99. Scandia House uses a 25% annual inventory holding cost rate; thus the holding cost is $0.04 per bookcase per day. The cost of placing an order with the firm's supplier is $30, and lead time is between 8 and 12 days with the following probability distribution:

$$P(\text{lead time} = 8 \text{ days}) = .10$$
$$P(\text{lead time} = 9 \text{ days}) = .15$$
$$P(\text{lead time} = 10 \text{ days}) = .20$$
$$P(\text{lead time} = 11 \text{ days}) = .25$$
$$P(\text{lead time} = 12 \text{ days}) = .30$$

The number of customers who arrive at Scandia House to purchase the teak bookcases each day can be approximated by a Poisson distribution with a mean of 1.5. Each customer who arrives to purchase bookcases buys between one and four units, with the following probability distribution:

Number of Bookcases Demanded	Probability
1	.50
2	.30
3	.15
4	.05

If a customer wants to purchase bookcases but the store does not have enough stock to satisfy the order, the store offers customers either a more expensive substitute bookcase or a discount of $20 per bookcase for each bookcase that is backordered. Scandia House management believes that 30% of customers will accept the substitute bookcase, while 50% of customers will take the discount and backorder. The other 20% of customers will go elsewhere for the bookcases, and their sales will be lost. The substitute bookcases cost the firm $80 each and are always available. (Note that if a customer elects to backorder and Scandia House has sufficient inventory to satisfy part of the order, the store will sell the customer as many bookcases as are available.)

Develop a simulation model to analyze this problem using Excel. Try numerous combinations of order quantity and reorder point values. Simulate at least 1000 days of demand. From the results of this model, prepare a business report to Gudrun Kroner, president of Scandia House, regarding a recommended inventory policy for the teak bookcases.

CASE STUDY 4 ON THE CD

APPENDIX A: TABLES

TABLE A.1 — Pseudo-Random Numbers

	1	2	3	4	5	6	7	8	9	10	11	12	13	14	15
1	6506	3338	2197	8927	6320	1094	1995	5971	5147	3620	0582	2982	8731	6037	4231
2	7761	9874	9834	8848	4630	7371	7971	6600	1296	5299	1374	9517	8177	2403	7443
3	6170	2631	6268	9089	8657	2809	3554	4814	7401	9983	5613	3199	6005	1879	9339
4	8800	9139	8305	2605	0030	5148	6300	1762	2499	5417	2607	7111	9892	3703	8408
5	4211	9651	0051	7982	5624	9115	5495	2710	2888	9620	5078	6541	5066	9082	8981
6	7452	4883	5619	5541	6728	1469	5165	1908	9619	2043	9221	6405	6559	6343	8920
7	1182	8260	3367	2624	5925	6480	9339	5104	7435	4121	9234	9031	3506	6230	1202
8	4012	2781	6140	1603	2829	2447	6997	4947	3343	3125	1070	2998	1236	9821	6438
9	0335	9636	1645	4063	7939	7031	1443	7610	9665	3357	6415	4994	3780	8437	6475
10	6299	4696	8036	6519	6476	8442	3574	4978	7911	0759	7991	2677	4401	9996	3878
11	5482	2016	7017	6406	3379	7384	0150	7199	7336	2121	1006	4066	5675	8784	6141
12	1085	4426	4988	6807	8134	1788	0933	7209	3054	0107	0033	2795	9978	4542	5388
13	1698	8464	8208	7589	1712	4891	7082	3021	4519	2000	7987	4122	8150	3058	1281
14	6969	9424	1524	6590	6317	1149	5025	8181	0013	1802	7521	6735	1511	4255	7643
15	1696	6693	9525	0882	6605	8822	4081	0722	8234	9257	3985	5061	2021	9265	9641
16	0267	6317	1051	3193	2734	9451	4100	1471	3270	1065	6001	4366	7642	2800	5028
17	3175	7529	1759	2084	0432	2990	7190	4648	8760	9085	4591	3874	7636	3983	7406
18	7659	0515	8149	4053	3441	8314	6822	0714	7731	6648	3007	5625	8682	8699	3711
19	4958	1069	0318	9941	0726	7176	5053	5177	6950	9598	0640	0297	7153	5379	3610
20	4281	1877	885	0967	6969	2766	8284	2528	0194	2496	4152	9645	3200	8762	1574
21	2231	0382	7782	7890	3434	5391	2022	6820	9294	8609	6437	3848	0668	2868	7085
22	0002	0786	2889	1522	0059	1313	9858	1336	4964	3223	3010	9118	6072	6432	1895
23	8434	7236	3686	8333	0617	1821	4297	9250	5737	2599	3785	4356	6943	1461	6921
24	8959	5886	9020	7247	5586	7136	0595	2432	0685	1058	6967	0202	8565	1423	6268
25	8975	6480	9478	5140	0996	6483	0881	4444	5587	4517	5402	4436	1516	8855	1132
26	1288	8758	5711	0916	1114	2046	2564	4713	5154	7742	1653	2428	8366	7530	8709
27	6412	0141	9310	7329	6063	4279	8996	6782	5013	1565	8090	8400	6118	5830	6202
28	6463	0315	2277	3642	4400	5030	9321	6107	8498	7832	8209	4891	8378	8816	2156
29	3856	1780	5371	1981	9871	2679	7859	1416	8795	4004	1302	2802	1445	8578	0356
30	6117	4088	7219	2557	6612	3386	2724	8737	6412	5548	5214	6804	4716	2134	6811
31	5396	2510	3168	9061	5963	2243	6824	6614	1074	6839	5576	8077	9191	2406	8859
32	1281	1710	4009	5721	5830	1755	1225	6382	4148	1870	3651	5876	9282	4682	6765
33	7644	0296	2395	7493	8626	4617	9388	2845	1363	4705	6759	2983	7857	8906	1027
34	8608	3656	0659	6827	2183	9893	4989	1855	9358	1041	4488	3197	1723	4120	6987
35	9359	0331	6735	1301	7891	5958	1119	8374	1817	4825	8018	2728	7241	6119	0439
36	4233	0282	0397	0646	0527	9247	2280	6931	3963	3227	9732	9148	6735	5047	0981
37	3871	1294	9059	7680	5964	5402	6068	1781	6103	3768	1999	2403	3006	3742	2539

A similar table can be generated in Excel by entering for each cell: =INT(RAND()*10000).

TABLE A.2 — Areas of the Standard Normal Distribution

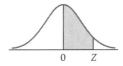

The entries in this table are the probabilities that a standard normal random variable is between 0 and Z (the shaded area).

Z	0.00	0.01	0.02	0.03	0.04	0.05	0.06	0.07	0.08	0.09
0.0	.0000	.0040	.0080	.0120	.0160	.0199	.0239	.0279	.0319	.0359
0.1	.0398	.0438	.0478	.0517	.0557	.0596	.0636	.0675	.0714	.0753
0.2	.0793	.0832	.0871	.0910	.0948	.0987	.1026	.1064	.1103	.1141
0.3	.1179	.1217	.1255	.1293	.1331	.1368	.1406	.1443	.1480	.1517
0.4	.1554	.1591	.1628	.1664	.1700	.1736	.1772	.1808	.1844	.1879
0.5	.1915	.1950	.1985	.2019	.2054	.2088	.2123	.2157	.2190	.2224
0.6	.2257	.2291	.2324	.2357	.2389	.2422	.2454	.2486	.2517	.2549
0.7	.2580	.2611	.2642	.2673	.2704	.2734	.2764	.2794	.2823	.2852
0.8	.2881	.2910	.2939	.2967	.2995	.3023	.3051	.3078	.3106	.3133
0.9	.3159	.3186	.3212	.3238	.3264	.3289	.3315	.3340	.3365	.3389
1.0	.3413	.3438	.3461	.3485	.3508	.3531	.3554	.3577	.3599	.3621
1.1	.3643	.3665	.3686	.3708	.3729	.3749	.3770	.3790	.3810	.3830
1.2	.3849	.3869	.3888	.3907	.3925	.3944	.3962	.3980	.3997	.4015
1.3	.4032	.4049	.4066	.4082	.4099	.4115	.4131	.4147	.4162	.4177
1.4	.4192	.4207	.4222	.4236	.4251	.4265	.4279	.4292	.4306	.4319
1.5	.4332	.4345	.4357	.4370	.4382	.4394	.4406	.4418	.4429	.4441
1.6	.4452	.4463	.4474	.4484	.4495	.4505	.4515	.4525	.4535	.4545
1.7	.4554	.4564	.4573	.4582	.4591	.4599	.4608	.4616	.4625	.4633
1.8	.4641	.4649	.4656	.4664	.4671	.4678	.4686	.4693	.4699	.4706
1.9	.4713	.4719	.4726	.4732	.4738	.4744	.4750	.4756	.4761	.4767
2.0	.4772	.4778	.4783	.4788	.4793	.4798	.4803	.4808	.4812	.4817
2.1	.4821	.4826	.4830	.4834	.4838	.4842	.4846	.4850	.4854	.4857
2.2	.4861	.4864	.4868	.4871	.4875	.4878	.4881	.4884	.4887	.4890
2.3	.4893	.4896	.4898	.4901	.4904	.4906	.4909	.4911	.4913	.4916
2.4	.4918	.4920	.4922	.4925	.4927	.4929	.4931	.4932	.4934	.4936
2.5	.4938	.4940	.4941	.4943	.4945	.4946	.4948	.4949	.4951	.4952
2.6	.4953	.4955	.4956	.4957	.4959	.4960	.4961	.4962	.4963	.4964
2.7	.4965	.4966	.4967	.4968	.4969	.4970	.4971	.4972	.4973	.4974
2.8	.4974	.4975	.4976	.4977	.4977	.4978	.4979	.4979	.4980	.4981
2.9	.4981	.4982	.4982	.4983	.4984	.4984	.4985	.4985	.4986	.4986
3.0	.4987	.4987	.4987	.4988	.4988	.4989	.4989	.4989	.4990	.4990
3.1	.4990	.4991	.4991	.4991	.4992	.4992	.4992	.4992	.4993	.4993
3.2	.4993	.4993	.4994	.4994	.4994	.4994	.4994	.4995	.4995	.4995
3.3	.4995	.4995	.4995	.4996	.4996	.4996	.4996	.4996	.4996	.4997
3.4	.4997	.4997	.4997	.4997	.4997	.4997	.4997	.4997	.4997	.4998
3.5	.4998									
4.0	.49997									
4.5	.499997									
5.0	.4999997									
6.0	.499999999									

TABLE A.3   Critical Values from the *t* Distribution

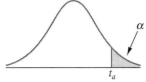

	Values of α for one-tailed test and $\alpha/2$ for two-tailed test					
df	$t_{.100}$	$t_{.050}$	$t_{.025}$	$t_{.010}$	$t_{.005}$	$t_{.001}$
1	3.078	6.314	12.706	31.821	63.656	318.289
2	1.886	2.920	4.303	6.965	9.925	22.328
3	1.638	2.353	3.182	4.541	5.841	10.214
4	1.533	2.132	2.776	3.747	4.604	7.173
5	1.476	2.015	2.571	3.365	4.032	5.894
6	1.440	1.943	2.447	3.143	3.707	5.208
7	1.415	1.895	2.365	2.998	3.499	4.785
8	1.397	1.860	2.306	2.896	3.355	4.501
9	1.383	1.833	2.262	2.821	3.250	4.297
10	1.372	1.812	2.228	2.764	3.169	4.144
11	1.363	1.796	2.201	2.718	3.106	4.025
12	1.356	1.782	2.179	2.681	3.055	3.930
13	1.350	1.771	2.160	2.650	3.012	3.852
14	1.345	1.761	2.145	2.624	2.977	3.787
15	1.341	1.753	2.131	2.602	2.947	3.733
16	1.337	1.746	2.120	2.583	2.921	3.686
17	1.333	1.740	2.110	2.567	2.898	3.646
18	1.330	1.734	2.101	2.552	2.878	3.610
19	1.328	1.729	2.093	2.539	2.861	3.579
20	1.325	1.725	2.086	2.528	2.845	3.552
21	1.323	1.721	2.080	2.518	2.831	3.527
22	1.321	1.717	2.074	2.508	2.819	3.505
23	1.319	1.714	2.069	2.500	2.807	3.485
24	1.318	1.711	2.064	2.492	2.797	3.467
25	1.316	1.708	2.060	2.485	2.787	3.450
26	1.315	1.706	2.056	2.479	2.779	3.435
27	1.314	1.703	2.052	2.473	2.771	3.421
28	1.313	1.701	2.048	2.467	2.763	3.408
29	1.311	1.699	2.045	2.462	2.756	3.396
30	1.310	1.697	2.042	2.457	2.750	3.385
40	1.303	1.684	2.021	2.423	2.704	3.307
50	1.299	1.676	2.009	2.403	2.678	3.261
60	1.296	1.671	2.000	2.390	2.660	3.232
70	1.294	1.667	1.994	2.381	2.648	3.211
80	1.292	1.664	1.990	2.374	2.639	3.195
90	1.291	1.662	1.987	2.368	2.632	3.183
100	1.290	1.660	1.984	2.364	2.626	3.174
150	1.287	1.655	1.976	2.351	2.609	3.145
200	1.286	1.653	1.972	2.345	2.601	3.131
∞	1.282	1.645	1.960	2.326	2.576	3.090

TABLE A.4
Percentage Points of the *F* Distribution

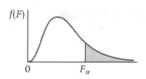

v_1	$\alpha = .10$								
	Numerator Degrees of Freedom								
v_2	**1**	**2**	**3**	**4**	**5**	**6**	**7**	**8**	**9**
1	39.86	49.50	53.59	55.83	57.24	58.20	58.91	59.44	59.86
2	8.53	9.00	9.16	9.24	9.29	9.33	9.35	9.37	9.38
3	5.54	5.46	5.39	5.34	5.31	5.28	5.27	5.25	5.24
4	4.54	4.32	4.19	4.11	4.05	4.01	3.98	3.95	3.94
5	4.06	3.78	3.62	3.52	3.45	3.40	3.37	3.34	3.32
6	3.78	3.46	3.29	3.18	3.11	3.05	3.01	2.98	2.96
7	3.59	3.26	3.07	2.96	2.88	2.83	2.78	2.75	2.72
8	3.46	3.11	2.92	2.81	2.73	2.67	2.62	2.59	2.56
9	3.36	3.01	2.81	2.69	2.61	2.55	2.51	2.47	2.44
10	3.29	2.92	2.73	2.61	2.52	2.46	2.41	2.38	2.35
11	3.23	2.86	2.66	2.54	2.45	2.39	2.34	2.30	2.27
12	3.18	2.81	2.61	2.48	2.39	2.33	2.28	2.24	2.21
13	3.14	2.76	2.56	2.43	2.35	2.28	2.23	2.20	2.16
14	3.10	2.73	2.52	2.39	2.31	2.24	2.19	2.15	2.12
15	3.07	2.70	2.49	2.36	2.27	2.21	2.16	2.12	2.09
16	3.05	2.67	2.46	2.33	2.24	2.18	2.13	2.09	2.06
17	3.03	2.64	2.44	2.31	2.22	2.15	2.10	2.06	2.03
18	3.01	2.62	2.42	2.29	2.20	2.13	2.08	2.04	2.00
19	2.99	2.61	2.40	2.27	2.18	2.11	2.06	2.02	1.98
20	2.97	2.59	2.38	2.25	2.16	2.09	2.04	2.00	1.96
21	2.96	2.57	2.36	2.23	2.14	2.08	2.02	1.98	1.95
22	2.95	2.56	2.35	2.22	2.13	2.06	2.01	1.97	1.93
23	2.94	2.55	2.34	2.21	2.11	2.05	1.99	1.95	1.92
24	2.93	2.54	2.33	2.19	2.10	2.04	1.98	1.94	1.91
25	2.92	2.53	2.32	2.18	2.09	2.02	1.97	1.93	1.89
26	2.91	2.52	2.31	2.17	2.08	2.01	1.96	1.92	1.88
27	2.90	2.51	2.30	2.17	2.07	2.00	1.95	1.91	1.87
28	2.89	2.50	2.29	2.16	2.06	2.00	1.94	1.90	1.87
29	2.89	2.50	2.28	2.15	2.06	1.99	1.93	1.89	1.86
30	2.88	2.49	2.28	2.14	2.05	1.98	1.93	1.88	1.85
40	2.84	2.44	2.23	2.09	2.00	1.93	1.87	1.83	1.79
60	2.79	2.39	2.18	2.04	1.95	1.87	1.82	1.77	1.74
120	2.75	2.35	2.13	1.99	1.90	1.82	1.77	1.72	1.68
∞	2.71	2.30	2.08	1.94	1.85	1.77	1.72	1.67	1.63

Denominator Degrees of Freedom

$\alpha = .10$										v_1	
Numerator Degrees of Freedom											
10	**12**	**15**	**20**	**24**	**30**	**40**	**60**	**120**	**∞**		v_2
60.19	60.71	61.22	61.74	62.00	62.26	62.53	62.79	63.06	63.33	1	
9.39	9.41	9.42	9.44	9.45	9.46	9.47	9.47	9.48	9.49	2	
5.23	5.22	5.20	5.18	5.18	5.17	5.16	5.15	5.14	5.13	3	
3.92	3.90	3.87	3.84	3.83	3.82	3.80	3.79	3.78	3.76	4	
3.30	3.27	3.24	3.21	3.19	3.17	3.16	3.14	3.12	3.10	5	
2.94	2.90	2.87	2.84	2.82	2.80	2.78	2.76	2.74	2.72	6	
2.70	2.67	2.63	2.59	2.58	2.56	2.54	2.51	2.49	2.47	7	
2.54	2.50	2.46	2.42	2.40	2.38	2.36	2.34	2.32	2.29	8	
2.42	2.38	2.34	2.30	2.28	2.25	2.23	2.21	2.18	2.16	9	
2.32	2.28	2.24	2.20	2.18	2.16	2.13	2.11	2.08	2.06	10	
2.25	2.21	2.17	2.12	2.10	2.08	2.05	2.03	2.00	1.97	11	
2.19	2.15	2.10	2.06	2.04	2.01	1.99	1.96	1.93	1.90	12	
2.14	2.10	2.05	2.01	1.98	1.96	1.93	1.90	1.88	1.85	13	
2.10	2.05	2.01	1.96	1.94	1.91	1.89	1.86	1.83	1.80	14	
2.06	2.02	1.97	1.92	1.90	1.87	1.85	1.82	1.79	1.76	15	
2.03	1.99	1.94	1.89	1.87	1.84	1.81	1.78	1.75	1.72	16	
2.00	1.96	1.91	1.86	1.84	1.81	1.78	1.75	1.72	1.69	17	
1.98	1.93	1.89	1.84	1.81	1.78	1.75	1.72	1.69	1.66	18	
1.96	1.91	1.86	1.81	1.79	1.76	1.73	1.70	1.67	1.63	19	
1.94	1.89	1.84	1.79	1.77	1.74	1.71	1.68	1.64	1.61	20	
1.92	1.87	1.83	1.78	1.75	1.72	1.69	1.66	1.62	1.59	21	
1.90	1.86	1.81	1.76	1.73	1.70	1.67	1.64	1.60	1.57	22	
1.89	1.84	1.80	1.74	1.72	1.69	1.66	1.62	1.59	1.55	23	
1.88	1.83	1.78	1.73	1.70	1.67	1.64	1.61	1.57	1.53	24	
1.87	1.82	1.77	1.72	1.69	1.66	1.63	1.59	1.56	1.52	25	
1.86	1.81	1.76	1.71	1.68	1.65	1.61	1.58	1.54	1.50	26	
1.85	1.80	1.75	1.70	1.67	1.64	1.60	1.57	1.53	1.49	27	
1.84	1.79	1.74	1.69	1.66	1.63	1.59	1.56	1.52	1.48	28	
1.83	1.78	1.73	1.68	1.65	1.62	1.58	1.55	1.51	1.47	29	
1.82	1.77	1.72	1.67	1.64	1.61	1.57	1.54	1.50	1.46	30	
1.76	1.71	1.66	1.61	1.57	1.54	1.51	1.47	1.42	1.38	40	
1.71	1.66	1.60	1.54	1.51	1.48	1.44	1.40	1.35	1.29	60	
1.65	1.60	1.55	1.48	1.45	1.41	1.37	1.32	1.26	1.19	120	
1.60	1.55	1.49	1.42	1.38	1.34	1.30	1.24	1.17	1.00	∞	

Denominator Degrees of Freedom

Continued

v_2 \ v_1	$\alpha = .05$ Numerator Degrees of Freedom								
	1	2	3	4	5	6	7	8	9
1	161.45	199.50	215.71	224.58	230.16	233.99	236.77	238.88	240.54
2	18.51	19.00	19.16	19.25	19.30	19.33	19.35	19.37	19.38
3	10.13	9.55	9.28	9.12	9.01	8.94	8.89	8.85	8.81
4	7.71	6.94	6.59	6.39	6.26	6.16	6.09	6.04	6.00
5	6.61	5.79	5.41	5.19	5.05	4.95	4.88	4.82	4.77
6	5.99	5.14	4.76	4.53	4.39	4.28	4.21	4.15	4.10
7	5.59	4.74	4.35	4.12	3.97	3.87	3.79	3.73	3.68
8	5.32	4.46	4.07	3.84	3.69	3.58	3.50	3.44	3.39
9	5.12	4.26	3.86	3.63	3.48	3.37	3.29	3.23	3.18
10	4.96	4.10	3.71	3.48	3.33	3.22	3.14	3.07	3.02
11	4.84	3.98	3.59	3.36	3.20	3.09	3.01	2.95	2.90
12	4.75	3.89	3.49	3.26	3.11	3.00	2.91	2.85	2.80
13	4.67	3.81	3.41	3.18	3.03	2.92	2.83	2.77	2.71
14	4.60	3.74	3.34	3.11	2.96	2.85	2.76	2.70	2.65
15	4.54	3.68	3.29	3.06	2.90	2.79	2.71	2.64	2.59
16	4.49	3.63	3.24	3.01	2.85	2.74	2.66	2.59	2.54
17	4.45	3.59	3.20	2.96	2.81	2.70	2.61	2.55	2.49
18	4.41	3.55	3.16	2.93	2.77	2.66	2.58	2.51	2.46
19	4.38	3.52	3.13	2.90	2.74	2.63	2.54	2.48	2.42
20	4.35	3.49	3.10	2.87	2.71	2.60	2.51	2.45	2.39
21	4.32	3.47	3.07	2.84	2.68	2.57	2.49	2.42	2.37
22	4.30	3.44	3.05	2.82	2.66	2.55	2.46	2.40	2.34
23	4.28	3.42	3.03	2.80	2.64	2.53	2.44	2.37	2.32
24	4.26	3.40	3.01	2.78	2.62	2.51	2.42	2.36	2.30
25	4.24	3.39	2.99	2.76	2.60	2.49	2.40	2.34	2.28
26	4.23	3.37	2.98	2.74	2.59	2.47	2.39	2.32	2.27
27	4.21	3.35	2.96	2.73	2.57	2.46	2.37	2.31	2.25
28	4.20	3.34	2.95	2.71	2.56	2.45	2.36	2.29	2.24
29	4.18	3.33	2.93	2.70	2.55	2.43	2.35	2.28	2.22
30	4.17	3.32	2.92	2.69	2.53	2.42	2.33	2.27	2.21
40	4.08	3.23	2.84	2.61	2.45	2.34	2.25	2.18	2.12
60	4.00	3.15	2.76	2.53	2.37	2.25	2.17	2.10	2.04
120	3.92	3.07	2.68	2.45	2.29	2.18	2.09	2.02	1.96
∞	3.84	3.00	2.60	2.37	2.21	2.10	2.01	1.94	1.88

Denominator Degrees of Freedom

$\alpha = .05$										v_1	
Numerator Degrees of Freedom											
10	12	15	20	24	30	40	60	120	∞		v_2
241.88	243.90	245.90	248.00	249.10	250.10	251.10	252.20	253.30	254.30	1	
19.40	19.41	19.43	19.45	19.45	19.46	19.47	19.48	19.49	19.50	2	
8.79	8.74	8.70	8.66	8.64	8.62	8.59	8.57	8.55	8.53	3	
5.96	5.91	5.86	5.80	5.77	5.75	5.72	5.69	5.66	5.63	4	
4.74	4.68	4.62	4.56	4.53	4.50	4.46	4.43	4.40	4.36	5	
4.06	4.00	3.94	3.87	3.84	3.81	3.77	3.74	3.70	3.67	6	
3.64	3.57	3.51	3.44	3.41	3.38	3.34	3.30	3.27	3.23	7	
3.35	3.28	3.22	3.15	3.12	3.08	3.04	3.01	2.97	2.93	8	
3.14	3.07	3.01	2.94	2.90	2.86	2.83	2.79	2.75	2.71	9	
2.98	2.91	2.85	2.77	2.74	2.70	2.66	2.62	2.58	2.54	10	
2.85	2.79	2.72	2.65	2.61	2.57	2.53	2.49	2.45	2.40	11	
2.75	2.69	2.62	2.54	2.51	2.47	2.43	2.38	2.34	2.30	12	
2.67	2.60	2.53	2.46	2.42	2.38	2.34	2.30	2.25	2.21	13	
2.60	2.53	2.46	2.39	2.35	2.31	2.27	2.22	2.18	2.13	14	
2.54	2.48	2.40	2.33	2.29	2.25	2.20	2.16	2.11	2.07	15	
2.49	2.42	2.35	2.28	2.24	2.19	2.15	2.11	2.06	2.01	16	
2.45	2.38	2.31	2.23	2.19	2.15	2.10	2.06	2.01	1.96	17	
2.41	2.34	2.27	2.19	2.15	2.11	2.06	2.02	1.97	1.92	18	
2.38	2.31	2.23	2.16	2.11	2.07	2.03	1.98	1.93	1.88	19	
2.35	2.28	2.20	2.12	2.08	2.04	1.99	1.95	1.90	1.84	20	
2.32	2.25	2.18	2.10	2.05	2.01	1.96	1.92	1.87	1.81	21	
2.30	2.23	2.15	2.07	2.03	1.98	1.94	1.89	1.84	1.78	22	
2.27	2.20	2.13	2.05	2.01	1.96	1.91	1.86	1.81	1.76	23	
2.25	2.18	2.11	2.03	1.98	1.94	1.89	1.84	1.79	1.73	24	
2.24	2.16	2.09	2.01	1.96	1.92	1.87	1.82	1.77	1.71	25	
2.22	2.15	2.07	1.99	1.95	1.90	1.85	1.80	1.75	1.69	26	
2.20	2.13	2.06	1.97	1.93	1.88	1.84	1.79	1.73	1.67	27	
2.19	2.12	2.04	1.96	1.91	1.87	1.82	1.77	1.71	1.65	28	
2.18	2.10	2.03	1.94	1.90	1.85	1.81	1.75	1.70	1.64	29	
2.16	2.09	2.01	1.93	1.89	1.84	1.79	1.74	1.68	1.62	30	
2.08	2.00	1.92	1.84	1.79	1.74	1.69	1.64	1.58	1.51	40	
1.99	1.92	1.84	1.75	1.70	1.65	1.59	1.53	1.47	1.39	60	
1.91	1.83	1.75	1.66	1.61	1.55	1.50	1.43	1.35	1.25	120	
1.83	1.75	1.67	1.57	1.52	1.46	1.39	1.32	1.22	1.00	∞	

Denominator Degrees of Freedom

Continued

v_2	\multicolumn{9}{c}{$\alpha = .025$}
	\multicolumn{9}{c}{**Numerator Degrees of Freedom**}
	1	**2**	**3**	**4**	**5**	**6**	**7**	**8**	**9**
1	647.79	799.48	864.15	899.60	921.83	937.11	948.20	956.64	963.28
2	38.51	39.00	39.17	39.25	39.30	39.33	39.36	39.37	39.39
3	17.44	16.04	15.44	15.10	14.88	14.73	14.62	14.54	14.47
4	12.22	10.65	9.98	9.60	9.36	9.20	9.07	8.98	8.90
5	10.01	8.43	7.76	7.39	7.15	6.98	6.85	6.76	6.68
6	8.81	7.26	6.60	6.23	5.99	5.82	5.70	5.60	5.52
7	8.07	6.54	5.89	5.52	5.29	5.12	4.99	4.90	4.82
8	7.57	6.06	5.42	5.05	4.82	4.65	4.53	4.43	4.36
9	7.21	5.71	5.08	4.72	4.48	4.32	4.20	4.10	4.03
10	6.94	5.46	4.83	4.47	4.24	4.07	3.95	3.85	3.78
11	6.72	5.26	4.63	4.28	4.04	3.88	3.76	3.66	3.59
12	6.55	5.10	4.47	4.12	3.89	3.73	3.61	3.51	3.44
13	6.41	4.97	4.35	4.00	3.77	3.60	3.48	3.39	3.31
14	6.30	4.86	4.24	3.89	3.66	3.50	3.38	3.29	3.21
15	6.20	4.77	4.15	3.80	3.58	3.41	3.29	3.20	3.12
16	6.12	4.69	4.08	3.73	3.50	3.34	3.22	3.12	3.05
17	6.04	4.62	4.01	3.66	3.44	3.28	3.16	3.06	2.98
18	5.98	4.56	3.95	3.61	3.38	3.22	3.10	3.01	2.93
19	5.92	4.51	3.90	3.56	3.33	3.17	3.05	2.96	2.88
20	5.87	4.46	3.86	3.51	3.29	3.13	3.01	2.91	2.84
21	5.83	4.42	3.82	3.48	3.25	3.09	2.97	2.87	2.80
22	5.79	4.38	3.78	3.44	3.22	3.05	2.93	2.84	2.76
23	5.75	4.35	3.75	3.41	3.18	3.02	2.90	2.81	2.73
24	5.72	4.32	3.72	3.38	3.15	2.99	2.87	2.78	2.70
25	5.69	4.29	3.69	3.35	3.13	2.97	2.85	2.75	2.68
26	5.66	4.27	3.67	3.33	3.10	2.94	2.82	2.73	2.65
27	5.63	4.24	3.65	3.31	3.08	2.92	2.80	2.71	2.63
28	5.61	4.22	3.63	3.29	3.06	2.90	2.78	2.69	2.61
29	5.59	4.20	3.61	3.27	3.04	2.88	2.76	2.67	2.59
30	5.57	4.18	3.59	3.25	3.03	2.87	2.75	2.65	2.57
40	5.42	4.05	3.46	3.13	2.90	2.74	2.62	2.53	2.45
60	5.29	3.93	3.34	3.01	2.79	2.63	2.51	2.41	2.33
120	5.15	3.80	3.23	2.89	2.67	2.52	2.39	2.30	2.22
∞	5.02	3.69	3.12	2.79	2.57	2.41	2.29	2.19	2.11

v_1

Denominator Degrees of Freedom

$\alpha = .025$										v_1	
Numerator Degrees of Freedom											
10	12	15	20	24	30	40	60	120	∞		v_2
968.63	976.72	984.87	993.08	997.27	1001.40	1005.60	1009.79	1014.04	1018.00	1	
9.40	39.41	39.43	39.45	39.46	39.46	39.47	39.48	39.49	39.50	2	
14.42	14.34	14.25	14.17	14.12	14.08	14.04	13.99	13.95	13.90	3	
8.84	8.75	8.66	8.56	8.51	8.46	8.41	8.36	8.31	8.26	4	
6.62	6.52	6.43	6.33	6.28	6.23	6.18	6.12	6.07	6.02	5	
5.46	5.37	5.27	5.17	5.12	5.07	5.01	4.96	4.90	4.85	6	
4.76	4.67	4.57	4.47	4.41	4.36	4.31	4.25	4.20	4.14	7	
4.30	4.20	4.10	4.00	3.95	3.89	3.84	3.78	3.73	3.67	8	
3.96	3.87	3.77	3.67	3.61	3.56	3.51	3.45	3.39	3.33	9	
3.72	3.62	3.52	3.42	3.37	3.31	3.26	3.20	3.14	3.08	10	
3.53	3.43	3.33	3.23	3.17	3.12	3.06	3.00	2.94	2.88	11	
3.37	3.28	3.18	3.07	3.02	2.96	2.91	2.85	2.79	2.72	12	
3.25	3.15	3.05	2.95	2.89	2.84	2.78	2.72	2.66	2.60	13	
3.15	3.05	2.95	2.84	2.79	2.73	2.67	2.61	2.55	2.49	14	
3.06	2.96	2.86	2.76	2.70	2.64	2.59	2.52	2.46	2.40	15	
2.99	2.89	2.79	2.68	2.63	2.57	2.51	2.45	2.38	2.32	16	
2.92	2.82	2.72	2.62	2.56	2.50	2.44	2.38	2.32	2.25	17	
2.87	2.77	2.67	2.56	2.50	2.44	2.38	2.32	2.26	2.19	18	
2.82	2.72	2.62	2.51	2.45	2.39	2.33	2.27	2.20	2.13	19	
2.77	2.68	2.57	2.46	2.41	2.35	2.29	2.22	2.16	2.09	20	
2.73	2.64	2.53	2.42	2.37	2.31	2.25	2.18	2.11	2.04	21	
2.70	2.60	2.50	2.39	2.33	2.27	2.21	2.14	2.08	2.00	22	
2.67	2.57	2.47	2.36	2.30	2.24	2.18	2.11	2.04	1.97	23	
2.64	2.54	2.44	2.33	2.27	2.21	2.15	2.08	2.01	1.94	24	
2.61	2.51	2.41	2.30	2.24	2.18	2.12	2.05	1.98	1.91	25	
2.59	2.49	2.39	2.28	2.22	2.16	2.09	2.03	1.95	1.88	26	
2.57	2.47	2.36	2.25	2.19	2.13	2.07	2.00	1.93	1.85	27	
2.55	2.45	2.34	2.23	2.17	2.11	2.05	1.98	1.91	1.83	28	
2.53	2.43	2.32	2.21	2.15	2.09	2.03	1.96	1.89	1.81	29	
2.51	2.41	2.31	2.20	2.14	2.07	2.01	1.94	1.87	1.79	30	
2.39	2.29	2.18	2.07	2.01	1.94	1.88	1.80	1.72	1.64	40	
2.27	2.17	2.06	1.94	1.88	1.82	1.74	1.67	1.58	1.48	60	
2.16	2.05	1.94	1.82	1.76	1.69	1.61	1.53	1.43	1.31	120	
2.05	1.94	1.83	1.71	1.64	1.57	1.48	1.39	1.27	1.00	∞	

Denominator Degrees of Freedom

Continued

v_2	$\alpha = .01$ Numerator Degrees of Freedom								
	1	2	3	4	5	6	7	8	9
1	4052.18	4999.34	5403.53	5624.26	5763.96	5858.95	5928.33	5980.95	6022.40
2	98.50	99.00	99.16	99.25	99.30	99.33	99.36	99.38	99.39
3	34.12	30.82	29.46	28.71	28.24	27.91	27.67	27.49	27.34
4	21.20	18.00	16.69	15.98	15.52	15.21	14.98	14.80	14.66
5	16.26	13.27	12.06	11.39	10.97	10.67	10.46	10.29	10.16
6	13.75	10.92	9.78	9.15	8.75	8.47	8.26	8.10	7.98
7	12.25	9.55	8.45	7.85	7.46	7.19	6.99	6.84	6.72
8	11.26	8.65	7.59	7.01	6.63	6.37	6.18	6.03	5.91
9	10.56	8.02	6.99	6.42	6.06	5.80	5.61	5.47	5.35
10	10.04	7.56	6.55	5.99	5.64	5.39	5.20	5.06	4.94
11	9.65	7.21	6.22	5.67	5.32	5.07	4.89	4.74	4.63
12	9.33	6.93	5.95	5.41	5.06	4.82	4.64	4.50	4.39
13	9.07	6.70	5.74	5.21	4.86	4.62	4.44	4.30	4.19
14	8.86	6.51	5.56	5.04	4.69	4.46	4.28	4.14	4.03
15	8.68	6.36	5.42	4.89	4.56	4.32	4.14	4.00	3.89
16	8.53	6.23	5.29	4.77	4.44	4.20	4.03	3.89	3.78
17	8.40	6.11	5.19	4.67	4.34	4.10	3.93	3.79	3.68
18	8.29	6.01	5.09	4.58	4.25	4.01	3.84	3.71	3.60
19	8.18	5.93	5.01	4.50	4.17	3.94	3.77	3.63	3.52
20	8.10	5.85	4.94	4.43	4.10	3.87	3.70	3.56	3.46
21	8.02	5.78	4.87	4.37	4.04	3.81	3.64	3.51	3.40
22	7.95	5.72	4.82	4.31	3.99	3.76	3.59	3.45	3.35
23	7.88	5.66	4.76	4.26	3.94	3.71	3.54	3.41	3.30
24	7.82	5.61	4.72	4.22	3.90	3.67	3.50	3.36	3.26
25	7.77	5.57	4.68	4.18	3.85	3.63	3.46	3.32	3.22
26	7.72	5.53	4.64	4.14	3.82	3.59	3.42	3.29	3.18
27	7.68	5.49	4.60	4.11	3.78	3.56	3.39	3.26	3.15
28	7.64	5.45	4.57	4.07	3.75	3.53	3.36	3.23	3.12
29	7.60	5.42	4.54	4.04	3.73	3.50	3.33	3.20	3.09
30	7.56	5.39	4.51	4.02	3.70	3.47	3.30	3.17	3.07
40	7.31	5.18	4.31	3.83	3.51	3.29	3.12	2.99	2.89
60	7.08	4.98	4.13	3.65	3.34	3.12	2.95	2.82	2.72
120	6.85	4.79	3.95	3.48	3.17	2.96	2.79	2.66	2.56
∞	6.63	4.61	3.78	3.32	3.02	2.80	2.64	2.51	2.41

v_1

Denominator Degrees of Freedom

			Numerator Degrees of Freedom							v_1	
10	12	15	20	24	30	40	60	120	∞		v_2
6055.93	6106.68	6156.97	6208.66	6234.27	6260.35	6286.43	6312.97	6339.51	6366.00	1	
99.40	99.42	99.43	99.45	99.46	99.47	99.48	99.48	99.49	99.50	2	
27.23	27.05	26.87	26.69	26.60	26.50	26.41	26.32	26.22	26.13	3	
14.55	14.37	14.20	14.02	13.93	13.84	13.75	13.65	13.56	13.46	4	
10.05	9.89	9.72	9.55	9.47	9.38	9.29	9.20	9.11	9.02	5	
7.87	7.72	7.56	7.40	7.31	7.23	7.14	7.06	6.97	6.88	6	
6.62	6.47	6.31	6.16	6.07	5.99	5.91	5.82	5.74	5.65	7	
5.81	5.67	5.52	5.36	5.28	5.20	5.12	5.03	4.95	4.86	8	
5.26	5.11	4.96	4.81	4.73	4.65	4.57	4.48	4.40	4.31	9	
4.85	4.71	4.56	4.41	4.33	4.25	4.17	4.08	4.00	3.91	10	
4.54	4.40	4.25	4.10	4.02	3.94	3.86	3.78	3.69	3.60	11	
4.30	4.16	4.01	3.86	3.78	3.70	3.62	3.54	3.45	3.36	12	
4.10	3.96	3.82	3.66	3.59	3.51	3.43	3.34	3.25	3.17	13	
3.94	3.80	3.66	3.51	3.43	3.35	3.27	3.18	3.09	3.00	14	
3.80	3.67	3.52	3.37	3.29	3.21	3.13	3.05	2.96	2.87	15	
3.69	3.55	3.41	3.26	3.18	3.10	3.02	2.93	2.84	2.75	16	
3.59	3.46	3.31	3.16	3.08	3.00	2.92	2.83	2.75	2.65	17	
3.51	3.37	3.23	3.08	3.00	2.92	2.84	2.75	2.66	2.57	18	
3.43	3.30	3.15	3.00	2.92	2.84	2.76	2.67	2.58	2.49	19	
3.37	3.23	3.09	2.94	2.86	2.78	2.69	2.61	2.52	2.42	20	
3.31	3.17	3.03	2.88	2.80	2.72	2.64	2.55	2.46	2.36	21	
3.26	3.12	2.98	2.83	2.75	2.67	2.58	2.50	2.40	2.31	22	
3.21	3.07	2.93	2.78	2.70	2.62	2.54	2.45	2.35	2.26	23	
3.17	3.03	2.89	2.74	2.66	2.58	2.49	2.40	2.31	2.21	24	
3.13	2.99	2.85	2.70	2.62	2.54	2.45	2.36	2.27	2.17	25	
3.09	2.96	2.81	2.66	2.58	2.50	2.42	2.33	2.23	2.13	26	
3.06	2.93	2.78	2.63	2.55	2.47	2.38	2.29	2.20	2.10	27	
3.03	2.90	2.75	2.60	2.52	2.44	2.35	2.26	2.17	2.06	28	
3.00	2.87	2.73	2.57	2.49	2.41	2.33	2.23	2.14	2.03	29	
2.98	2.84	2.70	2.55	2.47	2.39	2.30	2.21	2.11	2.01	30	
2.80	2.66	2.52	2.37	2.29	2.20	2.11	2.02	1.92	1.80	40	
2.63	2.50	2.35	2.20	2.12	2.03	1.94	1.84	1.73	1.60	60	
2.47	2.34	2.19	2.03	1.95	1.86	1.76	1.66	1.53	1.38	120	
2.32	2.18	2.04	1.88	1.79	1.70	1.59	1.47	1.32	1.00	∞	

$\alpha = .01$

Denominator Degrees of Freedom

Continued

v_1	$\alpha = .005$								
	Numerator Degrees of Freedom								
v_2	1	2	3	4	5	6	7	8	9
1	16212.46	19997.36	21614.13	22500.75	23055.82	23439.53	23715.20	23923.81	24091.45
2	198.50	199.01	199.16	199.24	199.30	199.33	199.36	199.38	199.39
3	55.55	49.80	47.47	46.20	45.39	44.84	44.43	44.13	43.88
4	31.33	26.28	24.26	23.15	22.46	21.98	21.62	21.35	21.14
5	22.78	18.31	16.53	15.56	14.94	14.51	14.20	13.96	13.77
6	18.63	14.54	12.92	12.03	11.46	11.07	10.79	10.57	10.39
7	16.24	12.40	10.88	10.05	9.52	9.16	8.89	8.68	8.51
8	14.69	11.04	9.60	8.81	8.30	7.95	7.69	7.50	7.34
9	13.61	10.11	8.72	7.96	7.47	7.13	6.88	6.69	6.54
10	12.83	9.43	8.08	7.34	6.87	6.54	6.30	6.12	5.97
11	12.23	8.91	7.60	6.88	6.42	6.10	5.86	5.68	5.54
12	11.75	8.51	7.23	6.52	6.07	5.76	5.52	5.35	5.20
13	11.37	8.19	6.93	6.23	5.79	5.48	5.25	5.08	4.94
14	11.06	7.92	6.68	6.00	5.56	5.26	5.03	4.86	4.72
15	10.80	7.70	6.48	5.80	5.37	5.07	4.85	4.67	4.54
16	10.58	7.51	6.30	5.64	5.21	4.91	4.69	4.52	4.38
17	10.38	7.35	6.16	5.50	5.07	4.78	4.56	4.39	4.25
18	10.22	7.21	6.03	5.37	4.96	4.66	4.44	4.28	4.14
19	10.07	7.09	5.92	5.27	4.85	4.56	4.34	4.18	4.04
20	9.94	6.99	5.82	5.17	4.76	4.47	4.26	4.09	3.96
21	9.83	6.89	5.73	5.09	4.68	4.39	4.18	4.01	3.88
22	9.73	6.81	5.65	5.02	4.61	4.32	4.11	3.94	3.81
23	9.63	6.73	5.58	4.95	4.54	4.26	4.05	3.88	3.75
24	9.55	6.66	5.52	4.89	4.49	4.20	3.99	3.83	3.69
25	9.48	6.60	5.46	4.84	4.43	4.15	3.94	3.78	3.64
26	9.41	6.54	5.41	4.79	4.38	4.10	3.89	3.73	3.60
27	9.34	6.49	5.36	4.74	4.34	4.06	3.85	3.69	3.56
28	9.28	6.44	5.32	4.70	4.30	4.02	3.81	3.65	3.52
29	9.23	6.40	5.28	4.66	4.26	3.98	3.77	3.61	3.48
30	9.18	6.35	5.24	4.62	4.23	3.95	3.74	3.58	3.45
40	8.83	6.07	4.98	4.37	3.99	3.71	3.51	3.35	3.22
60	8.49	5.79	4.73	4.14	3.76	3.49	3.29	3.13	3.01
120	8.18	5.54	4.50	3.92	3.55	3.28	3.09	2.93	2.81
∞	7.88	5.30	4.28	3.72	3.35	3.09	2.90	2.74	2.62

Denominator Degrees of Freedom

$\alpha = .005$										v_1	
Numerator Degrees of Freedom											
10	12	15	20	24	30	40	60	120	∞		v_2
24221.84	24426.73	24631.62	24836.51	24937.09	25041.40	25145.71	25253.74	25358.05	25465.00	1	
199.39	199.42	199.43	199.45	199.45	199.48	199.48	199.48	199.49	199.50	2	
43.68	43.39	43.08	42.78	42.62	42.47	42.31	42.15	41.99	41.83	3	
20.97	20.70	20.44	20.17	20.03	19.89	19.75	19.61	19.47	19.32	4	
13.62	13.38	13.15	12.90	12.78	12.66	12.53	12.40	12.27	12.14	5	
10.25	10.03	9.81	9.59	9.47	9.36	9.24	9.12	9.00	8.88	6	
8.38	8.18	7.97	7.75	7.64	7.53	7.42	7.31	7.19	7.08	7	
7.21	7.01	6.81	6.61	6.50	6.40	6.29	6.18	6.06	5.95	8	
6.42	6.23	6.03	5.83	5.73	5.62	5.52	5.41	5.30	5.19	9	
5.85	5.66	5.47	5.27	5.17	5.07	4.97	4.86	4.75	4.64	10	
5.42	5.24	5.05	4.86	4.76	4.65	4.55	4.45	4.34	4.23	11	
5.09	4.91	4.72	4.53	4.43	4.33	4.23	4.12	4.01	3.90	12	
4.82	4.64	4.46	4.27	4.17	4.07	3.97	3.87	3.76	3.65	13	
4.60	4.43	4.25	4.06	3.96	3.86	3.76	3.66	3.55	3.44	14	
4.42	4.25	4.07	3.88	3.79	3.69	3.59	3.48	3.37	3.26	15	
4.27	4.10	3.92	3.73	3.64	3.54	3.44	3.33	3.22	3.11	16	
4.14	3.97	3.79	3.61	3.51	3.41	3.31	3.21	3.10	2.98	17	
4.03	3.86	3.68	3.50	3.40	3.30	3.20	3.10	2.99	2.87	18	
3.93	3.76	3.59	3.40	3.31	3.21	3.11	3.00	2.89	2.78	19	
3.85	3.68	3.50	3.32	3.22	3.12	3.02	2.92	2.81	2.69	20	
3.77	3.60	3.43	3.24	3.15	3.05	2.95	2.84	2.73	2.61	21	
3.70	3.54	3.36	3.18	3.08	2.98	2.88	2.77	2.66	2.55	22	
3.64	3.47	3.30	3.12	3.02	2.92	2.82	2.71	2.60	2.48	23	
3.59	3.42	3.25	3.06	2.97	2.87	2.77	2.66	2.55	2.43	24	
3.54	3.37	3.20	3.01	2.92	2.82	2.72	2.61	2.50	2.38	25	
3.49	3.33	3.15	2.97	2.87	2.77	2.67	2.56	2.45	2.33	26	
3.45	3.28	3.11	2.93	2.83	2.73	2.63	2.52	2.41	2.29	27	
3.41	3.25	3.07	2.89	2.79	2.69	2.59	2.48	2.37	2.25	28	
3.38	3.21	3.04	2.86	2.76	2.66	2.56	2.45	2.33	2.21	29	
3.34	3.18	3.01	2.82	2.73	2.63	2.52	2.42	2.30	2.18	30	
3.12	2.95	2.78	2.60	2.50	2.40	2.30	2.18	2.06	1.93	40	
2.90	2.74	2.57	2.39	2.29	2.19	2.08	1.96	1.83	1.69	60	
2.71	2.54	2.37	2.19	2.09	1.98	1.87	1.75	1.61	1.43	120	
2.52	2.36	2.19	2.00	1.90	1.79	1.67	1.53	1.36	1.00	∞	

TABLE A.5   The Chi-Square Table

Values of χ^2 for Selected Probabilities

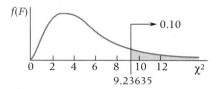

Example: df (Number of degrees of freedom) = 5, the tail above $\chi^2 = 9.23635$ represents 0.10 or 10% of the area under the curve.

Degrees of Freedom	Area in Upper Tail									
	.995	.99	.975	.95	.9	.1	.05	.025	.01	.005
1	0.0000393	0.0001571	0.0009821	0.0039322	0.0157907	2.7055	3.8415	5.0239	6.6349	7.8794
2	0.010025	0.020100	0.050636	0.102586	0.210721	4.6052	5.9915	7.3778	9.2104	10.5965
3	0.07172	0.11483	0.21579	0.35185	0.58438	6.2514	7.8147	9.3484	11.3449	12.8381
4	0.20698	0.29711	0.48442	0.71072	1.06362	7.7794	9.4877	11.1433	13.2767	14.8602
5	0.41175	0.55430	0.83121	1.14548	1.61031	9.2363	11.0705	12.8325	15.0863	16.7496
6	0.67573	0.87208	1.23734	1.63538	2.20413	10.6446	12.5916	14.4494	16.8119	18.5475
7	0.98925	1.23903	1.68986	2.16735	2.83311	12.0170	14.0671	16.0128	18.4753	20.2777
8	1.34440	1.64651	2.17972	2.73263	3.48954	13.3616	15.5073	17.5345	20.0902	21.9549
9	1.73491	2.08789	2.70039	3.32512	4.16816	14.6837	16.9190	19.0228	21.6660	23.5893
10	2.15585	2.55820	3.24696	3.94030	4.86518	15.9872	18.3070	20.4832	23.2093	25.1881
11	2.60320	3.05350	3.81574	4.57481	5.57779	17.2750	19.6752	21.9200	24.7250	26.7569
12	3.07379	3.57055	4.40378	5.22603	6.30380	18.5493	21.0261	23.3367	26.2170	28.2997
13	3.56504	4.10690	5.00874	5.89186	7.04150	19.8119	22.3620	24.7356	27.6882	29.8193
14	4.07466	4.66042	5.62872	6.57063	7.78954	21.0641	23.6848	26.1189	29.1412	31.3194
15	4.60087	5.22936	6.26212	7.26093	8.54675	22.3071	24.9958	27.4884	30.5780	32.8015
16	5.14216	5.81220	6.90766	7.96164	9.31224	23.5418	26.2962	28.8453	31.9999	34.2671
17	5.69727	6.40774	7.56418	8.67175	10.08518	24.7690	27.5871	30.1910	33.4087	35.7184
18	6.26477	7.01490	8.23074	9.39045	10.86494	25.9894	28.8693	31.5264	34.8052	37.1564
19	6.84392	7.63270	8.90651	10.11701	11.65091	27.2036	30.1435	32.8523	36.1908	38.5821
20	7.43381	8.26037	9.59077	10.85080	12.44260	28.4120	31.4104	34.1696	37.5663	39.9969
21	8.03360	8.89717	10.28291	11.59132	13.23960	29.6151	32.6706	35.4789	38.9322	41.4009
22	8.64268	9.54249	10.98233	12.33801	14.04149	30.8133	33.9245	36.7807	40.2894	42.7957
23	9.26038	10.19569	11.68853	13.09051	14.84795	32.0069	35.1725	38.0756	41.6383	44.1814
24	9.88620	10.85635	12.40115	13.84842	15.65868	33.1962	36.4150	39.3641	42.9798	45.5584
25	10.51965	11.52395	13.11971	14.61140	16.47341	34.3816	37.6525	40.6465	44.3140	46.9280
26	11.16022	12.19818	13.84388	15.37916	17.29188	35.5632	38.8851	41.9231	45.6416	48.2898
27	11.80765	12.87847	14.57337	16.15139	18.11389	36.7412	40.1133	43.1945	46.9628	49.6450
28	12.46128	13.56467	15.30785	16.92788	18.93924	37.9159	41.3372	44.4608	48.2782	50.9936
29	13.12107	14.25641	16.04705	17.70838	19.76774	39.0875	42.5569	45.7223	49.5878	52.3355
30	13.78668	14.95346	16.79076	18.49267	20.59924	40.2560	43.7730	46.9792	50.8922	53.6719
40	20.70658	22.16420	24.43306	26.50930	29.05052	51.8050	55.7585	59.3417	63.6908	66.7660
50	27.99082	29.70673	32.35738	34.76424	37.68864	63.1671	67.5048	71.4202	76.1538	79.4898
60	35.53440	37.48480	40.48171	43.18797	46.45888	74.3970	79.0820	83.2977	88.3794	91.9518
70	43.27531	45.44170	48.75754	51.73926	55.32894	85.5270	90.5313	95.0231	100.4251	104.2148
80	51.17193	53.53998	57.15315	60.39146	64.27784	96.5782	101.8795	106.6285	112.3288	116.3209
90	59.19633	61.75402	65.64659	69.12602	73.29108	107.5650	113.1452	118.1359	124.1162	128.2987
100	67.32753	70.06500	74.22188	77.92944	82.35813	118.4980	124.3421	129.5613	135.8069	140.1697

TABLE A.6 — Critical Values for the Durbin-Watson Test

Entries in the table give the critical values for a one-tailed Durbin-Watson test for autocorrelation. For a two-tailed test, the level of significance is doubled.

Significant Points of d_L and d_U: α = .05
Number of Independent Variables

k		1		2		3		4		5
n	d_L	d_U	d_L	d_U	d_L	d_U	d_L	d_U	d_L	d_U
15	1.08	1.36	0.95	1.54	0.82	1.75	0.69	1.97	0.56	2.21
16	1.10	1.37	0.98	1.54	0.86	1.73	0.74	1.93	0.62	2.15
17	1.13	1.38	1.02	1.54	0.90	1071	0.78	1.90	0.67	2.10
18	1.16	1.39	1.05	1.53	0.93	1.69	0.82	1.87	0.71	2.06
19	1.18	1.40	1.08	1.53	0.97	1.68	0.86	1.85	0.75	2.02
20	1.20	1.41	1.10	1.54	1.00	1.68	0.90	1.83	0.79	1.99
21	1.22	1.42	1.13	1.54	1.03	1.67	0.93	1.81	0.83	1.96
22	1.24	1.43	1.15	1.54	1.05	1.66	0.96	1.80	0.86	1.94
23	1.26	1.44	1.17	1.54	1.08	1.66	0.99	1.79	0.90	1.92
24	1.27	1.45	1.19	1.55	1.10	1.66	1.01	1.78	0.93	1.90
25	1.29	1.45	1.21	1.55	1.12	1.66	1.04	1.77	0.95	1.89
26	1.30	1.46	1.22	1.55	1.14	1.65	1.06	1.76	0.98	1.88
27	1.32	1.47	1.24	1.56	1.16	1.65	1.08	1.76	1.01	1.86
28	1.33	1.48	1.26	1.56	1.18	1.65	1.10	1.75	1.03	1085
29	1.34	1.48	1.27	1.56	1.20	1.65	1.12	1.74	1.05	1.84
30	1.35	1.49	1.28	1.57	1.21	1.65	1.14	1.74	1.07	1.83
31	1.36	1.50	1.30	1.57	1.23	1.65	1.16	1.74	1.09	1.83
32	1.37	1.50	1.31	1.57	1.24	1.65	1.18	1.73	1.11	1.82
33	1.38	1.51	1.32	1.58	1.26	1.65	1.19	1.73	1.13	1.81
34	1.39	1.51	1.33	1.58	1.27	1.65	1.21	1.73	1.15	1.81
35	1.40	1.52	1.34	1.58	1.28	1.65	1.22	1.73	1.16	1.80
36	1.41	1.52	1.35	1.59	1.29	1.65	1.24	1.73	1.18	1.80
37	1.42	1.53	1.36	1.59	1.31	1.66	1.25	1.72	1.19	1.80
38	1.43	1.54	1.37	1.59	1.32	1.66	1.26	1.72	1.21	1.79
39	1.43	1.54	1.38	1.60	1.33	1.66	1.27	1.72	1.22	1.79
40	1.44	1.54	1.39	1.60	1.34	1.66	1.29	1.72	1.23	1.79
45	1.48	1.57	1.43	1.62	1.38	1.67	1.34	1.72	1.29	1.78
50	1.50	1.59	1.46	1.63	1.421	1.67	1.38	1.72	1.34	1.77
55	1.53	1.60	1.49	1.64	1.45	1.68	1.41	1.72	1.38	1.77
60	1.55	1.62	1.51	1.65	1.48	1.69	1.44	1.73	1.41	1.77
65	1.57	1.63	1.54	1.66	1.50	1.70	1.47	1.73	1.44	1.77
70	1.58	1.64	1.55	1.67	1.52	1.70	1.49	1.74	1.46	1.77
75	1.60	1.65	1.57	1.68	1.54	1.71	1.51	1.74	1.49	1.77
80	1.61	1.66	1.59	1.69	1.56	1.72	1.53	1.74	1.51	1.77
85	1.62	1.67	1.60	1.70	1.57	1.72	1.55	1.75	1.52	1.77
90	1.63	1.68	1.61	1.70	1.59	1.73	1.57	1.75	1.54	1.78
95	1.64	1.69	1.62	1.71	1.60	1.73	1.58	1.75	1.56	1.78
100	1.65	1.69	1.63	1.72	1.61	1.74	1.59	1.76	1.57	1.78

This table is reprinted by permission of *Biometrika* Trustees from J. Durbin and G.S. Watson, "Testing for Serial Correlation in Least Square Regression II," *Biometrika*, vol. 38, 1951, pp. 159-78.

Continued

Significant Points of d_L and d_U: $\alpha = .01$
Number of Independent Variables

k	1		2		3		4		5	
n	d_L	d_U	d_L	d_U	d_L	d_U	d_L	d_U	d_L	d_U
15	0.81	1.07	0.70	1.25	0.59	1.46	0.49	1.70	0.39	1.96
16	0.84	1.09	0.74	1.25	0.63	1044	0.53	1.66	0.44	1.90
17	0.87	1.10	0.77	1.25	0.67	1.43	0.57	1.63	0.48	1.85
18	0.90	1.12	0.80	1.26	0.71	1.42	0.61	1.60	0.52	1.80
19	0.93	1.13	0.83	1.26	0.74	1.41	0.65	1.58	0.56	1.77
20	0.95	1.15	0.86	1.27	0.77	1.41	0.68	1.57	0.60	1.74
21	0.97	1.16	0.89	1.27	0.80	1.41	0.72	1.55	0.63	1.71
22	1.00	1.17	0.91	1.28	0.83	1.40	0.75	1.54	0.66	1.69
23	1.02	1.19	0.94	1.29	0.86	1.40	0.77	1.53	0.70	1.67
24	1.04	1.20	0.96	1.30	0.88	1.41	0.80	1.53	0.72	1.66
25	1.05	1.21	0.98	1.30	0.90	1.41	0.83	1.52	0.75	1.65
26	1.07	1.22	1.00	1.31	0.93	1.41	0.85	1.52	0.78	1.64
27	1.09	1.23	1.02	1.32	0.95	1.41	0.88	1.51	0.81	1.63
28	1.10	1.24	1.04	1.32	0.97	1.41	0.90	1.51	0.83	1.62
29	1.12	1.25	1.05	1.33	0.99	1.42	0.92	1.51	0.85	1.61
30	1.13	1.26	1.07	1.34	1.01	1.42	0.94	1.51	0.88	1.61
31	1.15	1.27	1.08	1.34	1.02	1.42	0.96	1.51	0.90	1.60
32	1.16	1.28	1.10	1.35	1.04	1.43	0.98	1.51	0.92	1.60
33	1.17	1.29	1.11	1.36	1.05	1.43	1.00	1.51	0.94	1.59
34	1.18	1.30	1.13	1.36	1.07	1.43	1.01	1.51	0.95	1.59
35	1.19	1.31	1.14	1.37	1.08	1.44	1.03	1.51	0.97	1.59
36	1.21	1.32	1.15	1.38	1.10	1.44	1.04	1.51	0.99	1.59
37	1.22	1.32	1.16	1.38	1.11	1.45	1.06	1.51	1.00	1.59
38	1.23	1.33	1.18	1.39	1.12	1.45	1.07	1.52	1.02	1.58
39	1.24	1.34	1.19	1.39	1.14	1.45	1.09	1.52	1.03	1.58
40	1.25	1.34	1.20	1.40	1.15	1.46	1.10	1.52	1.05	1.58
45	1.29	1.38	1.24	1.42	1.20	1.48	1.16	1.53	1.11	1.58
50	1.32	1.40	1.28	1.45	1.24	1.49	1.20	1.54	1.16	1.59
55	1.36	1.43	1.32	1.47	1.28	1.51	1.25	1.55	1.21	1.59
60	1.38	1.45	1.35	1.48	1.32	1.52	1.28	1.56	1.25	1.60
65	1.41	1.47	1.38	1.50	1.35	1.53	1.31	1.57	1.28	1.61
70	1.43	1.49	1.40	1.52	1.37	1.55	1.34	1.58	1.31	1.61
75	1.45	1.50	1.42	1.53	1.39	1.56	1.37	1.59	1.34	1.62
80	1.47	1.52	1.44	1.54	1.42	1.57	1.39	1.60	1.36	1.62
85	1.48	1.53	1.46	1.55	1.43	1.58	1.41	1.60	1.39	1.63
90	1.50	1.54	1.47	1.56	1.45	1.59	1.43	1.61	1.41	1.64
95	1.51	1.55	1.49	1.57	1.47	1.60	1.45	1.62	1.42	1.64
100	1.52	1.56	1.50	1.58	1.48	1.60	1.46	1.63	1.44	1.65

APPENDIX B: ANSWERS TO SELECTED PROBLEMS

CHAPTER 1

1.7 825

1.13
   a. .0548
   b. .7881
   c. .0082
   d. .8575
   e. .1664

1.15 11.11

1.17
   a. .9772
   b. .2385
   c. .1469
   d. .1230

1.19 .0000

1.21
   a. .1894
   b. .0559
   c. .0000
   d. 16.4964

1.23
   a. .1492
   b. .9404
   c. .1985
   d. .1445
   e. .0000

1.25 .26

1.27
   a. .1977
   b. .2843
   c. .9881

1.29
   a. .1020
   b. .7568

   c. .2981

1.31 55, 45, 90, 25, 35

1.37
   a. .3156
   b. .00003
   c. .1736

1.41 .0021, .9265, .0281

1.43
   a. .0314
   b. .2420
   c. .2250
   d. .1469
   e. .0000

1.45
   a. .8534
   b. .0256
   c. .0007

1.49 .6402, .0174, .0217

1.51 .9147

CHAPTER 2

2.1
   a. $24.11 \leq \mu \leq 25.89$
   b. $113.17 \leq \mu \leq 126.03$
   c. $3.136 \leq \mu \leq 3.702$
   d. $54.55 \leq \mu \leq 58.85$

2.3 $45.92 \leq \mu \leq 48.08$

2.5 $66, 62.75 \leq \mu \leq 69.25$

2.7 $5.3, 5.13 \leq \mu \leq 5.47$

2.9 $2.853 \leq \mu \leq 3.759$

2.11 $23.036 \leq \mu \leq 26.030$

2.13 $42.18 \leq \mu \leq 49.06$

2.15 $118.57 \leq \mu \leq 138.23$, 128.4

2.17 $15.631 \leq \mu \leq 16.545$, 16.088

2.19 $2.26886 \leq \mu \leq 2.45346$, 2.36116, $.0923$

2.21 $36.77 \leq \mu \leq 62.83$

2.23 **a.** $.316 \leq p \leq .704$

     b. $.777 \leq p \leq .863$

     c. $.456 \leq p \leq .504$

     d. $.246 \leq p \leq .394$

2.25 $.38 \leq p \leq .56$

     $.364 \leq p \leq .576$

     $.33 \leq p \leq .61$

2.27 $.4287 \leq p \leq .5113$

     $.2488 \leq p \leq .3112$

2.29 **a.** $.266$

     b. $.246 \leq p \leq .286$

2.31 $.5935 \leq p \leq .6665$

2.33 $18.24 \leq \sigma^2 \leq 106.66$

2.35 $1.37 \leq \sigma^2 \leq 10.54$

2.37 **a.** 200

     b. 114

     c. 299

     d. 57

2.39 166

2.41 62

2.43 385

2.45 $43.924 \leq \mu \leq 47.276$, $43.138 \leq \mu \leq 48.062$, $42.549 \leq \mu \leq 48.651$

2.47 **a.** $.4235 \leq p \leq .4965$

     b. $.6657 \leq p \leq .7543$

     c. $.4523 \leq p \leq .5077$

     d. $.5374 \leq p \leq .6446$

2.49 **a.** 827

     b. 196

     c. 849

     d. 897

2.51 722

2.53 $196.33 \leq \mu \leq 229.67$

2.55 196

2.57 $117.534 \leq \mu \leq 138.466$, 20.932

2.59 196

2.61 $.233 \leq p \leq .427$

2.63 $4.6736 \leq \mu \leq 4.9664$

2.65 $.28 \leq p \leq .38$

2.67 $1.69 \leq \mu \leq 2.51$

2.69 $1.209 \leq \mu \leq 1.379$

CHAPTER 3

3.1 **a.** $z = 2.77$, reject

     b. .0028

     c. 22.115, 27.885

3.3 **a.** $z = 1.59$, reject

     b. .0559

     c. 1212.04

3.5 $z = 1.84$, fail to reject

3.7 $z = 1.41$, fail to reject

3.9 $z = -5.46$, reject

3.11 $t = 0.56$, fail to reject

3.13 $t = 2.44$, reject

3.15 $t = 1.59$, fail to reject

3.17 $t = -2.06$, fail to reject

3.19 $z = 0.53$, fail to reject

3.21 $z = -0.60$, fail to reject

     .2743, .257 and .323

3.23 $z = -3.00$, reject

3.25 $z = 2.02$, fail to reject

3.27 $z = 2.08$, reject

3.29 $\chi^2 = 23.64$, reject

3.31 $\chi^2 = 49.93$, reject

3.33 **a.** .7852

     b. .8749

     c. .9671

3.35 .5160

3.37 $z = 0.96$, fail to reject, .8599, .5832, .2514, .0618

3.39 $z = 3.21$, reject

3.41 **a.** $z = 0.85$, fail to reject

     b. $z = -2.05$, reject

3.43 **a.** $\beta = .1003$

     b. $\beta = .6255$

3.45 $z = 1.05$, fail to reject

3.47 $\chi^2 = 24.63$, reject

3.49 **a.** $z = 1.38$, fail to reject

     b. $z = -2.52$, $\beta = .0059$

3.51 $z = 1.53$, fail to reject, .7704

3.53 $z = 2.05$, fail to reject, .01, .3300

3.55 $\chi^2 = 47.25$, reject

3.57 **a.** $z = -1.43$, fail to reject

     b. .3156

CHAPTER 4

4.1 $\hat{y} = 16.5 + 0.162x$

4.3 $\hat{y} = -46.29 + 15.24x$

4.5 $\hat{y} = 158881.1 - 0.48042x$

4.7 $\hat{y} = -2.31307 + 0.05557x$

4.9   18.4582, 19.9196, 21.0563, 17.8087, 19.7572, −1.4582, −4.9196, 0.9437, 1.1913, 4.2428

4.11 144.2053, 10.0953, 282.8873, 868.0945, 526.7236, 46.6708, 209.7364, 581.5868, 3.7947, 44.9047, 55.1127, 125.9055, 14.2764, 42.3292, −83.7364, −202.5868

4.13 4.7244, −0.9836, −0.3996, −6.7537, 2.7683, 0.6442

4.15 Error terms nonindependent.

4.17 Nonlinear regression.

4.19 SSE = 46.5692, s_e = 3.94, 3 out of 5

4.21 SSE = 70940, s_e = 108.7, 6 out of 8

4.23 s_e = 4.391

4.25 $\hat{y} = 118.257 - 0.1504x$, s_e = 40.5256

4.27 r^2 = .972

4.29 r^2 = .685

4.31 $\hat{y} = -599.3674 + 19.2204x$; s_e = 13.539; r^2 = .688

4.33 $t = -13.18$, reject

4.35 $t = -2.56$, fail to reject

4.37 $F = 8.26$, p-value = .021, not significant at α = .01, $t = 2.874$, not significant at α = .01.

4.39 $38.523 \le y \le 70.705$, $10.447 \le y \le 44.901$

4.41 $0.97 \le E(y_{10}) \le 15.65$

4.43 a. $\hat{y} = -11.335 + 0.355x$

      b. 7.48, 5.35, 3.22, 6.415, 9.255, 10.675, 4.64, 9.965; −2.48, −0.35, 3.78, −2.415, 0.745, 1.325, −1.64, 1.035

      c. SSE = 32.4649

      d. s_e = 2.3261

      e. r^2 = .608

      f. $t = 3.05$, reject

4.45 a. $20.92 < E(y_{60}) < 26.8$

      b. $20.994 < y < 37.688$

4.47 $\hat{y} = 9.728511 + 10.626383x$, s_e = 97.1277, r^2 = .652, $t = 4.33$, reject

4.49 $\hat{y} = -1004.9575 + 2.97366x$; $\hat{y}(700) = 1076.6044$; −287.5588 to 2440.7676; $t = 3.6124$, reject

4.51 $\hat{y} = 1268.685 + 0.01835x$

4.53 $\hat{y} = -54.35604 + 2.40107x$; s_e = 17.886; r^2 = .91; $t = 7.80$, reject; $\hat{y}(100) = 185.75$

CHAPTER 5

5.1 $\hat{y} = 25.03 - 0.0497x_1 + 1.928x_2$, 28.586

5.3 $\hat{y} = 121.62 - 0.174x_1 + 6.02x2 + 0.00026x_3 + 0.0041x_4$, 4

5.5   Per capita consumption = −538 + 0.23368 paper consumption + 18.09 fish consumption − 0.2116 gasoline consumption

5.7   9, fail to reject null overall at α = .05, only $t = 2.73$ for x_1, significant at α = .05, s_e = 3.503, R^2 = .408, adj. R^2 = .203

5.9   Per capita consumption = −538 + 0.23368 paper consumption + 18.09 fish consumption − 0.2116 gasoline consumption; $F = 24.63$, p =.002; $t_1 = 5.31$, p =.003; $t_2 = 0.98$, p = .373; $t_3 = −0.93$, p = .397; s_e = 2085; R^2 = .937; adj. R^2 = .899

5.11 $\hat{y} = 3.981 + 0.07322x_1 - 0.03232x_2 - 0.003886x_3$, $F = 100.47$ significant at α = .01, $t = 3.50$ for x_1 significant at α = .01, s_e = 0.2331, R^2 = .965, adj. R^2 = .955

5.13 3 predictors, 15 observations, $\hat{y} = 657.053 + 5.710 x_1 - 0.417 x_2 - 3.471 x_3$, R^2 = .842, adjusted R^2 = .630, s_e = 109.43, $F = 8.96$ with $p = .0027$, x_1 significant at α = .01, x_3 significant at α = .05

5.15 s_e = 9.722, R^2 = .515, adjusted R^2 = .404

5.17 s_e = 6.544, R^2 = .005, adjusted R^2 = .000

5.19 model with x_1, x_2: s_e = 6.333, R^2 = .963, adjusted R^2 = .957

      model with x_1: s_e = 6.124, R^2 = .963, adjusted R^2 = .960

5.21 heterogeneity of variance

5.23 2, $\hat{y} = 203.3937 + 1.1151x_1 - 2.2115x_2$, $F = 24.55$, reject, R^2 = .663, adjusted R^2 = .636

5.25 $\hat{y} = 362 - 4.75x_1 -13.9x_2 + 1.87x_3$; $F = 16.05$, reject; s_e = 37.07; R^2 = .858; adjusted R^2 = .804; x_1 only significant predictor

5.27 Employment = 71.03 + 0.4620 Naval Vessels + 0.02082 Commercial

      $F = 1.22$, fail to reject; R^2 = .379; adjusted R^2 = .068; no significant predictors

5.29 Corn = −2718 + 6.26 Soybeans − 0.77 Wheat; $F = 14.25$, reject; s_e = 862.4; R^2 = .803; adjusted R^2 = .746; Soybeans was a significant predictor

CHAPTER 6

6.1   Simple Model: $\hat{y} = -147.27 + 27.128 x$, $F = 229$ with $p = .000$, s_e = 27.27, R^2 = .97, adjusted R^2 = .966

Quadratic Model: $\hat{y} = -22.01 + 3.385x_1 + 0.9373x_2$, $F = 578.76$ with $p = .000$, $s_e = 12.3$, $R^2 = .995$, adjusted $R^2 = .993$, for x_1: $t = 0.75$, for x_2: $t = 5.33$

6.3 $\hat{y} = 1012 - 14.1x + 0.611x^2$; $R^2 = .947$; S = 605.7; adjusted $R^2 = .911$; $t(x) = -0.17$, fail to reject; $t(x^2) = 1.03$, fail to reject

6.5 $\hat{y} = -28.61 - 2.68x_1 + 18.25x_2 - 0.2135x_1^2 - 1.533x_2^2 + 1.226x_1x_2$; $F = 63.43$, reject; $s_e = 4.669$, $R^2 = .958$; adjusted $R^2 = .943$; no significant t ratios. Model with no interaction term: $R^2 = .957$

6.7 $\hat{y} = 13.619 - 0.01201x_1 + 2.988x_2$, $F = 8.43$ significant at $\alpha = .01$, $t = 3.88$ for x_2, (dummy variable) significant at $\alpha = .01$, $s_e = 1.245$, $R^2 = .652$, adj. $R^2 = .575$

6.9 x_1 is a significant predictor at $\alpha = .05$

6.11 Price = $7.066 - 0.0855$ Hours + 9.614 Probability + 10.507 French Quarter, $F = 6.80$ significant at $\alpha = .01$, $t = 3.97$ for French Quarter (dummy variable) significant at $\alpha = .01$, $s_e = 4.02$, $R^2 = .671$, adj. $R^2 = .573$

6.13 Step 1: x_2 entered, $t = -7.53$, $r^2 = .794$
Step 2: x_3 entered, $t_2 = -4.60$, $t_3 = 2.93$, $R^2 = .876$

6.15 4 predictors, x_2 ($c3$) and x_5($c6$) not in model.

6.17 Step 1: Dividends in the model, $t = 6.69$, $r^2 = .833$

Step 2: Net income and dividends in model, $t = 2.24$ and $t = 4.36$, $R^2 = .897$

6.19

	y	x_1	x_2
x_1	$-.653$		
x_2	$-.891$	$.650$	
x_3	$.821$	$-.615$	$-.688$

6.21

	Net Income	Dividends
Dividends	.682	
Underwriting	.092	$-.522$

6.23 $\hat{y} = 564 - 27.99 x_1 - 6.155 x_2 - 15.90 x_3$, $R^2 = .809$, adjusted $R^2 = .738$, $s_e = 42.88$, $F = 11.32$ with $p = .003$, x_2 only significant predictor x_1 is a non significant indicator variable

6.25 The procedure stopped at step 1 with only log x in the model, $= -13.20 + 11.64 \log x_1$, $R^2 = .9617$

6.27 The procedure went 2 steps, step 1: silver entered, $R^2 = .5244$, step 2: aluminum entered, $R^2 = .8204$, final model: gold $= -50.19 + 18.9$ silver + 3.59 aluminum

6.29 The procedure went 3 steps, step 1: food entered, $R^2 = .84$, step 2: fuel oil entered, $R^2 = .95$, step 3: shelter entered, $R^2 = .96$, final model: All $= -1.0615 + 0.474$ food $+ 0.269$ fuel oil $+ 0.249$ shelter

6.31 Grocery = $76.23 + 0.08592$ Housing $+ 0.16767$ Utility $+ 0.0284$ Transportation $- 0.0659$ Healthcare, $F = 2.29$ not significant; $s_e = 4.416$; $R^2 = .315$; Adjusted $R^2 = .177$; Utility only significant predictor.

CHAPTER 7

7.1 MAD = 1.367, MSE = 2.27

7.3 MAD = 5.375, MSE = 23.65

7.5 **a.** 44.75, 52.75, 61.50, 64.75, 70.50, 81

b. 53.25, 56.375, 62.875, 67.25, 76.375, 89.125

7.7 $\alpha = .3$: 9.4, 9, 8.7, 8.8, 9.1, 9.7, 9.9, 9.8

$\alpha = .7$: 9.4, 8.6, 8.1, 8.7, 9.5, 10.6, 10.4, 9.8

7.9 $\alpha = .2$: 332, 404.4, 427.1, 386.1, 350.7, 315, 325.2, 362.6, 423.5, 453, 477.4, 554.9

$\alpha = .9$: 332, 657.8, 532, 253, 213.4, 176.1, 347, 495.5, 649.9, 578.9, 575.4, 836; $\text{MAD}_{\alpha=.2} = 190.8$; $\text{MAD}_{\alpha=.9} = 168.6$

7.11 Members = $17206 - 62.7$ Year; $R^2 = .809$; $s_e = 158.8$; $F = 63.54$, reject

7.13 TC: 136.78, 132.90, 128.54, 126.43, 124.86, 122, 119.08, 116.76, 114.61, 112.70, 111.75, 111.36

SI: 93.30, 90.47, 92.67, 98.77, 111.09, 100.83, 113.52, 117.58, 112.36, 92.08, 99.69, 102.73

7.15 $D = 1.12$, reject

7.17 Assets = $1379 + 136.68$ failures, $R^2 = .379$, $D = 2.49$, fail to reject

7.19 1 lag model: $= 158 + 0.589 x$, $R^2 = .353$

2 lag model: $= 401 - 0.065 x$, $R^2 = .05$

7.21 **a.** 100, 139.9, 144.0, 162.6, 200, 272.8, 310.7, 327.1, 356.6, 376.9, 388.8

b. 32.2, 45.0, 46.4, 52.3, 64.4, 87.8, 100, 105.3, 114.8, 121.3, 125.1

7.23 100, 108.5, 112.0

7.25 121.6, 127.4, 131.4

7.27 **a.** Linear: $= 9.96 - 0.14 x$, $R^2 = 90.9\%$,

Quadratic: $= 10.4 - 0.252 x + .00445 x_2$, $R^2 = 94.4\%$

b. MAD = .3585

c. MAD ($\alpha = .3$) = .4374, MAD ($\alpha = .7$) = .2596

d. $\alpha = .7$ did best

7.29 100, 104.8, 114.5, 115.5, 114.1

7.31 $\text{MAD}_{\text{mov.avg.}} = 653.63$, $\text{MAD}_{\alpha=.2} = 1054.11$

7.33 Jan. 95.35, Feb. 99.69, March 106.75, April 103.99, May 100.99, June 106.96, July 94.53, Aug. 99.60, Sept. 104.16, Oct. 97.04, Nov. 95.75, Dec. 95.19

7.35 unweighted: 100, 101.5, 103.05; Laspeyres: 104.4, 106.4; Paasche: 104.3, 106.3

7.37 $\text{MSE}_{\text{ma}} = 49.06$; $\text{MSE}_{\text{wma}} = 32.07$

7.39 98.07, 103.84, 97.04, 101.05

7.43 $D = 0.99$, inconclusive

7.45 $D = 0.98$, reject

CHAPTER 8

1. 560 diagonal kites, 920 box kites; weekly profit = $6280

3. **b.** 80 GE45's, 53.3333 GE60's

  c. 106.6667 GE45's, 35.5556 GE60's

6. **a.** MAX $30000X_1 + 80000X_2$

  s.t. $X_1 \leq 26$

  $X_2 \leq 5$

  $2000X_1 + 8000X_2 \leq 40000$

  $X_1 \geq 8$

  $X_2 \geq 2$

  Solution: Place 12 daily ads and 2 Sunday ads—Exposure = 520,000

  Much of the same population is probably reading both the daily and Sunday newspapers—may not get this increase in exposure on Sunday.

  b. Given the budget, there can be a maximum of 20 daily ads or 5 Sunday ads.

  c. Place 20 daily ads and no Sunday ads—Exposure = 600,000

8. **a.** MIN $100X_1 + 140X_2$

  s.t. $20X_1 + 40X_2 \geq 800$

  $20X_1 + 25X_2 \geq 600$

  $20X_1 + 10X_2 \geq 500$

  $X_1, X_2 \geq 0$

  Purchase 2000 pounds of La Paz ore and 1000 pounds of Sucre ore

  b. La Paz—($70, $280), Sucre—($50, $200); within these limits the optimal solution remains unchanged.

  c. Outside the range of optimality; reduced cost = $50

  d. $3 for copper in the range (700, 2000); $0 for zinc in the range ($-\infty$, 6500); $2 for iron in the range (400, 800). Within these ranges the cost per extra pound of requirements will remain unchanged.

  e. Infeasible

10. **a.** $1.50 per cow **b.** Would cost $1.60 per cow

  c. 50 oz. Cow Chow per cow, 25 oz. Moo Town per cow—total savings $25/day

12. Participate in the program and plant 125 acres of wheat and 125 acres of corn; profit = $43,750; if he did not participate the optimal profit would be $43,050.

14. **a.** 1680 phone hours, 4570 door to door hours; 132,660 voters reached

b. 1260 phone hours, 4990 door to door hours; 217,440 voters reached

15. 4 magazine ads, 2 Internet ads

17. MIN $X_1 + X_2$

  s.t. $.06X_1 + .10X_2 \geq 4000$

  $.06X_1 + .03X_2 \geq 2000$

  $X_1 + X_2 \leq 60000$

  $X_1, X_2 \geq 0$

  Invest $19,047.62 in the C/D and $28,571.43 in the venture capital project. He can keep $12,380.95 for personal use.

19. **a.** 187.5 acres of garlic; 0 acres of onions; 12.5 acres of unfarmed land

  b. $412.50 **c.** 150 acres of garlic; 50 acres of onions **d.** $0

21. **a.** MIN $3000X_1 + 1000X_2$

  s.t. $X_2 \leq 5$

  $2000X_1 + 800X_2 \geq 10000$

  $X_1, X_2 \geq 0$

  Optimal: Lease 3 and Purchase 5; monthly payments = $14,000

  b. The solution is unbounded

  c. The number of machines leased and purchased must be integers

22. **a.** 120 8-sq. ft. crates; 60 4-sq. ft. crates; profit = $13,200

  No slack on hours or space; 20 slack in the max number of 8-sq. ft. crates shipped and 60 slack in the maximum number of 4-sq. ft. crates shipped—these will not be shipped

  b. $8.33 in the range (720–1320); crates must be integers—the optimal solution with one extra sq. ft. of loading space is not integer valued.

  c. The shadow price reduces to $6.33; extra hours are still worth $18.33.

23. MAX $.10X_1 + .12X_2$

  s.t. $X_1 + X_2 = 100000$

  $.000002X_1 + .000004X_2 \geq .25$

  $.000003X_1 + .000008X_2 \leq .50$

  $X_1, X_2 \geq 0$

  Invest $60,000 in Tater, Inc. and $40,000 in Lakeside

26. **a.** MAX $15X_1 + 25X_2$

  s.t. $12X_1 + 10X_2 \leq 150$

  $50X_1 + 40X_2 \leq 500$

  $5X_1 + 10X_2 \leq 90$

  $15X_2 \leq 120$

  $X_1, X_2 \geq 0$

Bake 4 2/3 dozen (=56) custard pies and 6 2/3 dozen (=80) fruit pies

b. No, $15 extra is within the Allowable Increase

c. No **d.** No change **e.** Yes $2.67 > $2.25

27. **a.** No **b.** Yes **c.** Same optimal solution; $28.50

28. Produce 300 KCU's and 600 KCP's; Profit = $180,000. Klone will use 1200 floppy drives (600 unused), 600 hard drives (100 unused) and 900 cases (100 unused). All 480 production hours are used.

32. Use 6 Nautilus machines and spend 21 minutes on the treadmill; 81 points

33. **a.** MAX $24000X_1 + 30000X_2$

$$\text{s.t.} \quad X_1 \qquad \leq \quad 3$$
$$X_2 \leq \quad 2$$
$$50X_1 \quad + 60X_2 \leq 160$$
$$X_1, X_2 \geq 0 \text{ and integer}$$

Sell 2 compactors and 1 drill press; profit = $78,000

b. Linear solution is (.8,2)—rounding up (or off) to (1,2) is infeasible; rounding down to (0,2) produces a feasible solution that is not optimal.

c. Fractional values would be work in progress.

34. **a.** MIN $3500X_1 + 800X_2$

$$\text{s.t.} \quad 150X_1 + 35X_2 \geq 750$$
$$X_1 \qquad \geq \quad 1$$
$$X_2 \leq \quad 20$$
$$X_1, X_2 \geq 0 \text{ and integer}$$

b. Rounded solution is 1 60-inch and 18 27-in. sets; cost = $17,900

c. 2 60-inch and 13 27-in. sets; No; $17,400

48. 22 using process 1 and 28 using process 2

50. **a.** MIN $60000X_1 + 40000X_2$

$$\text{s.t.} \quad X_1 + \quad X_2 \geq \quad 6$$
$$3000X_1 + 1000X_2 \geq 9000$$
$$2X_1 + \quad X_2 \geq \quad 18$$
$$X_1, X_2 \geq 0 \text{ and integer}$$

(i) 1.5 Safeco trucks, 4.5 Kluge trucks (ii) 2 Safeco trucks, 4 Kluge trucks

b. (i) $270,000 (ii) $280,000

c. The integer problem has more constraints (the integer constraints)

CHAPTER 9

1. 150 20-in. girls, 100 20-in. boys, 100 26-in. girls, 100 26-in. boys; profit = $16,150

2. **a.** 266.67 stoves, 448.72 washers, 133.33 refrigerators; work in progress

b. 266.67 stoves, 227.15 washers, 63.58 electric dryers, 163.58 gas dryers, 133.33 refrigerators

3. **a.** 22.94 standard Z345's, 22.94 standard W250's, 45.87 industrial W250's; work in progress

b. 75%; if the limit were loosened or eliminated, the profit would increase

c. (i) Yes (ii) No (iii) Yes

4. **a.** $7500 in EAL, $2500 in TAT, $30,000 in long term bonds, $10,000 in the TDA

b. 10.5%; 11%—the maximum increase for the shadow price for funds is $+\infty$

c. EAL, BRU, long term bonds

d. $0.11 increase for each extra dollar invested, $0.15 decrease per extra dollar required in tax deferred annuities, $0.16 decrease for each extra dollar invested in TAT above 25%, $0.10 increase for each extra dollar allowed in low-yield funds

6. 12.69 oz. of steak; 16.67 oz. of milk; no apples or cheese

9. Conduct 500 telephone and 500 personal interviews with large William and Ryde investors, 600 telephone interviews with small William and Ryde investors, 200 personal telephone interviews with large investors from other firms and 200 interviews with small investors from other firms

12. **a.** 101.80 plates, 150 mugs, 87.54 steins; total profit = $1083.42

b. 128 plates, 298.67 mugs, 0 steins; total profit = $1290.67; increase of $207.25

15. **a.** 142.86 ac. Wheat, 142.86 ac. Corn, 14.29 ac. Soybeans; profit = $197,200

b. $486.21; $3.92 **c.** Yes; $4400 **d.** Yes; $22,698.20 in additional profit

18. Invest $2,075.14 in Bonanza Gold, $47,924.53 in Cascade Telephone, $20,000 in the money market account, and $30,000 in treasury bonds. Expected return = $8,424.53 (8.42453%)

23. **a.** This could violate the additivity assumption of linear programming.

b. Spend $300,000 on TV, $100,000 on radio, and $300,000 on newspaper ads

c. No effect; it is not binding

26. 7550 2-oz. Go bars, 2500 2-oz. Power bars, 5050 2-oz. Energy bars, 437.5 8-oz. Energy bars; total daily profit $7,273.375.

27. **a.** $550,000 in ketchup only, $450,000 in spaghetti sauce only, $750,000 in taco sauce only,

$250,000 in joint advertising; $2,251,500; 12.575% return

28. Part-time: 7AM-11AM—7, 11AM-3PM—13, 3PM-7PM—12, 7PM-11PM—14

Full-time: 7AM-3PM—3, 11AM-7PM—6, 3PM-11PM—2; Total Cost = $1,661

29. 3 patrols only. Two possible solutions: (1) Sectors 3, 7, 11; (2) Sectors 1, 4, 14

34. **a.** Develop applications 1, 2, 3, 4; projected net worth $12,600,000

b. Develop applications 1, 2, 6; projected net worth $11,800,000

35. Hire 2 CPAs and 19 experienced accountants; total payroll = $19,500

38. Purchase 12 shares of TCS and invest $1,044.44 in MFI; total investment = $1,704.44

39. 1581 Fords, 8 Chevrolets, 1411 Macks, 576 Nissans, 1424 Toyotas; outlay = $17,021,000

41. **a.** 52 turkey, 100 beef, 76 ham, 40 club, 32 all meat; $67,200

b. Shadow price = $0.33; range of feasibility (336,448); in this range, each extra ounce of cheese will add $0.33 to the optimal profit

c. Beef

47. **a.** Make 60,000 Jeeptrykes only; profit = $160,000

b. Make 60,000 Herotrykes only; profit = $117,500

CHAPTER 10

1. **a.** 400 **b.** 320 **c.** 360

4. **a.** 2 commercials **b.** $170,000

6. **a.** 12 leases **b.** 9 leases

9. **a.**

Number of Adoptions

Plan	0	1	2	3	4	5	6
Plan 1	2000	2000	2000	2000	2000	2000	2000
Plan 2	1000	1300	1600	1900	2200	2500	2800
Plan 3	0	700	1400	2100	2800	3500	4200

b. Plan 2 **c.** Plan 1

12. **a.** (i) custom (ii) unfurnished (iii) unfurnished

b. $937.50 per lot. **c.** 58% **d.** GNP is not a good indicator. Other indicators that would specifically focus on the Atlanta housing market or economy (such as average per capita income) would be better.

14. **a.** 1 car **b.** 2 cars **c.** 3 cars

15. **a.** P(outstanding) = .15; King should order 3 cars **b.** $3950

17. **a.**

Order Quantity	Demand 10000	50000	100000
0	0	0	0
40000	−130000	130000	80000
80000	−250000	110000	360000
120000	−370000	−10000	440000

b. Order 80,000 **c.** Order 80,000 **d.** $58,899

19. .996

23. **a.** order 2 sets **b.** EVPI = $587.50

24. **a.** If survey shows that at least one customer is likely to buy order 2, otherwise order 1.

b. $82.50. **c.** 14% **d.** record number of survey customers who are likely to purchase.

28. **a.** introduce candy **b.** introduce candy **c.** EVSI = $1800; efficiency = 8%

29. **a.**

Number Built	Demand 0	1	2	3	4
1	−300000	−75000	−105000	−135000	−165000
2	−400000	−175000	50000	20000	−10000
3	−300000	−75000	150000	375000	345000
4	−400000	−175000	50000	275000	500000

b. Building 3 computers and building 4 computers are undominated strategies.

c. P(0) = .2401 P(1) = .4116 P(2) = .2646 P(3) = .0756 P(4) = .0081; – build 3 computers.

31. Select Plan II

34. **a.** $580 **b.** .9952 **c.** Approximately $1000

36. **a.** Bid $.02 **b.** Bid $.04

38. **a.** Spot + $.01 **b.** $116 **c.** Risk loving **d.** Spot + $.01

40. Import scooters and advertise only if tariff is not imposed.

43. Midge should wait two months before buying her ticket.

45. John should bid $1.2 million without having the survey done

47. **a.** Concave utility function—risk averse **b.** Hire consultant. If consultant predicts approval purchase the option. If the consultant predicts denial do nothing.

CHAPTER 11

Note: The answers in this chapter correspond to the approach illustrated in the Instructor's Solutions Manual. Your answers will probably differ due to a different probability ordering or random number selection; your results should approximate these values, however.

1.   **b.**   .0025, price in 30 days would be 32.075 **c.** 31.125

   d.   We would expect the simulation to give an answer close to the expected value, but not necessarily the same as the expected value.

3.   **a.**   D–E, expected completion time = 15 weeks

   b. $P(A) = .2$, $P(B) = .2$, $P(C) = .2$, $P(D) = .6$, $P(E) = .6$, $P(F) = .2$, $P(G) = .2$

   c.   (16.244, 19.756)

5.   It will take 8 days. There will be 4 backorders of ChannelMaster systems and 2 lost sales.

7.   ($32.09, $109.91)

10. W_q from simulation is .994 minutes, W_q from steady state results is 2.4 minutes. One reason for the difference between the two values is the start up bias of the simulation.

12.   The average waiting time, W, is .96 minutes.

14.   The Garden Grove-Orange Freeway combination appears to give the lowest average time (12.9 minutes).

18. $L_q = .35$

20.   The average waiting time appears to be much greater for full serve than for self serve (15.4 minutes versus 3.7 minutes).

22.   **c.**   Based on the two simulations, Family should take the supplier's offer; for the 10 weeks the total simulated cost under the current policy is $401.33 versus only $155 under the supplier's offer.

24.   Officer will give out 6 tickets.

26.   **a.**   1.938 **b.** (4.622, 10.978)

28.   **b.**   (31.99, 34.99)

31.   **a.**   (2.585, 2.593) **b.** .505

32.   102 loaves

36.   44%

39.   (33.47, 37.69)

41.   (397.820, 532,065)

45.   **b.**   ($212.94, $214.78)

48.   **b.**   Yes, profit over the 10 days increases from $284 to $287 if the new machine is added.

PHOTO CREDITS

Chapter 1:   Flat Earth

Chapter 2:   PhotoDisc Inc

Chapter 3:   Corbis Digital Stock

Chapter 4:   Michael Coqliantry, The Image Bank

Chapter 5:   Keith Brofsky, PhotoDisc, Inc

Chapter 6:   PhotoDisc, Inc

Chapter 7:   PhotoDisc, Inc

Chapter 8:   Courtesy San Miguel Corporation

Chapter 9:   1995–2001 FedEx. All rights reserved.

Chapter 10:   Photo courtesy of Lindal Cedar Homes, Inc., Seattle, Washington

Chapter 11:   Juan Silva/The Image Bank

INDEX

Areas of the Standard Normal Distribution

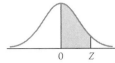

The entries in this table are the probabilities that a standard normal random variable is between 0 and Z (the shaded area).

Z	0.00	0.01	0.02	0.03	0.04	0.05	0.06	0.07	0.08	0.09
0.0	.0000	.0040	.0080	.0120	.0160	.0199	.0239	.0279	.0319	.0359
0.1	.0398	.0438	.0478	.0517	.0557	.0596	.0636	.0675	.0714	.0753
0.2	.0793	.0832	.0871	.0910	.0948	.0987	.1026	.1064	.1103	.1141
0.3	.1179	.1217	.1255	.1293	.1331	.1368	.1406	.1443	.1480	.1517
0.4	.1554	.1591	.1628	.1664	.1700	.1736	.1772	.1808	.1844	.1879
0.5	.1915	.1950	.1985	.2019	.2054	.2088	.2123	.2157	.2190	.2224
0.6	.2257	.2291	.2324	.2357	.2389	.2422	.2454	.2486	.2517	.2549
0.7	.2580	.2611	.2642	.2673	.2704	.2734	.2764	.2794	.2823	.2852
0.8	.2881	.2910	.2939	.2967	.2995	.3023	.3051	.3078	.3106	.3133
0.9	.3159	.3186	.3212	.3238	.3264	.3289	.3315	.3340	.3365	.3389
1.0	.3413	.3438	.3461	.3485	.3508	.3531	.3554	.3577	.3599	.3621
1.1	.3643	.3665	.3686	.3708	.3729	.3749	.3770	.3790	.3810	.3830
1.2	.3849	.3869	.3888	.3907	.3925	.3944	.3962	.3980	.3997	.4015
1.3	.4032	.4049	.4066	.4082	.4099	.4115	.4131	.4147	.4162	.4177
1.4	.4192	.4207	.4222	.4236	.4251	.4265	.4279	.4292	.4306	.4319
1.5	.4332	.4345	.4357	.4370	.4382	.4394	.4406	.4418	.4429	.4441
1.6	.4452	.4463	.4474	.4484	.4495	.4505	.4515	.4525	.4535	.4545
1.7	.4554	.4564	.4573	.4582	.4591	.4599	.4608	.4616	.4625	.4633
1.8	.4641	.4649	.4656	.4664	.4671	.4678	.4686	.4693	.4699	.4706
1.9	.4713	.4719	.4726	.4732	.4738	.4744	.4750	.4756	.4761	.4767
2.0	.4772	.4778	.4783	.4788	.4793	.4798	.4803	.4808	.4812	.4817
2.1	.4821	.4826	.4830	.4834	.4838	.4842	.4846	.4850	.4854	.4857
2.2	.4861	.4864	.4868	.4871	.4875	.4878	.4881	.4884	.4887	.4890
2.3	.4893	.4896	.4898	.4901	.4904	.4906	.4909	.4911	.4913	.4916
2.4	.4918	.4920	.4922	.4925	.4927	.4929	.4931	.4932	.4934	.4936
2.5	.4938	.4940	.4941	.4943	.4945	.4946	.4948	.4949	.4951	.4952
2.6	.4953	.4955	.4956	.4957	.4959	.4960	.4961	.4962	.4963	.4964
2.7	.4965	.4966	.4967	.4968	.4969	.4970	.4971	.4972	.4973	.4974
2.8	.4974	.4975	.4976	.4977	.4977	.4978	.4979	.4979	.4980	.4981
2.9	.4981	.4982	.4982	.4983	.4984	.4984	.4985	.4985	.4986	.4986
3.0	.4987	.4987	.4987	.4988	.4988	.4989	.4989	.4989	.4990	.4990
3.1	.4990	.4991	.4991	.4991	.4992	.4992	.4992	.4992	.4993	.4993
3.2	.4993	.4993	.4994	.4994	.4994	.4994	.4994	.4995	.4995	.4995
3.3	.4995	.4995	.4995	.4996	.4996	.4996	.4996	.4996	.4996	.4997
3.4	.4997	.4997	.4997	.4997	.4997	.4997	.4997	.4997	.4997	.4998
3.5	.4998									
4.0	.49997									
4.5	.499997									
5.0	.4999997									
6.0	.499999999									

Critical Values from the *t* Distribution

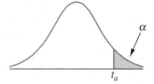

	Values of α for one-tailed test and α/2 for two-tailed test					
df	$t_{.100}$	$t_{.050}$	$t_{.025}$	$t_{.010}$	$t_{.005}$	$t_{.001}$
1	3.078	6.314	12.706	31.821	63.656	318.289
2	1.886	2.920	4.303	6.965	9.925	22.328
3	1.638	2.353	3.182	4.541	5.841	10.214
4	1.533	2.132	2.776	3.747	4.604	7.173
5	1.476	2.015	2.571	3.365	4.032	5.894
6	1.440	1.943	2.447	3.143	3.707	5.208
7	1.415	1.895	2.365	2.998	3.499	4.785
8	1.397	1.860	2.306	2.896	3.355	4.501
9	1.383	1.833	2.262	2.821	3.250	4.297
10	1.372	1.812	2.228	2.764	3.169	4.144
11	1.363	1.796	2.201	2.718	3.106	4.025
12	1.356	1.782	2.179	2.681	3.055	3.930
13	1.350	1.771	2.160	2.650	3.012	3.852
14	1.345	1.761	2.145	2.624	2.977	3.787
15	1.341	1.753	2.131	2.602	2.947	3.733
16	1.337	1.746	2.120	2.583	2.921	3.686
17	1.333	1.740	2.110	2.567	2.898	3.646
18	1.330	1.734	2.101	2.552	2.878	3.610
19	1.328	1.729	2.093	2.539	2.861	3.579
20	1.325	1.725	2.086	2.528	2.845	3.552
21	1.323	1.721	2.080	2.518	2.831	3.527
22	1.321	1.717	2.074	2.508	2.819	3.505
23	1.319	1.714	2.069	2.500	2.807	3.485
24	1.318	1.711	2.064	2.492	2.797	3.467
25	1.316	1.708	2.060	2.485	2.787	3.450
26	1.315	1.706	2.056	2.479	2.779	3.435
27	1.314	1.703	2.052	2.473	2.771	3.421
28	1.313	1.701	2.048	2.467	2.763	3.408
29	1.311	1.699	2.045	2.462	2.756	3.396
30	1.310	1.697	2.042	2.457	2.750	3.385
40	1.303	1.684	2.021	2.423	2.704	3.307
50	1.299	1.676	2.009	2.403	2.678	3.261
60	1.296	1.671	2.000	2.390	2.660	3.232
70	1.294	1.667	1.994	2.381	2.648	3.211
80	1.292	1.664	1.990	2.374	2.639	3.195
90	1.291	1.662	1.987	2.368	2.632	3.183
100	1.290	1.660	1.984	2.364	2.626	3.174
150	1.287	1.655	1.976	2.351	2.609	3.145
200	1.286	1.653	1.972	2.345	2.601	3.131
∞	1.282	1.645	1.960	2.326	2.576	3.090